A GUIDE TO
THE IDENTIFICATION OF THE

GENERA OF BACTERIA

A GUIDE TO
THE IDENTIFICATION OF THE
GENERA OF BACTERIA

With Methods and Digests of
Generic Characteristics

Based on
Bergey's Manual of Determinative Bacteriology,
Seventh Edition, Williams & Wilkins, Baltimore,
Topley and Wilson's Principles of
Bacteriology and Immunity,
Fifth edition, Arnold, London,
Prévot's Traité de Systematique Bacterienne,
Volume II, 1961, Dunod, Paris,
Krassilnikov's Diagnostik de Bakterien und Actinomyceten,
Gustav Fischer, Jena, and on original papers

By V. B. D. SKERMAN

Professor of Microbiology,
University of Queensland,
Brisbane, Australia

SECOND EDITION

THE WILLIAMS & WILKINS COMPANY
BALTIMORE • 1967

Made in the United States of America

Library of Congress Catalog
Card Number 66-28166

Printed and composed at the

Waverly Press, Inc.
Mt. Royal & Guilford Avenues
Baltimore, Md. 21202, U.S.A.

TO MY WIFE

*in Appreciation of Her Patience
and Forbearance*

CONTENTS

CONTENTS

PREFACE
TO THE FIRST EDITION

The Key to the Genera of Bacteria has been compiled with the aim of placing in the hands of research workers, teachers, and students, a volume in which general directives for the identification of bacteria are supported by a complete list of the techniques needed for the purpose. In addition, a Digest of data published for the various species in the seventh edition of *Bergey's Manual of Determinative Bacteriology* and in several original papers has been included. The publication of the Key and Methods in the one book should encourage a more general application of common procedures for the description of bacteria. The main purpose of the digests is to draw attention in a more definite way to the deficiencies in descriptions within the various genera in the hope that steps may be taken to rectify them. A Guide to Study has been provided to ease the burden associated with the assimilation of knowledge over this varied field of science.

The volume is intended as a supplement to the *Manual* itself, and it is hoped that its use will contribute materially to the development of future editions of the *Manual.*

I am indebted to the late Professor R. S. Breed, at whose invitation the present keys were written for inclusion in the seventh edition of *Bergey's Manual,* to the Board of Trustees of the *Manual* for permission to draw so freely on the contents of the *Manual,* and particularly to Dr. R. E. Buchanan for a very critical perusal of the manuscript.

I am also indebted to the numerous authors, organizations, and publishers who have so readily given their permission to reproduce the material which appears in the Methods and illustrations, and whose names appear in the references to the respective items.

In drawing up the Methods, I have made use of some which have been in use for a long period in this laboratory and for which the original references can not be traced. These methods bear no reference and acknowledgement is due to the original authors and publishers whoever they may be.

I should like to express my appreciation to the Carnegie Corporation of New York through whose financial assistance I was able to visit the late Professor Breed and many other people whose assistance to me in the compilation of the keys has proved invaluable; to Mrs. Anne Pope, Miss Barbara Carey, and Mr. Ian MacRae for the very great assistance which has made the publication of the volume possible; and to Miss Barbara Steele who typed the manuscript and whose unusual interest in the work has resulted in the elimination of many errors and omissions. I am also indebted to the Department of Photography, University of Queensland, for the preparation of line drawings and the development and printing of the photographic illustrations; and finally to those colleagues whose comments, acid and otherwise, have contributed to formulation of the Key.

V. B. D. SKERMAN
October, 1958

PREFACE
TO THE SECOND EDITION

The Key to the Genera of *Bacteria* has been compiled with the aim of placing in the hands of research workers, teachers, and students a volume in which general directives for the identification of the genera of bacteria are supported by a complete list of the methods needed for the purpose.

Because systematic bacteriology has a strong element of subjectiveness and views on the systematic relationships amongst the bacteria vary from one country to another, an attempt has been made to bridge the differences by integrating, within the Keys, the nomenclature adopted by four of the major publications in systematic bacteriology, listed on the title page, and at the same time to incorporate information from publications that have appeared since the publication of the first edition. The task has not been easy. It was not simply a matter of determining the names given to the same organism by the various authors; it was also one of assimilating and translating ideas, with which I may not have been entirely successful. This has made necessary some major changes in the contents of the keys, although the general framework has been left unchanged.

Since the publication of the seventh edition of the *Manual*, there have been several major contributions to systematic bacteriology that outdate certain sections of the *Manual*. This is inevitable. Notwithstanding this fact, I have retained in the section on Digest of Genera the information obtainable from *Bergey's Manual* itself, modified where necessary with new information and supplemented, particularly in the case of the *Enterobacteriaceae*, with the definitions given by International Subcommittees. The main purpose in doing this has been to provide some indication of the transitional changes that are taking place.

Genera that have been included in the Key but that did not appear in the seventh edition of the *Manual* have not been included in the Digest of Genera. The pertinent references to the original papers have been cited in the Key.

Supplementing the Digests are, in most instances, lists of references to some taxonomic papers that have appeared since the last edition of the *Manual*. The list should not, in any sense, be considered complete or the most appropriate.

The section on Methods has been expanded to accommodate additional methods made necessary by the additions to the Keys. It is quite apparent, however, that one set of methods will never suit all purposes. An appeal is made, however, for all workers to adopt some sets of common procedures in addition to their specialized needs to provide a better basis for comparison between different groups of bacteria.

I am particularly indebted to the United States Government Printing Office and to Dr. W. H. Ewing for permission to reproduce the methods from Publication 734 of the Public Health Service of the United States Department of Health, Education and Welfare, entitled "Enterobacteriaceae. Biochemical Methods for Group Differentiation." Some of these methods are reproduced without the full commentaries, for which the reader is referred to the original.

The Guide to Study has been modified to accommodate the new genera.

An addition to the *Guide* is a short chapter on Numerical Analysis. The rapid advances that are being made in the use of these methods, based on Adansonian principles, make it necessary that students in systematics become familiar with the technique in order to appreciate the significance of recently published work. The treatment is, perforce, elementary, but it is hoped that it is sufficient to serve its purpose.

In the course of preparation of this edition, reference has been made to over 5000 reprints dealing with all aspects of research on the bacteria. These have been supplied directly or at my request, and a general note of thanks is offered to those who have responded. At the same time an apology is offered for the omission of any significant contributions to which I have had no access or have inadvertently missed.

I owe a special debt of gratitude to Miss Lynne Clark, who was responsible for the translation of Prévot's *Traité de Systematique Bacterienne* and for the major portion of the work associated with the determination of relationships between the nomenclature of the *Manual* and that of

Krassilnikov, and to Mrs. Jan Grainger and Miss Eleanora Szabo and the University Department of Photography for painstaking work in the revision of the illustrations.

I also express my sincere appreciation to Miss Barbara Heron, Miss Dawn Ellis, Miss Wendy Loder, Miss Helen Gritton, Mr. John Kennedy, Mr. Alan Mortimer, Mr. John Bowyer, Dr. Chris Hayward, and my daughter Joan who, although new to this type of work, have responded magnificently to the inevitable pressures of getting the publication to press.

Finally, I express appreciation to my publisher, The Williams & Wilkins Company, for the cordial assistance given at all times and the extreme patience shown in waiting for the manuscript of this edition.

V. B. D. Skerman

INTRODUCTION

The Key is structurally the same as that which appeared in the previous edition of the *Guide*. There have been major alterations in the contents and, in some instances, the sequence of operation, made necessary by the different approaches used by various authors to construction of their taxa. Each termination in the Key indicates the genus (or group) into which each author places the relevant organism; the statements in parentheses following the generic names refer to the source of the information and bear no relationship to the authority for the name. The abbreviation I C N B used with the *Enterobacteriaceae* refers to the Reports of the Subcommittee on the *Enterobacteriaceae* of the International Committee on Nomenclature of Bacteria appearing in the International Bulletin for Bacteriological Nomenclature and Taxonomy, *8*, 1958, 25; *13*, 1963, 69. The abbreviation T and W refers to Topley and Wilson's *Principles of Bacteriology and Immunity* (Ed. 5, Arnold). References to Ewing refer principally to the paper by W. H. Ewing (Intern. Bull. Bacteriol. Nomen. Taxon., *13*, 1963, 95). Those to Prévot and Krassilnikov refer to their publications cited in the Preface.

The keys for the order *Myxobacterales* and the organisms in the class *Microtatobiotes* are both merely reconstructions of those provided in the *Manual* and are reproduced in this form with the permission of the authors and publishers.

The Key departs in several places from a simple dichotomy. Such departures occur where (a) there has been some doubt as to the validity of the insertion, and the use of other than a dichotomy permits subsequent removal without reconstruction and numbering of the key; (b) there has been a late insertion that would have necessitated a complete renumbering of the key; and (c) it appeared more convenient to depart from the dichotomy, as in Section B.

Shunts have been used where there is a divided opinion on interpretation or a test is of limited usefulness. By this device, organisms may be separated into two groups by a dichotomy. Certain genera are then separated from one group on specified tests and the remaining organisms rechanneled into the other group for subsequent treatment. One such shunt has been used in the treatment of the multicellular organisms and another in the separation of the cocci.

The definition of terms given as a footnote to Section A has been retained. The author has received some comments on the use of the term *trichome*—all indicating that its use is undesirable. In this the author agrees, but the term is still used in an attempt to define the different ways in which it has been employed in the *Manual*. Its elimination from subsequent editions of the *Manual* and from current literature is desirable.

The use of the term *multicellular* also warrants comment. In the Key those organisms which show a clear subdivision in the rods without resort to special staining methods are regarded as multicellular, *e.g.*, *Caryophanon*. Provision has been

1

made, however, for those smaller cells such as *Nocardia* by means of a shunt in the Key that admits them as multicellular, although special methods are needed to demonstrate this.

Page references following genera in the Key and in the Digest of Genera are in two forms. Those preceded by the letter *M* refer to the pages in the seventh edition of *Bergey's Manual of Derminative Bacteriology;* the others refer to pages in this volume.

In view of the remarks made by Palleroni and Doudoroff (J. Bacteriol., *89,* 1965, 264), it seems necessary to comment on the entry "not pathogenic or known to be pathogenic to plants." One frequently finds that organisms isolated from soil have the characteristics of genera of known plant pathogens. *Manual* and other keys are frequently based on evidence of pathogenicity, which in this instance is not known. One can either test pathogenicity over the entire plant world or, more rationally, attempt identification by other means. Until all our organisms have been redescribed and we are able to assess identity by means of computers, we must make the best of what we have. In these keys all plant pathogens have been treated as both pathogenic and nonpathogenic. Likewise, pigment-producing *Pseudomonas* and *Serratia* species have been treated also as nonpigmented and *Rhizobium* species as though we knew nothing of nodule formation. For this reason, knowledge of pathogenicity is not essential to generic identification but is a useful guide if present. For this reason the entry "not pathogenic or not known to be pathogenic" does not carry the implications that Palleroni and Doudoroff might infer. Nonetheless, because they appear to regard such information as useful to their diagnosis, it has been included in these keys.

The Methods have been collected from many sources. Most of them have been tested in the author's laboratory. In most instances the original procedure has been followed, but, particularly in the case of synthetic media for autotrophic bacteria, a complete new series of alternative media, founded on a common synthetic base, has been provided in addition to the original methods. The methods are not to be regarded as "standard methods." It is hoped, however, that general application of them in conjunction with the Key will lead to a greater uniformity in descriptions at the generic level. In the presentation of the methods, a few procedures for isolation of cultures, which have a direct bearing on the operation of the Key, have been included.

A fundamental objection to the use of a common procedure is that there is no guarantee that it is, in fact, the one used by the original author or, if so, that subsequent authors have used a similar procedure. The objection is valid, but it is not impossible, even now, to re-examine species on a common pattern and continue to use such a pattern in the future.

The present indiscriminate use of tests is leading only to chaos. The adoption of a more uniform approach should result in a much clearer picture of the present state of knowledge and should act as a stimulus to more productive research.

It is very desirable that some measure of international agreement be reached on the matter of methods.

The Digest of Genera has been prepared from an analysis of data given in the *Manual.* In many instances, particularly in the case of older German literature on the sulfur or iron bacteria and of more recently described genera, a search of the original literature has been made. The object of the Digest is to present the facts relating to the descriptions of species in a manner that accentuates the deficiencies. With the exception of those organisms placed in the *Manual* in the class *Microtatobiotes*, the digests are in two sections, namely, Differentiating Characters and

Notes. The author has had no personal experience with the class *Microtatobiotes* and has given under the heading of Differentiating Characters the generic description provided for each genus in the *Manual*. The differentiating characters given for the other genera are those derived by manipulation of the Key in reverse.

In the construction of the Key numerous assumptions had to be made to cope with lack of information. Where there has been any serious doubt, the character has been treated as positive or negative. Where an assumption has seemed to be legitimate, such as the absence of chlorophylls from colorless organisms, it has been made. It is possible, of course, that some assumptions may not have been legitimate.

The material included in the Notes should not be regarded as unimportant to the generic description. In some cases characters relegated to this section are uniform throughout the genus but have not appeared in the manipulation of the Key. In the compilation of the data in the Notes, the number of species described has been listed, and for individual tests the number positive over the number tested is also given. For example, there may be 82 species in the genus. The indole test may have been cited for 47 and may have been positive for 28. In the text these facts would be summarized as "indole produced 28/47." A perusal of these data will give an idea of the extent to which species in each genus have been uniformly examined.

A Guide to Study has been included to aid students in taxonomic studies.

Reference to the higher taxa has been generally avoided. This has been done purposely to encourage a reconsideration of the evidence at the generic level.

ELEMENTS OF NUMERICAL ANALYSIS

Prominent amongst the developments in research in the systematics of bacteria over recent years has been the return to Adansonian principles in classification. The application of these principles to bacteria must be credited to Sneath. Sokal and Sneath (1963), in *Principles of Numerical Taxonomy* (W. H. Freeman and Co.), have exhaustively reviewed the various proposals. It is my intention here to give only a brief but operative outline of the procedures and to emphasize the importance of some of their aspects to the future of systematics. Because the form of analysis has to deal with numbers, the discipline has become generally referred to as Numerical Taxonomy.

Numerical analysis is applied to the data accumulated by laboratory investigation of strains of bacteria. Each strain is an Operational Taxonomic Unit (OTU) and is the most important element in any system of classification. Each strain is defined by a series of unit characters, which may be anatomical, cultural, biochemical, or serological, or may relate to sensitivities to attack by bacteriophages, although the last two are not considered desirable characteristics (see Sokal and Sneath). For statistical reasons, the number of unit characters should not be less than about 60. The unit characters should be independent of one another, representing even distribution amongst taxonomic categories, *i.e.*, morphology, physiology, biochemistry, etc. Because it is not always possible to determine independence, the influence of interdependence is largely offset by increasing the number of unit characters, which, in some recent studies, has exceeded 150. Each unit character chosen should be determined for every strain in the collection.

Characters chosen may be qualitative, such as the Gram stain, or quantitative, such as sensitivity to an antibiotic. If the latter, then some arbitrary means must be devised to express the quantitative value in discrete units. For example, sensitivity to streptomycin may be expressed as sensitivity to 0 to 5, 6 to 10, 11 to 20, or 21 to 50 μg. per ml. The question of handling quantitative data will be discussed later.

All tests should be performed under a set of standard conditions, and in any publication of data all the information, including the methods, should be specified. This is sound taxonomic practice, not in any way restricted to numerical analysis.

For the purpose of illustration of method, a small number of OTU's, characterized by an equally small number of tests, will be used. Table 1 (I) shows the reaction of 11 OTU's (A_1 to A_{11}) to 12 independent qualitative tests.

In what has become termed "conventional" taxonomy, one searches through such a table and tries to rearrange the groupings so that organisms which appear to share common characteristics are grouped together in a manner similar to that which appears in Table 1 (II). If the groups that form seem to be sufficiently different from one another, one may be inclined to give each group a specific name within a common genus or, if the character-

TABLE 1

Adansonian analysis—group of strains "A"

I Features

Strain	1	2	3	4	5	6	7	8	9	10	11	12
A 1	+	+	−	+	+	+	−	+	+	−	−	+
A 2	+	−	−	+	+	−	+	+	−	+	+	+
A 3	+	−	−	+	−	−	+	+	−	−	+	+
A 4	+	+	−	+	+	−	−	+	−	+	−	+
A 5	+	+	−	+	+	+	−	+	+	+	−	+
A 6	+	−	−	+	−	+	+	+	−	−	−	+
A 7	+	−	−	+	+	−	+	+	−	+	+	+
A 8	+	+	−	+	+	−	+	+	−	−	+	+
A 9	+	+	−	+	+	−	−	+	+	+	−	+
A10	+	−	−	+	+	−	+	−	−	−	+	+
A11	+	−	−	+	+	+	+	+	−	−	+	+

III "A" Strains

Strain	1	2	3	4	5	6	7	8	9	10	11
1	100										
2	50	100									
3	50	83	100								
4	75	75	58	100							
5	83	50	42	75	100						
6	67	67	83	58	50	100					
7	50	100	83	75	50	67	100				
8	92	58	58	83	75	58	58	100			
9	75	58	42	83	92	42	58	83	100		
10	58	92	92	67	42	75	92	67	50	100	
11	75	75	75	67	58	83	75	75	50	83	100

II Features

Strain	1	2	3	4	5	6	7	8	9	10	11	12
A 1	+	+	−	+	+	+	−	+	+	−	−	+
A 8	+	+	−	+	+	−	−	+	+	−	−	+
A 5	+	+	−	+	+	+	−	−	+	+	−	+
A 9	+	+	−	+	+	−	−	+	+	+	−	+
A 4	+	+	−	+	+	−	−	+	+	+	−	+
A 2	+	−	−	+	+	−	+	+	−	+	−	+
A 7	+	−	−	+	+	−	+	+	−	−	+	+
A10	+	−	−	+	+	−	+	+	−	−	+	+
A 3	+	−	−	+	−	−	+	−	−	−	+	+
A11	+	−	−	+	+	+	+	+	−	−	+	−
A 6	+	−	−	+	−	+	+	+	−	−	−	+

IV "A" Strains

Strain	1	8	5	9	4	2	7	10	3	11	6
1	100										
8	92	100									
5	83	75	100								
9	75	83	92	100							
4	75	83	75	83	100						
2	50	58	50	58	75	100					
7	50	58	50	58	75	100	100				
10	58	67	42	58	67	92	92	100			
3	50	58	42	50	58	83	83	92	100		
11	75	67	58	42	67	75	75	83	75	100	
6	67	58	50	42	58	67	67	75	83	83	100

(X and Y denote clustered regions delineated by the diagonal in Table IV.)

istics of each group are grossly dissimilar, to set up species within different genera.

If one is faced, as in Table 1, with the results, without any knowledge of the nature of the characters or the origin of the OTU's, the rearrangement will be unbiased, and each characteristic will be considered of equal value. This is one essential element of Adansonian (M. Adanson, 1763, *Familles des Plantes*, Vincent, Paris) analysis. Another is that no test need be uniformly positive within any group, the grouping being based on a measure of overall similarity between pairs of OTU's placed in a group. Although this is true of the method of analysis, the chance that all the OTU's that finally form a single group will in fact possess a number of common characters is very high, and in practice this is found to be the case.

In the jargon of numerical analysis, a group formed in this fashion is called a *polythetic group*. If, on the other hand, one insists that *all* the organisms within a group *must* share certain common characters, the group is said to be *monothetic*. Most naturally occurring polythetic groups are in fact monothetic to a degree.

Estimation of Similarity

As stated above, "conventional" matching of strains is usually done by eye, aided very materially, and quite often conditioned, by the operator's detailed knowledge of the strains involving information not usually committed to paper. Unfortunately, when one has a large mass of data, it is extremely tedious, if not impossible, to assess the similarities accurately by direct observation. Thus, one must resort to mathematical estimation of the number of tests in which individual strains agree (either positively or negatively) and the number in which they disagree; one must also express the measure of agreement in some specific way.

If one is going to do this, then the characters must be expressed in some discrete form amenable to mathematical treatment.

The insistence on this, which makes it necessary for the operator to think seriously about the mode of expression of a character and to reduce it to its elements, is perhaps one of the great contributions that numerical method has given to taxonomy.

Several methods of estimating similarity between OTU's have been proposed. One in common use in microbiology is the matching coefficient (S_{SM}) of Sokal and Michener, which will be used here without prejudice to claims of greater validity of other proposals, which include the use of *correlation coefficients, measures of distance,* and *measures of central tendency.*

$$S_{SM} = \frac{\text{Sum of positive and negative matches}}{\text{Total number of tests}}$$

A modification in common use is

$$S_{SM} = \frac{\text{Sum of positive and negative matches}}{\text{Total number of tests} - \text{number of invalid tests}}$$

The modification has been introduced to cope with the situation when information about one or more tests is not available, such as occurs when comparing one's own work with published data or when special methods are adopted to reduce the "weight" that a quantitative test may have over a qualitative test. It is common, but not mandatory, to express the similarity as a percentage.

Comparing OTU's A_1 and A_2 in Table 1 (I), we find that the number of positive matches is 5 and that of negative matches is 1; the total number of tests is 12.

$$S_{SM} = \frac{5+1}{12} \times \frac{100}{1} = 50\%$$

In Table 1 (III) the similarities between each OTU and every other OTU under investigation are set out in the form of a triangular matrix.

The next step in the procedure is the formation of clusters in which each individual OTU has a minimum level of similarity with at least one other member of the cluster. A search is first made for independent pairs with the highest level of similarity, around which the other OTU's are clustered. This one does by searching the matrix column by column for the highest level of similarity, ignoring the 100 per cent matches on the diagonal but not in the matrix. In Table 1 (III), the highest level within the matrix is 100 per cent between OTU's A_2 and A_7, indicating exact identity (a very rare phenomenon in practice).

The pair is set aside from the matrix in storage. The matrix is again searched for the pair(s) with the next highest level of similarity (92 per cent in this case). The first pair to be encountered in the progressive searching of the columns is A_1 and A_8. This is transferred to a second "storage" for 92 per cent matches, but, before putting the pair in that store, a search is made of the first (100 per cent) store to see if either OTU of the pair has been previously stored. In this case neither has, so the pair is placed in the new store. The search is continued, the next pair at 92 per cent being OTU's A_2 and A_{10}. Because A_2 has already been matched with A_7 in the 100 per cent store, the other member of the pair (A_{10}) is joined to the A_2-A_7 pair and the group is stored in the 92 per cent store. This is termed a *single-linkage group* because no attempt is made to verify whether A_{10} agrees with A_7 at 92 per cent. It is sufficient, *under this particular form* of "cluster" analysis, for an OTU to have the required level of similarity with *any* member of the existing group to be joined to that group. The fact that it *may* have a very low level of similarity with some other members of the cluster is one of the weaknesses of the method, which the scope of this article does not permit me to discuss (see, however, Sokal and Sneath).

Inasmuch as the whole matrix is examined at each level of similarity, several clusters may be forming at one time. Linkage between clusters will occur when a pair is located in which the two members have already been clustered in two separate clusters at a higher level of similarity.

If the analysis is continued in this fashion, all the OTU's in Table 1 will have formed into a single cluster at the 75 per cent level in the manner indicated in Table 2. In this table the connecting lines indicate the OTU's through which each successive addition to a cluster has been made or through which separate clusters have been joined. The *final sequence* determines the order in which the OTU's should be rearranged for the formation of "clusters" within the matrix, as has been done in Table 1 (IV). Table 2 shows that two clusters had been formed at the 83 per cent level. These have been outlined in Table 1 and constitute clusters X and Y, respectively.

Note that, despite the fact that we have an 83 per cent single linkage cluster in each case, the similarities between pairs of OTU's in the cluster may fall well below this level (67 in Y). A further inspection of cluster X will show that the minimum value for similarity in the cluster is 75 per cent. One may refer to the cluster as a 75 per cent *multilinkage* cluster because every OTU agrees with every other OTU to *not less than* this value.

The interrelationship between clusters X and Y is obtained, in Sneath's procedure, by determining the average value of all the matching coefficients in the rectangle joining the two triangles. In this case, the value is 57 per cent.

Table 1 (II) shows the original data rearranged in accordance with the results of the cluster analysis.

A similar analysis of a second series of OTU's examined over the same series of characteristics is shown in Table 3. The results of the analysis of the B group of OTU's will show that two clusters (1-7-8-3-10 and 2-5-6-4) form at the 83 per cent level with OTU 9 excluded. Linkage between the two groups occurs first between OTU's 2 and 8 at the 75 per cent level.

TABLE 2

100%	2-7
92%	1-8　2-7-10-3　5-9
83%	1-8-5-9-4　2-7-10-3-6-11
75%	1-8-5-9-4　2-7-10-3-6-11

Note: The clusters 1-8-5-9-4 and 2-7-10-3-6-11 formed at the 83% level are clusters X and Y in Table 1.

OTU 9 joins the combined cluster through B_5 at the 75 per cent level. The purpose in presenting the second table is to illustrate the importance of publishing the details of OTU data and the accessibility of such data to workers in different laboratories.

Before proceeding to discuss this, an alternative method of publishing the triangular matrix resulting from the cluster analysis must be considered. One may publish the actual values of the matching coefficients or a shaded diagram, which is somewhat easier for the eye to interpret. Such a diagram for Table 1 is shown in Figure 1. This method certainly assists the operator in assessing the existence of possible clusters in the matrix, but it is of little value to another worker attempting to correlate his observations with those of the published work.

Publication of Information

The form in which the rearrangements given in Tables 1 (II) and 3 (II) are customarily published in journals is shown in Table 4. Attempts to compare the OTU's from the two sources (A and B) are made virtually impossible by the pooled expressions for each cluster, particularly where the variability is expressed as "V." It is little better when the magnitude of the variation is shown in terms of the percentage of positive reactions, as in the lower part of Table 4.

There is reason to suspect some relationship between clusters Y and W from the lower half of Table 4, inasmuch as they agree over 5 of the 12 characters and show a high level of agreement in percentage-positive reactions on characters 4, 8, 10, and 12.

The true solution to comparative study lies in access to strain data. In Table 5 the two sets of data from Tables 1 and 3 have been pooled. Some interesting information is apparent from a cursory inspection of the similarity matrix before analysis. OTU's A_5 and B_9 are identical, as are A_6 and B_1, a fact impossible to discover without access to OTU data. From the analysis of the matrix in Table 5, all OTU's are found to merge at the 75 per cent level, as would be expected from the previous analysis. At the 83 per cent level there are three groups, with OTU B_9, which clusters only at the 75 per cent level in the B group alone, entering an A group at the 83 per cent level.

The rearrangement of the matrix in Table 6 reveals three 83 per cent single-linkage clusters, one of which combines the original clusters W and Y. There are three high-level (83 to 92 per cent) multi-linkage clusters within the major cluster. The interrelationships between X and W + Y, X and Z, and Z and W + Y are 52, 58, and 60 per cent, respectively.

For these reasons, it is strongly recommended that the original OTU data be included in a standardized format in publications.

Nomenclature

Sneath refers to each individual cluster as a *phenon* and prefers, at this stage, not to attempt seriously to relate a phenon to any conventional taxon (taxonomic group), such as a genus or species. The caution is well merited. We still do not know the best form of expressing similarities, and the single-linkage system, despite the marked contribution it has made to the development of ideas in numerical analysis, is not

TABLE 3

Adansonian analysis—group of strains "B"

I — Features

Strain	1	2	3	4	5	6	7	8	9	10	11	12
B 1	+	−	−	+	−	+	+	+	−	−	−	+
B 2	−	−	−	+	+	+	+	−	−	+	−	+
B 3	+	−	−	−	+	+	+	−	−	−	−	+
B 4	−	+	−	+	+	+	+	−	−	+	+	+
B 5	−	+	−	+	+	+	+	−	−	+	−	+
B 6	−	−	−	+	−	+	+	+	−	−	+	+
B 7	+	−	−	+	−	+	+	+	−	+	+	+
B 8	+	+	−	+	−	+	+	+	−	+	−	+
B 9	+	+	−	+	+	+	−	−	+	+	−	+
B10	+	−	−	−	+	+	+	−	+	−	−	−

III — "B" Strains

Strain	1	2	3	4	5	6	7	8	9	10
1	100									
2	67	100								
3	83	67	100							
4	50	83	50	100						
5	58	92	58	92	100					
6	58	92	58	92	83	100				
7	92	58	75	58	50	67	100			
8	92	75	75	58	67	67	83	100		
9	50	67	50	67	75	58	42	58	100	
10	75	58	92	42	50	50	67	67	42	100

II — Features

Strain	1	2	3	4	5	6	7	8	9	10	11	12
B 1	+	−	−	+	−	+	+	+	−	−	−	+
B 7	+	−	−	+	−	+	+	+	−	−	+	+
B 8	+	−	−	+	−	+	+	+	−	+	−	+
B 3	+	−	−	−	−	+	+	−	−	−	−	+
B10	+	−	−	−	−	+	+	−	−	−	−	−
B 2	−	−	−	+	+	+	+	−	−	+	−	+
B 5	−	−	−	+	+	+	+	−	−	+	−	+
B 6	−	+	−	+	+	+	+	−	−	+	−	+
B 4	−	−	−	+	+	+	+	−	−	+	+	+
B 9	+	+	−	+	+	+	−	−	+	+	−	+

IV — "B" Strains

Strain	1	7	8	3	10	2	5	6	4	9
1	100									
7	92	100								
8	92	83	100							
3	83	75	75	100						
10	75	67	67	92	100					
2	67	58	75	67	58	100				
5	58	50	67	58	50	92	100			
6	58	67	67	58	50	92	92	100		
4	50	58	58	58	42	83	83	92	100	
9	50	42	58	50	42	67	75	58	67	100

W   Z

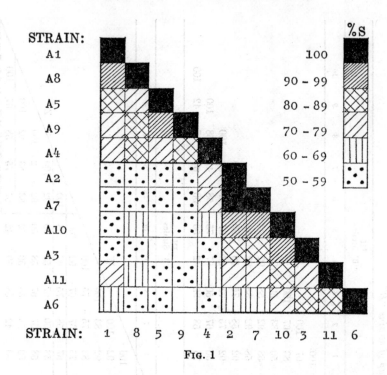

STRAIN: 1   8   5   9   4   2   7   10   3   11   6

%S
100
90 - 99
80 - 89
70 - 79
60 - 69
50 - 59

Fig. 1

TABLE 4
Condensation of data for strains "A" and "B" by two methods

	Features											
	1	2	3	4	5	6	7	8	9	10	11	12
X	+	+	−	+	+	v	−	v	v	v	−	+
Y	+	−	−	+	v	v	+	+	−	v	v	+
W	+	−	−	v	−	+	+	v	−	v	v	v
Z	v	v	−	+	+	+	v	−	v	+	v	+
X	+	+	−	+	+	40	−	60	80	60	−	+
Y	+	−	−	+	66	33	+	+	−	33	66	+
W	+	−	−	60	−	+	+	60	−	20	20	80
Z	20	60	−	+	+	+	80	−	20	+	40	+

Note: Figures quote percentage-positive reactions.

regarded as the most suitable; much research has yet to be done before a satisfactory solution is reached. We also do not know what level of similarity should be used to define taxonomic categories such as species, genera, etc. However, a survey of a large mass of data from descriptions of existing species has shown that a 65 per cent single-linkage cluster gives a rough approximation of the current conventional genus and 75 per cent, a species. There have been exceptions, and higher levels have been suggested for both. We are thus faced with the same problem in "numerical" analysis as in "conventional" analysis.

Notwithstanding this fact, we still have the formation of the phenon, and much can be gained from the use of the concept. Some idea of the relationship of the phenon to conventional nomenclature can be gained from the inclusion of *type* and *neotype* cultures and other *authentic* cultures in the OTU survey in the initial investigations. Where a named culture is found to fall with other OTU's into a well-defined phenon, it is reasonable to suggest that the phenon assumes the name of the "marker" culture.

This practice will inevitably cause several so-called "species" to merge into the one

TABLE 5

Extraction of linkage groups at decreasing levels of similarity according to the method proposed by Sneath—combined analysis of "A" and "B" strains

	A 1	A 2	A 3	A 4	A 5	A 6	A 7	A 8	A 9	A 10	A 11	B 1	B 2	B 3	B 4	B 5	B 6	B 7	B 8	B 9	B 10
A1	100																				
A2	50	100																			
A3	50	83	100																		
A4	75	75	58	100																	
A5	83	50	42	75	100																
A6	67	67	83	58	83	100															
A7	50	100	83	75	50	67	100														
A8	92	58	58	75	58	58	58	100													
A9	75	58	42	83	92	42	92	42	100												
A10	58	92	92	67	42	92	75	58	75	100											
A11	75	75	75	67	58	75	75	67	50	67	100										
B1	67	67	83	58	83	67	67	58	67	83	83	100									
B2	50	67	50	58	58	50	50	58	67	50	50	67	100								
B3	50	50	67	42	42	67	83	58	42	67	67	83	75	100							
B4	50	67	50	58	58	50	50	58	58	50	50	50	58	50	100						
B5	58	58	42	67	67	58	58	58	67	58	58	58	67	58	92	100					
B6	42	75	58	50	50	75	67	58	33	75	75	92	67	58	92	92	100				
B7	58	75	92	75	58	75	50	67	50	75	83	92	58	58	58	92	83	100			
B8	58	75	75	67	75	75	50	42	50	50	67	50	75	58	75	58	50	67	100		
B9	83	50	33	75	50	33	92	50	92	75	58	75	50	67	50	67	67	75	58	100	
B10	42	42	58	33	42	58	33	50	33	42	42	58	42	58	42	50	42	50	50	42	100

100%   2-7 92%   5-9   6-1   1-8 83%   75%

1-8 5-9-9-4   2-7-10-3-7-6-1-8-11   1-8-5-9-9-4   2-7-10-3-7-6-1-8-11-3-10   2-5-6-4

Note: In the details of cluster formation in the upper right-hand side of the table the "B" strains are underlined.

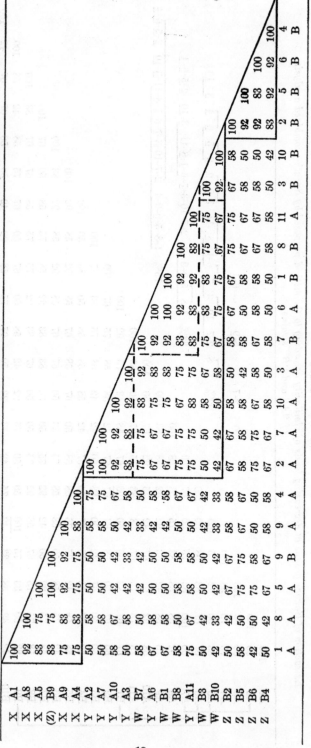

TABLE 6

Rearrangement of strains "A" and strains "B" on the basis of linkage groups obtained by analysis of the combined strain data

species (see Colwell and Mandel, J. Bacteriol., *89*, 1965, 454) or even several genera, for example, *Xanthomonas* and *Pseudomonas*, to merge into one genus. This "lumping" will at least be based on objective analysis.

Another purpose for which the phenon has been used is to attempt to define which of several OTU's within the phenon should constitute a type or neotype culture when no such culture has been designated. Normally, when a type culture no longer exists, a strain is selected that as nearly resembles the original description as possible, and this is recommended to the Judicial Commission of the Permanent International Committee on Nomenclature of Bacteria for approval. A current proposal is that selection of the neotype should rest upon numerical analysis of a large group of strains and that the most representative strain of the group should be chosen. There are again different proposals for the execution of this idea, and, without prejudice to the issue, I will quote the one of Liston, Wiebe, and Colwell (J. Bacteriol., *85*, 1963, 1067). This proposal has been described in detail in their paper. Its essentials will be discussed here. These authors describe what they term a *hypothetical median organism*. Its mode of assessment can best be understood by reference to Table 7 from their data on *Pseudomonas aeruginosa*. The first step is to determine the frequency with which each test is positive for the OTU's. These are set down in descending order and, from the table, the probability of occurrence of each test individually is determined. For example, tests 16, 59, 68, and 74 are positive for 32 of the 33 OTU's. The probability of the test being positive with any selected OTU is $32/33 = 0.97$. Similarly, test 5 is positive for 25 of the 33, and the probability of any one OTU being positive with test 5 is $25/33 = 0.76$.

The next step is the computation of probability of mutual occurrence of positive tests. This is obtained by multiplying

TABLE 7

Frequency of character occurrence in samples of 33 Pseudomonas aeruginosa strains

Character*	Occurrence	Computed probability
11, 14, 17, 18, 28, 38, 41, 51, 56, 60, 62, 64, 65, 69, 71, 72, 76	33	1.00
16, 59, 68, 74	32	0.97
43	31	0.94
45	30	0.91
29, 54	29	0.88
21, 25, 36	28	0.85
22	26	0.79
5	25	0.76
27, 32	24	0.73
42	20	0.61
8	19	0.58
30	17	0.52
7	14	0.43
58	13	0.39
26	10	0.30
4, 33, 73	9	0.27
44	7	0.21
20, 67	6	0.18
24, 75	5	0.15
31, 37	4	0.12
1, 46	2	0.06
3, 39, 52, 53, 55, 63, 70	1	0.03

* Minimum calculated organism defined by characters 11, 14, 17, 18, 28, 38, 41, 51, 56, 60, 62, 64, 65, 69, 71, 72, 76; maximum calculated organism defined by all positive characters (11 through 70). Reproduced by permission from Liston, Wiebe and Colwell, J. Bacteriol., *85*, 1963, 1067.

together the individual probabilities for *each* test. Inasmuch as the first 17 tests listed each have a probability of 1, the product of their probabilities is also 1. The probability of mutual occurrence of these 17 with the next 4 (tests 16, 59, 68, and 74) is $1^{17} \times 0.97^4 = 0.89$. The probability of mutual occurrence reaches a value of 0.02 at test 30 (35th test). With the addition of test 7, it falls to 0.01, and with test 58, to 0.004. It is thus unlikely that organisms will be found that have more than these 35 tests positive. However, some do occur because of lack of independence of some characters. When compensation is made for this, the *hypothetical median organism* can be defined as one with the 35 ± 3 tests positive. In this case, it will include all tests up to and including test 30.

It has been suggested that the hypothetical median organism should be designated as the neotype. There are some objections to this. With the acquisition of new data, the designation is apt to change, albeit very slightly. It is impossible to lyophilize it or deposit it in a culture collection for re-examination by others. The best alternative is to select the naturally occurring strain that most nearly approximates it. This has been done in the case of *Pseudomonas aeruginosa*.

Apart from serving the purpose of designating a type or neotype, the *hypothetical median organism* can also serve as the focus for assessment of the limits of the species. Liston, Wiebe, and Colwell have suggested that all OTU's that have similarities of 75 per cent or greater with the hypothetical median organism should constitute the species. It should be noted that, in the particular case cited, these authors estimated similarities scoring positive matches only. Additional study of these strains with the negative matches showed that, in general, the only effect on the results was to produce a higher level of similarity.

These recommendations must await further research before they can be generally accepted, but in the meantime they serve a very useful purpose.

Problems of Quantitation

I have deliberately deferred further discussion on quantitation in order to present as clear a picture as possible of the elements of the analysis. Use of quantitative characters introduces an element of "weighting" into the process of analysis by according more states to a quantitative than to a qualitative character.

Table 8 shows two slightly different proposals for what is called "nonadditive" coding, originally proposed by Sneath (J. Gen. Microbiol., *17*, 1957, 201) and by Beers and Lockhart (J. Gen. Microbiol., *28*, 1962, 633). In each case the results of scoring are based on two different methods of estimating similarities. In one, S (I), only the positive matches are scored. Both the negative matches and the "not considered (nc)" characters are deducted from the total number of tests in the denominator. The second, S (II), is the modified matching coefficient of Sokal and Michener. In this example I have chosen the quantitation of *size*. With the use of S (I), the denominator in each comparison in the method of Beers and Lockhart is 1 and, in that of Sneath, 2. These numbers are independent of the number of states into which the quantitative character is divided. With the use of S (II), the denominator varies with the circumstances. Although this is undesirable, it is regarded by Sokal and Sneath as of minor consequence, being balanced by other factors in the overall analysis.

Table 9 shows a method of additive coding compared with nonadditive coding, with determinations of similarity based on the modified matching coefficient of Sokal and Michener. With the additive coding, the score allocated to a multistate character is equal to the number of states into which it is divided. Weighting can become serious unless the number of states is kept to a minimum—at most, 4.

There is no real solution to the question of quantitation available yet. Experience may show that any one of several methods may yield satisfactory results.

Dendrogram

Another mode of expressing relationships between OTU's after an analysis is to

TABLE 8

Quantitative scoring methods

Compensation for weighting

Example: For size using 5 organisms A = 1.7, B = 3.0, C = 4.0, D = 1.5, E = 6.0 microns in length.

Scoring: Method I ignores all negative matches and all "nc" statements.
Method II includes all negative matches and all "nc" statements.

$$ S\ (I) = \frac{(\sum +)}{all - ((\sum -) + (\sum nc))} \qquad S\ (II) = \frac{(\sum +) + (\sum -)}{all - \sum nc} $$

Beers and Lockhart

Size	Coding 1	2	3	4	Features	1	2	3	4	Similarities	S (I)	S (II)
2	+	−	−	−	A	+	−	−	−	A-B	$\frac{0}{1}$	$\frac{2}{3}$
2-5	nc	+	−	−	B	nc	+	−	−			
5-8	nc	nc	+	−	C	nc	+	−	−	A-C	$\frac{0}{1}$	$\frac{2}{3}$
8	nc	nc	nc	+	D	+	−	−	−			
					E	nc	nc	+	−	A-D	$\frac{1}{1}$	$\frac{4}{4}$
										A-E	$\frac{0}{1}$	$\frac{1}{2}$

Sneath

Size	1	2	3	4	5		1	2	3	4	5		S (I)	S (II)
2	+	+	−	−	−	A	+	+	−	−	−	A-B	$\frac{1}{2}$	$\frac{3}{4}$
2-5	+	nc	+	−	−	B	+	nc	+	−	−			
5-8	+	nc	nc	+	−	C	+	nc	+	−	−	A-C	$\frac{1}{2}$	$\frac{3}{4}$
8	+	nc	nc	nc	+	D	+	+	−	−	−			
						E	+	nc	nc	+	−	A-D	$\frac{2}{2}$	$\frac{5}{5}$
												A-E	$\frac{1}{2}$	$\frac{2}{3}$

convert the information of the type given in Tables 2 and 5 into a dendrogram, such as has been done in Figure 2 for the data from Table 5.

Automatic Clustering and Plotting of Data Results by the Computer

In each of the methods described for presentation of the data there is the inference that the high-speed computer can present the investigator with the tabulated results in final, finished (for publication) format. This is indeed the case, and, in fact, the "on line" (*i.e.*, connected to the console of the computer and automatically operated) plotter can be used to good advantage. Plotting by machine of such informational parameters as $\bar{S}$ *vs.* $\mp$ provides both visual and numerical assessment of group homogeneity (Quadling and Colwell, 1963). In a matter of minutes, or seconds, plots of the computational results

TABLE 9
Coding multistate characters

Additive coding							Nonadditive coding				
Or-ganism	State		1	2	3	4	Or-ganism	State	X	Y_1	Y_2	Y_3
A	Absent	0	—	—	—	—	A	0 (undetecta-ble)	—	nc	nc	nc
B	+	1	+	—	—	—	B	1 (weak +)	+	+	—	—
C	++	2	+	+	—	—	C	2 (moderate +)	+	nc	+	—
D	+++	3	+	+	+	—	D	3 (strong +)	+	nc	nc	+
E	++++	4	+	+	+	+						

Similarities

$$S = \frac{(\sum +)}{\sum \text{all} - \sum \text{nc}}$$

B-D	$\frac{1}{4}$	Scored as two state characters with no attempt to reduce the weighting of the multistate characters	$\frac{1}{2}$
B-C	$\frac{1}{4}$		$\frac{1}{3}$
C-D	$\frac{2}{4}$		$\frac{1}{2}$
A-D	$\frac{0}{4}$		$\frac{0}{1}$

Note: Adapted from Sokal and Sneath, *Principles of Numerical Taxonomy*, W. H. Freeman.

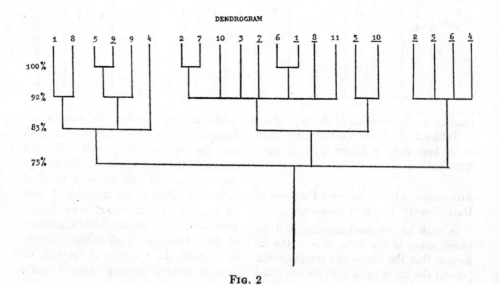

Fig. 2

are available for scanning and recomputing if necessary to omit OTU's obviously not related to the majority of the OTU's in the cluster within the standard deviations serving as boundaries.

Monothetic Groupings

Lockhart and Hartman (J. Bacteriol., *85*, 1963, 68) have described a method for the extraction of monothetic groups. The reader is referred to this paper for information.

Conventional *vs.* Numerical Analysis

Conventional methods have to date yielded relatively satisfactory results, which have, in the main, been confirmed by numerical methods. This has been due largely to the gradual mode of development of conventional systematics, starting with relatively small groups to which additional species have been added, and to periodic revision. Conventional methods cannot deal adequately with the mass handling of cultures, which has become the practice of "modern" taxonomists and for which numerical methods are suitable and provide objective analysis of the data.

This does not mean that conventional methods should be disregarded. The laboratory aspect of the two is the same, and much good work can be expected from both lines of approach. What is absolutely essential is that methods should be standardized and details of strain data published or filed in a suitable repository for subsequent reference.

The Place of the Computer

It should be noted that computers are machines and are not the analysts. Computers will only do what they are programmed to do, objecting more often, perhaps, than the human operator when the instruction is nonsensical. They are ideal for handling the type of $+$, $-$ information that characterizes descriptions of microbes and can take the tedium out of the task, often rendering possible analyses that would otherwise be impracticable, if not impossible.

The possession of a computer is desirable but not essential. The majority of those with access to machines are only too willing to process data for other investigators, provided it is presented in an intelligent form. What is essential is that the people concerned be thoroughly familiar with the operations that the program performs, and this requires little more than an ability to read and understand the data manipulations represented by a clearly set out flowchart, usually prepared and made available by the operator.

A COMPREHENSIVE KEY TO THE GENERA OF BACTERIA

USE OF THE KEY

First, determine the characters of the organism and then consult the Key, *always* commencing from the beginning. The Key poses a series of questions, which can be answered in the affirmative or negative. Boldface numbers on the right-hand side of the Key indicate the next number on the left to be consulted. The sequence should be followed until the right-hand number is replaced by a generic name. Keys to the particular genus in the *Manual* should then be consulted for species identification.

1. Organisms green, blue-green or yellowish green, brown or red, containing chlorophyll "a" either in well-defined chloroplasts or in the cytoplasm..............**Algae**
Organisms colorless or pigmented; if the latter, green pigments do not have the characteristics of chlorophyll "a"..........**2**

2. Diameter or width of cells exceeds 2.0 μ; proceed to...........Section A p. *19*
Diameter or width does not exceed 2.0 μ; proceed to..............Section B p. *26*

Note: a. In the assessment of diameter or width, measurement must be made of the cells themselves and not of any capsular structures or sheaths that may surround them. In Section A some cells have widths up to 100 μ and are clearly visible to the unaided eye.

b. To avoid confusion, the following terms have been used in the sense indicated below (for comment on the use of them, see the Introduction):

Multicellular Organism: a group of cells, arranged uniseriately, which are joined for the whole or major part of their width and result in an organism that has a lateral wall with little or no indentation and lack of articulation at the septa. The septa are clearly visible in unstained cells after the removal of inclusion substances, such as sulfur or fat.

In the Key, small organisms that appear to be unicellular in unstained preparations and in preparations stained by Gram's method, but which are distinctly multicellular after being stained to show cell walls, are treated with the unicellular organisms. A note to this effect appears at the appropriate place.

Unicellular Organism: an organism that shows no evidence of dividing septa, other than those involved in a normal division, in unstained preparations or in preparations stained to reveal cell walls.

Cell: a unicellular organism.

Filament: an elongated rod that shows no evidence of multicellularity without the application of special techniques designed to demonstrate cell walls.

Chain of Organisms: a group of unicellular or multicellular organisms, arranged uniseriately, which are completely separated or are attached for only a minor part of their width and are freely articulate at the point of attachment.

18

The presence or absence of a sheath should not be taken into consideration.

Trichome: this term, as used in the Key, may refer to (a) multicellular, nonflagellated, gliding organisms; (b) chains of unicellular, nonflagellated, gliding organisms; (c) nonmotile, multicellular organisms; and (d) multicellular flagellated organisms. These cover the different kinds of bacteria for which the term has been employed in descriptions in the *Manual*.

The presence of a sheath should not be taken into consideration.

Sheath: a hollow structure surrounding a chain of cells or a trichome. It may be close fitting but is not in intimate contact with the cells. Sheath-forming organisms usually produce a gum-like holdfast and a gum-like secretion resembling a capsule, but as the length of the chain or trichome increases, the gum-like secretion is replaced by a hollow structure, the sheath, which lacks intimate contact with the cells.

Capsule: a substance secreted by microorganisms that forms an envelope around the cell and remains in intimate contact with it. Its margin may be sharply defined or, owing to its relative solubility in water, merge imperceptibly into the surrounding fluids.

SECTION A

1. Multicellular organisms with or without a sheath *or* unicellular organisms arranged in chains and surrounded by a sheath.. **2**
Unicellular organisms................ **18**
2. Multicellular organisms not in a sheath
   a. Colorless *Anabaena*-like cells found in guinea pigs
      Anabaeniolum* (in Krass.)
              (*A. langeroni*)
   b. **3**
Organisms in a sheath.............. **11**
3. Both trichomes and abstricted cells are nonmotile and are not flagellated....... **4**
Either trichomes or abstricted cells or both

* See Krassilnikov, p. 643. These are possibly colorless mutants of *Anabaena*.

are motile. Motility may be either by gliding on solid surfaces (nonflagellated) or by means of flagella. (Apparently nonmotile but flagellated cells are included in this section)........................... **5**
4. Trichomes up to 5000 μ in length attached basally by means of a globular holdfast; endospores produced in any or all cells within the trichome and obliquely situated; recorded from the alimentary canal of millipedes, cockroaches, and toads
         Arthromitus p. *195*
               M p. 835
      Arthromitus (in Prévot)
      Arthromitus (in Krass.)
Note: See also *Bacillus enterothrix* (in Krass., p. 564).

Long trichomes arranged in bundles; each cell contains one or more gas vacuoles which gleam reddish in transmitted light; do not deposit sulfur internally
         Peloploca p. *137*
              M p. 270
      Peloploca (in Prévot)
5. Trichomes flagellated, peritrichous.. **6**
Trichomes or abstricted cells not flagellated; motility of a gliding type on solid surfaces or along adjacent cells........ **7**
6. Organisms approximately 5 μ in width and straight to curved; develop a large endospore apparently by fusion of several cells within the trichome. The spore is normally centrally located. Division of the organisms is preceded by formation of biconcave discs within the trichome somewhat similar to those produced by the blue-green alga *Oscillatoria;* found in large numbers in the cecum of the guinea pig
         Oscillospira p. *195*
              M p. 834
      Oscillospira (in Prévot)
      Oscillospira (in Krass.)
Organisms 3 μ or more wide; actively motile; do not produce endospores; common in fresh dung......**Caryophanon** p. *194*
              M p. 831
      Caryophanon (in Prévot)
      Caryophanon (in Krass.)

Note: Provost and Doetsch (J. Gen. Microbiol., *28*, 1962, 547) state that *Caryophanon latum* is Gram positive.

7. Spiral cells...**Thiospirillopsis** p. *197*
M p. 840
Thiospirillopsis (in Prévot)
Not spirals..........................**8**
8. Entire trichomes are motile........**9**
Entire trichomes are not motile; attached by means of a holdfast; taper from the base to the tip; single cells formed by abstriction from the tip are motile by a gliding motion on a solid surface; trichomes characteristically arranged in rosettes but may occur singly; do not deposit sulfur internally
Leucothrix p. *200*
M p. 850
Leucothrix (in Prévot)
Pontothrix (in Krass.)
Entire trichomes are not motile; attached by means of a holdfast; taper from the base to the tip; single cells formed by abstriction from the tip are motile by a gliding motion on a solid surface; trichomes characteristically arranged in rosettes but may occur singly; deposit sulfur internally when growing in sulfide-containing waters
Thiothrix p. *198*
M p. 842
Thiothrix (in Prévot)
Thiothrix (in Krass.)
Note: Harold and Stanier (Bacteriol. Revs., *19*, 1955, 49) were unable to find a sheath on *Leucothrix*, although the original description cited a prominent sheath. Pringsheim (Bacteriol. Revs., *21*, 1957, 69) reports that a prominent sheath does exist but cannot be demonstrated by means of nigrosin. It stains pink with methylene blue, whereas the cells stain a dark indigo. Winogradsky (Schwefelbacterien, Leipzig, 1888) also notes that the sheath of *Thiothrix* is almost indistinguishable in living specimens but becomes visible at the tip, where hormogonia are separating, or may be observed when degeneration occurs after removal of sulfide.

The insertion of *Leucothrix* and *Thiothrix* at this point in the Key is made to cover

the possibility that sheaths may be overlooked.
9. Trichomes flat and ribbon-like.....**9a**
Trichomes cylindrical..............**9b**
9a. Trichomes with end cells hemispherical
Simonsiella p. *196*
M p. 833
Oscillospira (in Krass.)
Cells concave: tend to break up into groups of 4 cells....................**Alysiella**
Note: See Steed (J. Gen. Microbiol., *29*, 1963, 615).
9b. Elemental sulfur is deposited in a globular form in the cells when they are growing in waters containing hydrogen sulfide..............**Beggiatoa** p. *197*
M p. 838
Beggiatoa (in Prévot)
Beggiatoa (in Krass.)
Elemental sulfur is not deposited internally............................**10**
10. Cells within the trichomes contain one or more gas vacuoles, which gleam bluish or reddish in transmitted light; described from surface films in pond waters
Pelonema p. *137*
M p. 271
Pelonema (in Prévot)
Note: Pelonema is described as having a thin sheath and as possibly being motile. It seems unlikely that floating motile filaments would be ensheathed, and for this reason *Pelonema* is included here.

Not as above........**Vitreoscilla** p. *199*
M p. 845
Vitreoscilla (in Prévot)
11. Width of sheath increasing from base to tip; cells within the sheath divide transversely and longitudinally towards the tip to produce large numbers of coccoid elements; attached by means of a holdfast
12
Width of the sheath uniform or variable; division of cells in transverse direction only............................**13**
12. Cells within the basal portion of the sheath longer than wide; when growing in

iron-bearing waters, the sheath becomes heavily impregnated with iron

Crenothrix p. *137*

M p. *272*

Crenothrix (in Prévot)

Crenothrix (in Krass.)

Cells within the basal portion of the sheath much wider than long; sheaths remain colorless in iron-bearing waters

Phragmidiothrix p. *137*

M p. *273*

Phragmidiothrix (in Prévot)

13. Cells within the base of the sheath 2 by 10 µ with rounded ends; divide transversely near the tip to produce spherical, nonmotile cells, which are extruded either singly or in chains. The sheath becomes heavily impregnated with iron or manganese, becoming wide at the base and tapering towards the tip; attached by a holdfast; false branching is common . Clonothrix p. *138*

M p. *274*

Spirally wound to straight chains up to 250 µ long; sheaths heavily encrusted with iron................Leptothrix p. *136*

(*L. pseudovacuolata*)

M p. *264*

Leptothrix (in Prévot)

Leptothrix (in Krass.)

Note: The single species may be a *Sphaerotilus.*

Not as above..................... 14

14. Chains of cells enclosed in a sheath of uniform width; attached by means of a conspicuous holdfast; free cells motile by means of subpolar flagella

Sphaerotilus p. *134*

M p. *263*

Sphaerotilus (in Prévot)

Sphaerotilus (in Krass.)

Note: Species of *Sphaerotilus* have been shown to precipitate iron in the sheath, in which state they strongly resemble species of *Leptothrix*. Skerman, Dementjeva, and Carey (J. Bacteriol., *73*, 1957, 504) have shown that *S. natans* will also deposit sulfur internally. Although it has a superficial resemblance to *Thiothrix*, it differs in having flagella.

Not as above; if motile, not flagellated.. 15

15. Sulfur deposited internally when grown in water containing hydrogen sulfide.... 16

Sulfur not deposited internally........ 17

16. Several trichomes within a common sheath...............Thioploca p. *198*

M p. *841*

Thioploca (in Prévot)

Thioploca (in Krass.)

A single trichome within each sheath; usually attached by a holdfast

Thiothrix p. *198*

M p. *842*

Thiothrix (in Prévot)

Thiothrix (in Krass.)

17. Colorless trichomes, attached at the base, tapering from the base to the tip; most characteristically arranged in rosettes but may occur singly. Constriction of the outer wall near the tips produces a beaded appearance. Single cells are abstricted and may exhibit a gliding motility on a solid surface. The trichomes themselves are immobile..............Leucothrix p. *200*

M p. *850*

Leucothrix (in Prévot)

Pontothrix (in Krass.)

Note: Harold and Stanier (Bacteriol. Revs., *19*, 1955, 49) were unable to find a sheath on *Leucothrix*, although the original description cited a prominent sheath. Pringsheim (Bacteriol. Revs., *21*, 1957, 69) reports that a prominent sheath does exist but cannot be demonstrated by means of nigrosin. It stains pink with methylene blue, whereas the cells stain a dark indigo.

Colorless trichomes up to 500 µ in length; each cell contains one or more gas vacuoles, which gleam reddish or bluish in transmitted light; enclosed in a thin, transparent sheath; occur singly...Pelonema p. *137*

M p. *271*

Pelonema (in Prévot)

Note: Peloploca, which has a similar cellular morphology, although described as "no sheath evident," and which occurs in bundles, should be compared carefully with *Pelonema*.

18. Spiral cells.................... **19**
Not as above...................... **23**
19. Cells contain bacteriochlorophyll and carotenoid pigments; cell masses various shades of red or purple.............. **20**
Not as above...................... **21**
20. Oxidize hydrogen sulfide, depositing sulfur internally...**Thiospirillum** p. *100*
M p. 46
Thiospirillum (in Prévot)
Thiospirillum (in Krass.)
Do not oxidize hydrogen sulfide
Rhodospirillum p. *104*
M p. 58
Rhodospirillum (in Prévot)
Rhodospirillum (in Krass.)
21. Cells actively motile, with flagella.
a. Sulfur deposited internally when growing in waters containing hydrogen sulfide.......**Thiospira** p. *110*
M p. 82
Thiospira (in Prévot)
Thiospira (in Krass.)
b. Sulfur not deposited.
i. Sporulating.....**Sporospirillum***
Spirillum† (in Krass.)
ii. Non-sporulating
Spirillum† (in Krass.)
Flexible cells; not flagellated; do not deposit sulfur internally................ **22**
22. Large, spiral cells with tapered ends, up to 100 μ long; protoplast wound spirally around a well-defined axial filament; no cross striations; motile by means of a flexuous movement......**Spirochaeta** p. *207*
M p. 893
Spiral cells with a round cross section and blunt ends; up to 60 μ long; cells have a ridge or crista composed of numerous fibrils running along one side of the spiral; cross striations distinct; found in the intestinal tract of molluscs
Cristispira p. *207*
M p. 895

* See Delaporte, Ann. Inst. Pasteur, *107*, 1964, 246. She places *Spirillum praeclarum* in *Sporospirillum*.
† *Spirillum praeclarum* and *Spirillum kolkwitzii*.

Cristispira (in Prévot)
Cristispira (in Krass.)
23. Stalked cells; aquatic in habit..... **24**
Cells not borne on stalks............ **25**
24. Cells rod-shaped; 2 by 6 to 12 μ; single cells attached terminally and at right angles to branches of a lobose, dichotomously branched stalk; form globular bush-like or plate-like growth on the surface of waters............... **Nevskia** p. *139*
M p. 216
Nevskia (in Prévot)
Gallionella (in Krass.)
Cells pear-shaped to spherical; multiply by budding; cells attached by a long, slender stalk to a holdfast, with several stalks frequently arising from one holdfast. (This organism has so far been found only in lake waters where the temperature does not exceed 23° C.).......**Blastocaulis** p. *140*
M p. 279
Blastocaulis (in Prévot)
Blastocaulis‡ (in Krass.)
Cells pear-shaped; borne on a very short stalk; cells grow attached to one another in a cauliflower-like mass and reproduce by longitudinal division and budding. Colonies break up at intervals, and liberated cells start new colonies. Cells and methods of reproduction resemble those found in *Chamaesiphon*, a blue-green alga; discovered in the body cavity of fresh water crustaceans..........**Pasteuria** p. *139*
M p. 279
Pasteuria (in Prévot)
Pasteuria‡ (in Krass.)
25. Endospores produced........... **26**
No endospores produced............ **27**
26. Rod-shaped cells, fusiform; containing 2 to 8 large, cylindrical endospores when mature; found in the cecum of the guinea pig.................. **Metabacterium**
(See Chatton and Pérard, Compt. rend. Soc. Biol. Paris, *65*, 1913, 1232.)
Spindle-shaped cells up to 100 μ long with

‡ *Genus incertae sedis.*

two endospores each 1 to 3 by 8 μ; found in the alimentary tract of tadpoles

Fusosporus*

Rod-shaped cells containing only a single endospore.

a. Aerobic; spores do not distend the rod: See *Bacillus oxalaticus, B. apicum, B. giganteus, B. fastidiosus, B. enterothrix,* and *B. camptospora* in Krassilnikov.

b. Spores distend the rods; anaerobic, motile....... **Clostridium** p. *180*

M p. 634

Clostridium (in Prévot)

Note: This entry covers *Manual* species 12 and 30, not listed by Krassilnikov.

Spherical cells in cubical packets

Sarcina p. *162*

M p. 467

Sarcina (in Prévot)

Planosarcina (in Krass.)

27. Cells contain bacteriochlorophyll and carotenoid pigments; cell masses are various shades of red, brown, and purple; proceed to............ Section J p. *90*

Not as above...................... **28**

28. Iron deposited on the cells or in capsules........................... **29**

Note: In the absence of further information, these organisms are identified on their iron-depositing characteristics. Most iron organisms studied in pure culture metabolize the organic compound that forms the iron chelate, and the liberated iron chelates with some cell component. Citrate-utilizing organisms will, for example, release iron from ferric ammonium citrate. Accumulation of the iron in or on the cell may depend only upon the nature of the cell substance. Pure culture studies may place these organisms in more commonly recognized genera. Many more organisms, if tested, may fall into the following genera. They should also be treated as non-iron-depositing cells and should be followed through the Key.

* See Delaporte, Ann. Inst. Pasteur, *107*, 1964, 845.

Not as above...................... **32**

29. Iron deposited as a torus, a solid ring partially or completely surrounding the cell in one area only, giving the cells the appearance of open or closed links of a chain.. **30**

Iron deposited uniformly over the cells or capsules........................... **31**

30. Cells completely surrounded by a torus

Naumanniella p. *121*

M p. 223

Naumanniella (in Prévot)

Naumanniella (in Krass.)

Cells only partially enclosed, appearing like a horseshoe. Flagella of unequal length borne at the open end

Ochrobium p. *121*

M p. 225

Ochrobium (in Prévot)

Ochrobium (in Krass.)

Note: The type of flagellation suggests that this may be an alga.

31. Spherical cells 1 to 2 μ in diameter, 2 to 60 or more cells occurring in a primary capsule 10 to 20 μ wide; secondary capsules unite to form a mucilaginous colony; iron or manganese compounds are stored in the secondary capsules.. **Siderocapsa** p. *119*

M p. 218

Cells coccoid to ovoid, 4.8 to 5.0 by 6.5 μ, forming short chains embedded in a thin mucilaginous layer; iron compounds stored in the surface membrane of the cells

Sideronema p. *120*

M p. 220

Sideronema (in Prévot)

Cells rod-shaped, 2.5 by 6 to 15 μ, straight or slightly bent; not encapsulated; iron or manganese stored on the surface or in the membrane of the cell

Siderobacter p. *122*

M p. 226

Siderobacter (in Prévot)

Siderobacter† (in Krass.)

32. Strict intracellular parasites occurring in the cytoplasm of conjunctival cells in cattle, goats, and sheep. Elliptical, coccoid, rod-shaped, and comma-shaped cells occur

† *Genus incertae sedis.*

Colettsia p. *211*
M p. 961
See also Section K............... p. *93*
Not as above...................... **33**
33. Cells spherical to cylindrical, varying from spheres 5 μ in diameter to large cylindrical organisms 35 to 100 μ long; sulfur deposited internally when growing in the presence of hydrogen sulfide. In one of the two recorded species, large crystals of calcium carbonate fill the cells; motile with a slow, jerky, rotating action when in contact with solid surfaces

Achromatium p. *200*
(*A. oxaliferum*)
M p. 852
Achromatium (in Prévot)
Achromatium (in Krass.)

Note: Cells similar to the above but lacking calcium carbonate are recognized as *Achromatium volutans* by the *Manual*, which considers the species synonymous with *Thiophysa volutans, Thiophysa macrophysa,* and *Thiosphaerella amylifera,* recognized by Krassilnikov (p. 657).
Not as above...................... **34**
34. Cells spherical to ovoid, 5 to 20 μ in diameter, with the cytoplasm compressed in one end of the cell; sulfur deposited in the cytoplasmic layer; exhibits an extremely rapid darting motion in free solution; peritrichate* flagella; found in waters containing hydrogen sulfide, forming a tenacious web-like growth in a zone of critical hydrogen sulfide-oxygen concentration...............**Thiovulum** p. *110*
M p. 81
Thiovulum (in Prévot)
Thiovulum (in Krass.)
Not as above...................... **35**
35. Colorless rod-shaped cells containing sulfur embedded in a gelatinous matrix resembling the finger-like processes of *Zoogloea ramigera*......... **Thiodendron**
(*T. mucosum*)
(See Lackey and Lackey, J. Gen. Microbiol., *26*, 1961, 29, nov. gen.)

* See de Boer, La Rivière, and Houwink, Antonie van Leeuwenhoek, *27*, 1961, 447.

Not as above...................... **36**
36. Large, cylindrical, pear-shaped or slightly curved rods 3 to 14 μ wide; actively motile by means of a single polar flagellum; contain large spherules of calcium carbonate and may also contain sulfur

Macromonas p. *109*
M p. 80
Macromonas (in Prévot)
Achromatium† (in Krass.)
Curved rods with polar flagella; 1.7 to 2.4 by 6.6 to 14.0 μ; contain small globules of sulfur in the center of the cell and large volutin granules at each end

Thiospira p. *110*
M p. 882
Thiospira (in Prévot)
Thiospira (in Krass.)
Not as above...................... **37**
37. Cells spherical.................. **38**
Cells rod-shaped................... **47**
38. Cells always coccal............. **39**
Cells coccal only as a stage in the life cycle of a rod-shaped cell................ **43**
39. Arranged in cubical packets

Sarcina p. *162*
M p. 467
Sarcina (in Prévot)
Sarcina (in Krass.)
(See also *Azotobacter macrocytogenes* in Prévot.)
Not as above...................... **40**
40. Cocci varying in diameter from 0.5 to 4.0 μ; grow in a mineral salts-bicarbonate medium with formate as the only known source of available carbon, fermenting it to methane, CO_2, and possibly hydrogen; pH range, 7.4 to 9.2

Methanococcus p. *162*
(*M. vannielii*)
M p. 473
Methanococcus (in Prévot)
Not as above...................... **41**
41. Aerobic....................... **42**
Anaerobic spherical cells; pleomorphic, ranging in diameter from 0.7 to 2.5 μ; occurring in pairs, in short chains, and in irregular groups; dependent upon glycine

† Only for *M. mobilis.*

for growth in organic media. Glycine is decomposed to CO_2, NH_3, and acetic acid

Peptococcus p. *163*
(*P. glycinophilus*)
M p. *474*
Diplococcus (in Prévot)

42. Gram positive; cells occur in irregular clusters............Micrococcus p. *158*
M p. *455*
Micrococcus (in Prévot)
Micrococcus (in Krass.)

Gram negative; fix atmospheric nitrogen

Azotobacter p. *140*
M p. *283*
Azotobacter (in Prévot)
Azotobacter (in Krass.)
Azotococcus (in Tchan)

(See Tchan, Proc. Linnean Soc. N.S. Wales, *78*, 1953, 85.)

43. Aerobic....................... 44
Anaerobic large cocci, 3 to 4 μ wide, sometimes bearing rod-shaped protuberances on opposite sides and at an obtuse angle to one another, a pleomorphic stage of a rod-shaped cell 0.8 by 2.4 to 10 μ; produce copious gas from peptone

Sphaerophorus p. *157*
(*S. ridiculosis*)
M p. *441*
Sphaerophorus (in Prévot)

44. Pleomorphic cultures consisting of large and small cocci and small rod-shaped cells, which are motile by means of a single polar flagellum; strongly halophilic, requiring 20 to 30 per cent salt for optimal growth; Gram negative

Halobacterium p. *119*
(*H. cutirubrum*)
M p. *207*
Serratia (in Prévot)
Pseudomonas (in Krass.)
(*P. carnea*)

Not as above....................... 45

45. Cells coccoid only at pH 7.0 on peptone yeast extract acetate agar; develop into multicellular rods with peritrichous flagella under other conditions; do not fix atmospheric nitrogen

Caryophanon p. *194*
M p. *831*
Caryophanon (in Prévot)
Caryophanon (in Krass.)

Not as above....................... 46

46. Spherical cells produced in macroscopic fruiting bodies on decaying vegetable material or in culture; fruiting bodies sessile or nearly so. The cocci germinate to produce rod-shaped cells, which glide on a solid surface; not flagellated

Myxococcus p. *204*
M p. *883*
Myxococcus (in Prévot)
Myxococcus (in Krass.)

Or.............Chondrococcus p. *205*
M p. *886*
Chondrococcus (in Prévot)
Chondrococcus (in Krass.)

See Section L for criteria for separation
p. *94*

Cells grow in nitrogen-free mineral salts media containing a suitable source of carbon, fixing atmospheric nitrogen

Azotobacter p. *140*
M p. *283*
Azotobacter (in Prévot)
Azotobacter (in Krass.)

Not as above....................... 47

47. Thick, long, straight or curved nonseptate filaments frequently having a bacillus-like body attached to one end; dichotomous branching frequently seen in microcolonies on brain heart infusion agar with or without 0.2 per cent yeast extract incubated 24 hours under 5 per cent CO_2 plus 95 per cent N_2 at 37° C. Gram positive. Reproduce by fragmentation. Facultative. Occasional strains anaerobic. Found in the oral cavity..............Bacterionema
(*B. matruchotii*)

(See Gilmour, Howell, and Biddy, Bacteriol. Revs., *25*, 1961, 131. This organism is also known as *Leptotrichia*.)

Not as above....................... 48

48. Curved rods with a bunch of flagella inserted laterally in the concave part of the cell; anaerobic; recorded from the cecum of

the guinea pig, the buccal cavity of man, and the rumen of the herbivore

Selenomonas p. *127*

M p. *258*

.... Selenomonas (in Prévot)

Note: Prévot regards *S. ruminantium* and *S. sputigena* as *species incertae sedis.*
Straight rods and pleomorphic rods.... 49
49. Large anaerobic, gram negative, non-sporeforming, nonmotile rods have been isolated from the feces of turkeys. These bacteria average 1 to 2.5 μ in diameter and 5 to 20 μ in length. They do not form hydrogen sulfide, reduce nitrate, or form appreciable catalase. They grow only in the presence of fermentable carbohydrates and related compounds, producing no visible gas, and from glucose form acetic acid, propionic acid, and dextro-lactic acid

Bacteroides

(See Harrison and Hansen, Antonie van Leeuwenhoek, *29*, 1963, 22.)
Not as above...................... 50
50. Motile with polar flagella........ 51
Motile by means of peritrichous flagella; grow in a nitrogen-free mineral salts medium, fixing atmospheric nitrogen

Azotobacter p. *140*

M p. *283*

.... Azotobacter (in Prévot)

Azotobacter (in Krass.)

51. Cells 1.4 to 2.0 by 4.0 to 5.0 μ; motile by means of polar flagella; anaerobic to microaerophilic; ferments glucose, producing ethyl alcohol, carbon dioxide, and lactic acid............. Zymomonas p. *117*

M p. *199*

Zymomonas (in Prévot)

Pleomorphic cultures consisting of large and small cocci and small rod-shaped cells, which are motile by means of a single polar flagellum; strongly halophilic, requiring 20 to 30 per cent salt for optimal growth; Gram negative

Halobacterium p. *119*

(*H. cutirubrum*)

M p. *207*

Serratia (in Prévot)

Pseudomonas (in Krass.)

(*P. carnea*)

SECTION B

Note: Criteria for the separation of the small, colorless, flagellated protozoan forms from bacteria are very limited. Organisms that (*a*) when stained with Giemsa show a clearly differentiated nucleus and cytoplasm without preliminary acid hydrolysis, (*b*) divide along the longitudinal axis, and (*c*) possess flagella or cilia that are clearly discernible without staining are possibly protozoa. A cross section of the flagella of protozoa examined with the electron microscope shows a structure quite unlike that of bacterial flagella. The flagella of protozoa consist of a pair of central fibrils surrounded by nine pairs of peripheral fibrils, all enclosed in a sheath (C. K. Pine, Exptl. Cell Research, *14*, 1958, 388). The nucleus of the protozoan cell is surrounded by a nuclear membrane.

1. Ultramicroscopic and filterable forms; strict intracellular parasites of animals and plants not cultivable on artificial media but transferable by contact or by arthropod vectors...................... Viruses
2. Strict parasites occurring within tissue cells of animal hosts or on or in erythrocytes. With few exceptions, which are treated under Section H, they cannot be or have not been cultivated in artificial media. Some can be cultivated in chick embryos or in tissue cultures. In the tissues or blood stream they occur *either* as spherical elementary bodies and initial bodies from 0.2 to 2.0 μ in diameter or slightly larger (usually 0.20 to 0.35 μ), singly or in aggregations in plaques several microns in diameter, or as bacillary, triangular, ring-shaped, horseshoe-shaped, and other pleomorphic forms. Bacillary forms may be as long as 3 μ. Stain with Giemsa's or Macchiavello's stain without differentiation into cytoplasmic and nuclear structures, a condition that would be suggestive of protozoa

Section K p. *93*

3. Small, spherical bodies, 150 to 300 mμ in diameter, which germinate to produce filaments approximately 0.2 μ wide and from 2 to 50 μ long, sparsely or richly

branching. At a later stage of growth, small endomycelial corpuscles develop in the filaments by a process of successive condensation and constriction. As a result, the homogeneous filaments are retransformed into chains of close-set spherical bodies, which are released by fragmentation; highly resistant to penicillin and sulfathiazole; colonies on agar have a dense, granulated central area, which penetrates into the agar and which is surrounded by a translucent, flat, peripheral zone, or consist of a pearly film containing numerous spots due to calcium or magnesium soaps; do not ferment lactose, sucrose, mannitol, or dulcitol............. **Mycoplasma** p. *208*
M p. 914
Asterococcus (in Prévot)

Note: a. L-phase colonies of some bacteria bear a strong resemblance to the colonies of *Mycoplasma*. They are generally more opaque and more heavily marked on the surface, tend to revert to the normal bacillary form in penicillin-free, semisolid media, are more difficult to subculture, do not require cholesterol for growth, and ferment the same carbohydrates as the parent organism.

b. Zavarzin (Mikrobiologia, *30*, 1961, 952; and *32*, 1963, 1020) describes a very thin filamentous organism active in the oxidation of manganese in a manganese carbonate medium. The organism is named
Metallogenium
(*M. symbioticum*)

4. Spiral cells; proceed to
Section C p. *28*
This section does not include (*a*) all forms like *Vitreoscilla*, which, through their great length and extreme flexibility, are apt to coil in one plane in watch spring fashion; (*b*) spiral cells of the *Streptomyces* type, which arise from branching Gram positive filaments; or (*c*) chains of vibrios. The latter do not possess the true helical twist of the spiral organisms.

5. Spherical to ovoid cells that reproduce by production of a tubular outgrowth, 0.2 to 0.3 μ wide, from the cell, on the end of which a daughter cell is formed. The tubular outgrowths may be simple or branched. Daughter cells are initially spherical but are later ovoid to rod-shaped; colorless or contain photosynthetic pigments.

Colorless cells, ovoid, 0.5 to 1.0 μ when mature; motile by means of a single polar flagellum; daughter cells may break loose from the tubular outgrowth and form tubes of their own while still actively motile
Hyphomicrobium p. *105*
M p. 277
Hyphomicrobium (in Prévot)
Hyphomicrobium* (in Krass.)

Cell masses salmon pink to deep orange-red; cells ovoid, 1.2 by 2.8 μ; nonmotile; contain photosynthetic pigments; grow only under anaerobic conditions when exposed to light
Rhodomicrobium p. *105*
M p. 277
Rhodomicrobium (in Prévot)

Note: Zavarzin (Mikrobiologia, *30*, 1961, 952), in a review on the stalked bacteria, describes a genus *Pedomicrobium* originally described by Aristovskaya, which resembles *Hyphomicrobium* and *Rhodomicrobium* but is heavily coated with oxides of manganese.

6. Spherical cells that reproduce by binary fission or by budding. Well-defined stalks are secreted by some species, the budding form of reproduction being confined to the stalked types; proceed to
Section D p. *31*

7. Vegetative cells, rod-shaped, not spirally twisted; Gram negative. Microcysts produced in macroscopically visible fruiting bodies or occur loosely among elongated S-shaped, twisted, or straight, flexible Gram negative rods; germinate to produce rod-shaped cells, which are motile only by a creeping action on solid surfaces. These rods may contract to form spherical microcysts or may combine in groups to form fruiting bodies in which the spherical or rod-shaped microcysts are formed.. Section L p. *94*

* Considers systematic position uncertain.

8. Rod-shaped cells, 0.5 to 1.5 by 2 to 5 μ, which grow in colonies on the surface of water containing sulfide and which deposit sulfur either inside or outside the cells. One species forms bladder-like gelatinous colonies, with the bacteria embedded in the surface..........**Thiobacterium** p. *109*
M p. 79
Thiobacterium (in Prévot)
Note: This very poorly defined group is separated here because of a complete lack of information of other properties. It is suggested that any such forms, if found, should be keyed out in the section on rods to determine their possible taxonomic relationship. The presence of the sulfur around the cells in such a location may not be significant.*

9. Rod-shaped and filamentous forms reproducing by binary fission, by fragmentation of the mycelium, by the production of endospores or conidia, or by the production of microcysts; proceed to
Section E p. *37*

10. Colorless, spherical cells, 0.8 to 1.0 μ in diameter, arranged in parallel rows in flat sheets on the surface of liquid manure and culture media. The sheets break characteristically into squares, each of 16 cells. Grows well on acetate plus beef extract plus yeast extract agar. Single cells are rare
Lampropedia
Note: a. This genus does not appear in the seventh edition of the *Manual*. The description given by Pringsheim (J. Gen. Microbiol., *13*, 1955, 285) does not give a clear indication of the shape or size of the cells, emphasis being placed on the peculiar colony form, of which an excellent illustration has been given. The information on morphology given above was obtained by phase contrast examination of a culture kindly supplied by Dr. Pringsheim. In preparations heat-fixed and stained by Gram, the cells are Gram negative and appear to be lenticular in shape (see Plate 31, Fig. 4).

* Janke (Mikroskopie, wien Zentralblatt fur Mikroskopische Forschung und Methodik, Jg. 1959, Bd 14, Heft 11/12, Seite 364) agrees that the systematic status of *Thiobacterium* and possibly other members of the *Thiobacteriales* is uncertain.

b. Schad, Knowles, and Meerovitch (Can. J. Microbiol., *10*, 1964, 801) report the occurrence of *Lampropedia* in the gut contents of nematodes of the genus *Tachygonetria*, which occur in the colon of the tortoise *Testudo graeca*. Identification was made only by optical means.

c. The fine structure of *Lampropedia* has been studied by Murray (Can. J. Microbiol., *9*, 1963, 593).

For further information see Chapman, Murray, and Salton, Proc. roy. Soc. B., *158*, 1963, 498; Kuhn and Starr, Archiv. Mikrobiol., *52*, 1965, 350; and Pangborn and Starr, J. Bacteriol., *91*, 1966, 2025.

11. *Note:* Attention is drawn to a new group of microorganisms described by A. E. Kriss and I. N. Mitzkevich (J. Gen. Microbiol., *20*, 1959, 1) in a paper entitled "Krassilnikoviae: A New Class of Microorganisms found in the Sea and Ocean Depths." The authors give the following diagnosis: "Filaments, non-septate, non-ramified, diameter 0.4–0.5 μ may be enclosed in a sheath. At one end form a cluster-shaped head, consisting of rounded bodies of diameter 0.5–2.0 μ. The number of round bodies in a cluster on one filament may amount to several scores. The organisms are widely spread in seas and oceans. May be found in considerable number at deep horizons. Have not been obtained in laboratory culture. Do not grow in conventional media or in isolated sea water samples. Rapidly develop on submerged fouling slides." (Plate 8, Fig. 4.)

SECTION C

1. Organisms contain chlorobium chlorophyll *or* bacteriochlorophyll with carotenoid pigments......................**2**
Organisms do not contain photosynthetic pigments..........................**4**

2. Nonmotile cells containing only chlorobium chlorophyll; appear distinctly green even under a microscope; may be found in *pure cultures* associated with other morphological forms, such as rods and streptococcal forms, with the latter often predominating;

strictly anaerobic cells, which oxidize sulfide, depositing sulfur outside the cells

Chlorobium   p. *101*
M p. 62
Chlorobium (in Prévot)
Chlorobium (in Krass.)

Note: This pleomorphism, recorded by van Niel, has been disputed by later investigators.

Cells contain bacteriochlorophyll and carotenoid pigments; red or purple in masses of cells; actively motile by means of polar flagella............................ 3

3. Organisms grow autotrophically under anaerobic conditions exposed to light; oxidize sulfide and thiosulfate to sulfur, which is deposited inside the cells

Thiospirillum   p. *100*
M p. 46
Thiospirillum (in Prévot)
Thiospirillum (in Krass.)

Organisms will grow anaerobically when exposed to light but will not grow under strictly autotrophic conditions; require growth factors available in yeast extract; may oxidize sulfide but do not oxidize thiosulfate; sulfur is not deposited in the cells

Rhodospirillum   p. *104*
M p. 58
Rhodospirillum (in Prévot)
Rhodospirillum (in Krass.)

4. Uniseriate chains of cells enclosed in a sheath; impregnated with iron when in ironbearing waters; spirally wound around themselves or algal filaments

Leptothrix   p. *136*
M p. 264
Leptothrix (in Prévot)
Leptothrix (in Krass.)

Note: Species of *Sphaerotilus*, considered by Pringsheim (Phil. Trans. Roy. Soc. London, Ser. B, *233*, 1949, 453) and others as identical with *Leptothrix*, frequently show spirally twisted, sheathed forms among normally straight ones.

Chains of curved rods wound into a ball within a nearly spherical capsule; do not store iron or manganese

Myconostoc   p. *127*
M p. 260
Myconostoc (in Prévot)

Spiral cells bearing a torus of iron hydroxide..............Naumanniella   p. *121*
M p. 223
Naumanniella (in Prévot)
Naumanniella* (in Krass.)

Very thin cells wound into tight cylindrical coils, 15 to 20 μ long; may be embedded in a capsular material when grown on silica gel. Slowly oxidize ammonia to nitrite

Nitrosospira   p. *106*
M p. 70
Nitrosospira (in Prévot)

Not as above....................... 5

5. Motile trichomes having a slow, creeping, rotating type of motility on solid surfaces; no flagella

a. Sulfur deposited internally

Thiospirillopsis   p. *197*
M p. 840
Thiospirillopsis (in Prévot)

b. No sulfur deposited internally. Spiral cells, 0.5 to 1.2 μ wide and 60 to 80 μ long, with a spiral amplitude of 4 to 25 μ; cross striations in stained cells distinct; no axial filament or crista;[†] motile but not flagellated; found in oysters and also free living

Saprospira   p. *197*
M p. 894
Saprospira (in Prévot)
Saprospira (in Krass.)

Nonmotile trichomes spirally wound around one another in bundles; not unsheathed; cells within the trichomes contain gas vacuoles, which have a reddish gleam in transmitted light

Peloploca   p. *137*
M p. 270
Peloploca (in Prévot)

Not as above....................... 6

6. Cells parasitic on the protozoan, *Paramecium*............................ 7

Not as above....................... 8

* Systematic position considered uncertain.
† See Lewin, Can. J. Microbiol., *8*, 1962, 555.

7. Cells contain 1.5 to 2.5 spiral turns; tapered at the ends; parasitic within the micronucleus of *Paramecium aurelia*, causing marked enlargement of the micronucleus, which is filled with spirals

Holospora
(*H. undulata*)
M p. 929
Holospora (in Prévot)

Cells twisted in two spiral turns that are not abrupt; one end pointed and the other rounded; no flagella; movement helicoid; endospores are formed; parasitic in the cytoplasm of *Paramecium caudatum*

Drepanospira
M p. 928
Drepanospira (in Prévot)

8. Cells, not more than 10 μ long, which may appear spiral in heat-fixed and stained preparations; flexible rods in the living state; motile by means of a creeping action on solid surfaces

possibly **Cytophaga** p. *201*
M p. 858
Cytophaga (in Prévot)
Cytophaga (in Krass.)

See also Section L..................p. *94*
Not as above; cells actively motile in free solution............................. 9

9. Cells relatively rigid; motile by means of polar flagella.................... 10
Cells flexible; motile by means of a helicoid flexing action: no flagella............. 12

10. Cells oxidize hydrogen sulfide, depositing sulfur as small globules in the center of the cell with volutin granules towards the ends.................Thiospira p. *110*
M p. 82
Thiospira (in Prévot)
Thiospira* (in Krass.)

Not as above..................... 11

11. Cells consisting of a single complete spiral twist; rather sharply angulated; cells 1.5 to 2.0 μ wide at the center and tapering towards both ends. In the center of the cell is an ovoid to rounded body almost as wide as the cell and clearly visible without

* Krassilnikov recognizes three species in addition to those listed in the *Manual*.

staining. It stains deeply with neutral red in killed cells and with Heidenhain's iron-hematoxylin or Giemsa's stain in fixed cells and is considered to be a nucleus; motile by means of polar flagella; when attached to an object at one end, cells are capable of contraction to a more angulated spiral

Paraspirillum p. *127*
M p. 257
Paraspirillum (in Prévot)

Note: The author has seen in pond waters several cells very similar morphologically to these cells, except that the central body appeared pale green and may be a chloroplast.

Not as above; spirals quite rigid; movement of a definite helical type in liquids

Spirillum p. *126*
M p. 253
Spirillum (in Prévot)
Spirillum (in Krass.)

Note: Several species of vibrios (*V. sputigenus*, *V. jejuni*, *V. coli*, *V. indicus*, *V. luminosus*, and *V. marinopraesens*) are described as forming spiral chains. If a vibrio is curved along only one axis, formation of a true spiral is not possible. Cells forming a true spiral when in chains must have the basic helical twist in the axis of the individual cells and should be classified as *Spirillum*. All of these species of *Vibrio* are recognized as species of *Vibrio* by Prévot. Only two are listed by Krassilnikov (*V. sputigenus* and *V. indicus*, the latter as a synonym of *V. caraibicus*). Krassilnikov regards *S. serpens* as a synonym of *S. undula* and *S. virginianum* as a synonym of *S. tenue* and does not recognize *S. minus*. He regards *S. itersonii* as synonymous with *Vibrio desulfuricans* (*Desulfovibrio*). He lists a further species *S. endoparagogicum* (p. 536). Prévot lists *S. muris*, which does not appear in the *Manual*. Reference should be made to the monograph by Williams and Rittenberg (Intern. Bull. Bacteriol. Nomen. Taxon., *7*, 1957, 49) for a revised classification of the spirillae.

12. Cells 20 to 300 μ long and 0.25 to 2.0 μ wide (generally 0.25 to 0.5 μ), with the

protoplast wound around a well-defined axial filament; cells very flexible and actively motile; flagella absent; fresh water and salt water forms

Spirochaeta p. *207*
M p. 893
Spirochaeta (in Prévot)
Spirochaeta (in Krass.)

Spiral cells, 0.5 to 3.0 μ wide and 10 to 100 μ long with a spiral amplitude of 6 to 8 μ; flexible cells characterized by a thin membrane or crista on one side of the body, which extends the entire length of the cell; cross striations in stained cells are distinct; actively motile without flagella; recorded from the cystalline style sac in the alimentary canal of molluscs

Cristispira p. *207*
M p. 895
Cristispira (in Prévot)
Cristispira* (in Krass.)

Not as above...................... **13**

13. Not readily stained; stain with Giemsa's stain or by silver impregnation methods; visible unstained under dark ground but rarely by ordinary light microscopy........................ **14**
Cells stain readily; Gram negative; cells rarely more than 1 μ wide; spirals frequently irregular and of variable amplitude

Borrelia p. *207*
M p. 897
Borrelia (in Prévot)
Borrelia (in Krass.)
Borrelia (in T and W, 5th ed.)

14. Aerobic; cells 0.1 to 0.2 μ thick; wound in a very fine coil and hooked at one or both ends; can be cultivated *in vitro* in semisolid rabbit plasma media

Leptospira p. *207*
M p. 907
Leptospira (in Prévot)
Leptospira (in Krass.)

Anaerobic; very fine coiled cells of uniform amplitude; may be pointed at both ends but not hooked; not yet cultivated *in vitro*

* Krassilnikov lists several additional species, which are cited in the appendix to the genus *Cristispira* in the sixth edition of the *Manual*.

Treponema p. *208*
M p. 904
Treponema (in Prévot)
Treponema (in Krass.)

Note: Only six of the eight species of *Treponema* recognized in the *Manual* are listed by Krassilnikov. Prévot lists them all but regards *T. genitalis* as *T. minutum*, as does Krassilnikov. *T. ambigua, T. comandoni,* and *T. phagedenis* of Prévot and *T. elusum, T. macrodentium,* and *Borrelia phagedenis* of Krassilnikov are listed in the appendix to *Borrelia* in the sixth edition of the *Manual. T. skoliodonta* and *T. macrodentium* from Prévot are listed in the appendix to *Treponema* in the sixth edition of the *Manual*, whereas *T. trimerodonti* of Prévot is listed in the appendix to *Leptospira* in the sixth edition of the *Manual. T. pernortha* and *T. enterogyrata* from Prévot could not be traced in the *Manual*.

SECTION D

1. Organisms contain photosynthetic pigments alone or with carotenoid pigments. Cells in masses appear green to greenish yellow or red to purple. These organisms will grow in certain media under anaerobic conditions only when exposed to light. Certain species are also capable of aerobic growth in the dark.................. **31**
Not as above....................... **2**
2. Single cells borne on the end of elongated stalks; aquatic forms................. **3**
Cells not borne on stalks............. **4**
3. Stalks band-shaped and twisted into a flat spiral; dumbbell-shaped in cross section; composed entirely of or impregnated with ferric hydroxide; dissolves completely in dilute mineral acids; a single cell is borne at the end of each stalk

Gallionella p. *138*
M p. 214
Gallionella (in Prévot)
Gallionella (in Krass.)

(See Note on *Gallionella*, p. *139*.)
Stalks long and slender; attached to some solid object by means of a holdfast; cells spherical to pear-shaped; reproduce by

budding, with the daughter cells subsequently secreting individual stalks

> **Blastocaulis** p. *140*
> *M p. 279*
> **Gallionella** (in Prévot)
> **Gallionella** (in Krass.)

4. Cells or their capsules impregnated with iron or manganese.................... 5

Note: In the absence of further information, these organisms are identified on their iron-depositing characteristics. Most iron organisms studied in pure culture metabolize the organic compound that forms the iron chelate, and the liberated iron chelates with some cell component. Citrate-utilizing organisms, for example, will release iron from ferric ammonium citrate. Accumulation of the iron in or on the cell may depend only on the nature of the cell substance. Pure culture studies may place these organisms in more commonly recognized genera. Many more organisms, if tested, may fall into the following genera. They should also be treated as non-iron-depositing cells and should be followed through the Key.

Not as above...................... 7

5. Not encapsulated

> **Siderococcus** p. *121*
> *M p. 225*
> **Siderococcus** (in Prévot)
> **Siderococcus*** (in Krass.)

Cells encapsulated.................. 6

6. Groups of cocci arranged in pairs in a common capsule..**Siderosphaera** p. *120*
> *M p. 220*
> **Siderosphaera** (in Prévot)

Cocci occur singly or in unordered groups in a common capsule

> **Siderocapsa** p. *119*
> *M p. 218*
> **Siderocapsa** (in Prévot)
> **Siderocapsa**† (in Krass.)

7. Cells coccal only as a stage in a definite life cycle *or* as a pleomorphic phase of rod-

---

* Krassilnikov notes that the systematic position of *S. limoniticus* is uncertain.

† Krassilnikov considers *S. monoeca* and *S. coronata* as synonymous with *S. treubii*. He does not list *S. botryoides* or *S. eusphaera*.

---

shaped bacteria...................... **8**
Cells coccal at all stages of growth..... **15**

8. Cells have a definite cyclic form of development; spherical cells germinate at one or more points to produce rod-shaped cells, which elongate and divide. At the point of division, growth of the cells continues at an angle to the original axis. When the side branch is equal in size to the parent cell, division occurs at the angle. This process is repeated during the growth of the colony. *In older colonies, the rods transform entirely into a mass of cocci.* Rods are most frequently Gram negative with Gram positive granules; cocci are frequently Gram positive; soil inhabitants

> **Arthrobacter** p. *177*
> *M p. 605*
> **Arthrobacter** (in Krass.)

Note: a. Prévot does not list the genus. Krassilnikov lists only three of the species: *A. globiformis* as *Mycobacterium globiforme; A. simplex* as *Mycobacterium flavum* var. *simplex*, and *A. tumescens* as *Mycobacterium globiforme* var. *tumescens*.

b. The emphasis lies on the final transformation into cocci. Some authorities may consider that limited true branching may occur. If this is admitted, the dividing line between *Arthrobacter* and *Nocardia* becomes very slim. The author's observations of *Arthrobacter globiformis* fit the above statement, and it is suggested that these criteria be adopted, with true branching forms, which later disintegrate, being assigned to *Nocardia*.

Not as above...................... **9**

9. Gram positive.................. **10**
Gram negative...................... **11**

10. Organisms occur as cocci under anaerobic conditions in neutral media; in media becoming acid, they assume a diphtheroid form; extremely pleomorphic under aerobic conditions; *produce propionic acid from lactic acid*.. **Propionibacterium** p. *173*
> *M p. 569*
> **Propionibacterium** (in Prévot)
> **Propionibacterium** (in Krass.)

Note: Krassilnikov regards *P. pentosa-*

ceum, P. shermanii, P. raffinosaceum, and *P. petersonii* as synonyms of *P. freuden-reichii; P. arabinosum* and *P. jensenii* as synonyms of *P. zeae;* and *P. theonii* as a synonym of *P. rubrum.* Prévot does not list *P. raffinosaceum.*

Not as above
possibly **Mycococcus** p. *183*
M p. *707*
Mycococcus (in Prévot)
Mycococcus (in Krass.)

Note: Cells of *Mycococcus* species are irregular in size and shape. They develop by an apparent budding process, yielding cell clumps resembling yeasts. *Micrococcus cinnabareus* and *M. rhodochrous* are included here. Prévot recognizes both of these as species of *Micrococcus;* Krassilnikov regards them as synonymous with *M. cinnabareus.*

11. Anaerobic; nonmotile; Gram negative; principally rod-shaped cells exhibiting a coccoid phase; recorded from genital and alimentary tracts of man and other animals
Sphaerophorus p. *157*
M p. *441*
Sphaerophorus (in Prévot)
Sphaerophorus (in Krass.)

Note: The type species of this genus is listed as *Fusiformis necrophorus* in Topley and Wilson, fifth edition. Four species that terminate here are *S. glycolyticus, S. ridiculosis, S. siccus,* and *S. inaequalis.* Krassilnikov recognizes *S. siccus* as *Pseudobacterium necroticum* and *S. inaequalis* as *Pseudobacterium fragilis.*

Aerobic............................ **12**
12. Obligate halophiles requiring 16 to 30 per cent salt for growth: not luminescent.
a. Motile; colonies red or purple
Halobacterium p. *119*
M p. *207*
Serratia (in Prévot)
Pseudomonas (in Krass.)
b. Nonmotile; colonies yellow or orange
Halobacterium p. *119*
M p. *207*
Empedobacter (in Prévot)
Note: Krassilnikov lists *H. cutirubrum* as

Pseudomonas carnea. He does not list *H. halobium, H. trapanicum,* or *H. marismortui.*

Not obligate halophiles............. **13**
13. Parasites attacking erythrocytes and endothelial cells of man; extremely pleomorphic within the host; straight and curved rods, ring forms, and cocci occur; grow in semisolid rabbit serum agar mainly as rods and cocci; polar flagella
Bartonella p. *211*
M p. *969*
Bartonella (in Prévot)
Bartonella (in Krass.)

Note: This genus is selected as an example of a large group of intracellular parasites that are pleomorphic and have coccal stages. Only an odd species has been cultivated. For other genera see Section K. p. *93*
Animal parasites: produce tularemia or tularemia-like infections in rodents.

a. Motile........**Pasteurella** p. *127*
(*P. pseudotuberculosis*)
M p. *395*
Cillopasteurella (in Prévot)
Pasteurella (in T and W, 5th ed.)
b. Nonmotile......**Pasteurella** p. *127*
M p. *395*
Pasteurella (in Prévot)
Bacterium (in Krass.)
Pasteurella (in T and W, 5th ed.)

Note: Topley and Wilson list *Pasteurella tularensis* as *Brucella tularensis.*

Organisms occurring as diplococci on primary isolation on solid media; give rise to a proportion of rod-shaped organisms in liquid, which increases as the culture ages. Rod forms may show bipolar staining and are capsulated:

a. No acid from carbohydrates
Mima p. *133*
b. Acid or acid and gas from carbohydrates
i. Acid from carbohydrates
Herellea p. *134*
ii. Acid and gas from carbohydrates
Colloides p. *134*
Note: The genera *Mima, Herellea,* and *Colloides* do not appear in the *Manual.*

They are described by de Bord (Iowa State Coll. J. Sci., *16*, 1942, 471) and have been mentioned by a number of authors in connection with a species described as *Bacterium anitratum*. They appear to merit consideration. Isolates were obtained from conjunctival and vaginal specimens.

Not as above.......................... **14**

14. Bioluminescent when grown on fish agar or meat infusion agar containing 3 per cent salt........**Photobacterium** p. *116*
M *p. 193*
Photobacterium (in Prévot)
Photobacterium (in Krass.)

Organisms not fitting into any of the above groups are probably pleomorphic forms of rod-shaped cells; proceed to
Section E p. *37*

15. Organisms parasitic within the cytoplasm or nucleus of flagellated protozoa............................ **16**

Not as above...................... **17**

16. Parasitic on the nucleus or nucleolus
Caryococcus
M *p. 927*
Caryococcus (in Prévot)

Parasitic in the cytoplasm of *Trichomonas batrachorum*

Micrococcus (*M. batrachorum*)
M *p. 929*
Micrococcus (in Prévot)

17. Strict autotrophs; will not grow on organic media; oxidize ammonia to nitrite, or nitrite to nitrate.................. **18**

Heterotrophic...................... **19**

18. Oxidize ammonia to nitrite; nonmotile; not encapsulated
Nitrosococcus p. *106*
M *p. 69*

Other than above; proceed to
Section G p. *45*

19. Obligate anaerobes...............**20**

Aerobic or microaerophilic........... **23**

20. Gram variable; cells occur singly or in masses; ferment acetate vigorously with the production of methane; discovered in mud......... **Methanococcus** p. *162*
M *p. 473*

subgenus **Methanococcus** (in Prévot)
Micrococcus (in Krass.)

Not as above...................... **21**

21. Gram positive.................. **22**

Gram negative:

a. Arranged in pairs
Veillonella p. *164*
M *p. 485*
Neisseria (in Prévot)
Neisseria (in Krass.)

b. Arranged in clusters
Veillonella p. *164*
M *p. 485*
Veillonella (in Prévot)
Micrococcus (in Krass.)

Note: a. Krassilnikov lists only *N. reniformis* amongst the above anaerobic *Neisseria*. Prévot lists four anaerobic species under *Neisseria*. Under *Veillonella* he lists *V. parvula* (*M. parvula* in Krass.), *V. alcalescens* (*M. gasogenes* in Krass.), and an additional species, *V. variabilis*.

b. Hobson, Mann, and Oxford (J. Gen. Microbiol., *19*, 1958, 462) described but did not name a large (1.5 μ) Gram negative *Diplococcus* from the rumen of young calves.

22. Organisms arranged in pairs and chains; ferment cellulose and cellobiose but rarely glucose to produce succinic, acetic, and formic acid; rumen organisms
Ruminococcus*
Streptococcus (in Prévot)

Organisms arranged in pairs and/or chains; no cellulose fermented:

a. Organisms arranged predominantly in pairs ..**Peptostreptococcus** p. *168*
M *p. 533*
Diplococcus (in Prévot)
Diplococcus (in Krass.)

Note: Included in *Diplococcus* are *P. magnus, P. plagarumbelli, D. paleopneumoniae,* and *P. morbillorum*. (The last named is regarded as a synonym of *D.*

---

* See A. Kaars Sijpesteijn (J. Gen. Microbiol., *5*, 1951, 869); see also Hungate (Can. J. Microbiol., *3*, 1957, 289), Bryant *et al.* (J. Bacteriol., *76*, 1958, 529), and Kistner and Gouws (J. Gen. Microbiol., *34*, 1964, 447).

paleopneumoniae by Krassilnikov). See also note to *Peptococcus.*

b. Organisms predominantly in chains

Peptostreptococcus p. *168*
M p. 533
Streptococcus (in Prévot)
Streptococcus (in Krass.)

Note: Krassilnikov lists seven *Manual* species under the one species *Streptococcus anaerobius. P. evolutus* is listed separately and *P. productus* is not cited. Topley and Wilson list the organisms in the genus *Peptotreptococcus* under the general heading "*anaerobic streptococci.*"

Organisms arranged in cubical packets

Sarcina p. *162*
M p. 467
Sarcina (in Prévot)
Sarcina (in Krass.)

Organisms arranged singly, in pairs, and in irregular clusters; rarely in chains:

a. Smooth clusters*

Peptococcus p. *163*
M p. 474
Staphylococcus (in Prévot)
Micrococcus (in Krass.)

b. Rough clusters*

Peptococcus p. *163*
M p. 474
Micrococcus (in Prévot)
Micrococcus (in Krass.)

Note: Peptococcus constellatus may belong to *Peptostreptococcus.* Both Prévot and Krassilnikov place the organism in the genus *Diplococcus.* Prévot also recognizes an anaerobic species of *Gaffkya* (*G. anaerobia*). See also *Micrococcus pseudosarcina* in Krassilnikov.

The species of this genus are referred to under the general heading of "*anaerobic micrococci*" by Topley and Wilson.

23. Gram negative, kidney-shaped to hemispherical cells, occurring basically in pairs with the flat sides adjacent; animal parasites............ **Neisseria** p. *163*
M p. 480

* Characters used by Prévot.

Neisseria (in Prévot)
Neisseria (in Krass.)

Note: a. *Micrococcus morrhuae, M. roseus,* and *M. sphaeroides* (in Krassilnikov) are described as Gram negative and occur singly and in pairs. Prévot placed *M. morrhuae* in the genus *Neisseria.* Krassilnikov lists *N. sicca* under *N. catarrhalis; N. flavescens* and *N. perflava* under *N. flava;* and *N. meningitidis* as a synonym of *N. intracellularis.* He does not list *N. caviae* or *N. subflava.* Eisenberg and Evans (Can. J. Microbiol., *9*, 1963, 633) have made a detailed study of *M. roseus* but do not quote the Gram stain.

b. Compare with the genera *Mima, Herellea,* and *Colloides* in Section D, **13.**

c. Berger (Intern. Bull. Bacteriol. Nomen. Taxon., *11*, 1961, 17) suggests the separation of *N. haemolysans* into the monotypic genus **Gemella,** which is oxidase negative compared with the oxidase positive species of the genus *Neisseria.*

Gram negative cocci, nonmotile, capsulated (usually in diplococci); thermotolerant; grow in a mineral salts base aerobically solely at the expense of methane or methanol............**Methylococcus**†
(*M. capsulatus*)

Not as above...................... **24**

24. Organisms arranged in cubical packets

Sarcina p. *162*
M p. 467
Sarcina (in Prévot)

a. Motile
  i. Sporulating
Sporosarcina (in K and M)
Planosarcina (in Krass.)
  ii. Nonsporulating
Planosarcina (in Krass.)
b. Nonmotile..... **Sarcina** (in Krass.)

Note: See Kocur and Martinec (Intern. Bull. Bacteriol. Nomen. Taxon., *13*, 1963, 201) for discussion on *Sporosarcina.* Krassilnikov does not recognize *S. hansenii* or *S. litoralis.* He lists four species of *Planosarcina* and ten additional species of *Sar-*

† See Foster and Davis, J. Bacteriol. *91*, 1966, 1924.

cina, which are cited in the *Manual,* sixth edition, in an appendix.

Organisms from liquids are arranged singly, in pairs or as tetrads, and occasionally in short chains; tetrads common in acid media; produce at least 0.5 to 0.7 per cent acid in yeast extract-glucose-tryptone-phosphate broth, lowering the pH below 4.0; *lactic acid produced is optically inactive;* found in fermented liquids and foods

Pediococcus p. *167*

M p. 529

Pediococcus (in Prévot)

Micrococcus (in Krass.)

Note: Krassilnikov lists both *Manual* species of *Pediococcus* under *Micrococcus albicans.* For a detailed study of the genus *Pediococcus,* see J. Gen. Microbiol., *26,* 1961, 185. See also Note c to *Gaffkya* in Section D, **28.** For recent papers, see Digest of Genera.

Not as above...................... **25**

25. Organisms arranged in pairs only or in chains of varying lengths when growing in liquid media...................... **26**

Organisms arranged singly, in pairs, and in clusters in liquid media; occasional species are motile...................... **28**

26. Organisms produce gas in Eldredge tubes when growing in yeast-extract-glucose-tryptone-phosphate broth; *lactic acid produced is levorotatory;* frequently produce a copious gum (dextran) in sucrose broth

Leuconostoc p. *168*

M p. 531

Leuconostoc (in Prévot)

Streptococcus (in Krass.)

Not as above; lactic acid produced is *dextrorotatory*...................... **27**

27. Parasitic; cells usually in pairs, particularly in pathological material, in which they are encapsulated; chains are common in culture media; bile-soluble; found in the respiratory tract of man

Diplococcus p. *165*

Diplococcus (in Prévot)

Diplococcus (in Krass.)

Streptococcus (in T and W, 5th ed.)

Note: The following organisms are listed

by Krassilnikov as occurring singly and in pairs: *M. elasticus, M. vividus,* and *Planococcus casei.* Only the last named is recorded in an appendix in the *Manual,* sixth edition. See also *M. halodenitrificans.*

Other than above; parasitic or saprophytic

Streptococcus p. *166*

M p. 508

Streptococcus (in Prévot)

Streptococcus (in Krass.)

Note: a. *S. anginosis, S. dysgalactiae, S. equisimilis, S. sanguis,* and *S. zooepidemicus* are not listed by Krassilnikov. He recognizes *S. pastorianus.* He places *S. durans* and *S. cremoris* under *S. lactis; S. agalactiae, S. equi,* and *S. uberis* under *S. pyogenes; S. acidominimus, S. bovis, S. equinus, S. faecalis, S. mitis,* and *S. thermophilus* under *S. salivarius;* and lists *S. faecalis* var. *liquefaciens* as *S. liquefaciens* and *S. faecalis* var. *zymogenes* as *Micrococcus subtilis.*

b. The following species of *Micrococci* are listed by Krassilnikov as forming pairs and chains. Except *M. polychromus,* they are listed as species (*M. aurantiacus*) or in the appendix to *Micrococcaceae* in the *Manual,* sixth edition: *M. albatus, M. gummosus, M. hauseri, M. utriculosis,* and *M. viticulosis.*

28. Cells occur predominantly as tetrads and are encapsulated in body fluids; occur as tetrads and in irregular masses in cultures................. **Gaffkya** p. *161*

M p. 466

Gaffkya (in Prévot)

Micrococcus (in Krass.)

Micrococcus (in T and W, 5th ed.)

Note: a. Prévot includes three additional species, *G. verneti, G. tardissima,* and *G. anaerobia,* which are listed as species (*G. anaerobia*) or in the appendix to *Gaffkya* in the *Manual,* sixth edition. Krassilnikov recognizes only *Micrococcus tetragenus.* He also lists the following species in the genus *Micrococcus,* which form singly or in tetrads only, *M. albescens* and *M. chlorinus* (in appendix to *Micrococcaceae* in *Manual*, sixth edition).

b. Aaronson (J. Gen. Microbiol., *15*, 1956, 478) describes saprophytic cultures otherwise identical with *G. homari*.

c. Deibel and Niven (J. Bacteriol., *79*, 1960, 175) note that *G. homari* is very similar to *Aerococcus viridans* and suggest that both should be placed in the genus *Pediococcus*. However, the lactic acid produced is dextrorotatory.

d. Kocur and Martinec (Intern. Bull. Bacteriol. Nomen. Taxon., *15*, 1965, 177) suggest that *Gaffkya tetragena* is an atypical strain of *Staphylococcus aureus* and recommend the rejection of the genus *Gaffkya*.

Not as above...................... **29**

29. Organisms grow on media containing 40 per cent bile; produce a pronounced greening on blood agar....**Aerococcus**

Not as above..................... **30**

Note: See Williams, Hirch, and Cowan (J. Gen. Microbiol., *8*, 1953, 475); see also Note c in Section D, **28**; Clausen (J. Gen. Microbiol., *35*, 1964, 1) proposes a new species, *A. catalasicus*, which is catalase and nitratase positive. Topley and Wilson (fifth edition) list the genus *Aerococcus* with the enterococci (p. 719).

30. Glucose fermented in the Hugh and Leifson test....**Staphylococcus** p. *160*

M p. *464*

Staphylococcus (in Prévot)

Micrococcus (in Krass.)

Staphylococcus (in T and W, 5th ed.)

Glucose oxidized in the Hugh and Leifson test, or not attacked

Micrococcus p. *158*

M p. *455*

Micrococcus (in Prévot)

Micrococcus (in Krass.)

Micrococcus (in T and W, 5th ed.)

Note: a. Placed in the genus *Staphylococcus*, in the *Manual*, are *S. aureus* and *S. epidermidis*.

b. Evans, Bradford, and Niven (Intern. Bull. Bacteriol. Nomen. Taxon., *5*, 1955, 61) recommended the separation of the genus *Staphylococcus* from *Micrococcus* on the basis of glucose fermentation or oxidation. The suggestion has the support of Baird-Parker (J. Gen. Microbiol., *30*, 1963, 409) and Cowan and Steel (J. Bacteriol., *88*, 1964, 804), and a modified Hugh and Leifson test has been recommended by the Subcommittee on Taxonomy of *Staphylococcus* and *Micrococcus* (Intern. Bull. Bacteriol. Nomen. Taxon., *15*, 1965, 109).

c. Krassilnikov lists *M. colpogenes* as a variety of *M. ochraceus* and lists, in addition, 30 species not listed in the *Manual*, seventh edition. Three of these are motile and are placed in the genus **Planococcus;** 24 are listed in the appendix to the *Micrococcaceae* in the *Manual*, sixth edition.

d. Friedemann and Kern (Can. J. Microbiol., *2*, 1956, 515) described a new species of *Micrococcus* which digests beeswax, and Eisenberg and Evans (Can. J. Microbiol., *9*, 1963, 633) have made a detailed study of *M. roseus*.

See also Section B, **10.**

31. Cell masses are green or yellowish green; probably contain chlorobium chlorophyll and not bacteriochlorophyll...... **32**

Cell masses red, brown, or purple; proceed to................... Section J p. *90*

32. Spherical to ovoid cells, occurring in chains and forming flat sheets in which the chains are parallel. Oxidize hydrogen sulfide but do not store sulfur inside the cells............... **Pelodictyon** p. *102*

M p. *63*

Pelodictyon (in Prévot)

Pelodictyon (in Krass.)

Spherical cells united in loose trellis-like aggregates. Sulfur is deposited internally

Clathrochloris p. *102*

M p. *64*

Clathrochloris (in Prévot)

Pelodictyon (in Krass.)

SECTION E

1. Multicellular organisms (sheathed or not sheathed) *or* chains of unicellular organisms enclosed in a sheath........ **2**

Note: This does not include chains of individually encapsulated cells or cells in zoogloeal masses.
Not as above; proceed to
Section F p. *40*

2. Organisms enclosed in a common sheath
3

Not as above...................... **14**

3. Width of the sheath increasing from the base to the tip; cells within the sheath divide transversely and longitudinally towards the tip to produce large numbers of coccoid elements; attached by means of a holdfast.......................... **4**
Not as above........................ **5**

4. Cells within the basal portion of the sheath longer than wide; when growing in iron- or manganese-bearing waters, become heavily impregnated with iron or manganese..............**Crenothrix** p. *137*
M p. 272
Crenothrix (in Prévot)
Crenothrix (in Krass.)

Cells within the basal portion of the sheath are wider than long; no iron deposited
Phragmidiothrix p. *137*
M p. 273
Phragmidiothrix (in Prévot)

5. Sheaths become impregnated with iron or manganese when growing in iron- or manganese-bearing waters or media.... **6**
Not as above........................ **8**

6. Organisms in which the sheaths split longitudinally into fine, hair-like sections. The chain of cells remains attached to hairs at several points and, with continued growth, causes arching of the hairs and of the chain of cells within its new sheath, resulting in the formation of a helm-like mass................**Toxothrix** p. *136*
M p. 269
Toxothrix (in Prévot)
Leptothrix (in Krass.)

Not as above........................ **7**

7. Cells within the base of the sheath 2 by 10 μ, with rounded ends; divide transversely near the tip to produce spherical, nonmotile cells, which are extruded either singly or in chains. The sheath is heavily impregnated

with iron or manganese, becoming much wider at the base and tapering towards the tip; attached by a holdfast; false branching is common..........**Clonothrix** p. *138*
M p. 274
Clonothrix (in Prévot)

In the absence of iron, cells within the sheath are of uniform size except during division. During deposition of iron in the sheath, cells in the more heavily impregnated areas become much narrower than normal; extruded cells are of the same dimensions as those within the sheath
Leptothrix p. *136*
M p. 264
Leptothrix (in Prévot)
Leptothrix (in Krass.)

Note: a. Krassilnikov does not list *L. major, L. skujae, L. thermalis,* and *L. winogradskii.* He regards *L. discophora* as a synonym of *L. ochracea* and *L. epiphytica* as a synonym of *L. volubilis.*

b. Species of *Sphaerotilus* will also be found to terminate at this point if grown in ferric ammonium citrate media. The genera are considered to be identical by Pringsheim (Phil. Trans. Roy. Soc. London, Ser. B, *233*, 1949, 605) and others, but this relationship has been disputed by Beger and Bringmann (Zentr. Bakteriol., Parasitenk., Abt. II, *107*, 1953, 318) and by Mulder and van Veen (Antonie van Leeuwenhoek, *29*, 1963, 121).

8. Endospores produced within the cells of the trichome and located in an oblique position........... **Coleomitus** p. *195*
M p. 836
Coleomitus (in Prévot)
Coleonema* (in Krass.)

No endospores...................... **9**

9. Organisms oxidize hydrogen sulfide, depositing sulfur inside the cells....... **10**
Organisms do not oxidize hydrogen sulfide and do not deposit sulfur internally.... **11**

10. Several trichomes within a sheath
Thioploca p. *198*
M p. 841

---

* In an appendix.

Thioploca (in Prévot)
Thioploca (in Krass.)
A single trichome in each sheath
Thiothrix p. *198*
M p. 842
Thiothrix (in Prévot)
Thiothrix (in Krass.)

Note: Skerman, Dementjeva, and Carey (J. Bacteriol., *73*, 1957, 504) have demonstrated that *Sphaerotilus*, when exposed to hydrogen sulfide, deposits sulfur internally. Superficially such cells show a very striking resemblance to illustrations of *Thiothrix*. However, the isolated cells of *Sphaerotilus* are motile with subpolar flagella, whereas those of *Thiothrix* are nonflagellated and exhibit a gliding motility.

11. Single cells in chains within a common sheath; free cells motile by means of subpolar flagella or nonmotile
Sphaerotilus p. *134*
M p. 263
Sphaerotilus (in Prévot)
Sphaerotilus (in Krass.)
(See notes on *Leptothrix* and *Thiothrix*, *vide supra*, 7 and 10.)

Trichomes........................ **12**

12. Trichomes attached; free cells formed by abstriction from the terminal portion are motile by a gliding action on a solid surface............ Leucothrix p. *200*
M p. 850
Leucothrix (in Prévot)
Pontothrix (in Krass.)

Note: Although Harold and Stanier claim that *Leucothrix* does not form a sheath, they consider it to be identical with *Pontothrix*, which was originally recorded as a sheathed organism.*

Not as above; if motile, whole trichomes move; cells within the trichomes each contain one or more pseudovacuoles, which give a reddish gleam in transmitted light
13

* Pringsheim (Bacteriol. Revs., *21*, 1957, 69) reports a prominent sheath exists but cannot be demonstrated by means of nigrosin. It stains pink with methylene blue, whereas the cells stain a dark indigo.

13. Trichomes occur singly
Pelonema p. *137*
M p. 271
Pelonema (in Prévot)
Trichomes occur in bundles
Peloploca p. *137*
M p. 270
Peloploca (in Prévot)

Note: Peloploca is described in the *Manual* as "sheath not demonstrated." It is included here on the possibility that it is sheathed and because of the morphological similarity to *Pelonema*.

14. Trichomes 6 to 20 μ long; motile by means of peritrichous flagella; rigid, multicellular, bacillary forms, in which the stained cells are differentiated into a series of light and dark bands; end cells rounded; commonly form chains up to 200 μ long. Individual cells in a trichome may separate as discoid elements and may grow out into trichomes; common in peat and cow dung
Caryophanon p. *194*
M p. 831
Caryophanon (in Prévot)
Caryophanon (in Krass.)

Not as above...................... **15**

15. Long trichomes attached by a globular holdfast to the intestinal walls of some insects and millipedes; a single endospore may be produced in any or all cells of the trichome, and, if so, it usually lies in an oblique position.. Arthromitus p. *195*
M p. 835
Arthromitus (in Prévot)
Arthromitus (in Krass.)

Note: Krassilnikov does not list *A. nitidus.*

Trichomes 1.5 to 22.0 μ long; found in the cytoplasm of the rhizopod *Pelomyxa palustris*, generally aggregated close to the nucleus.................... Cladothrix
M p. 930
Cladothrix (in Prévot)

Not as above...................... **16**

16. Entire trichomes unattached and actively motile by a gliding action on a solid surface; no flagella................. **17**
Trichomes attached or free; nonmotile;

abstricted cells may be motile with a gliding action on solid surfaces.............. 21

Note: References have been made in the literature to the multicellular nature of many small cells previously regarded as unicellular. They are mostly cells not more than 6 μ long, and they stain uniformly or more frequently show a granulated or barred staining with simple stains but show a multicellular character when special techniques are applied to show cell walls. They will be found by other characteristics to belong to genera located in Section F *et seq.*

17. Trichomes flat and ribbon-like..... **18**
Trichomes cylindrical................ **19**
18. Trichomes with end cells hemispherical

Simonsiella p. *196*

M p. 833

Simonsiella (in Prévot)

Oscillospira (in Krass.)

Trichomes with end cells concave; tend to break up into groups of four cells

Alysiella

Note: See Steed (J. Gen. Microbiol., *29*, 1962, 615).

19. Organisms oxidize hydrogen sulfide, depositing sulfur inside the cell

Beggiatoa p. *197*

M p. 838

Beggiatoa (in Prévot)

Beggiatoa (in Krass.)

Not as above...................... **20**
20. Trichomes composed of cells that are not clearly articulated at the junctions; complete trichomes very flexible

Vitreoscilla p. *199*

M p. 845

Vitreoscilla (in Prévot)

Trichomes composed of rod-like elements with little individual flexibility; bending occurs freely at the junctions

Bactoscilla p. *199*

M p. 848

Bactoscilla (in Prévot)

21. Colorless trichomes; attached; cells are abstricted from the terminal position and are motile by a gliding action on a

solid surface. Sulfur is not deposited internally............ **Leucothrix** p. *200*

M p. 850

Leucothrix* (in Prévot)

Pontothrix (in Krass.)

Colorless trichomes; arranged in bundles; nonmotile; each cell in the trichome contains one or more gas vacuoles, which gleam reddish in transmitted light

Peloploca p. *137*

M p. 270

Peloploca* (in Prévot)

Cells deposit sulfur internally

Thiothrix p. *198*

M p. 842

Thiothrix* (in Prévot)

Thiothrix (in Krass.)

SECTION F

1. Pear-shaped cells; 1.0 to 2.0 by 4.0 to 5.0 μ; nonmotile; grow attached to one another or to solid surfaces by a holdfast secreted from the narrow end; sessile; multiply by longitudinal fission and by budding at the free end

Pasteuria p. *139*

M p. 279

Pasteuria (in Prévot)

Pasteuria† (in Krass.)

Not as above........................ **2**
2. Curved or straight rods that produce a well-differentiated stalk by which they *may* attach to a surface; a single cell occurs at the end of each stalk, except during the process of multiplication.............. **3**
Not as above........................ **6**
3. Unicellular stalked bacteria. The stalk arises from the pole of the cell, and adhesive material is secreted at the distal end of the stalk. Multiplication occurs by division of the stalked cell, giving rise to a nonstalked sibling, which is motile by means of a single polar flagellum. This cell secretes adhesive material at the base of the flagel-

---

* Inserted here although classical descriptions indicate a sheath, which is often very difficult to see.
† Listed under *Gallionella pediculata* as of uncertain systematic position.

lum, develops a stalk at this site, and enters the immotile vegetative phase. The adhesive material allows cells in either phase to attach to other microorganisms, inanimate substrates, or to one another's holdfasts to form rosettes. The cells are rod-shaped or vibrioid. They may be colorless or contain yellow or orange pigments related to carotenoids. Several morphological types exist, which are distinguished from one another by cell shape. The deoxyribonucleic acid is composed of approximately 65 per cent guanine plus cytosine

Caulobacter p. 138

M p. 213

Caulobacter (in Prévot)

Caulobacter* (in Krass.)

Caulobacter† (in Poindexter)

Unicellular stalked bacteria. The stalk arises from a site on the cell that is not coincidental with the center of the pole of the cell. The stalk does not possess adhesive material. Multiplication occurs by division of the stalked cell, giving rise to a non-stalked sibling, which is smaller than the stalked sibling and is motile by means of a single flagellum, which arises in an eccentric position on the pole of the cell. This cell develops a stalk and enters the immotile vegetative phase. Adhesive material is secreted by cells in both phases at or near the pole of the cell at a site different from that at which the stalk develops. The adhesive material allows cells to attach to a variety of solid substrates, or to one another's holdfasts to form rosettes. The cells of known types are rod-shaped and colorless.. Asticcacaulis† (in Poindexter)
Not as above; cells produce a stalk at right angles to the main axis of the cell...... 4
4. Large rods, 2.0 by 6.0 to 12.0 μ, borne on the end of lobose, dichotomously branched stalks composed of gum, forming

---

* Listed under *Gallionella pediculata* as of uncertain systematic position.
    † Poindexter, Bacteriol. Revs., *28*, 1964, 231).

a gummy colony, which floats on water; may become attached.. **Nevskia** p. 139

M p. 216

Nevskia (in Prévot)

Gallionella (in Krass.)

Not as above; stalks composed of or impregnated with ferric hydroxide; dissolve completely in hydrochloric acid; cells curved with the stalk secreted from the concave side; reported only from iron-bearing waters............................. 5
5. Stalks ribbon-like and usually twisted; cells located terminally

Gallionella p. 138

M p. 214

Gallionella (in Prévot)

Gallionella (in Krass.)

Note: Krassilnikov lists three additional species of *Gallionella*. (See Note on *Gallionella*, p. 138.) Aristovskaya (Mikrobiologica, *33*, 1964, 929) describes another organism similar to *Gallionella* under the name of **Seliberia.** He notes that the peculiar features of the new family are as follows: spiral coiling of the filiform or rod-like cells, formation through budding of rounded, oval, or bean-like generative cells, and a developmental cycle involving a flagellar, filiform, or rod-like, cluster-like and zooglea stage.

Stalks horn-shaped; not twisted; round in cross section.... **Siderophacus** p. 139

M p. 216

Siderophacus (in Prévot)

Gallionella (in Krass.)

6. Obligate autotrophs, which oxidize ferrous to ferric iron at low pH in mineral synthetic media; Gram negative rods... 7
Not as above....................... 8
7. Thiosulfate is oxidized

Thiobacillus p. 110

(*T. ferrooxidans*)

M p. 83

Thiobacillus (in Prévot)

Thiosulfate is not oxidized

Ferrobacillus p. 122

(*F. ferrooxidans*)

M p. 227
Ferrobacillus (in Prévot)
(See also Kinsel, J. Bacteriol., *80*, 1960, 628, for *Ferrobacillus sulfooxidans*, which oxidizes sulfur but not thiosulfate.)

8. Organisms that store oxides of manganese or iron either in the cell membrane, in the cell wall, or in the surrounding capsules; found in water and mud......... **9**

Note: a. In the absence of further information, these organisms are identified on the basis of their iron-depositing characteristics. Most iron organisms studied in pure culture metabolize the organic compound that forms the iron chelate, and the liberated iron then chelates with some cell component. Citrate-utilizing organisms will, for example, release iron from ferric ammonium citrate. Accumulation of the iron in or on the cell may depend only on the nature of the cell substance. Pure culture studies may place these organisms in more commonly recognized genera. They should also be treated as non-iron-depositing cells and should be followed through the Key.

b. In addition to the species in genera listed below, see also *Chromobacterium manganicum* (in Krassilnikov); *Perabacterium spelei* Caumartin (in Prévot); and *Metallogenium* (see Section B, **3**, Note b).

Not as above...................... **13**
9. Cells encapsulated or embedded in mucus or surrounded by a torus of iron
10
Not as above; iron or manganese stored in cell membrane or cell wall
Siderobacter p. *122*
M p. 226
Siderobacter (in Prévot)
Siderobacter (in Krass.)
Note: Krassilnikov lists only *S. lineare* and *S. duplex* as *species incertae sedis*.
10. Encapsulated cells occurring singly or in short chains, each capsule being completely surrounded by a ring (torus) heavily impregnated with iron or manganese, giving the general appearance of links in a chain

Naumanniella p. *121*
M p. 223
Naumanniella (in Prévot)
Naumanniella (in Krass.)
Note: Krassilnikov lists only *N. minor* and *N. neustonica* as *species incertae sedis*.

Not as above...................... **11**
11. Cells surrounded by a ring (torus), which is open at one end; cells motile by means of two unequal polar flagella
Ochrobium p. *121*
M p. 225
Ochrobium (in Prévot)
Ochrobium (in Krass.)
Note: The unequal lengths of the flagella suggest that this may be an algal or a protozoan cell.
Not as above...................... **12**
12. Rods arranged at random in zoogloea; encrusted with iron . **Sideromonas** p. *121*
(Including *Siderocapsa major*)
M p. 222
Sideromonas (in Prévot)
Sideromonas (in Krass.)
Cells arranged in pairs or chains in capsules
Ferribacterium p. *120*
M p. 221
Ferribacterium (in Prévot)
Note: Krassilnikov lists *F. duplex* under *Ochrobium tectum* and *F. rectangulare* in the genus *Sideroderma*, both as *species incertae sedis*.
Cells arranged in two angulated and intertwined chains, embedded in mucus encrusted with iron. . **Lieskeella** (in Krass.)
Note: Not included in the *Manual* or by Prévot. This organism can be found in bottom muds of Lake Windermere (author's observation).
13. Cells *in mass* appear green to greenish yellow; contain a photosynthetic pigment that is not bacteriochlorophyll or chlorophyll "a" but that may be chlorobium chlorophyll; individual cells usually colorless; grow anaerobically when exposed to light, oxidizing sulfide to sulfur, which is deposited outside the cell; no growth aerobically...................... **14**

Not as above...................... **18**
14. Cells found adherent to the surface of other organisms, apparently living in symbiosis with them................ **15**

Note: The taxonomic significance of these groups is doubtful, but until they are isolated from the supposed symbiont and studied separately, they must be treated in this fashion.

Cells free-living..................... **17**
15. Green cells attached to the surface of a protozoan cell

> **Chlorobacterium** p. *102*
> *M p. 65*
> **Chlorobacterium** (in Prévot)
> **Pelodictyon** (?) (in Krass.)

Green cells attached to bacteria....... **16**
16. Aggregates small, barrel-shaped; actively motile, consisting of a central, polar flagellated, rod-shaped cell covered with the green organisms; green cells 0.5 to 1.0 by 1.0 to 2.5 μ, usually 8 to 16 surrounding the central cell; aggregates measure 2.5 to 5.0 by 7 to 12 μ

> **Chlorochromatium** p. *102*
> *M p. 65*
> **Chlorochromatium** (in Prévot)
> **Pelodictyon** (in Krass.)

Aggregates large, long, and cylindrical; nonmotile; consist of green cells, 0.5 to 1.0 by 2.0 to 4.0 μ, lying on the surface of a slime capsule, which covers the inner cylindrical cell. They are themselves covered by a layer of slime. Aggregates measure 7.0 to 8.0 μ wide by up to 50 μ long...........**Cylindrogloea** p. *103*
> *M p. 66*
> **Cylindrogloea** (in Prévot)

17. Encapsulated cells forming characteristic aggregates consisting of net-like structures, irregular three-dimensional or two-dimensional masses, in which cells lie in parallel strands

> **Pelodictyon** p. *102*
> *M p. 63*
> **Pelodictyon** (in Prévot)
> **Pelodictyon** (in Krass.)

Cells may produce slime but usually remain dispersed; small cells which grow anaerobi-

ally exposed to light, oxidizing inorganic sulfur compounds to elemental sulfur which is deposited externally; absorption maxima for the purified green pigment in ethyl ether at 660, 432, and 412 mμ; maxima in intact cells at 457 and 750 mμ;

a. Nonmotile; do not oxidize organic compounds....**Chlorobium** p. *101*
> *M. p. 62*
> **Chlorobium** (in Prévot)
> **Chlorobium** (in Krass.)

b. Motile; oxidize organic compounds in the presence of sulfate, especially ethanol......**Chloropseudomonas***

Note: Krassilnikov lists only one species of *Chlorobium*.

18. Cell masses are various shades of red or purple.......................... **19**
Not as above...................... **20**
19. Cells contain bacteriochlorophyll and carotenoid pigments; capable of growth anaerobically when exposed to light; proceed to............ Section J p. *90*
Not as above...................... **20**
20. Cells motile only by a gliding movement on solid surfaces or along one another; single cells nonmotile when free in solution. Motility can be observed at the glass-water interface on a slide or on the surface of agar plates, where cells move singly or in groups, frequently leaving a trail of slime behind. Cells are flexible, the extent of the flexibility being dependent on length and turgidity (see note below)............ **21**

Note: This subdivision is represented by two main groups. In one the cells are usually less than 10 μ long, frequently only 2.0 to 5.0 μ; Gram negative; in wet preparations fixed with osmic acid, they may appear as blunt-ended rods; in stained preparations subjected to heat fixation, they are frequently curved, S-shaped, bent, or spirilliform. In the other, the cells are usually longer than 10 μ and may form articulated chains.

There are, however, much shorter representatives of this subdivision, which,

---

* See Shaposnikov, Kondratieva, and Fedorov, Nature, London, *187*, 1960, 167.

because of their shortness, are more rigid and resemble ordinary bacteria in many respects, except for the gliding movement and lack of flagella. Species of both groups so far described have been found in fresh and salt water and in soil and decomposing organic matter, especially dung.

The genus **Moraxella**, long considered as nonmotile, has been shown to exhibit a peculiar form of gliding motility (see Lautrop, Intern. Bull. Bact. Nomen. Taxon. *11*, 1961, 107, and Piéchaud, Ann. Inst. Pasteur, *104*, 1963, 291). Both authors describe methods for examining the motility.

Not as above; cells nonmotile or motile, when free in solution, by means of flagella; proceed to.............. Section G p. *45*
21. Cells that, on rabbit dung or bacterial cell agar or other suitable media, produce spherical or rod-shaped microcysts either lying free among the rods or borne in macroscopically visible fruiting bodies formed by transformation of whole or part of the population of rod-shaped cells; cells rarely more than 10 μ long; proceed to
Section L p. *94*
Not as above....................... **22**
22. Rod-shaped cells forming articulated chains............ **Bactoscilla** p. *199*
M p. 848
Bactoscilla (in Prévot)
Not as above....................... **23**
23. Filaments from 12 to 100 μ or more in length, highly flexible and actively motile by gliding motion; cells may bend and wave but do not rotate
Microscilla p. *199*
M p. 849
Microscilla (in Prévot)
Note: Soriano (Rev. Arg. Agron., *12*, 1945, 120) described a number of species of *Flexibacter*, including *F. flexilis* (10 to 20 μ), *F. elegans* (20 to 50 μ), and *F. giganteus* (100 μ or greater), which are morphologically similar to *Microscilla*.

Inasmuch as *Flexibacter* antedates *Microscilla*, it would seem to have precedence as

a name for the group. This seems also to be the opinion of Fox and Lewin (Can. J. Microbiol., *9*, 1963, 753), whose descriptions of new species of *Flexibacter* I have been unable to locate. These authors describe the nature of the pigment in some species of *Flexibacter*.
Not as above....................... **24**
24. Cells usually less than 12 μ long.
a. If the colonies are pigmented yellow, pink, green, orange, or black, they probably belong to the genus
Cytophaga p. *201*
M p. 858
Cytophaga (in Prévot)
Note: Krassilnikov divides this genus into two groups:
i. Spindle-shaped with pointed ends
Cytophaga
ii. Rods with rounded ends
Promyxobacterium
Note: Promyxobacterium includes the *Manual* species *Cytophaga johnsonii* and two other species, *P. flavum* and *P. lanceolatus*. See also *C. succinicans* of Anderson and Erling (J. Bacteriol., *81*, 1961, 130) and *C. fermentans* and *C. salmonicolor* (Veldkamp, J. Gen. Microbiol., *26*, 1961, 331).
b. If they are white and albuminous, they may belong to.. **Flexibacter***
M p. 858
Flexibacter (in Prévot)
(*F. albuminosus, F. aureus*)
Cells usually short and plump and arranged as diplobacilli; growth best under humid conditions; usually oxidase positive and sensitive to penicillin; may liquefy coagulated serum; parasites of mucous membranes of man and animals.... **Moraxella**
M. p. 132
Moraxella (in Prévot)
Bacterium (in Krass.)
(As *B. duplex* and *B. cancrosi*)

---

* Not recognized in the *Manual*. See Soriano (Rev. Arg. Agron., *12*, 1945, 120); (Antonie van Leeuwenhoek, *12*, 1947, 215).

SECTION G

1. Organisms will not grow on meat extract or other complex organic media; strict autotrophs, which use carbon dioxide as the sole source of carbon and which obtain their energy from the oxidation of carbon monoxide or other inorganic substances.. **2**

Note: The genus *Methanomonas* has to be considered here. The information in the *Manual* does not indicate whether the organism is a strict or facultative autotroph. Dworkin and Foster (J. Bacteriol., *72*, 1956, 646) described an organism under the name of *Pseudomonas methanica* that they considered to be identical with *Methanomonas methanica* (Sohngen) Orla-Jensen. Methane and methanol were the only carbon compounds of those tested which proved satisfactory for growth. Foster* states that the organic growth factors described as necessary in the original paper are not necessary and that the organism grows well in a completely inorganic medium (see section on media) in the presence of methane. Polar flagellates should be tested under these conditions for their ability to oxidize methane.

Not as above........................ **6**

2. Organisms oxidize ammonia to nitrite†
3
Organisms oxidize nitrite to nitrate.... **5**
Organisms oxidize inorganic sulfur compounds...........**Thiobacillus** p. *110*
M p. 83
Thiobacillus (in Prévot)
Sulfomonas† (in Krass.)
Thiobacterium† (in Krass.)
(*T. denitrificans*)

Note: There is a disagreement between the authors on the flagellation of *Thiobacillus denitrificans*. The *Manual* and Prévot

* Personal communication, October 10, 1957.
† Engel (J. Bacteriol., *81*, 1961, 833) questions the advisability of continuing recognition of genera other than Nitrosomonas. See also Notes to *Nitrosocystis*, p. 106.

quote polar flagella and Krassilnikov quotes peritrichate flagella.

Organisms oxidize ferrous iron
Ferrobacillus p. *122*
M p. 227
Ferrobacillus (in Prévot)
Organisms oxidize carbon monoxide
Carboxydomonas p. *109*
M p. 77
Carboxydomonas (in Prévot)
Proactinomyces (in Krass.)

Note: It is reasonably certain that *Carboxydomonas* is also heterotrophic and may be identical with *Hydrogenomonas*. See "Discussion" in the *Manual* (p. 77) in relation to this and the inclusion of the organism in *Proactinomyces*.

3. Cells encapsulated; form zoogloea... **4**
Cells not encapsulated
Nitrosomonas p. *106*
M p. 68
Nitrosomonas (in Prévot)
Nitrosomonas (in Krass.)
(*N. europaea*)

Note: Krassilnikov recognizes only *N. europaea* of the *Manual* species. He lists *N. monocella* under the name *Nitrosomonas javanensis*. The latter species is listed in the *Manual* as *Nitrosocystis javanensis*.

4. Zoogloea encysted
Nitrosocystis p. *106*
M p. 70
Nitrosocystis (in Prévot)
Nitrosomonas (in Krass.)

Note: See note to *Nitrosomonas* in Section G, **3**. *N. coccoides* is not recognized by Krassilnikov.
Zoogloea not encysted
Nitrosogloea p. *107*
M p. 71
Nitrosogloea (in Prévot)
Nitrosogloea (in Krass.)

Note: Krassilnikov recognizes only *Nitrosogloea merismoides*, regarding the other species as synonyms.

5. Zoogloea formed...**Nitrocystis** p. *108*
M p. 73

Nitrocystis (in Prévot)
Nitrobacter (in Krass.)
Zoogloea not formed
Nitrobacter p. *107*
M p. 72
Nitrobacter (in Prévot)
Nitrobacter (in Krass.)
Note: Krassilnikov recognizes only one species of *Nitrobacter* (*N. winogradskyi*), with which *Nitrocystis micropunctata* and *N. sarcinoides* are grouped. He places *Nitrobacter agilis* in the genus *Pseudomonas*.
6. Gram positive.................... 7
Gram negative; proceed to
Section H   p. *59*
7. Aerobic......................... 8
Anaerobic, microaerophilic.......... 35
Note: Some species are described as "anaerobic to microaerophilic" or "anaerobic, aerotolerant." Opinions differ on the same organism, probably due to different strains and different methods of culture. In the Key provision is made for most aerotolerant species as either aerobic or anaerobic. The aerotolerant endospore-producing organisms have been treated as anaerobes, but a note to G **8** indicates which species have been so treated.
8. No endospores produced........... 9
Endospores produced....**Bacillus** p. *179*
M. p. 613
Bacillus (in Krass.)
a. Motile........**Bacillus** (in Prévot)
Nonmotile.**Bacteridium** (in Prévot)
Note: The following endospore-producing organisms are described as aerotolerant. Generic names are those used by Prévot. The *Manual* names are given in parentheses. *Plectridium* (*Clostridium*) *carnis*, *Plectridium* (*Clostridium*) *pectinovorum*, *Plectridium* (*Clostridium*) *tertium*, *P. haemolysans*, *P. cellulolyticum*, *Acuformis caninus*, *Clostridium* (*Clostridium*) *histolyticum*, *Clostridium* (*Clostridium*) *lacunarum*, *Clostridium sextum*, and *Clostridium amylobacter*.
9. Organisms show distinct branching in young cultures..................... 10
Organisms do not branch............ 19
Note: No provision appears to be made for organisms that, under optimal growth conditions, produce long, *unbranched* filaments, which, like *Nocardia*, eventually disintegrate into a series of short rods. The *Manual* descriptions of *Nocardia globerula* and *N. rubropertincta* suggest such forms. The author has observed others in rabbit dung media. It would seem better to assign such forms to a new genus to retain the branching character in *Nocardia*.

10. Branching mycelium produced in microcolonies....................... **11**
Branching very rudimentary, limited to simple branching or bifurcation of isolated rods; no mycelium formed............ **16**
11. Organisms show dichotomous branching in young cultures. Filaments later divide into unicellular, rod-shaped segments, which become arranged in zigzag fashion. Subsequently, a narrow tube is produced from one end of each rod and grows out, finally developing to the same width as the original rod. Filaments may also reproduce by breaking down into spore-like elements reminiscent of the sporogenous hyphae of *Streptomyces*. L-forms common. Found in the mouth
Leptotrichia   (in B-P and D)
(*L. dentium*)
Bacterionema (in G, H, and B)
(*B. matruchotii*)
(This genus is not listed in the *Manual*. See Baird-Parker and Davis, J. Gen. Microbiol., *19*, 1958, 446, and Gilmour, Howell, and Biddy, Bacteriol. Revs., *25*, 1961, 131.)
Not as above..................... **11a**
11a. Organisms produce branching mycelium in the early stages of development, which completely fragments to short, nonmotile bacillary forms. When aerial mycelium is produced, it may fragment into rods and coccal elements by complete fragmentation of the hyphae (see Note a). Fragmentation of the mycelium may commence within a few hours or be delayed several days. No conidia formed:
  i. Branching, at most, limited to very short branches on filamentous growth, followed by rapid fragmentation and

"slipping" of the cells. Cells weakly or strongly acid-fast

Mycobacterium p. *182*
M. p. 695
Mycobacterium (in Prévot)
Mycobacterium (in Krass.)

ii. Mycelium initially well developed and ramifying; usually non-acid-fast

Nocardia p. *184*
M p. 713
Nocardia (in Prévot)
Proactinomyces (in Krass.)

Note: a. For discussion on differentiation of these forms, see Gordon and Mihm (J. Bacteriol., *73*, 1957, 1527). Gordon (J. Bacteriol., *75*, 1958, 239) claims that aerial chains of spores are produced by *Nocardia asteroides* and that they are indistinguishable morphologically from those of *Streptomyces*. This claim should be examined in the light of Bisset and Moore's claim (see Note b) for multi-cellularity of the *Nocardia* with the view to transferring the species to *Streptomyces*. It is difficult to accept the retention of organisms of this type in the genus *Nocardia* if the formation of the aerial spore chains is identical to that of *Streptomyces*. If, on the other hand, there is a complete fragmentation of the aerial mycelium in the manner of arthrospore formation in fungi, this would seem to be differentiated from the mode of conidium formation in *Streptomyces*, revealed by electron microscope sections of sporophores (Vernon, Nature, *176*, 1955, 935; Glauert and Hopwood, J. Biochem. Biophys. Cytol., *10*, 1961, 505).

b. *Actinomyces*, generally regarded as anaerobic, is considered by some to be microaerophilic. Organisms growing poorly aerobically but better anaerobically should be compared carefully with the *Actinomyces* spp. According to Bisset and Moore (J. Gen. Microbiol., *3*, 1949, 387), component rods of *Nocardia* are each composed of a number of very short cells, *i.e.*, they are multicellular, whereas component rods of *Actinomyces* are unicellular. They also note that branches occurring in *Nocardia*

and *Actinomyces* are separated by a septum at the point of origin whereas in *Streptomyces* the branch arises from the component cell without the development of a septum. Since a limited number of species was examined, these claims require further substantiation.

c. Cultures of *Actinoplanes*, when cultured on certain media, fail to produce sporangia and resemble *Nocardia*.

d. See also the following *Proactinomyces* species, which are not listed in the *Manual: alni, cyaneus, elaeagnii, gabritschewski, myricae, putorii, pyogenes, sendaiensis variabilis;* see also *P. freeri*, which is considered as a synonym of *Nocardia asteroides* in the *Manual*. See also the following species of *Mycobacterium: album, convolutum, cyaneum, ferrosiliceum, filiforme, fluorescens, oligonitrophilum.*

e. Krassilnikov does not list the *Manual* species 9, 10, 27 to 31, 35, 39, 40, 42, and 43. He lists *N. leishmani* under *Actinomyces spumalis, N. pretoriana* under *Actinomyces phenotolerans, N. rubropertincta* under *Mycobacterium rubrum, N. coeliaca* under *Mycobacterium flavum,* and *N. madurae* as *Actinomyces madurae*.

Gordon and Mihm (J. Bacteriol., *73*, 1957, 15) list the following species under *Mycobacterium rhodochrous: N. corallina, N. erythropolis, N. globerula, N. lutea, N. opaca, N. rhodnii, N. rubra,* and *N. polychromogenes.*

Not as above......................... **11b**

11b. Branching mycelium produced from coccoid bodies undergoes a primary subdivision by transverse septa laid down progressively 5 to 30 μ behind the tip of the hypha as growth proceeds. This is followed by progressive division of each cell by further transverse septa until individual cells are only 0.3 to 0.5 μ long. Then longitudinal and radial division of each cell occurs with progressive widening of the hypha sometimes eight to ten fold, producing sarcina or mulberry-like packets of coccoid cells. At this stage the hyphal-cell mass is enclosed in mucus. Individual cocci may germinate to produce hypha but most ultimately swell and produce motile cocci, which free themselves from the gelatinous matrix. . **Dermatophilus** (See Roberts, Aust. J. Exp. Biol. Med. Sci., *39*, 1961, 463; Gordon and Edwards, J. Bacteriol., *86*, 1963, 1101; and Gordon, J. Bacteriol., *88*, 1964, 509.)

Note: There is some uncertainty whether the mucous sheath represents a sporangium.

Not as above...................... **11c**

11c. Organisms produce a branching mycelium, which breaks into short bacillary or coccoid forms. Colonies have a mealy consistency and are bare or covered with a hardly perceptible felt of aerial mycelium. Spores are produced in short chains on short sporophores by successive abstriction of spores from the tip

Promicromonospora
(See Krassilnikov, Hindustan Antibiotics Bull., *7*, 1964, 1; compare with *Micropolyspora.*)

Not as above...................... **12**

12. Organisms do not form any spores; saprophytic, aerobic, mesophilic organisms, which produce a fine, well-developed, nonseptate branching substrate mycelium, which does not fragment; forms large, spherical sclerotia-like bodies in large aggregate masses of mycelium 16 to 75 μ wide, enveloped in a covering mass of mycelium................... **Chainia**
(See Thirumalachar, Nature, *176*, 1955, 935.)

Organisms produce spores in pycnidia. Cultures of this genus differ from *Streptomyces* only in that on the surface of colonies they form pycnidia, *i.e.*, fruiting bodies, having spherical or oval form, inside which spores are developed. These organisms have well-developed aerial mycelium with spiral or nonspiral fruiting structures with numerous spores in long chains. Mycelium is nonseptate

Actinopycnidium
(See Krassilnikov, Hindustan Anti-

biotics Bull., 7, 1964, 1; compare with *Streptosporangium.*)

Organisms produce spores in sporangia

13

Organisms produce conidia but not in sporangia......................... **14**

13. Sporangia small and club-shaped, arise as bud-like processes from both substrate and aerial mycelium; the contents of which divide into a short chain of spores, which swell to give the sporangium a beaded appearance, looking, at first glance, like *Waksmania* or *Micropolyspora*. When mounted in an aqueous medium, the sporangia erupt to release the spores. Usually two spores in substrate sporangia and two to five in aerial sporangia

Microellobosporia
(See Cross, Lechevalier, and Lechevalier, J. Gen. Microbiol., *31*, 1963, 495.)

Sporangia large; containing numerous spores.

i. Spores rod-shaped............. **13a**

ii. Spores spherical............. **13b**

13a. i. Spores produced in straight chains; motile; sporangia spherical, urceolate, oval, cylindrical, bell-shaped, or in other forms; spores 0.8 to 1.5 μ by 2 to 3 μ; sporangia range from 3 to 9 μ by 6 to 14 μ to 5 to 14 μ by 8 to 30 μ. . **Ampullariella**
(Couch, J. Elisha Mitchell Scientific Society, *79*, 1963, 54.)

ii. Spores rod-shaped, straight, curved, or spiral, developed from one or more coiled hyphae within the sporangium; weakly but definitely motile; sporangia spherical, subspherical to elongate and borne on branched sporophores. The mycelium also forms compact regular and irregular coils without a surrounding wall, and such coils, when flooded, at times break up into motile spores

Spirillospora
(See Couch, *loc cit.*)

iii. Spores rod-shaped; nonmotile, occurring in very irregular sporangia

Amorphosporangium
(See Couch, *loc cit.*)

13b. Mycelium penetrates the submerged

plant tissue; conidia, 1.0 to 1.5 μ in diameter, produced in coils or irregularly within the sporangia; conidia globose to slightly angular; sporangia, 8.4 to 22.0 μ in diameter, borne on long aerial hyphae; conidia *motile;* germinate to produce a branched mycelium........ **Actinoplanes** p. *193*

M p. 826

Actinoplanes (in Prévot)

Mycelium grows over the surface of submerged plant tissue; conidia spherical, 1.8 to 2.0 μ in diameter, produced in coils within the sporangia; sporangia 7 to 19 μ in diameter produced apically or on branches of aerial hyphae; conidia *nonmotile* and forcibly ejected from a protuberance formed from the sporangium wall when the sporangia are immersed in water.... **Streptosporangium** p. *193*

M p. 828

Streptosporangium (in Prévot)

14. Conidia produced singly on short conidiophores...................... 15
Conidia produced in longitudinal pairs either sessile on the nonseptate mycelium or on monopodially arranged short conidiophores........... **Waksmania** p. *190*

Microbispora (in Nonomura and Ohara)

Note: This genus does not appear in the *Manual.* See Lechevalier and Lechevalier (J. Gen. Microbiol., *17*, 1957, 104) and Lechevalier (Intern. Bull. Bacteriol. Nomen. Taxon., *15*, 1965, 139). Although it was discovered at the same time priority has been accorded to the name *Microbispora.* Included here is the organism *Thermopolyspora bispora* Henssen.

Conidia produced acropetally in unbranched straight, curved, or spiral chains from sharply defined unbranched aerial mycelium only. Substrate mycelium nonseptate............ **Thermopolyspora**

(See Henssen, Archiv. Mikrobiol., *26*, 1957, 373, and Corbaz et al., J. Gen. Microbiol., *32*, 1963, 449.)

Conidia produced acropetally from short sporophores on the aerial *and* the substrate mycelium. The substrate mycelium is septate and breaks up readily when

disturbed. Spores sometimes produced in coiled aggregates on the agar

Micropolyspora

(See Lechevalier, Solotorovsky, and McDurmont, J. Gen. Microbiol., *26*, 1961, 11.) Lechevalier—personal communication—is of the opinion that the species named *Thermopolyspora glauca*, *T. flexuosa*, and *T. rectivirgula* by Krassilnikov and Agre, Hindustan Antibiotics Bull., *6*, 1964, 97, belong to the genus *Micropolyspora.*)

Conidia large, of variable length and cylindrical; produced by transformation of unbranched septate aerial mycelium; substrate mycelium septate and *Nocardia*-like but does not disintegrate

Pseudonocardia p. *185*

Conidia produced in long straight, flexed, or spiral chains by conversion of aerial hyphae into spore chains by total reorganization within the already formed hyphae........ **Streptomyces** p. *187*

M p. 744

Streptomyces (in Prévot)

Actinomyces (in Krass.)

Note: Krassilnikov does not list 47 of the *Manual* species and disagrees with the speciation of many of the others. He lists 11 species that do not appear in the *Manual* under the names assigned to them and lists *Streptomyces gedanensis* and *S. somaliensis* under *Proactinomyces.*

(See Vernon, Nature, *176*, 1955, 935, and Glauert and Hopwood, J. Biochem. Biophys. Cytol., *10*, 1961, 505, for notes on spore formation in *Streptomyces.* See also note to *Microellobosporia.*)

15. Conidia produced singly on short, unbranched conidiophores.......... **15a**
Conidia produced singly on the bifurcated tips of dichotomously branched conidiophores.................. **Actinobifida**

(See Krassilnikov and Agre, Mikrobiologia, *33*, 1964, 935, and *34*, 1965, 284.)

15a. No secondary mycelium formed; mycelium nonseptate; no growth between 50° and 65° C

Micromonospora p. *191*
M p. 822
Micromonospora (in Prévot)
Micromonospora (in Krass.)
(See also *M. elongata* and *M. bicolor* in Krassilnikov.)
Secondary aerial mycelium formed; growth at 50° to 65° C.

a. Spores on nonseptate aerial mycelium only.......... **Thermomonospora** (See Henssen, Arch. Mikrobiol., *26*, 1957, 373, and also Kuster and Locci, Intern. Bull. Bacteriol. Nomen. Taxon., *45*, 1963, 188.)

b. Spores on both aerial and substrate mycelium
Thermoactinomyces p. *192*
M p. 824
Thermoactinomyces (in Prévot)
Micromonospora (in Krass.)

16. Acid-fast.. **Mycobacterium** p. *182*
M p. 695
Non-acid-fast..................... **17**

17. Rudimentary branching rods only under aerobic conditions or in acid media anaerobically; produce chains of cocci or short rods in neutral media under anaerobic conditions; *propionic acid produced from lactic acid*.. **Propionibacterium** p. *173*
M p. 569
Propionibacterium (in Prévot)
Propionibacterium (in Krass.)

Note: Krassilnikov lists *Manual* species 1, 2, 7, 8, and 11 as *P. freudenreichii;* 5, 9, and 10 as *P. zeae;* and 3 and 4 as *P. rubrum.*

Cells have a definite cyclic development; spherical cells germinate at one or more points to produce rod-shaped cells, which elongate and divide. At the point of division, growth of the cells continues at an angle to the original axis. When side branches are equal in size to the parent, cell division occurs at the angle. This process is repeated during the growth of the colony. *In older colonies the rods transform entirely into a mass of cocci.* Rods are most frequently Gram negative with Gram

positive granules; the coccal forms are frequently Gram positive. Recorded mainly from soils...... **Arthrobacter** p. *177*
M p. 605
Mycobacterium (in Krass.)

Note: The emphasis lies on the final transformation into cocci. Some authorities may consider that limited true branching may occur. If this is admitted, the dividing line between *Arthrobacter* and *Nocardia* becomes very slim. The author's observations of *Arthrobacter globiformis* fit the above statement, and it is suggested that these criteria be adopted, with true branching forms that later disintegrate being assigned to *Nocardia.*

Coccoid cells, irregular in shape and size, reproducing by a budding process yielding assemblages of cells like flowering yeasts. Under low magnification these assemblages have a definite appearance of branching, hence the name. Common on lichens.
Mycococcus p. *183*
M p. 707
Mycococcus (in Prévot)
Mycococcus (in Krass.)

Note: The descriptions given for species in this genus are like early descriptions given for *Arthrobacter* and in some instances could fit *Nocardia.*
Not as above....................... **18**

18. Organisms disintegrate filter paper in 0.5 per cent peptone water; produce clearing on precipitated cellulose agar plates
Cellulomonas p. *177*
M p. 601

a. Motile.. **Cellulomonas** (in Prévot)
i. Yellow
Chromobacterium (in Krass.)
(*C. biazoteum*)
ii. Colorless.. **Bacterium** (in Krass.)
b. Nonmotile
Aplanobacter (in Prévot)
(*A. flavigenum*)
Pseudobacterium (in Krass.)
(*P. liquatum*)

Note: Krassilnikov lists *Cellulomonas fimi* under *Mycobacterium.*

Not as above
>   *possibly* **Corynebacterium**   p. *174*
>   *M p. 579*
>   **Corynebacterium** (in Prévot)
>   **Mycobacterium** (in Krass.)

(See also *Corynebacterium cutis* and *C. endocarditis* in Prévot and *Mycobacterium citreochromogenes, M. luteum,* and *M. salivarium* in Krassilnikov.)

>   *or*   **Jensenia**   p, *186*

Note: Bisset and Moore (J. Gen. Microbiol., *3*, 1949, 387) described the genus *Jensenia* to include the "soil diphtheroids." According to these authors, rod-shaped elements of the true *Corynebacterium* are multicellular and do not branch, whereas those of the majority of "soil diphtheroids" are unicellular, with the branches separated from the parent cell at the point of origin by a septum.

(See comments by Gordon and Mihm and by Adams and McClung under *Jensenia* in Digest of Genera.)

19. Motile at 37° or at 25° C........ **20**
Nonmotile......................... **27**
20. Organisms pathogenic to warm-blooded animals, causing monocytosis; catalase positive; acid produced from glucose, salicin, and esculin*

>   **Listeria**   p. *176*
>   *M p. 597*
>   **Listeria** (in Prévot)
>   **Listerella** (in Krass.)
>   **Listeria** (in T and W, 5th ed.)

Note: The name *Listerella* is invalid.

Not as above..................... **21**
21. Pathogenic to plants............ **22**
Not pathogenic or not known to be pathogenic to plants.................... **24**
22. Yellow colonies; polar flagella

>   *possibly*   **Corynebacterium**   p. *174*
>   (*C. flaccumfaciens* or *C. tritici*)
>   *M p. 579*
>   **Bacterium** (in Prévot)

>   **Pseudomonas** (in Krass.)
>   *or*   **Xanthomonas**   p. *113*
>   (*X. proteamaculans* or *X. conjac*)
>   *M p. 152*
>   **Xanthomonas** (in Prévot)
>   **Pseudomonas†** (in Krass.)

Yellow colonies; peritrichous flagella

>   **Erwinia**   p. *146*
>   (*E. citrimaculans*)
>   *M p. 349*
>   **Erwinia** (in Prévot)
>   **Bacterium** (?) (in Krass.)

Colonies not yellow................. **23**
23. Flagella polar

>   *either*   **Corynebacterium**   p. *174*
>   (*C. poinsettiae* or *C. hypertrophicans*)
>   *M p. 579*

Note: C. hypertrophicans is listed under *Bacterium* (*species incertae sedis*) by Prévot and under *Pseudomonas melopthora* by Krassilnikov.

>   or   **Pseudomonas**   p. *111*
>   (*P. polygoni*)
>   *M p. 89*
>   **Pseudobacterium** (in Krass.)

Flagella peritrichous.. **Erwinia** p. *146*
>   (*E. carnegieana*)
>   **Erwinia** (in Prévot)

Note: Erwinia species are generally regarded as Gram negative. Gram variable species are recorded. See also *Bacterium nadsonii* and *Bacterium dahliae* in Krassilnikov.

24. Organisms disintegrate filter paper in 0.5 per cent peptone water; produce clearing on precipitated cellulose agar plates

>   **Cellulomonas**   p. *177*
>   (*C. galba*)
>   *M p. 601*
>   **Cellulomonas** (in Prévot)
>   **Chromobacterium** (in Krass.)
>   (*C. aurogenes*)

Not as above..................... **25**
25. No acid from carbohydrates...... **26**

---

* Prévot described another organism, which ferments glucose only and reduces nitrates, which he calls *L. denitrificans.*

† Krassilnikov lists *X. proteamaculans* under *P. pelargonii* and *X. conjac* under *P. oryzae.*

Acid from carbohydrates
>Brevibacterium   p. *164*
>M p. *490*
>Bacterium (in Krass.)

(Including *Flavobacterium suaveolens* and *F. marinum*).

Note: a. Included here are *B. acetylicum, B. incertum, B. imperiale, B. lipolyticum.* Krassilnikov lists *B. lipolyticum* under *Bacterium liquefaciens* and *B. acetylicum* under *Chromobacterium sulphureum*, which also includes *Flavobacterium marinum* and *Flavobacterium suaveolens*. Prévot does not list the species included here under *Brevibacterium* but recognizes both species of *Flavobacterium* as such.

b. Bolcato (Antonie van Leeuwenhoek, *23*, 1957, 351) has described a new organism, *Microbacterium mobile*, which has most of the characteristics assigned to *Microbacterium* in Section G, *29*, except that the cells occur singly and in chains and are motile with peritrichous flagella; lactic acid produced is mainly optically inactive.

c. Harrison and Hansen (J. Bacteriol., *59*, 1950, 444) also record a new variety of *Lactobacillus plantarum* (var. *mobilis*), which is motile with peritrichous flagella and produces dextrorotatory lactic acid.

26. Organisms occur in long chains; colonies colorless and spreading
>Kurthia   p. *165*
>M p. *503*
>Kurthia (in Prévot)
>Bacterium (in Krass.)
>(*B. zopfii* only)

Organisms arranged singly; colonies yellow
>Brevibacterium   p. *164*
>(*B. sulfureum*)
>M p. *490*
>Chromobacterium (in Krass.)
>(*C. sulphureum*)

27. Acid-fast.. Mycobacterium   p. *182*
>M p. *695*
>Mycobacterium (in Prévot)
>Mycobacterium (in Krass.)

Note: Prévot lists two species, *M. anabanti* and *M. chelonei*, not cited in the

Manual. Krassilnikov does not list the species 3, 6, 7, 10, and 14 and lists *M. thamnopheos* under *M. marinum* and *M. bovis* and *M. avium* under *M. tuberculosis.*

Not acid-fast...................... **28**

28. Organisms 0.2 to 0.4 by 0.5 to 2.5 μ; long filaments common in rough colonies; occur singly and also in chains; pinpoint transparent colonies on agar in 24 hours at 37° C., extending on further incubation to 1.5 mm.; acid only produced from glucose and lactose and some other carbohydrates but not from esculin; final pH in glucose broth, approximately 6.0; hydrogen sulfide is produced; causes swine erysipelas, human erysipeloid, mouse septicemia, and infections in sheep, birds, and fish........**Erysipelothrix**   p. *176*
>M p. *599*
>Erysipelothrix (in Prévot)

Not as above...................... **29**

29. Rods 0.4 to 0.7 by 1 to 3 μ; show granular staining with methylene blue; arranged in angular fashion similar to the corynebacteria; only two species recorded, both of which produce acid from glucose, fructose, and mannose; catalase positive; resist heating to 72° C. for 15 minutes; normally found in dairy products and equipment.... **Microbacterium**   p. *177*
>M p. *600*
>Microbacterium (in Prévot)
>Pseudobacterium (in Krass.)

Not as above...................... **30**

30. Organisms grow on agar under aerobic conditions only if heavy inocula are used; slightly pleomorphic, including branched forms; *propionic acid is produced from glucose and also from lactic acid;* catalase positive... **Propionibacterium**   p. *173*
>(*P. arabinosum*)
>M p. *569*
>Propionibacterium (in Prévot)
>Propionibacterium (in Krass.)
>(*P. zeae*)

Not as above...................... **31**

31. Small spindle-shaped cells, usually occurring in long, intertwined chains in liquid media; microaerophilic; ferments glucose with the production of ethyl alcohol with small amounts of CO_2 and acetic acid and possibly lactic and formic acids; acid and gas in glucose in 3 to 5 days

Zymobacterium p. *174*
M p. 577
Eubacterium (in Prévot)

Not as above...................... **32**

32. Colonies usually 1 mm. or less in diameter, colorless, little or no growth on media devoid of carbohydrates; rods frequently arranged in chains, grow in glucose broth, producing a pH much below 6.0; acid produced from lactose by all species except *L. delbrueckii* with *L. brevis* and *L. viridescens* (Niven and Evans, J. Bacteriol., *73*, 1957, 758)

Lactobacillus p. *169*
M p. 543
Lactobacillus (in Prévot)
Lactobacterium* (in Krass.)

(See also *Lactobacterium orientale*, in Krassilnikov, and *L. heterohiochi*, in Demain *et al.*, J. Bacteriol., *81*, 1961, 147.)

Not as above...................... **33**

33. Lactose fermented; cells pleomorphic; arranged in palisades and Chinese letter forms; frequently bar-shaped, beaded, and clubbed.... **Corynebacterium** p. *174*
M p. 579

Note: a. Bisset (J. Gen. Microbiol., *3*, 1949, 93) states that the apparent barred and beaded staining is due to the fact that the so-called rods of corynebacteria are multicellular.

b. This entry includes species 4, 5, 7, 8, 11, 18, 21, 22, and 23. Of these, Prévot places 18 and 23 (*C. agropyri* and *C. insidiosum*) in the genus *Aplanobacter* and the rest in *Corynebacterium*. Krassilnikov does not list species 11 (*C. phocae*); he lists 22 and 23 (*C. rathayi* and *C. agropyri*) in *Pseudobacterium* and the remainder in *Mycobacterium*. See also *Pseudobacterium opacum*, *P. erythrogloeum*, *P. subluteum*, and *P. flavum* in Krassilnikov. See also *Actinomyces nitritogenes* in Prévot.

* See Note b to Section G **33**.

Lactose not fermented.............. **34**

34. Organisms occur singly, in pairs or in short chains; not pleomorphic

Brevibacterium p. *164*
M p. 490
Brevibacterium (in Prévot)
(*except species 6*)
Species 1, 2, 23: **Mycobacterium** (in Krass.)
Species 3 to 15: **Pseudobacterium** (in Krass.)
(*except 6* and *14*)
Species 14, 16, 17: **Bacterium** (in Krass.)

Note: Krassilnikov lists 11 additional species of *Pseudobacterium*. In his system the genus differs from *Mycobacterium* on lack of branching and from *Lactobacterium* (*Lactobacillus*) in not having a lactic fermentation. He includes in it *Corynebacterium fascians.*

(See also *B. healii.*)

Organisms normally found in palisade or Chinese letter forms, pleomorphic; barred and beaded and club-shaped forms common

Corynebacterium p. *174*
M p. 579
Corynebacterium (in Prévot)
Mycobacterium (in Krass.)

Note: a. Criteria for separation of these two genera are inadequate. Multicellularity in *Corynebacterium* may be the decisive factor (see note to Section G, **33**).

b. Included at this point are species 1, 2, 3, 6, 10, 12 to 15, 16, 17, 19, 20, 24, and 30. Krassilnikov does not list species 16, 17, and 20. He lists 12 further species not listed in the *Manual*. There is some difference of opinion between these authors and the *Manual* on nomenclature of species. See also *Corynebacterium cutis* and *C. endocarditis* in Prévot.

35. Organisms produce a true branching mycelium, which later disintegrates into simple rods, cocci, and rods with remnants of branches; catalase negative

Actinomyces p. *186*
M p. 742
Actinobacterium (in Prévot)
Proactinomyces (in Krass.)

Organisms produce a branching mycelium, which does not readily disintegrate; conidia produced singly on short condiophores...... **Micromonospora** p. *191*
Actinobacterium (in Prévot)
(*A. propionici*)

Note: a. The *Manual* does not list any anaerobic species of *Micromonospora*. Hungate (J. Bacteriol., *51*, 1946, 51) describes an anaerobic cellulose-digesting organism belonging to this genus. Prévot named this organism *Actinobacterium propionici*.

b. Bisset (J. Gen. Microbiol., *17*, 1957, 562) describes a monosporous actinomycete.

Organisms show dichotomous branching in young cultures. Filaments later divide into unicellular, rod-shaped segments, which become arranged in zigzag fashion. Subsequently a narrow tube is produced from one end of each rod and grows out, finally developing to the same width as the original rod. Filaments may also reproduce by breaking down into spore-like elements reminiscent of the sporogenous hyphae of *Streptomyces*. L-forms common. Found in the mouth
Leptotrichia (in B-P and D)
(*L. dentium*)
Bacterionema (in G, H, and B)
(*B. matruchotii*)
(This genus is not listed in the *Manual*. See Baird-Parker and Davis, J. Gen. Microbiol., *19*, 1958, 446, and Gilmour, Howell, and Biddy, Bacteriol. Revs., *25*, 1961, 131.)

Organisms do not branch, or if branching occurs, it is limited to bifurcations and branching of isolated rods; no mycelium formed.......................... **36**
36. Endospores produced........... **37**
No endospores produced............. **38**
37. Organisms reduce CO_2 to CH_4 while oxidizing secondary alcohols to ketones and primary alcohols to acids
Methanobacterium p. *125*
(*M. omelianskii*)
M p. 250

Note: Both Prévot and Krassilnikov consider this organism to be Gram negative, placing it in the genus *Terminosporus* (in Prévot) and *Bacterium* (in Krassilnikov).

Not as above..... **Clostridium** p. *180*
M p. 634
a. Spores terminal................. **b**
Spores subterminal or central..... **c**
b. Motile... **Plectridium** (in Prévot)
Nonmotile.. **Acuformis** (in Prévot)
c. Spores distend the rods.......... **d**
Spores do not distend the rods..... **f**
d. Nonmotile..................... **e**
Motile.. **Clostridium** (in Prévot)
e. Capsulated.... **Welchia** (in Prévot)
Noncapsulated
Inflabilis (in Prévot)
f. Motile..... **Bacillus** (in Prévot)
Nonmotile
Bacteridium (in Prévot)

Note: Prévot includes a large number of species, spread over the foregoing genera, which do not appear in the *Manual*. Disagreement with the ability of the spore to swell the rod occurs with some *Manual* species regarded by Prévot as having a nonswelling type of spores and placed in the genus *Inflabilis*.

Similar difficulty is encountered in attempting to correlate Krassilnikov's treatment of the *Bacillaceae* with that of the *Manual*. He lays emphasis on the swelling of rods by the spores and the production of granulose. There is so much conflict on interpretation of the former that no attempt is made here to equate Krassilnikov's nomenclature with that of Prévot or the *Manual*.

38. Cells motile; gas produced from peptone in the absence of carbohydrates
Cillobacterium p. *172*
M p. 566
Cillobacterium (in Prévot)
Note: a. Glucose and other carbohydrates are fermented by all species; butyric acid is frequently among the byproducts. Smith and Hungate (J. Bacteriol., *75*, 1958, 713) describe an organism that

produces methane from hydrogen and formate, which they call *Methanobacterium ruminantium*. Data given do not permit comparison beyond this point.

b. Prévot lists three additional species of *Cillobacterium*. See also Bryant, *et al.* (J. Bacteriol., *76*, 1958, 529).

Cells motile with a single polar flagellum; curved rods with pointed ends; isolated or in pairs or chains, gelatin not liquefied; acid and gas from carbohydrates; Voges-Proskauer positive; nitrates not reduced; indole negative; ferments glucose, producing CO_2, H_2, ethanol, acetic, formic, and lactic acids.. **Lachnospira** (in Prévot)

Note: Species incertae sedis in Prévot. See Bryant and Small (J. Bacteriol., *72*, 1956, 22).

Chain-forming rods, producing motile colonies.. **Catenabacterium** (in Prévot)
(*C. rotans*)

Cells nonmotile..................... **39**

39. Visible gas produced in culture media in either the presence or the absence of carbohydrates..................... **40**

Note: In the ensuing Sections 40 to 44 inclusive, the phrase "acid from" infers "acid" or "acid and gas," because it is not clear whether gas produced in the presence of carbohydrate arises from the fermentation of the sugar or action on the peptone.

There are some organisms that produce visible gas in culture media in either the presence or the absence of carbohydrates; glucose fermentation not recorded; pathogenic to guinea pigs; rods occur singly, in pairs, in V-formation, in short chains, and in clumps. (See *Eubacterium niosii*, *Eubacterium quintum*, and *Corynebacterium renale cuniculi*, in Prévot.)

No visible gas produced in culture media in the presence or absence of carbohydrates
45

40. Acid produced from glucose, lactose, and fructose...................... **41**

Acid produced from glucose and fructose but not from lactose................. **42**

Acid produced from glucose and lactose but not from fructose.................. **43**

Acid produced from glucose but not from lactose or fructose................... **44**

41. Large rods with rounded ends, occurring as short, swollen forms and long, curved forms; bifurcation common; acid produced also from maltose, galactose, and sucrose; strict anaerobes

Catenabacterium p. *171*
(*C. filamentosum*)
M p. *560*

Catenabacterium (in Prévot)
Slender rods, sometimes undulating and filamentous; form acute V- and Y-shaped angles, giving an appearance of false branching; acid also from galactose and trehalose; strict anaerobes

Ramibacterium p. *172*
(*R. pseudoramosum*)
M p. *563*

Ramibacterium (in Prévot)
Microaerophilic, pleomorphic organisms, occurring as chains of cocci in acid media anaerobically and as rods with branching forms aerobically; aerobic growth very poor; propionic acid produced from lactic acid; limited gas from carbohydrates but none from peptone

Propionibacterium p. *173*
M p. *569*

Small, spindle-shaped cells, usually occurring in long, intertwined chains in liquid media; ferment glucose with the production of ethyl alcohol and small amounts of CO_2 and acetic and possibly lactic and formic acids; *no butyric or propionic acid produced;* acid and gas from glucose in three to five days

Zymobacterium p. *174*
(*Z. oroticum*)
M p. *577*

Rods occurring singly, in pairs, or in short or long chains; strict anaerobes

Eubacterium p. *171*
M p. *552*

Eubacterium (in Prévot)
Note: Krassilnikov does not recognize the genus *Eubacterium*. Species 10, 12, and 14 appear in the genus *Pseudobacterium* and 7 in *Mycobacterium*.

(See also *Lactobacillus brevis*, *Corynebacterium avidum*, and *Eubacterium cadaveris*.)

42. Organisms occur in long chains; acid from glucose, fructose, maltose, sucrose, galactose, xylose, and arabinose; propionic acid produced among the byproducts; strict anaerobes

Catenabacterium p. *171*

(*C. contortum*)

M p. 560

Catenabacterium (in Prévot)

Organisms arranged in chains and in acute V- and Y-shaped forms suggestive of false branches; gelatin not liquefied; nitrites not produced from nitrates; no acid from maltose; butyric acid is produced; strictly anaerobic.... **Ramibacterium** p. *172*

(*R. dentium* and *R. alactolyticum*)

M p. 563

Ramibacterium (in Prévot)

Microaerophilic pleomorphic organisms, occurring as chains of cocci in acid media anaerobically and as rods with branching forms aerobically; aerobic growth very poor; propionic acid produced from lactic acid; limited gas from carbohydrates but none from peptone

Propionibacterium p. *173*

M p. 569

Other than above; organisms occur singly or in short chains; acid from maltose; butyric acid is produced by one species; strict anaerobes.. **Eubacterium** p. *171*

M p. 552

Eubacterium (in Prévot)

(*E. foedans, E. quartum, E. limosum*)

Note: Krassilnikov lists *E. foedans* in *Pseudobacterium* and *E. limosum* in *Mycobacterium*.

(See also *Lactobacillus brevis* and *Corynebacterium avidum*.)

43. Organisms occur in short or long chains with zigzag arrangement and acute V- and Y-forms suggestive of false branching; propionic acid produced by one species

Ramibacterium p. *172*

(*R. ramosum* and *R. ramosoides*)

M p. 563

Ramibacterium (in Prévot)

Organisms occur singly or in a long, sinuous chain of cells.... **Eubacterium** p. *171*

(*E. rectale*)

M p. 552

Eubacterium (in Prévot)

Pseudobacterium (in Krass.)

Note: There is a strong resemblance between *Ramibacterium ramosoides* and *Eubacterium rectale*.

44. Organisms occur in short chains and as long, pleomorphic filaments; acid produced from glucose, maltose, sucrose, galactose, and glycerol; hydrogen sulfide is produced; gelatin is liquefied; butyric acid is produced

Catenabacterium p. *171*

(*C. helminthoides*)

M p. 560

Catenabacterium (in Prévot)

Organisms arranged singly; butyric acid, acetic acid, and CO_2 produced from glucose, maltose, and lactic acid

Butyribacterium p. *174*

(*B. rettgeri*)

M p. 577

Eubacterium (in Prévot)

Organisms arranged singly; amines, ammonia, and nitrogen produced

Eubacterium p. *171*

(*E. obstii*)

M p. 552

Eubacterium (in Prévot)

Pseudobacterium (in Krass.)

Organisms arranged predominantly in Y-shaped forms, suggestive of false branching; acid from glucose and galactose; gelatin not liquefied

Ramibacterium p. *172*

(*R. pleuriticum*)

M p. 563

Ramibacterium (in Prévot)

(See also *Corynebacterium diphtheroides* —*Mycobacterium anaerobium* in Krassilnikov—and *Bifidobacterium bifurcatum* in Prévot, p. 510.)

45. No acid from carbohydrates

Eubacterium p. *171*

M p. 552

Eubacterium (in Prévot)
Pseudobacterium (in Krass.)
(Includes *E. lentum*, *E. minutum* and *E. poeciloides*. See also *Corynebacterium adamsoni* in Prévot.)
Acid from carbohydrates............ **46**
46. Rods 5 to 15 μ long, often fusiform, occurring singly, in pairs, or in long chains; Gram positive when young but Gram negative in old cultures; no evidence of branching; ferment glucose, maltose, sucrose, fructose, mannose, and usually salicin and occasionally other sugars. Voges-Proskauer negative; gelatin not liquefied; indole not produced, lactic acid (racemic) produced from glucose; catalase negative; found in the human mouth........ **Leptotrichia**
(*L. buccalis*)
Note: This is the *L. buccalis* of Hamilton and Zahler (J. Bacteriol., *73*, 1957, 386) and Gilmour, Howell, and Biddy (Bacteriol. Revs., *25*, 1961, 131).
Not as above...................... **47**
47. Acid from glucose, lactose, and fructose.......................... **53**
Acid from glucose and lactose but not from fructose.... **Catenabacterium** p. *171*
(*C. lottii*)
M p. *560*
Catenabacterium (in Prévot)
(See also *Lactobacillus caucasicus*.)
Acid from glucose and fructose but not from lactose...................... **48**
Acid from glucose but not from lactose or fructose.......................... **57**
48. Rod-shaped cells with rounded ends, occurring singly, in pairs, and in chains: not pleomorphic; produce acid without gas from glucose, fructose, maltose, galactose, and sucrose; H$_2$S not produced; indole negative; gelatin not liquefied; nitrates not reduced; peptones and volatile amines produced.... **Eubacterium** (in Prévot)
(*E. ventriosum*)
(See also *Catenabacterium rotans* in Prévot.)
Not as above...................... **49**
49. Organisms pathogenic to mice and rabbits; cause urinary tract infection in horses, cattle, sheep, and dogs; propionic acid not produced from lactic acid; strictly anaerobic... **Corynebacterium** p. *174*
(*C. renale*)
M p. *579*
Corynebacterium (in Prévot)
Mycobacterium (in Krass.)
Not as above...................... **50**
50. Organisms found mainly in fermenting foods; *propionic acid produced from lactic acid;* microaerophilic to anaerobic
Propionibacterium p. *173*
M p. *569*
Not as above...................... **51**
51. Organisms isolated from infections in animals; propionic and/or acetic acid produced from glucose............... **52**
No propionic acid produced from lactic acid; predominantly lactic acid from glucose........ **Lactobacillus** p. *169*
M p. *542*
Bifidobacterium (in Prévot)
Note: Hayward, Hale, and Bisset (J. Gen. Microbiol., *13*, 1955, 292) suggest that *Lactobacillus bifidus* should be placed in the genus *Bidifobacterium* Orla-Jensen 1924: see also *B. cornutum* and possibly *B. bifurcatum* (in Prévot).
52. Cells 3 μ or more long; rudimentary branching evident in some cells; pleomorphic
possibly **Actinobacterium** (in Prévot)
(See *A. cellulitis*, *A. liquefaciens*, *A. meyeri*.)
Cells less than 3 μ long; diphtheroid; catalase positive;
Corynebacterium (in Prévot)
(See *C. pyogenes bovis* and *C. lymphophilum* in Prévot.)
53. Butyric acid produced........... **54**
Propionic acid produced............ **55**
No propionic or butyric acid produced.. **56**
54. Organisms occurring in very long chains
Catenabacterium p. *171*
(*C. catenaforme*)
M p. *560*
Catenabacterium (in Prévot)
Mycobacterium (in Krass.)
(*M. anaerobium*)

Organisms occurring singly, in pairs, and in clumps..........**Eubacterium** p. *171*
(*E. parvum*)
M p. *552*
Eubacterium (in Prévot)
Pseudobacterium (in Krass.)
(*P. niosii*)
(See also *Corynebacterium avidum—Mycobacterium* in Krassilnikov—and *Bifidobacterium appendicitis* in Prévot.)

55. Propionic acid produced from lactic acid: catalase positive
Propionibacterium p. *173*
M p. *569*
Propionibacterium (in Prévot)
Propionibacterium (in Krass.)
Not as above; rods 0.5 to 0.7 μ by 0.3 to 0.4 μ with rounded ends; arranged singly and in pairs; no growth in gelatin
Eubacterium p. *171*
(*E. disciformans*)
M p. *552*
Eubacterium (in Prévot)
Not as above; rods 1.5 to 3.0 μ by 0.4 μ; club-shaped; contains metachromatic granules; gelatin slowly liquefied
Corynebacterium (in Prévot)
(*C. anaerobium*)

56. Long rods, 0.3 by 8.0 μ, with tapered, rounded, or swollen ends; often occurring in short or long chains
Catenabacterium p. *171*
(*C. leptotrichoides*)
M p. *560*
Catenabacterium (in Prévot)
Slender rods, 0.5 to 0.7 by 2 to 8 μ, occurring in short or long chains; bifurcations common; produce lactic and volatile acids from glucose; microaerophilic to anaerobic
Lactobacillus p. *169*
(*L. bifidus*)
M p. *542*
Bifidobacterium (in Prévot)
Lactobacterium (in Krass.)
(See also *Bifidobacterium appendicitis* in Prévot. See also Clarke, J. Gen. Microbiol., *20*, 1959, 549, and Gibbons and Doetsch, J. Bacteriol., *77*, 1959, 417.)
Rods 1.0 by 3.0 μ; produced in short or

long chains; acetic and lactic acids produced from glucose
Eubacterium p. *171*
M p. *552*
Note: E. crispatum has a sugar fermentation range similar to that of *Lactobacillus bifidus*, but acetic acid appears to predominate.

57. Propionic acid produced.......... **59**
Butyric acid produced from lactic acid; acid from glucose and maltose
Butyribacterium p. *174*
(*B. rettgeri*)
M p. *577*
Eubacterium (in Prévot)
No propionic or butyric acid produced.. **58**

58. Organisms arranged in short to very long chains
Catenabacterium p. *171*
(*C. nigrum*)
M p. *560*
Catenabacterium (in Prévot)
Organisms occurring singly and in groups arranged in a palisade or Chinese letter fashion...... **Corynebacterium** p. *174*
(*C. granulosum* and *C. parvum*)
M p. *579*
Corynebacterium (in Prévot)
Mycobacterium (in Krass.)
(See also *C. granulomatis, C. hepatodystrophicans* and *Bifidobacterium intestinalis* in Prévot.)

59. Catalase positive; propionic acid produced from lactic acid
Propionibacterium p. *173*
M p. *569*
Propionibacterium (in Prévot)
Propionibacterium (in Krass.)
Catalase positive; propionic acid produced from glucose but not from lactic acid
Corynebacterium p. *174*
(*C. acnes*)
M p. *579*
Corynebacterium (in Prévot)
Mycobacterium (in Krass.)
Note: Moon and Cato (J. Bacteriol., *85*, 1963, 870) have shown that all strains of *Corynebacterium acnes* consistently fermented lactate to propionate, thus remov-

ing the validity of this separation. They support Douglas and Gunter (J. Bacteriol., *52*, 1946, 15) in placing *C. acnes* in the genus *Propionibacterium.*

SECTION H

1. Aerobic............................ 2
Anaerobic; proceed to.... Section I p. *86*
2. Cells 1.4 to 1.6 μ wide and 10 to 50 μ long, forming chains usually over 100 μ in length; individual rods are characterized by constrictions, which later develop into cross walls followed by division; cells may branch, the branch appearing at or near the site of constriction but not visibly connected with the main axis; motile by means of peritrichous flagella; form small, bluish white, iridescent colonies on peptone yeast extract agar, particularly with added acetate........ **Lineola** p. *195*
M p. 832
Not as above........................ 3
3. Organisms isolated from cases of granuloma inguinale; grow only in the yolk sac of the developing chick embryo or in condensation water of a sloped medium prepared by adding 50 per cent unheated embryonic yolk to melted and cooled nutrient agar
Calymmatobacterium p. *132*
M p. 418
Donovania (in T and W, 4th ed.)
Calymmatobacterium (in Prévot)
Bacterium (in Krass.)
Pleomorphic organisms parasitic on or within erythrocytes of man and other vertebrates, causing infections of lower animals; stain by Giemsa's stain without visible differentiation into nucleus and cytoplasm; grown with variable success in semisolid agar containing whole blood. Proceed to.......... Section K p. *93*
Organisms grow in glucose-blood-bouillon agar as Gram negative rods 1.0 μ in length; occur in masses as coccoid and ellipsoidal cells 0.3 to 0.5 μ in diameter, extracellularly lining the intestinal epithelium of the sheep ked, *Melophagus ovinus*
Wolbachia p. *210*

(W. melophagi)
M p. 953
Not as above........................ **4**
4. Organisms isolated from nodules on the roots of leguminous plants and capable of producing nodules on the host plant
Rhizobium p. *141*
M p. 285
Rhizobium (in Prévot)
Rhizobium (in Krass.)
Not as above........................ **5**
5. Organisms capable of continued growth in a glucose, sucrose, or mannitol mineral salts medium devoid of nitrogen compounds........................... **6**
Not as above........................ **7**
6. Motile with polar flagella
Azotomonas p. *117*
M p. 198
Pseudomonas (in Prévot)
Azotomonas (in Krass.)
Motile with peritrichous flagella or nonmotile:
a. Straight or slightly curved or irregular, locally swollen or buckled rods, characterized by the presence at the extremities of highly refractile spherical bodies, presumably consisting of lipoids; grow in acid media at pH 4.5
Azotobacter p. *140*
M p. 283
Azotobacter (in Krass.)
Beijerinckia Derx 1950
Beijerinckia (in Prévot)
Note: Krassilnikov lists five species.
b. Spherical to oval yeast-like cells, exceeding 2 μ in width, which do not form cysts (arthrospores). Do not produce acid from carbohydrates or grow at pH 4.5
Azotobacter p. *140*
M p. 283
Azotobacter (in Prévot)
Azotobacter (in Krass.)
Azotococcus Tchan 1953
(See Tchan, Proc. Linnean Soc. N. S. Wales, *78*, 1953, 85.)
c. Rod-shaped to spherical cells 2 μ or more in width, which produce cysts

(arthrospores). Do not produce acid from carbohydrates or grow at pH 4.5

> Azotobacter p. 140
>
> M p. 283
>
> Azotobacter (in Krass.)

Not as above........................ 7

Note: Nitrogen fixation has also been recorded for *Aerobacter aerogenes* and some other organisms, which will key out in a subsequent section.

7. Endospores produced

> Bacillus p. 179
>
> M p. 613

a. Endospores do not distend the rods

> Bacillus (in Krass.)

1. Subterminal or central

> Innominatus (in Prévot)

Note: Krassilnikov places all sporing cells, in which the spore does not distend the cell, into **Bacillus**. Prévot places the Gram negative rods of the nonswelling type into the genus. **Innominatus.** There were no entries for aerobic Gram negative organisms with distended spores, or for nondistending terminal spores.

Endospores not produced............ 8

8. Organisms grow well on yeast water medium containing up to 10 per cent alcohol, with oxidation of the latter to acetic acid; growth very poor or absent on media containing no carbohydrates or alcohols.

a. Polar flagella; do not oxidize acetate

> Acetomonas Leifson* 1954
>
> Gluconobacter Asai
>
> Acetobacter p. 113
>
> M p. 183
>
> Acetobacter (in Prévot)
>
> Acetobacter (in Krass.)

Note: De Ley (J. Gen. Microbiol., *24*, 1961, 31) favors the use of *Gluconobacter* instead of *Acetomonas.*

b. Peritrichous flagella or nonmotile; oxidize acetate to CO_2 and H_2O

> Acetobacter Leifson† 1954
>
> Acetobacter p. 113
>
> M p. 183

---

* See Digest of Genera p. *115*.
† See notes on *Acetobacter*, p. *113*.

> Acetobacter (in Prévot)
>
> Acetobacter (in Krass.)

Note: a. Kimmett and Williams (J. Gen. Microbiol., *31*, 1963, 447) recommend that *Gluconobacter liquefaciens* be placed in the genus *Acetobacter sensu* Leifson.

b. *Erwinia carotovora* is recorded to be able to oxidize 5 per cent ethyl alcohol.

Not as above........................ 9

9. Organisms grow poorly on peptone media in the absence of carbohydrates; good growth of white, raised, round colonies 1 mm. in diameter on wort agar under anaerobic conditions; only slight growth, if any, aerobically in the presence of sugars; glucose fermented with the production of carbon dioxide, lactic acid, and up to 10 per cent ethyl alcohol; motile by means of a single polar flagellum

> Zymomonas p. 117
>
> M p. 199
>
> Zymomonas (in Prévot)

Organisms that will not grow on common laboratory media; grow in sucrose broth containing less than 0.5 per cent NaCl and a very low concentration of meat extract; will grow in selected synthetic media with the use of pneumococcal capsular polysaccharide as the sole source of carbon

> Saccharobacterium
>
> Saccharobacterium (in Krass.)

Note: This genus is recorded in the sixth but not in the seventh edition of the *Manual.*

Not as above........................ 10

10. Colonies with a purple pigment

> Chromobacterium p. 142
>
> M p. 292
>
> Chromobacterium (in Prévot)
>
> Chromobacterium (in Krass.)
>
> Chromobacterium (in T and W, 5th ed.)

Note: a. *Chromobacterium marismortui* has a bluish-brown pigment; see also *Pseudomonas iodinum* and *Pseudomonas beijerinckii* and *Halobacterium halobium* in the *Manual* and *Pseudomonas amethystinum, P. indigofera, P. ianthina, P. pseudoviolacea, P. laurentia,* and *Chromobacterium amethystinum,* and *C. lividum* in Krassilnikov.

b. Leifson (J. Bacteriol., *71*, 1956, 393) and Sneath (J. Gen. Microbiol., *15*, 1956, 70 and 99) give somewhat conflicting views on the genus.

Colonies red at 37° C. or 25° C., sometimes with a red, water-soluble pigment... **11**

Other than above.................. **17**

11. Red color due to prodigiosin; motile by means of peritrichous flagella or nonmotile

Serratia p. *153*

M p. 359

Serratia (in Prévot)

Chromobacterium (in Krass.)

Serratia (in T and W, 5th ed.)

Note: Colwell (J. Bacteriol., *89*, 1965, 454) has recommended recognition of only one species—*S. marcescens.* Prévot lists three additional species—*S. marinorubra, S. rubida,* and *S. rubrolutea.*

Red color not due to prodigiosin.... **12**

12. Obligate halophiles requiring 20 to 30 per cent salt for growth; highly pleomorphic

Halobacterium p. *119*

M p. 207

Serratia (in Prévot)

Pseudomonas (in Krass.)

Note: Krassilnikov lists only *P. salinaria* and *P. carnea (H. cutirubrum).* Prévot lists *H. marismortui* in the genus *Chromobacterium.*

Not obligately halophilic............. **13**

13. Organisms metabolize alkylamines.

a. Motile with a polar flagellum

Protaminobacter p. *117*

(P. ruber)

M p. 200

Serratia (in Prévot)

Pseudomonas (in Krass.)

(P. rubra)

b. Nonmotile

Protaminobacter p. *117*

(P. alboflavum)

M p. 240

Empedobacter (in Prévot)

Pseudobacterium (in Krass.)

Not as above...................... **14**

14. Motile by means of polar flagella;

straight or curved rods.............. **15**

Motile by means of peritrichous flagella

16

Nonmotile

Pseudobacterium (in Krass.)

(P. rubricum, P. corallinum, P. lacticolum, P. latericeum)

15. Straight rods

Pseudomonas p. *111*

M p. 89

Pseudomonas* (in Prévot)

Pseudomonas (in Krass.)

Note: In addition to two *Manual* species *(P. melophthora, P. erythra),* Krassilnikov lists five species, which terminate here.

Curved rods............ **Vibrio** p. *122*

(V. extorquens and *V. hyphalus)*

M p. 229

Vibrio (in Prévot)

Vibrio (in Krass.)

Note: Manual species listed here are *V. extorquens* and *V. hyphalus.* Krassilnikov does not list the latter and places the former in *Pseudomonas.* He lists two others —*V. hydrosulfureus* and *V. saprophiles*— as having red colonies.

16. Methyl red positive; Voges-Proskauer negative.......... **Escherichia** p. *149*

(E. aurescens)

M p. 335

Flavobacterium (in Prévot)

Bacterium (in Krass.)

Methyl red negative; Voges-Proskauer positive; pathogenic on rhubarb

Erwinia p. *146*

(E. rhapontica)

M p. 349

Erwinia (in Prévot)

Pseudobacterium (in Krass.)

Note: Other peritrichously flagellated organisms listed by Krassilnikov are *Chromobacterium aurantiacum, C. rubefaciens, Bacterium rubidum,* and *Photobacterium cyanophosphorescens.*

17. Organisms produce a water-soluble, blue, green, or yellow pigment...... **18**

Not as above...................... **19**

* Prévot lists *P. melophthora* in the genus *Phytobacterium.*

18. Agar hydrolyzed; alginic acid decomposed.......... **Alginomonas** p. *118*
(*A. fucicola*)
Pseudomonas (in Prévot)
Pseudomonas (in Krass.)
(See also *P. proteus* in Prévot. See also *P. gelatica* and *Vibrio fuscus* in the *Manual*.)
Agar not hydrolyzed.
  a. Nonmotile.. **Pseudomonas** p. *111*
M p. 89
Aplanobacter (in Prévot)
Pseudobacterium (in Krass.)
  b. Motile..... **Pseudomonas** p. *111*
M p. 89
Pseudomonas (in Prévot)
Pseudomonas (in Krass.)
Note: Both Prévot and Krassilnikov include in the genus *Pseudomonas* several species not listed in the seventh edition of the *Manual*. Most are in appendices to the sixth edition. The nonmotile organisms listed here are *P. betle* and *P. cissicola*, *P. eisenbergii* and *P. smaragdina*. Krassilnikov places *P. betle* in *Pseudobacterium* and the others in *Pseudomonas*. He also lists *P. synxantha* under *Chromobacterium rheni*. See also *Chromobacterium sauromali* in Krassilnikov.

19. Plant pathogens................. **20**
Not pathogenic or known to be pathogenic to plants.......................... **24**
Note: In view of the remark made by Palleroni and Doudoroff (J. Bacteriol., *89*, 1965, 264), attention is drawn to comment on this statement in the Introduction.

20. Nonmotile
Aplanobacter (in Prévot)
Pseudobacterium (in Krass.)
Note: Two *Manual* species, *Xanthomonas stewartii* and *Corynebacterium agropyri*, terminate here. Prévot places them both in *Aplanobacter*. He also includes *A. betlis*, *A. cepivorum*, *A. fleuryi*, *A. magroni*, *A. rhizoctonia*, *A. robici*, and *A. stewartii*. Krassilnikov lists only *A. betle* and *A. rhizoctonia*. See also *Achromobacter nicotinophagum* in Hylin (J. Bacteriol., *76*,

1958, 36) and *Xanthomonas clerodendri* and *X. sesbaniae*.
Motile; produce hyperplastic diseases such as galls and hairy root
Agrobacterium p. *142*
M p. 288
Pseudomonas (in Prévot)
Pseudomonas (in Krass.)
Note: Prévot places the yellow-pigmented *A. gypsophilae* in *Xanthomonas*. Krassilnikov does not list *A. pseudotsugae* and *A. rubi*.
Not as above...................... **21**
21. Colonies yellow.................. **22**
Colonies not yellow............... **23**
22. Flagella polar, oxidative
Xanthomonas p. *113*
M p. 152
Xanthomonas (in Prévot)
Pseudomonas (in Krass.)
Note: Starr and Stephens (J. Bacteriol., *87*, 1964, 293) state that species of *Xanthomonas* are characterized by the presence of a distinctive carotenoid alcohol with absorption maxima at 418, 437, and 463 mμ in petroleum ether.
(There is some measure of disagreement amongst the authors on nomenclature of species. See also *P. destructans*, *P. trifolii*, *P. panicimiliacei*, *P. radiciperda*, and *P. levistici* in the *Manual*; *X. fici*, *X. glycines*, *X. itoana*, *X. lactucae*, *X. lactucaescariolae*, *X. rubefaciens*, and *X. suberfaciens* in Prévot; and *P. glycines* and *P. necrosis* in Krassilnikov.
Flagella peritrichous.... **Erwinia** p. *146*
M p. 349
Erwinia (in Prévot)
Note: This entry includes *E. ananas*, *E. cassaviae*, and *E. vitivora*, which Krassilnikov places in the genus *Chromobacterium*, and *E. citrimaculans*, *E. milletiae*, and *E. mangiferae*, which he places in *Bacterium*. See also *E. cacticida*, *E. edgeworthiae*, *E. cytolytica*, *E. erivanensis*, and *E. lathyri* in Prévot. Krassilnikov lists the last three of these in *Chromobacterium* together with *C. flavidum*, *C. orchitidis*, and *C. sacchari*.

23. Flagella polar...**Pseudomonas** p. *111*
M p. 89
Phytobacterium (in Prévot)
Pseudomonas (in Krass.)
Note: Manual species that terminate here are 67, 72, 86, 91, 107, 112, 119, 121 to 128, 130 to 132, 134, 135, 137 to 139, 141, 142, 144, 145, 148, and 149. There is disagreement between Prévot and the *Manual* on pigmentation of the *Manual* species. Prévot places the colorless species in *Phytobacterium*. See also the *Manual* species *Xanthomonas panici*, *X. proteamaculans*, *X. manihotis*, *X. rubrisubalbicans*, *X. cannae*, *X. zingiberi*, and *X. translucens; Phytobacterium destructans* in Prévot; and *Pseudomonas trifoliorum* and *P. leguminiperdus* in Krassilnikov.
Flagella peritrichous... **Erwinia** p. *146*
M p. 349
Erwinia (in Prévot)
Bacterium (in Krass.)
Note: Located here are *Manual* species 1, 5 to 10, 12, and 14. Prévot lists eleven additional species. Krassilnikov places *E. nimipressuralis* in the genus *Chromobacterium* on the basis of pigmentation, not recorded in the *Manual*, and *E. salicis* in the genus *Pseudobacterium*. See also *Bacterium burgeri*, *B. melanogenum*, *B. phytophthorum*, and *B. scabiegenum* in Krassilnikov.
24. Curved and irregular cells; may branch in young cultures; capable of using phenolic compounds as the sole source of carbon; gas, presumably nitrogen, produced in 0.1 per cent nitrate broth, but no nitrites are produced; no acid from carbohydrates
Mycoplana p. *118*
M p. 204
Mycoplana (in Prévot)
Note: Listed in the appendix to *Rhizobium* by Krassilnikov (p. 410). See also *Achromobacter cycloclastis* in Prévot.
Not as above...................... **25**
25. Curved rods, very small, about 1.0 μ in length, which, during growth, produce closed rings, 2.0 to 3.0 μ in diameter, which later change to two horseshoe-shaped

halves fastened together without any evidence of divisional lines. These divide into separate rods, which reproduce the cycle; encapsulated; grow well in 0.5 per cent peptone water
Microcyclus p. *126*
M p. 253
Microcyclus (in Prévot)
Not as above...................... **26**
26. Curved or S-shaped rods, 0.1 to 0.2 by 6 to 8 μ or longer; very poor growth on peptone agar; *or* short, straight rods 0.5 by 1 to 2 μ; good growth on peptone agar; on inorganic thiosulfate agar, small, watery colonies are produced, which turn white from the deposition of sulfur; grow autotrophically, oxidizing thiosulfate to sulfur and sulfate...... **Thiobacillus** p. *110*
M p. 83
Thiobacillus (in Prévot)
Sulfomonas (in Krass.)
Not as above...................... **27**
27. Curved cells, 1 by 5 to 10 μ, which form chains that may twist around one another to form coiled, nonseptate, nonmotile colorless bundles; enclosed in a spherical, solid, gelatinous mass from 10 to 17 μ in diameter; found floating on water containing decomposing plant material
Myconostoc p. *126*
M p. 260
Myconostoc (in Prévot)
Cellulose hydrolyzed in either a peptone or a mineral salts medium.............. **28**
Cellulose not hydrolyzed............ **30**
28. Curved organisms that grow on precipitated cellulose-mineral salts agar producing a clearing of the medium around the colonies; also grow in 0.5 per cent peptone water in which a strip of filter paper is half immersed, weakening the filter paper sufficiently for the fibers to separate on slight agitation or reducing it to a pulpy mass; organisms are arranged in palisade fashion similar to the *Corynebacterium* spp.
Cellulomonas p. *177*
M p. 601

Cellulomonas (in Prévot)
(except *C. flavigena*)

Note: Krassilnikov does not recognize the genus. He classifies *Manual* species 1, 2, 5, 7, and 8 as *Chromobacterium biazoteum, Bacterium cellaseum, Mycobacterium fimi, Bacterium albidum,* and *Pseudobacterium liquatum.* See also *Pseudobacterium lucrosum.* Prévot lists the nonmotile *C. flavigena* as *Aplanobacter flavigenum.*

Curved organisms that grow on a filter paper-mineral salts medium, oxidizing the cellulose to oxycellulose.............. **29**

Note: There appears to be no justification for recognizing this so-called "oxidation" or the genera whose existence is based on it; see notes in Methods.

29. Sickle-shaped; cells no longer than 2.0 μ; stain more intensely at the center than at the ends; no growth on a mineral salts agar containing starch; green, cream-colored, or brownish on filter paper

Cellfalcicula p. *125*
M p. 252
Cellfalcicula (in Prévot)

Note: Placed in appendix to *Cytophaga* in Krassilnikov (p. 696).

Curved cells 1.5 to 5.0 μ in length, with rounded ends; grow moderately well on mineral salts agar containing starch; cream-colored, brown, or no pigment on filter paper.......... **Cellvibrio** p. *125*
M p. 250
Cellvibrio (in Prévot)
Vibrio (in Krass.)

(See Hulcher and King, J. Bacteriol., *76*, 1958, 565, and also *V. fuscus* and *V. agarliquefaciens* in the *Manual.*

30. Curved rods that transform completely into coccoid forms during growth of the colony. Rods elongate and divide. At the point of division the rods grow out at an angle to the original axis and divide again at the angle when the cell has doubled its length. This process continues until a colony is formed. *Ultimately the rods transform completely into cocci*

Arthrobacter p. *177*
M p. 605

Mycobacterium (in Krass.)

Note: a. Krassilnikov recognizes only two of the species in the *Manual.*

b. The emphasis lies on the final transformation into cocci. Some authorities may consider that limited true branching may occur. If this is admitted, the dividing line between *Arthrobacter* and *Nocardia* becomes very slim. The author's observations of *Arthrobacter globiformis* fit the above statement, and it is suggested that these criteria be adopted, with true branching forms, which later disintegrate, being assigned to *Nocardia.*

Not as above...................... **31**
31. Curved rods; motile by means of polar flagella.......................... **32**
Straight rods....................... **34**
32. Oxidize hydrogen sulfide, depositing sulfur inside the cell.. **Thiospira** p. *110*
M p. 82
Thiospira (in Prévot)
Thiospira (in Krass.)

Note: If *Thiospira* should prove to be anaerobic, this insertion would be invalid.

Not as above...................... **33**
33. *Predatory cells* about 0.3 μ wide, with a single polar flagellum; lytic on various Gram negative bacteria

Bdellovibrio Stolp and Starr

Note: For full description of the single species *B. bacteriovorus,* see Stolp and Starr (Antonie van Leeuwenhoek, *29*, 1963, 217). (See also Scherff, Deoay, and Carroll, Phytopathology, *56*, 1966, 627; Shilo and Bruff, J. Gen. Microbiol., *40*, 1965, 317; and Starr and Baigent, J. Bacteriol., *91*, 1966, 2006.)

Not as above...................... **33a**
33a. No action on carbohydrates; alkaline reaction in the Hugh and Leifson test; indole negative; cholera red negative; methyl red and Voges-Proskauer tests negative; gelatin not liquefied; citrate not utilized; no growth in the presence of KCN; phenylalanine deaminase and Moeller's lysine, arginine, and ornithine tests negative; urease, catalase, and oxidase tests positive;

no pigment or fluorescence under ultra-violet light; lophotrichous flagella

Vibrio p. *122*

M p. *229*

Comamonas (Davis and Park)

(See Davis and Park, J. Gen. Microbiol., *27*, 1962, 101, and Hugh, Intern. Bull. Bacteriol. Nomen. Taxon., *12*, 1962, 33.)

Note: Sebald and Véron (Ann. inst. Pasteur, *105*, 1963, 897) state that the DNA base ratio (GC%) of *Comamonas* is *c.* 64 and assign to the genus *Vibrio per-colans*, *V. cyclosites*, *V. neocistes*, and *V. alcaligenes.*

Not as above..................... **33b**

33b. Motile by means of monopolar flagella; carbohydrates *fermented* without gas production............. **Vibrio** p. *122*

M p. *229*

Vibrio (in Prévot)

Vibrio (in Krass.)

(This is the genus *Vibrio* as defined by Davis and Park, J. Gen. Microbiol., *27*, 1962, 101. They add that all the species are pleomorphic and grow at pH 9.0. Sebald and Véron, *vide supra*, affirm the designation of *Vibrio* to the fermentative, monopolar curved rods. They add that the DNA base ratio—GC%—is 47.)

Note: a. Dependence upon curvature in the rod to define the genus *Vibrio* is a hazardous procedure, as has been pointed out by many authors. Shewan, Hodgkiss, and Liston (Nature, London, *173*, 1954, 208) have recommended the use of the vibriostatic agent 0/129. The test may be useful if positive, but the reagent is not marketed (1965) and its prescription presumes a prior knowledge of the parameters of the genus *Vibrio.*

b. See also *V. agarlyticus*, *V. albis*, *V. anguillarum*, *V. aquatilus*, *V. aureus*, *V. canalis*, *V. frequens*, *V. marinus*, *V. mobile*, *V. nasalis*, *V. nigricans*, and *V. suis* in Krassilnikov. Krassilnikov places *V. ex-torquens* in *Pseudomonas.*

Motile with polar monotrichous or multi-trichous flagella; do not produce acid from sugars; reduce nitrates to nitrites; non-proteolytic

Campylobacter Sebald and Véron

(Sebald and Véron, *vide supra*, state that this genus, created to include *Vibrio fetus* and *V. bubulus*, is characterized by a DNA base ratio—GC%—of 30 to 34.)

Not as above...................... **34**

34. Acid produced from lactose within 40 days............................... **35**

No acid produced from lactose........ **71**

35. Agar is digested................. **36**

Agar is not digested; organisms parasitic on the cytoplasm of the rhizopod, *Pelomyxa palustris..* **"Bacterium"*** *parapelomyxae*

Not as above...................... **38**

36. Yellow colonies................. **37**

Colonies not yellow

"Bacterium"* *nenckii*

(*Manual*, 6th ed.)

"Bacterium" *nenckii* (in Krass.)

37. Polar flagella **Pseudomonas** p. *111*

M p. *89.*

Pseudomonas (in Krass.)

(Including *P. segnis* and *P. lacunogenes*, placed in the appendix to *Xanthomonas* in the *Manual* and both under *P. gelatica* in Krassilnikov. Not listed by Prévot.)

Motile by means of peritrichous flagella or nonmotile...... **Agarbacterium** p. *145*

M p. *322*

Flavobacterium (in Prévot)

(*F. aurantiacum*)

Note: Krassilnikov does not recognize the genus. In his book, *A. uliginosum* is placed in *Pseudobacterium*; *A. pastinator* is placed in *Bacterium*, and *A. aurantiacum* is placed in *Chromobacterium.*

38. Motile at 37° or at 21° C......... **39**

Nonmotile........................ **59**

Motility not recorded (see *Xanthomonas clerodendri* and *X. sesbaniae*).

39. Acid and gas from glucose........ **40**

Acid only from glucose.............. **52**

40. Gelatin liquefied................. **41**

Gelatin not liquefied................ **46**

41. Flagella polar; colorless colonies; litmus milk acid, coagulated and slowly digested,

* The genus *Bacterium* is not recognized in the *Manual*, but (pp. 926 to 930) a few unplaced species in the addendum to Class II still appear under this generic name.

2,3-butylene glycol produced from glucose; cause a fatal septicemia in fish and frogs

> **Aeromonas**   p. *116*
> *M p. 189*
> **Aeromonas** (in T and W, 5th ed.)

Flagella polar; colorless colonies; not as above.......... **Pseudomonas**   p. *111*

> (*P. colurnae*)
> *M p. 89*
> **Phytobacterium** (in Prévot)
> **Pseudomonas** (in Krass.)

(See also *Pseudomonas betae-gelatae* and *Phytobacterium vitrosum* in Prévot.)

Flagella polar; yellow colonies

> possibly **Xanthomonas**   p. *113*
> *M p. 152*

(See also *X. hemmiana* in the *Manual* and *Pseudomonas destructans* in Krassilnikov.)

Flagella peritrichous................. **42**

42. Soft rot produced in sterile plant tissues

> **Erwinia**   p. *146*
> *M p. 349*
> **Erwinia** (in Prévot)
> **Bacterium** (in Krass.)

Note: This entry includes *E. atroseptica*, *E. carnegieana*, and *E. chrysanthemi* (from the *Manual*); *Erwinia flavida* (from Prévot); and *Bacterium phytophthorum* and *B. melanogenum* and *Chromobacterium sacchari* (from Krassilnikov).

Not as above...................... **43**

43. Lactose fermented in two days.... **44**

Lactose fermentation delayed

> **Paracolobactrum**   p. *155*
> *M p. 346*
> **Paracolon group** (in T and W, 5th ed.)

(*P. arizonae*—rare strains of the *Arizona group* of the *Enterobacteriaceae*—and *P. aerogenoides* strains 4611, 1721, and 19111; see also *Erwinia chrysanthemi* and strains of *Serratia*.)

Organisms keying out here should be further examined from Section H, **44** onwards to determine affinities with recognized groups.

44. Methyl red positive; Voges-Proskauer positive or negative................. **45**

Methyl red negative; Voges-Proskauer positive.

a. Acid from cellobiose

> **Aerobacter**   p. *151*
> *M p. 341*
> **Aerobacter** (in Prévot)
> **Bacterium** (in Krass.)
> **Enterobacter** (in Ewing*)
> **Klebsiella** (in T and W, 5th ed.)

b. No acid from cellobiose:

i. Colorless strains of

> **Serratia group** (I C N B)
> **Serratia**   p. *153*
> *M p. 359*
> **Serratia** (in Prévot)
> **Chromobacterium** (in Krass.)
> **Serratia** (in T and W, 5th ed.)
> **Serratia** (in Ewing*)

45. No gas produced from lactose in two days........ **Paracolobactrum**   p. *155*

> *M p. 346*
> **Paracolobactrum** (in Prévot)
> **Paracolon group** (in T and W, 5th ed.)

(*P. intermedium* strains 8011, 13311, and 11411. These should be checked against the following groups in Section H, **45**.)

Gas produced from lactose within 2 days. (*Erwinia carnegieana* and *E. atroseptica* may terminate in one of the following groups.)

a. Growth in KCN; lysine decarboxylase negative..... **Escherichia**   p. *149*

> (*E. freundii*)
> *M p. 335*
> **Escherichia** (in Prévot)
> **Bacterium** (in Krass.)
> **Citrobacter** (in T and W, 5th ed.)
> **Citrobacter group** (I C N B)
> **Citrobacter** (in Ewing)

Note: The entry covers the gelatin-liquefying strains of *E. freundii* in the *Manual*. Although the I C N B Report (Intern. Bull. Bacteriol. Nomen. Taxon., *13*, 1963, 69) reports *Citrobacter* as gelatin negative, Edwards and Ewing, in "Identification of the Enterobacteriaceae," 1962, state "gelatin usually not liquefied."

b. No growth with KCN; lysine decarboxylase positive

> **Arizona group** (I C N B)
> (Rare strains)

* See W. H. Ewing, Intern. Bull. Bacteriol. Nomen. Taxon., *13*, 1963, 69.

Arizona (in Prévot)
Arizona group (in T and W, 5th ed.)
Arizona (in Ewing)
46. Flagella polar; litmus milk unchanged; starch hydrolyzed; hydrogen sulfide produced; wide range of sugars fermented; organisms will grow in a nitrogen-free medium fixing atmospheric nitrogen
Azotomonas p. *117*
M p. 198
Pseudomonas (in Prévot)
Azotomonas (in Krass.)
Flagella polar; acid only in lactose; indole negative; luminescent on a variety of media at pH 8.0
Photobacterium p. *116*
M p. 193
Photobacterium (in Prévot)
Photobacterium (in Krass.)
Flagella polar, not as above.......... **47**
Note: The polar-flagellated plant pathogens *Pseudomonas petasitis* (colorless) (*Phytobacterium* in Prévot), *Xanthomonas conjac* (yellow pigmented) (*Pseudomonas* in Krassilnikov), if the latter is lactose positive, and *Chromobacterium gilvum* (in Krassilnikov) may terminate here.
Not as above; flagella peritrichous.... **47**
47. Alginate fermented with the production of acid and gas; hydrogen sulfide produced; methyl red positive; Voges-Proskauer weak; citrate utilized; nitrite produced from nitrate
Alginobacter p. *146*
M p. 348
Not as above...................... **48**
48. Methyl red positive; Voges-Proskauer negative......................... **49**
Methyl red negative; Voges-Proskauer positive........................... **51**
Note: Erwinia nimipressuralis and *E. dissolvens* should be compared with genera terminating between Sections **49** to **51** inclusive.
49. Lactose fermented within two days
50
Note: Some organisms that produce acid within two days, but no gas, from lactose are placed in the genus *Paracolobactrum* in the *Manual.* The entry covers *P. interme-*

dium strains 14011 and 12611. In the following part of the key these fall into the genus *Citrobacter.*
Lactose fermentation delayed
Paracolobactrum p. *155*
M p. 346
Paracolobactrum (in Prévot)
Paracolon group (in T and W, 5th ed.)
Note: These organisms have been reallocated into other groups by the following tests:
a. Growth on citrate; H_2S positive; growth with KCN
Citrobacter group (I C N B)
Citrobacter (in Ewing*)
(Includes *P. intermedium* strains 14011, 12611, and 1421; Bethesda and Ballerup Groups.)
b. No growth on citrate or with KCN; H_2S negative
Escherichia group (I C N B)
Escherichia (in Ewing*)
(Includes *P. coliforme* strains 28221, 5511, 6611, 2611, 31611, 111, 15411, 1811, 33811, and 4361.)
50. Methyl red negative at 22° C.; acid or acid and gas from mannitol but not from dulcitol, adonitol, or inositol; indole negative; urease negative; growth with KCN
Hafnia group (I C N B)
Hafnia group (in T and W, 5th ed.)
(See Intern. Bull. Bacteriol. Nomen. Taxon., *8*, 1958, 25.)
Not as above..................... **50a**
50a. Growth on citrate; H_2S produced
50b
No growth on citrate; H_2S not produced
Escherichia p. *149*
M p. 335
Escherichia (in Prévot)
Bacterium (in Krass.)
Escherichia group (I C N B)
Escherichia (in Ewing*)
50b. Growth with KCN; no growth on malonate; lysine decarboxylase negative
Escherichia p. *149*

* W. H. Ewing, Intern. Bull. Bacteriol. Nomen. Taxon., *13*, 1963, 95.

(*E. intermedia*)
M p. 335
Escherichia (in Prévot)
(*E. intermedia*)
Bacterium (in Krass.)
(*B. freundii*)
Citrobacter group (I C N B)
Citrobacter (in T and W, 5th ed.)
Citrobacter (in Ewing*)
No growth with KCN; growth with malonate; lysine decarboxylase positive
Arizona group (I C N B)
Arizona (in Prévot)
Arizona group (in T and W, 5th ed.)
Arizona (in Ewing*)
51. Lactose fermented in two days; no acid from sorbitol... Aerobacter p. 151
M p. 341
Aerobacter (in Prévot)
Bacterium (in Krass.)
Klebsiella (in T and W, 5th ed.)
Enterobacter group (I C N B)
Enterobacter (in Ewing*)
Lactose fermentation delayed; acid from sorbitol..... Paracolobactrum p. 155
M p. 346
Paracolobactrum (in Prévot)
Bacterium (in Krass.)
Hafnia group (I C N B)
Hafnia group (in T and W, 5th ed.)
Enterobacter (in Ewing*)
(See *P. aerogenoides* strains 721, 37711, and 37211.)
52. Organisms cause a glanders-like infection (melioidosis) in rats, guinea pigs, rabbits, and man; colonies on agar small, circular, slightly raised, thick, opaque, and cream colored with an irregular margin; litmus milk slowly coagulated; blood serum slowly liquefied; acid from glucose, glycerol, galactose, and sometimes from lactose; no acid from dulcitol and salicin; optimal temperature, 37° C... Pseudomonas p. 111
(*P. pseudomallei*) *M p. 89*
Loefflerella (*whitmori*) (in T & W, 5th ed.)
Whitmorella (in Prévot)
Pseudobacterium (in Krass.)

* W. H. Ewing, Intern. Bull. Bacteriol. Nomen. Taxon., *13*, 1963, 95.

Organisms that produce granular conjunctivitis in monkeys and apes are believed to be a cause of trachoma in man; optimal temperature, between 28° and 31° C. with motility only at low temperatures; colonies on blood agar small, circular, grayish, and translucent, becoming sticky and mucoid.........Noguchia p. 133
M p. 421
Noguchia (in Prévot)
Pseudomonas (in Krass.)
Note: Krassilnikov places both species in *P. granulosis.*
Not as above...................... 53
53. Organisms grow in 0.5 per cent peptone water containing a filter paper strip, weakening the latter sufficiently to cause disintegration on slight agitation or reducing it to a pulp; produce clearings around colonies on precipitated cellulose agar plates; cells commonly arranged in angular fashion like *Corynebacterium* spp.
Cellulomonas p. 177
M p. 601
Cellulomonas (in Prévot)
a. Pigmented colonies
Chromobacterium (in Krass.)
b. Colorless.... Bacterium (in Krass.)
Note: a. Prévot lists several additional species, all of which were classified in the genus *Cellulomonas* in the *Manual*, sixth edition. In addition, he includes *Bacterium bibulum* (*Manual*, sixth edition, and Krassilnikov) in *Cellulomonas.*
b. See also *Pseudomonas arguta* and *P. tralucida,* and also *P. ephemerocyanea* if the latter produces no pigment and *P. caesia* (in Krassilnikov).
Not as above...................... 54
54. Colonies yellow................. 55
Colonies not yellow................ 57
55. Flagella polar
Xanthomonas p. 113
M p. 152
Xanthomonas (in Prévot)
Pseudomonas (in Krass.)
Note: Terminating here are the *Manual* species 1, 2, 5, 7 to 11, 13 to 16, 18, 21, 22, 24, 25, 29 to 34, 36 to 40, 42 to 45, 48, and

52, and Prévot species *X. lactucae* and *X. rubefaciens;* see also the *Manual* species *Pseudomonas perlurida, P. subcreta, P. cepacia,* and *P. radiciperda* and possible colorless mutants of species 62, 65, 88, and 108 of the genus *Pseudomonas.*

Flagella peritrichous.................. **56**

56. Marine organisms; nitrites not produced from nitrates; starch hydrolyzed

Flavobacterium p. *144*
M p. 309
Flavobacterium (in Prévot)
Chromobacterium (in Krass.)

(Includes *F. halohydrium* and *F. neptunium.* See also *Serratia anolium* in Prévot and *Chromobacterium citricum* in Krassilnikov.)

Not as above

possibly **Erwinia** p. *146*
M p. 349

Note: Erwinia ananas, E. maniferae, E. vitivora, and *E. milletiae* terminate here.

(See also *Erwinia lathyri* and *E. cytolytica* in Prévot and *Chromobacterium citricum, C. flavidum, C. lathyri,* and *C. orchitidis* in Krassilnikov.)

57. Organisms found in the cytoplasm of the rhizopod *Pelomyxa*

Bacterium* *parapelomyxae*

Note: This entry is valid only if the organism is motile.

Not as above...................... **58**

58. Flagella polar, Oxidative metabolism

Pseudomonas p. *111*
M p. 89
Pseudomonas (in Krass.)
Pseudomonas (in Prévot)
Phytobacterium (in Prévot)

Note: a. This includes the *Manual* species 23, 67, 72, 86, 121, 123, 128, 137, 138, 141, and 145. Of these species 128, 137, 141, and 145 are listed by Prévot under *Phytobacterium,* which he regards as colorless pseudomonads. The remainder he places in *Pseudomonas,* disagreeing with the *Manual* on the question of pigmentation. All of these species are plant pathogens and will key out here if pathogenicity is not known;

* See p. *65* of *Guide.*

see also *Pseudomonas periphyta* and *P. pleomorpha* and *Achromobacter azotogenus* (in Prévot). Of these species Krassilnikov lists only 86, 121, 123, 137, 141, and 145.

b. Colorless mutants of the pigmented *Pseudomonas* species 59, 73, 78, 81 to 83, 89, 94, and 109 (from the *Manual*) and *P. felthami* and *P. dispersum* (from Prévot) will also terminate here.

Flagella polar, monotrichous, or multitrichous in the stationary phase of growth but capable of having in the exponential phase one or several lateral flagella; aerobic to facultative; oxidase positive; *ferments* glucose without gas production; nitrates reduced to nitrites; gelatin not liquefied; GC% of DNA about 51

Fergusonia Sebald and Véron

(The single species *F. shigelloides* is the *Aeromonas shigelloides* of Ewing, Hugh, and Johnson, 1961, Studies on the *Aeromonas* group, U. S. Department of Health, Education and Welfare, Communicable Diseases Center, Atlanta, Georgia.)

Flagella peritrichous

Paracolobactrum p. *155*
(anaerogenic strains)
M p. 346
Paracolobactrum (in Prévot)
Bacterium (in Krass.)

Paracolon group (in T and W, 5th ed.)

No provision is made in the fourth report on *Citrobacter* (Intern. Bull. Bacteriol. Nomen. Taxon., *13*, 1963, 69) for non-gas-producing strains. It is possible that such strains belong to *Serratia* or the *Hafnia* group.

a. No acid from cellobiose or glycerol; gelatin liquefied.......... **Serratia**

b. Acid from cellobiose and glycerol; gelatin not liquefied...... **Hafnia**

(See also *Achromobacter pinnatus* in Prévot.)

Note: From published data the following organisms, if isolated from the soil, may terminate here: *Agrobacterium rhizogenes, Erwinia amylovora, E. aroideae, Rhizobium leguminosarum, R. trifolii,* and *R. phaseoli* (from the *Manual*) and *Erwinia croci*, *E. melonis*, *E. papaveris*, and *E. phytophthora* (from Prévot). In addition, the following may also be listed if they prove to be lactose fermenters: *Achromobacter delicatulum*, *A. superficiale*, *Agrobacterium tumefaciens*, *Rhizobium meliloti*, and *Erwinia salicis*.

59. Acid and gas from glucose........ 60

Acid only from glucose............. 64

60. Bioluminescent

Photobacterium p. *116*

(*P. pierantonii*)

M p. *193*

Photobacterium (in Prévot)

Photobacterium (in Krass.)

Not as above..................... 61

61. Methyl red positive; Voges-Proskauer negative........................ 62

Methyl red negative; Voges-Proskauer positive........................ 63

Methyl red positive; Voges-Proskauer positive.

a. Gelatin liquefied; indole produced

Oxytoca group

(See Hugh, Can. J. Microbiol., *5*, 1959, 251.)

b. Not as above.......... **Klebsiella***

Note: Included here are *K. edwardsii* var. *atlantae*, Cowan, *et al.* (J. Gen. Microbiol., *23*, 1960, 601), and also strains of *Escherichia* (*Citrobacter*) *freundii* in the *Manual* (see Parr, J. Bacteriol., *36*, 1938, 1).

62. Lactose fermented in two days.

a. Growth on malonate and citrate: lysine decarboxylase positive; urease positive.. **Klebsiella** (*pneumoniae*)*

b. No growth on malonate; urease negative; no growth on citrate

Escherichia p. *149*

M p. *335*

Escherichia (in Prévot)

Bacterium (in Krass.)

Escherichia group (I C N B)

Escherichia (in Ewing†)

* As described by Cowan *et al.* (J. Gen. Microbiol., *23*, 1960, 601). This is in disagreement with the definition of *Klebsiella* given by the subcommittee on *Enterobacteriaceae*.

† W. H. Ewing, Intern. Bull. Bacteriol. Nomen. Taxon., *13*, 1963, 95.

Escherichia (in T and W, 5th ed.)

c. De Bord (Iowa State Coll. J. Sci., *16*, 1942, 471) describes an organism under the name of *Colloides anoxydana*, which terminates here. Isolated from the normal vagina and in cases of vaginitis and conjunctivitis, it appears as diplococci on solid media on primary isolation but as a mixture of rods and cocci in liquids. It is citrate positive and indole positive.

Lactose fermentation delayed.

a. No growth with KCN

Paracolobactrum p. *155*

M p. *346*

Paracolobactrum (in Prévot)

Bacterium (in Krass.)

Escherichia (in T and W, 5th ed.)

Escherichia (I C N B)

Escherichia (in Ewing†)

(*P. coliforme* strains 311, 17611, and 16911.)

b. Growth with KCN

possibly **Klebsiella‡** (*ozaenae*)

63. Encapsulated organisms; pathogenic, causing infections in man and animals, principally of the respiratory tract; conform to the description given for *Klebsiella* by the subcommittee on *Enterobacteriaceae* (see p.*151*)...........**Klebsiella** p. *150*

M p. *344*

Klebsiella (in T and W, 5th ed.)

Klebsiella (in Prévot)

Bacterium (in Krass.)

Klebsiella (in Ewing†)

Note: In the first edition of the *Guide*, provision was made for separation of the nonmotile strains of *Aerobacter* from *Klebsiella* on the grounds of capsulation and pathogenicity. Since that time it has become clear that nonmotile strains of *A. aerogenes* are indistinguishable from *Klebsiella* and have been merged with that genus. The motile strains have been placed in the genus *Enterobacter* as *Enterobacter aerogenes*. Cowan *et al.* (J. Gen. Micro-

‡ As described by Cowan *et al.* (J. Gen. Microbiol., *23*, 1960, 601).

biol., *23*, 1960, 601), have not accepted this and have merged the genus *Aerobacter* entirely with *Klebsiella*. Their proposal appears to have been adopted in Topley and Wilson, fifth edition.

Not as above; indole positive; urease positive, and possibly gelatin liquefied

Oxytoca group

(See Hugh, Can. J. Microbiol., *5*, 1959, 251.)

Note: a. As indicated in the third report of the subcommittee on *Enterobacteriaceae* (Intern. Bull. Bacteriol. Nomen. Taxon., *8*, 1958, 25), *Klebsiella ozaenae* does not fit the general description. (See entry Section H, **62**.)

b. Nonmotile variants of *Enterobacter* may perhaps be separated from *Klebsiella* by their production of ornithine decarboxylase.

64. Small ovoid coccobacilli, causing septicaemia in lambs and pneumonia in sheep and cattle and in rodents. Acid produced without gas from glucose, lactose (slow), sucrose, arabinose, xylose, and possibly from other "sugars"; methyl red and Voges-Proskauer negative; H_2S negative; catalase positive; oxidase positive; nitrate reduced to nitrite; methylene blue reduced; starch not hydrolyzed

Pasteurella p. *127*
M p. 395
Pasteurella (in Prévot)
Pasteurella (in T and W, 5th ed.)
(Includes *P. haemolytica* and *P. pneumotropica*. For the latter see Heyl, Antonie van Leeuwenhoek, *29*, 1963, 79. See also *Acinetobacter nasalis* in Prévot. See also rare lactose positive, H_2S positive, strains of *Pasteurella septica*.)

Organisms that produce mucoid to cartilaginous colonies adherent to the medium; grow on meat infusion agar; colonies usually 1 mm. in diameter in 24 hours but may enlarge to 3 to 6 mm. upon further incubation; produce a granulated growth on the walls of the tube in liquid media; occur in necrotic lesions as granules resembling actinomycotic granules in cases of actino-

bacillosis of cattle and joint ill of foals or in complicating actinomycotic infections. One species may be commensal in the alimentary canal of solipeds

Actinobacillus p. *131*
M p. 414
Actinobacillus (in Prévot)
Proactinomyces (in Krass.)

Note: A. equuli is listed under *Bacterium dysenteriae* by Krassilnikov and as **Acinetobacter** *equirulis* by Prévot.

Not as above...................... **65**

65. Fastidious organisms; do not grow on meat infusion agar in the absence of X-factor on primary isolation under aerobic conditions but may be trained to grow without it; colonies on blood agar 0.5 mm. in diameter but may be much larger on Levinthal agar; coccobacillary, arranged singly, in short chains, or in clumps

Haemophilus p. *130*
M p. 406
Haemophilus (in Prévot)
Bacterium (in Krass.)
Haemophilus (in T and W, 5th ed.)

Species represented here cause bronchopneumonia of sheep (*H. ovis*), respiratory infection in mice (*H. influenzae-murium*), and endocarditis (*H. aphrophilus*).

Fastidious organisms; require blood or ascitic fluid; highly pleomorphic; rod-shaped or filamentous; may reach 100 to 150 μ in length; homogeneous in young cultures but become granulated, beaded, and swollen in old cultures and tend to fragment into rods and cocci; large, spherical swellings packed with granules common; cholesterol globules appear among the growth; only rods and short filaments appear in pathological material; nonbranching; non-acidfast; colonies on ascitic agar 1 to 2.5 mm. in three days, circular, low convex, colorless; L-phase variants are common; highly virulent for mice, causing polyarthritis. Causes ratbite or Haverhill fever in man

Streptobacillus p. *158*
(*S. moniliformis*)
M p. 451

Streptobacillus (in Prévot)
Proactinomyces (in Krass.)
Actinobacillus (*muris*) (in T and W, 5th ed.)
Not as above: grow well on media without blood or serum...................... **66**
66. Colonies colorless................ **67**
Colonies yellow.................... **70**
67. Organisms grow in 0.5 per cent peptone containing filter paper and cause the latter to disintegrate; gelatin liquefied; nitrite produced from nitrate; starch hydrolyzed
Cellulomonas p. *177*
(*C. uda*)
M p. 601
Aplanobacter (*udum*) (in Prévot)
Pseudobacterium (*liquatum*) (in Krass.)
Not as above...................... **68**
68. Lactose fermentation delayed; growth with KCN; Voges-Proskauer positive; malonate and citrate positive; urease produced.................... **Klebsiella***
Not as above...................... **69**
69. Lactose fermentation delayed; no growth in KCN; Voges-Proskauer negative; malonate and citrate negative; urease negative.............. **Shigella** p. *150*
M p. 384
Shigella (in Prévot)
Bacterium (in Krass.)
Shigella (in T and W, 5th ed.)
Shigella group (I C N B)
Shigella (in Ewing†)
(See *Alkalescens Dispar* group and *Acinetobacter nasalis* in Prévot.)
Not as above... **Achromobacter** p. *143*
(*A. delmarvae*)
M p. 300
Acinetobacter (in Prévot)
Bacterium (in Krass.)
70. Curved rods that transform completely into coccoid forms during growth of the colony. Rods elongate and divide. At the point of division the rods grow out at an

angle to the original axis and divide again at the angle when the cell has doubled its length. This process continues until a colony is formed. *Ultimately the rods transform completely into cocci*
Arthrobacter p. *177*
M p. 605
Note: The emphasis lies on the final transformation into cocci. Some authorities may consider that limited true branching may occur. If this is admitted the dividing line between *Arthrobacter* and *Nocardia* becomes very slim. The author's observations of *Arthrobacter globiformis* fit the above statement, and it is suggested that these criteria be adopted, with true branching forms that later disintegrate being assigned to *Nocardia*.
Not as above; starch hydrolyzed
Flavobacterium p. *144*
(*F. ferrugineum*)
M p. 309
Empedobacter (in Prévot)
Pseudobacterium (in Krass.)
(*P. brunneum*)
In addition to the above, the following species, two of which are plant pathogens, terminate at this point: *Pseudomonas iridescens, Corynebacterium agropyri,* and *Xanthomonas stewartii.*
71. Nonmotile...................... **72**
Motile.......................... **103**
72. Acid and gas from glucose....... **73**
Acid but no gas from glucose........ **77**
No acid or gas from glucose......... **85**
73. Only a small amount of gas from glucose; causes dysentery in man; agglutinated by polyvalent antiserum to *Shigella flexneri*.............. **Shigella** p. *150*
M p. 384
Shigella (in Prévot)
Bacterium (in Krass.)
Shigella (in T and W, 5th ed.)
Shigella group (I C N B)
Shigella (in Ewing†)
(Newcastle strain)
Organisms that cause bacillary white diarrhea of chickens; agglutinated with

---

* *K. edwardsii* var. *edwardsii* (see Cowan, *et al.,* J. Gen. Microbiol., *23*, 1960, 601).
† W. H. Ewing, Intern. Bull. Bacteriol. Nomen. Taxon., *13*, 1963, 95.

Salmonella group D "O" antiserum

Salmonella p. *147*

(*S. pullorum*)

M p. 368

Salmonella (in Prévot)

Bacterium (in Krass.)

Salmonella (in T and W, 5th ed.)

Salmonella group (I C N B)

Salmonella (in Ewing*)

Not as above...................... **74**

74. Bioluminescent on 3 per cent salt agar, especially with a fish base; pleomorphic and branching rods on asparagine-sugar media; 2,3-butylene glycol produced

Photobacterium p. *116*

M p. 193

Photobacterium (in Prévot)

Photobacterium† (in Krass.)

Not bioluminescent................. **75**

75. Gelatin liquefied; nitrites produced from nitrates; methyl red negative; starch hydrolyzed; pathogenic to the fish *Salmonidae*.......... **Aeromonas** p. *116*

M p. 189

Not as above...................... **76**

76. Yellow pigment produced; nitrates reduced to nitrites

Empedobacter (*proteus*) (in Prévot)

Flavobacterium (*M*, 6th ed.)

(See also *Aplanobacter fleuryi* in Prévot.)
Colonies not yellow: Voges-Proskauer positive........ **Paracolobactrum** p. *155*

M p. 346

Paracolobactrum (in Prévot)

Bacterium (in Krass.)

Paracolon group (in T and W, 5th ed.)
(*P. aerogenoides* strains 32011 and 32811: possibly nonmotile strains of the **Hafnia group**.)

77. Obligate halophiles requiring 20 to 30 per cent salt for growth; pleomorphic; yellow colonies. **Halobacterium** p. *119*

M p. 207

Halobacterium (in Prévot)

Not as above...................... **78**

78. Organisms will not grow on meat in-

---

* W. H. Ewing, Intern. Bull. Bacteriol. Nomen. Taxon., *13*, 1963, 95.

† As *P. indicum.*

fusion agar without the addition of blood or ascitic fluid or X- and V-factors or other enrichments........................ **79**

Not as above...................... **80**

79. Pleomorphic coccobacillary organisms; grow well on blood agar, producing colonies up to 4 mm. in diameter on prolonged incubation; hydrogen sulfide produced from cystine media; slight acid from glucose, fructose, and mannose and possibly from other sugars. Pathogenic, producing tularemia or tularemia-like infections in laboratory animals.. **Pasteurella** p. *127*

M p. 395

Pasteurella (in Prévot)

Bacterium (in Krass.)

Pasteurella (*novicida*) (in T and W, 5th ed.) and **Brucella** (*tularensis*) (in T and W, 5th ed.).

Francisella (Dorofeev‡)

Organisms usually 0.2 to 0.5 μ wide and 0.5 to 2.0 μ long but frequently produce long filaments; do not grow on nutrient agar or on MacConkey's lactose bile salt agar; grow on nutrient agar with the addition of X-factor or V-factor or both or with the addition of diphosphothiamine or adenosine triphosphate; colonies on suitable media rarely more than 1 mm. in diameter after two days of incubation; nitrites produced from nitrates; various species have been reported as responsible for or associated with viruses in:

(i) Purulent meningitis and conjunctivitis in man (*H. influenzae*).

(ii) Subacute endocarditis (*H. hemolyticus*).

(iii) Acute and subacute conjunctivitis in man (*H. aegyptius*).

(iv) Soft chancre (*H. ducreyi*).

(v) Vesicular eruptions in the genitals of cattle (*H. citreus*).

(vi) Ulcers of trout (*H. piscium*).

(vii) Commonly present in the respiratory tract of man (various species)

---

‡ K. A. Dorofeev, Symp. Res. Works Inst. Epidem. Mikrobiol. in Chita, *1*, 1947, 177. This genus includes both *Pasteurella novicida* and *P. tularensis.*

and preputial secretions of dogs (*H. haemoglobinophilus*).

(viii) Pharyngitis (*H. parahaemolyticus*).

(ix) Nonpathogenic (*H. parainfluenzae*).

(x) Fowl coryza (*H. gallinarum*).

(xi) Swine influenza (*H. suis*).

(xii) Respiratory tract of ferrets (*H. putoriorum*)

Haemophilus p. *130*

M p. 406

Haemophilus (in Prévot)

Bacterium (in Krass.)

Haemophilus (in T and W, 5th ed.)

Note: a. Krassilnikov groups several of the *Manual* species. See also *Haemophilus vaginalis* (Dubes and Gardner, J. Bacteriol., *81*, 1961, 277).

b. This is the main entry for the genus *Haemophilus*. Owing to variable biochemical characteristics, other entries occur in other parts of the Key.

Fastidious organisms; require blood or ascitic fluid; highly pleomorphic; rod-shaped or filamentous; may reach 100 to 150 μ in length; homogeneous in young cultures but become granulated, beaded, and swollen in old cultures and tend to fragment into rods and cocci; large, spherical swellings packed with granules common; cholesterol globules appear among the growth; only rods and short filaments appear in pathological material; nonbranching; non-acid-fast; colonies on ascitic agar 1 to 2.5 mm. in three days; circular, low convex, colorless. L-phase variants are common. Highly virulent for mice, causing polyarthritis; causes ratbite or Haverhill fever in man . . . .**Streptobacillus** p. *158*

(*S. moniliformis*)

M p. 451

Streptobacillus (in Prévot)

Proactinomyces (in Krass.)

Actinobacillus (in T and W, 5th ed.)

80. Slender rods; 1.0 to 3.0 μ long and often arranged in angular fashion; pleomorphic; produce smooth, entire, butyrous, translucent, grayish-yellow colonies 0.5 to 1.0 mm. in diameter in two days at 37° C. on meat infusion agar; may increase

slightly in size upon further incubation; light brown on potato; nonhaemolytic; does not liquefy inspissated serum; no growth on bile media; acid only in glucose; indole negative; methyl red and Voges-Proskauer negative; nitrate reduced to nitrite; H_2S weakly positive; methylene blue not reduced; catalase positive; oxidase positive (weak). Straus reaction produced in guinea pigs; strict parasites, causing glanders in man and animals. **Actinobacillus** p. *131*

(*A. mallei*)

M p. 414

Malleomyces (in Prévot)

Pseudobacterium (in Krass.)

Loefflerella (in T and W, 5th ed.)

Small, ovoid coccobacilli, arranged singly and in pairs or in small bundles; sometimes pleomorphic; frequently exhibit bipolar staining; colonies on meat infusion agar 0.1 to 1.0 mm. in diameter in 24 hours at 37° C.; may increase in size up to 4 to 6 mm. in 5 days at 37° C. A slight, thin layer or no growth on potato; organisms cause plague in man and rodents or hemorrhagic septicemia in various other animals and in birds . . . .**Pasteurella** p. *127*

M p. 395

Pasteurella (in Prévot)

Bacterium (in Krass.)

Pasteurella (in T and W, 5th ed.)

Note: Topley and Wilson recognize only some of the *Manual* species. See also *P. ureae* (Hodgendijk, Antonie van Leeuwenhoek, *28*, 1962, 315). Mollaret and Le Minor (Ann. Inst. Pasteur, *102*, 1962, 649) have shown that *Pasteurella pestis* and *P. pseudotuberculosis* both produce β-galactosidase, whereas *P. septica* and *P. tularense* do not. They place the galactosidase positive organisms in the genus **Yersinia** proposed by van Loghem (Ann. Inst. Pasteur, *72*, 1946, 975).

Organisms cause actinobacillosis in man and other animals and may also be found in actinomycotic lesions; colonies on agar small, circular, bluish gray, translucent, with a smooth surface and an entire edge, up to 1.5 mm. in diameter in 24 hours at 37° C., but increase considerably in size on further incubation; on alkaline potato a slight, glistening, graying-yellow growth is produced; acid in glucose, maltose, mannitol and sucrose, xylose and dextrin; litmus milk acid; nitrates reduced; catalase positive; oxidase negative; H_2S positive; methyl red negative; Voges-Proskauer positive

Actinobacillus p. *131*

M p. 414

Actinobacillus (in Prévot)

Proactinomyces (in Krass.)

Actinobacillus (in T and W, 5th ed.)

Rods 0.5 to 0.6 μ by 1 to 2.2 μ arranged in pairs and short chains; tear-drop cells and rosette clusters and occasional filaments; rounded ends; Gram negative with Gram positive granules; fatty and metachromatic granules; require high humidity for growth; regularly ferment glucose, sucrose, fructose, mannose, and sorbitol; urease negative; catalase negative; indole positive; nitrates not reduced; gelatin not liquefied; H_2S produced; isolated from cases of endocarditis in man.......**Cardiobacterium**

(See Slotnick and Dougherty, Antonie van Leeuwenhoek, *30*, 1964, 261.)

Not as above...................... **81**

81. Curved rods that transform completely into coccoid forms during growth of the colony. Rods elongate and divide. At the point of division the rods grow out at an angle to the original axis and divide again at the angle when the cell has doubled its length. This process continues until a colony is formed. *Ultimately the rods transform completely into cocci.*

Colonies yellow or colorless

Arthrobacter p. *177*

M p. 605

(See note to *Arthrobacter* in Section H, **30.**)

Not as above...................... **82**

82. Colonies yellow

Flavobacterium p. *144*

M p. 309

Empedobacter (in Prévot)

Chromobacterium (in Krass.)

Pseudobacterium (in Krass.)

Flavobacterium (in T and W, 5th ed.) (Includes species 1, 5, and 8: see also *E. flavotenue* in Prévot and *Pseudobacterium picrum* in Krassilnikov: see also *"Marine Flavobacteria*—Group I" in Hayes, J. Gen. Microbiol., *30*, 1963, 1.)

Note: Smith (J. Gen. Microbiol., *33*, 1963, 263) described *"Bacterium" salmonicida* as a fermentative organism, producing no gas from glucose. Its colonies are greyish yellow, and a brown water-soluble pigment is produced. She proposes the name **Necromonas** *salmonicida* for the organism.

Colorless......................... **83**

83. Methyl red positive: Voges-Proskauer negative: no growth with KCN; no acid from sucrose, salicin, or adonitol; no growth in malonate..................... **83a**

Methyl red positive: Voges-Proskauer negative; growth with KCN; acid from sucrose, salicin, and adonitol; growth on malonate............**Klebsiella** p. *150*

(*K. rhinoscleromatis*)

M p. 344

(See Cowan *et al.*, J. Gen. Microbiol., *23*, 1960, 601.)

Not as above...................... **83b**

83a. Enteric pathogens of man: agglutinate with *Shigella* antisera; no growth on ammonium citrate; H_2S not produced

Shigella p. *150*

M p. 384

Shigella (in Prévot)

Bacterium (in Krass.)

Shigella (in T and W, 5th ed.)

Shigella group (I C N B)

Shigella (in Ewing*)

Organisms pathogenic to birds; grow on ammonium citrate; H_2S produced; agglutinate with *Salmonella* group D "O" antiserum.........**Salmonella** p. *147*

(*S. gallinarum*)

M p. 368

Salmonella (in Prévot)

Bacterium (in Krass.)

Salmonella (in T and W, 5th ed.)

* W. H. Ewing, Intern. Bull. Bacteriol. Nomen. Taxon., *13*, 1963, 95.

Salmonella group (I C N B)
Salmonella (in Ewing*)

83b. Organisms that occur as diplococci resembling *Neisseria* on primary isolation on solid media but as a mixture of cocci and rods in liquids, the latter predominating as the culture ages; isolated from normal vagina and from cases of conjunctivitis

Herellea p. *134*
(*H. vaginicola*)

Note: This genus does not appear in the *Manual.* See de Bord, Iowa State Coll. J. Sci., *16*, 1942, 471.

Not as above...................... **84**

84. Organisms cause disintegration of filter paper in 0.5 per cent peptone water

Cellulomonas p. *177*
(*C. acidula*)
M p. *601*

Aplanobacter (in Prévot)
Pseudobacterium (in Krass.)

Not as above....**Achromobacter** p. *143*
(*A. eurydice*)
M p. *300*

Acinetobacter (in Prévot)
Bacterium (in Krass.)

(See also *Acinetobacter anitratum, A. larvae, A. winogradskyi*, and *Moraxella lwoffi* in Prévot.)

85. Soil organisms; curved rods that transform completely into coccoid forms during growth of the colony. Rods elongate and divide. At the point of division the rods grow out at an angle to the original axis and divide again at the angle when the cell has doubled its length. This process continues until a colony is formed; *ultimately the rods transform completely into cocci;* colonies yellow or colorless. .**Arthrobacter** p. *177*
M p. *605*

(See note to *Arthrobacter* in Section H, **30.**)

Not as above........................**86**

86. Agar digested

Agarbacterium p. *145*
M p. *322*

Empedobacter (in Prévot)

* W. H. Ewing, Intern. Bull. Bacteriol. Nomen. Taxon., *13*, 1963, 95.

Pseudobacterium (in Krass.)

Note: Species 8 to 12 are included here. Prévot lists only species 8 (*A. bufo*), and Krassilnikov lists species 8 as *Bacterium granii* var. *bufo* and species 10 to 12 as varieties of *Pseudobacterium iridescens.*

Agar not digested................... **87**

87. Colonies yellow................. **88**

Colonies not yellow................. **92**

88. Organisms will grow in a mineral salts medium, using CO_2 as a source of carbon and oxidizing hydrogen

Hydrogenomonas p. *108*
(*H. vitrea*)
M p. *75*

Hydrogenomonas (in Prévot)
Pseudobacterium (in Krass.)

Organisms grow in a mineral salts medium using alkylamines as the sole source of carbon and nitrogen

Protaminobacter p. *117*
(*P. alboflavus*)
M p. *200*

Empedobacter (in Prévot)
Pseudobacterium (in Krass.)

Not as above...................... **89**

89. Obligate halophiles requiring 20 to 30 per cent salt for growth

Halobacterium p. *119*
(*H. trapanicum*)
M p. *207*

Empedobacter (in Prévot)

Not as above...................... **90**

90. Litmus milk acid or unchanged

Flavobacterium p. *114*
M p. *309*

Empedobacter (in Prévot)
Pseudobacterium (in Krass.)

Note: This includes *Flavobacterium* species 4, 6, 9, 10, and 11. Krassilnikov does not list 9 and 11; see also *Empedobacter serwanense, Aplanobacter betlis*, and *Cellulomonas flava* (in Prévot), *Photobacterium luminosum* (in Krassilnikov), and "*Marine Flavobacteria*—Group III" of Hayes (J. Gen. Microbiol., *30*, 1963, 1).

Litmus milk alkaline................ **91**

91. Nitrites produced from nitrates

Flavobacterium p. *144*

(*F. lutescens* and *F. fucatum*)
M p. 309
Empedobacter (in Prévot)
Pseudobacterium (in Krass.)
Note: See also *E. esteroaromaticum*
(in Prévot as *species incertae sedis*) and
Pseudobacterium rhizoctonia (in Krass.) and
"*Marine Flavobacteria*—Group II" of
Hayes (J. Gen. Microbiol., *30*, 1963, 1)
(nitrate reduction not stated).
Nitrites not produced from nitrates
Alcaligenes p. *143*
(*A. marshallii*)
M p. 297
Acinetobacter (in Prévot)
Pseudobacterium (*lactis*) (in Krass.)
(See also *P. decidiosum* in Krassilnikov.)
92. Loeffler's inspissated serum liquefied
93
Not as above...................... **94**
93. Recorded from septicemia in ducks
Pasteurella p. *127*
(*P. anatipestifer*)
M p. 395
Pasteurella (in Prévot)
Bacterium (*avicidum*) (in Krass.)
Cause acute ophthalmia (pink eye) of cattle
and granular conjunctivitis in man, mon-
keys, and apes and recorded as a possible
cause of trachoma in man
Moraxella p. *132*
M p. 419
Moraxella (in Prévot)
Bacterium (in Krass.)
(As *B. duplex* and *B. cancrosi.*)
(See notes on motility in Section F, **20.**
Some species show gliding motility.)
Not as above...................... **94**
94. Organisms recorded from an enzootic
of chronic pneumonia in calves; thin Gram
negative rods arranged in groups in tissues
and as coccoid and bacillary forms in culture; in the condensation water of blood
serum, produce mulberry-like flakes up to
1 mm. in diameter, consisting of cells arranged in chains, the latter encased in a
nonstainable material, which usually is
swollen at the tip
Actinobacillus p. *131*

(*A. actinoides*)
M p. 414
Actinobacillus (in Prévot)
Proactinomyces (in Krass.)
Actinobacillus (in T and W, 5th ed.)
Not as above...................... **95**
95. Slender rods; 1.0 to 3.0 μ long, often
arranged in angular fashion; pleomorphic;
produce smooth, entire, butyrous, translucent, grayish-yellow colonies 0.5 to 1.0
mm. in diameter in two days at 37° C. on
meat infusion agar; may increase slightly
in size upon further incubation; *café au lait*
colored on potato; Straus reaction produced in guinea pigs; strict parasite causing
glanders in man and other animals
Actinobacillus p. *131*
(*A. mallei*)
Malleomyces (in Prévot)
Pseudobacterium (in Krass.)
Loefflerella (in T and W, 5th ed.)
Not as above...................... **96**
96. Organisms cause brucellosis in man and
other animals; often cause abortion in animals; good growth on liver extract agar or
tryptose phosphate agar; increased CO_2
tension necessary for isolation of one species; litmus milk alkaline. **Brucella** p. *129*
M p. 404
Brucella (in Prévot)
Bacterium (in Krass.)
Brucella (in T and W, 5th ed.)
(Includes *Brucella abortus*, *B. melitensis*,
and *B. suis*, all of which Krassilnikov
lists under *Bacterium melitensis*.)
Not as above...................... **97**
97. Organisms causing whooping cough in
man, principally in children. One species
(*B. pertussis*) will not grow on primary isolation on meat extract agar but does not
require X- or V-factor; the other species
(*B. parapertussis*) grows profusely on meat
extract agar. Both species grow well on
Bordet-Gengou medium, producing
smooth, raised, entire, pearly, glistening
colonies in 48 to 72 hours at 37° C.;
nitrites not produced from nitrates; inspissated serum not liquefied. After intraperi-
toneal injection into mice, death occurs in

two to four days. Autopsy shows extensive hyperemia of the peritoneal wall, infiltration of glands, and the presence of an extremely mucoid exudate in the peritoneal cavity; hemorrhagic necrosis occurs after intradermal inoculation of the rabbit; agglutinated by antisera to *Bordetella pertussis*

> **Bordetella**   p. *128*
> *M p. 402*
> **Bordetella** (in Prévot)
> **Bacterium** (in Krass.)
> **Bordetella** (in T and W, 5th ed.)

Not as above...................... **98**
98. Organisms usually 0.2 to 0.5 μ wide and 0.5 to 2.0 μ long but frequently produce long filaments; do not grow on nutrient agar without the addition of X-factor or V-factor or both or the addition of diphosphothiamine or adenosine triphosphate; colonies on suitable media rarely more than 1 mm. in diameter after two days of incubation. Various species have been reported as responsible for or associated with viruses in a number of diseases (see H, **79**, p. *73*). *H. ducreyi* and *H. putoriorum* are the ones most likely to terminate here. The others may do so owing to variation in biochemical reactions

> **Haemophilus**   p. *130*
> *M p. 406*
> **Haemophilus** (in Prévot)
> **Bacterium** (in Krass.)

Haemophilus (in T and W, 5th ed.) Organisms do not require X- or V-factors. Grow well on meat infusion agar. Occur as diplococci resembling *Neisseria* on agar media and as a mixture of cocci and rods in liquid media, the latter predominating as the culture ages; occur in the normal vagina

> **Mima**   p. *133*
> (*M. polymorpha*)

Note: This genus is not listed in the *Manual*. See de Bord, Iowa State Coll. J. Sci., *16*, 1942, 471.

Not as above...................... **99**
99. Organisms grow in a mineral salts medium with an alkylamine as the sole source of carbon and nitrogen

> **Protaminobacter**   p. *177*
> *M p. 200*
> **Empedobacter** (in Prévot)
> **Pseudobacterium** (in Krass.)

Not as above..................... **100**
100. Organisms found growing in waters among decomposing plant tissue; coccobacillary forms embedded in a gelatinous matrix, which usually forms in long fingerlike processes in which the cells are well isolated from one another; produce a zoogloeal mass and cartilaginous colonies in culture...............**Zoogloea**   p. *118*
> *M p. 206*
> **Zoogloea** (in Prévot)
> **Bacterium** (in Krass.)

Not as above..................... **101**
101. Litmus milk alkaline........... **102**
Litmus milk acid or unchanged

> **Achromobacter**   p. *143*
> *M p. 300*
> **Acinetobacter** (in Prévot)
> **Bacterium** (in Krass.)

(This includes *Achromobacter* species 11, 12, and 15 from the *Manual* and *Acinetobacter spermophilum* from Prévot. Krassilnikov lists species 12 as *Achromobacter butyri*. Colorless mutants of the following *Manual* species of *Pseudomonas* may terminate here: *P. betle*, *P. cissicola*, *P. eisenbergii*, *P. smaragdina*. See also *P. graveolens* (in Krassilnikov) and *Aplanobacter cepivorum* and *A. robici* (in Prévot).
102. Colonies on nutrient agar colorless; up to 1 mm. in diameter in five days at 28° C.; grow autotrophically, oxidizing sodium thiosulfate to sodium sulfate and sulfuric acid....... **Thiobacillus**   p. *110*
> *M p. 83*

Note: This entry applies to *T. novellus* if it produces no acid from carbohydrates.
Not as above........**Alcaligenes**   p. *143*
> *M p. 297*
> **Acinetobacter** (in Prévot)
> **Bacterium** (in Krass.)

(This includes *A. metalcaligenes* and *A. viscolactis* from the *Manual:* see also *Acinetobacter candicans*, *A. coccoideum*,

Aplanobacter magroni, and *A. rhizoctonia* in Prévot and *Bacterium cyprinicida, Achromobacter cystinovorum,* and *Pseudobacterium grongingensis* in Krassilnikov.

103. Acid and gas from glucose at 37° C. or 22° C........................ **104**

Acid but no gas from glucose at 37° C or 22° C......................... **109**

No acid or gas from glucose at 37° C or 22° C......................... **120**

104. Colonies yellow; flagella polar

> **Xanthomonas** p. *113*
> *M* p. *152*

(*X. plantaginis* and *X. conjac,* if lactose negative, terminate here.)

Colonies yellow; flagella peritrichous:

a. Cellulose hydrolyzed

> **Cellulomonas** (*folia*) (in Prévot)

b. Cellulose not hydrolyzed

> **Erwinia** (in Prévot)
> **Chromobacterium** (in Krass.)

(*E. flavida, E. erivanense,* and *C. sauromali.*)

Colonies not yellow................. **105**

105. Organisms produce a luminescent growth on agar containing 2.8 to 3.0 per cent salt; usually no luminescence on media with the usual 0.5 per cent salt

> **Photobacterium** p. *116*
> *M* p. *193*
> **Photobacterium** (in Prévot)
> **Photobacterium** (in Krass.)

Not as above...................... **106**

106. Flagella polar; gelatin liquefied; some species are pathogenic to fish, frogs, and snakes, whereas others are saprophytic

> **Aeromonas** p. *116*
> *M* p. *189*
> **Bacterium** (in Krass.)

Note: Krassilnikov lists *Pseudomonas noctuarum* and *P. sphingidis,* and Prévot lists *Phytobacterium irtrosum,* which terminate here. Colorless polar-flagellated variants of *Serratia marcescens* and the species *Aeromonas margarita* (Stevenson, J. Gen. Microbiol., *21,* 1959, 366) also terminate here. Stevenson (*loc. cit.*) draws attention to the similarities with *Pseudomonas noctuarum* but claims that the latter

has peritrichous flagella. See also *P. polygoni* and *P. colurnae* (if lactose is not fermented).

Flagella peritrichous................ **107**

Note: Erwinia *betivora, E. dahliae,* and *E. serbinowi* (in Prévot) may fall into one of the groups between Section H, **107,** and H, **109.** There is insufficient information given to proceed from this point.

107. Voges-Proskauer positive at 37°C. or 22° C.; growth in the presence of KCN; indole negative; acid from mannitol but not dulcitol; urease negative; phenylalanine deaminase not produced... **107a**

Voges-Proskauer negative; methyl red positive; no growth in the presence of KCN; phenylalanine deaminase not produced........................ **107b**

Voges-Proskauer negative; methyl red positive; growth in the presence of KCN; growth on ammonium citrate; phenylalanine deaminase not produced:

a. No acid from adonitol; H_2S produced; gelatin not liquefied

> **Citrobacter group** (I C N B)
> **Citrobacter** (in T and W, 5th ed.)
> **Citrobacter** (in Ewing*)

(Includes strains 12611 and 1421 of Stuart *et al., loc. cit.,* and belongs to *Paracolobactrum intermedium* in the *Manual.*)

b. Acid from adonitol; no H_2S produced; gelatin liquefied

> **Enterobacter group** (I C N B)
> (Rare strains of subgroup C)
> **Aerobacter** p. *151*
> *M* p. *341*
> **Enterobacter** (in Ewing*)
> **Klebsiella** (in T and W, 5th ed.)

Voges-Proskauer negative; methyl red positive; growth in the presence of KCN; phenylalanine deaminase produced; no acid from dulcitol; no growth on malonate; no lysine decarboxylase or arginine dihydrolase produced.................. **108**

Note: Section H, **108,** covers the **Proteus-Providence group** (I C N B).

* W. H. Ewing, Intern. Bull. Bacteriol. Nomen. Taxon., *13,* 1963, 95.

107a. Gelatin liquefied

   Serratia group (I C N B)
   (Colorless mutants)

Or......**Enterobacter group** (I C N B)
   Subgroup C

(See also *Pseudomonas noctuarum* in Stevenson, J. Gen. Microbiol., *21*, 1959, 366.)

Gelatin not liquefied

   Hafnia group (I C N B)
  Hafnia group (in T and W, 5th ed.)
   Enterobacter (in Ewing*)

Note: Paracolon strains 32011, 3711, 35611, 37511, and 32811 of Stuart *et al.* (J. Bacteriol., *45*, 1943, 101), which essentially constitute **Paracolobactrum** (*P. aerogenoides*) (*Manual* p. 346), belong to (32011) or are closely related to the *Hafnia* group.

(See also *Bacterium apium* in Krassilnikov.)

107b. *Growth on ammonium citrate; H₂S produced; indole negative;* no acid produced from sucrose, salicin, or adonitol; urease negative; lysine and ornithine decarboxylases and arginine dihydrolase produced:

a. No growth on malonate

   Salmonella p. *147*
   M p. 368
   Salmonella (in Prévot)
   Bacterium (in Krass.)
   Salmonella group (I C N B)
  Salmonella (in T and W, 5th ed.)
   Salmonella (in Ewing*)

Note: Anaerogenic cultures redirected to Section H, **107**, from H, **119**, include *Salmonella typhi*, which terminates here. Prévot lists the organism in the genus **Eberthella.**

b. Growth on malonate

   Arizona group (I C N B)
   Arizona (in Prévot)
   Bacterium (in Krass.)
  Paracolobactrum p. *155*
   M p. 346
  Arizona group (in T and W, 5th ed.)

* W. H. Ewing, Intern. Bull. Bacteriol. Nomen. Taxon., *13*, 1963, 95.

   Arizona (in Ewing*)

No growth on ammonium citrate; H₂S not produced; indole positive

   Paracolobactrum p. *155*
   (*P. coliforme*)
   M p. 346
  Paracolobactrum (in Prévot)

(Includes strains 4361 and 33811 of Stuart *et al., loc cit.*)

  probably **Escherichia** (I C N B)

108. Urease negative; gas producing strains of..... **Providence subgroup** (I C N B)
  Proteus (*inconstans*) (*M p. 367*)
   Providencia (in Prévot)
  Providence group (in T and W, 5th ed.)
   Providencia (in Ewing*)

Note: Prévot does not equate *Proteus inconstans* with *Providencia* as does the *Manual.*

Urease positive........ **Proteus** p. *154*
   M p. 364
   Proteus (in Prévot)
   Bacterium (in Krass.)
  Proteus (in T and W, 5th ed.)
   Proteus (in Ewing*)

Note: The urease positive organisms are further subdivided into subgroups recognized as genera by Rauss (Intern. Bull. Bacteriol. Nomen. Taxon., *13*, 1963, 85). They may be separated as follows:

a. *Urease positive; gelatin liquefied; H₂S produced*

  Proteus subgroup (I C N B)
   Proteus (in Rauss)

(Includes *P. vulgaris* and *P. mirabilis.*)

b. *Urease positive; gelatin not liquefied; H₂S not produced*

i. Ornithine decarboxylase produced; no growth on ammonium citrate; no acid from mannitol, adonitol, or inositol

  Morganella subgroup (I C N B)
   Morganella (in Rauss)

(Includes *P. morganii.*)

ii. No ornithine decarboxylase produced; growth on ammonium citrate; acid from mannitol, adonitol, and inositol

Rettgerella subgroup (I C N B)
Rettgerella (in Rauss)
(Includes *P. rettgeri.*)
109. Colonies yellow.............. 110
Colonies not yellow............... 113
110. Bioluminescent on media containing 3 per cent salt.**Photobacterium** p. *116*
M p. 193
Photobacterium (in Prévot)
Photobacterium (in Krass.)
Not as above..................... 111
111. Flagella polar
Xanthomonas p. *113*
M p. 152
Note: This entry covers *Manual* species 3, 4, 6, 12, 17, 20, 26, 35, 47, 49 and 51, isolated from soils and not known to be pathogenic. See also the *Manual* species *Pseudomonas xanthe, P. xanthochlora,* and *P. pictorum* and also *P. trifolii, P. radiciperda,* and *Xanthomonas tardicrescens* if they produce no acid from lactose. See also *P. elongata, P. sessilis, Flavobacterium enalium,* and *F. oceanica* in Prévot and *P. necrosis* in Krassilnikov.
Flagella peritrichous............... 112
112. Chitin and starch hydrolyzed; gelatin liquefied............. **Beneckea** p. *145*
(*B. indolthetica*)
M p. 328
Flavobacterium (in Prévot)
(See also *F. chitinochroma* in Prévot, which is placed in *Chromobacterium* by Krassilnikov.)
Not as above...**Flavobacterium** p. *144*
M p. 309
Flavobacterium (in Prévot)
Chromobacterium (in Krass.)
Flavobacterium (in T and W, 5th ed.)
Note: a. The *Manual* species 12, 14, 15, 20, 21, and 25 terminate here. See also *Cellulomonas folia, Flavobacterium meningitidis,* and *F. resinovorum* (in Prévot) and *Chromobacterium flavum* and *C. denitrificans* (in Krassilnikov).
b. Hayward and Hodgkiss (J. Gen. Microbiol., *26*, 1961, 133) note that *Xantho-*

monas uredovorus is peritrichously flagellated and ferments carbohydrates. It also terminates here.
c. The following plant pathogens also terminate at this point: *Erwinia cassavae, E. citrimaculans,* and *Agrobacterium gypsophilae* (in the *Manual*) and *E. cacticida* (in Prévot).
113. Animal parasites; colonies mucoid; isolated from the eye of the Rhesus monkey................ **Noguchia** p. *133*
M p. 421
Noguchia (in Prévot)
Pseudomonas (in Krass.)
"**Bacterium**" (in T and W, 5th ed.)
(Krassilnikov and Topley and Wilson include here *N. granulosis* and *N. simiae;* Krassilnikov places *N. cuniculi* in the genus *Bacterium.*)
Small, translucent colonies; mucoid, small, slender rods in smooth colonies; ovoid rods with bipolar staining in rough colonies; motile at 37° C.; organisms cause meliodiosis in man and other animals
Pseudomonas p. *111*
(*P. pseudomallei*)
M p. 89
Whitmorella (in Prévot)
Pseudobacterium (in Krass.)
Loefflerella (in T and W, 5th ed.)
(*L. whitmori*)
Note: This insertion covers strains that have lost their ability to produce acid from lactose.
Small, umbonate colonies; translucent, with a dull, finely granular, "beaten copper" surface; entire; butyrous; organisms cause pseudotuberculosis in rodents
Pasteurella p. *127*
M p. 395
Cillopasteurella (in Prévot)
Pasteurella (in T and W, 5th ed.)
(See note to *Pasteurella* at H **80.**)
Organisms found in the cytoplasm of the rhizopod *Pelomyxa palustris*
Myxococcus
(*M. pelomyxae*)
M p. 930
Not as above..................... 114

114. Agar is digested

    Agarbacterium p. *145*
         M p. 322
    Bacterium (in Krass.)
(See also *Achromobacter perfectomarinus*,
a polar flagellate, in Prévot.)
Agar is not digested................ **115**

115. Chitin is hydrolyzed

      Beneckea p. *145*
         M p. 328
    Beneckea (in Prévot)
(Includes species 1, 2, 3, 4, and 6: see
also *Bacterium chitinophilum* in Krassilnikov.)
Chitin not hydrolyzed.............. **116**

116. Bioluminescent on media containing
3 per cent salt; may not be luminescent on
0.5 per cent salt

    Photobacterium p. *116*
         M p. 193
    Photobacterium (in Prévot)
    Pseudomonas (in Krass.)
Not as above...................... **117**

117. Flagella polar:

a. Capable of strictly autotrophic development oxidizing hydrogen and
utilizing carbon dioxide as a sole
carbon source; not known to be
pathogenic to whales or sweet potatoes; production of indole in eggnog
agar not reported

    probably **Hydrogenomonas**
Note: This entry includes *Pseudomonas
saccharophila* (see Doudoroff, Enzymologia,
9, 1940, 59, and Palleroni and Doudoroff,
J. Bacteriol., *89*, 1965, 264, who supplied
the above information). Unfortunately, the
authors do not state whether acid is produced from glucose oxidatively. See also
note in the Introduction.

b. Not as above................ **118**

118. Flagella polar

      Pseudomonas p. *111*
         M p. 89
    Pseudomonas (in Krass.)
(Includes *Manual* species 30 to 32, 37,
39 to 41, 51, 53, 55, and 58, which are
colorless and are not listed as plant
pathogens. In addition, the following

species of plant pathogens may terminate
here if not known to be pathogenic: 91,
107, 112, 122, 124, 125, 126, 127, 139,
and 142. Prévot places 30 to 32, 37, and
39 to 41 in *Pseudomonas;* 51, 53, 55, and
58 in *Achromobacter;* and 125, 126, 139,
and 142 in *Phytobacterium*. See also
*Pseudomonas centrifugans, P. gracilis,
P. liquefaciens,* and *P. mycophaga* and
Rhizobium ornithopi in Krassilnikov. See
also *Pseudomonas membranula, P. ob-
scura, Achromobacter echinodermis,* and
A. grypheae in Prévot. See also *Xanthomonas manihotis, X. proteamaculans,* and
Rhizobium meliloti and *Pseudomonas
castanae* (if lactose negative) in the
Manual. Colorless mutants of the following species, reported to produce green
fluorescent pigments, in the *Manual*,
would terminate here: 3 to 5, 10, 12, 13,
16, 60 to 61, 63, 64, 66, 68 to 71, 74 to
77, 79, 80, 84, 85, 87, 90, 92, 93, 95 to
101, 110 to 117, and 129. See also *Pseudomonas berolinensis* and *P. vignae* in
Krassilnikov.)

Flagella peritrichous................ **119**

119. Cause hyperplastic disease of plants

    Agrobacterium p. *145*
         M p. 288
(*A. rubi, A. tumefaciens,* if lactose negative, and *A. pseudotsugae.*)

    Agrobacterium (in Prévot)
    Pseudomonas (in Krass.)
    (*P. tumefaciens* only)
Cause wilts or necrotic diseases of plants

      Erwinia p. *146*
         M p. 349
    Erwinia (in Prévot)
(*E. amylovora, E. tracheiphila,* and *E.
salicis,* if lactose negative, in the *Manual*.
Krassilnikov places the last named in
Pseudobacterium and the others in
Bacterium. See also *E. solanisapra* and
E. papavae in Prévot.)

Not as above, return to..Section H, **107**
If the organism does not belong to one of
the categories under Section H, **107**, and
H, **108**, it possibly belongs to

Achromobacter p. *143*
M p. 300
Achromobacter (in Prévot)
Bacterium (in Krass.)
(This includes species 2, 5, 6, and 7 from the *Manual*. Species 5 and 6 are listed as *B. album* and 2 as *B. cycloclastes* by Krassilnikov. See also *A. echinodermis*, *A. litoralis* in Prévot and *Bacterium entericum* and *B. intrinsectum* in Krassilnikov.)

120. Curved rods, which transform completely into coccoid forms during growth of the colony. Rods elongate and divide. At the point of division the rods grow out at an angle to the original axis and divide again at the angle when the cell has doubled its length. This process continues until a colony is formed. *Ultimately the rods transform completely into cocci*

Arthrobacter p. *177*
M p. 605
Note: The emphasis lies on the final transformation into cocci. Some authorities may consider that limited, true branching may occur. If this is admitted the dividing line between *Arthrobacter* and *Nocardia* becomes very slim. The author's observations of *Arthrobacter globiformis* fit the above statement, and it is suggested that these criteria be adopted, with true branching forms that later disintegrate being assigned to *Nocardia*.

Organisms that will grow in a mineral salts medium, using phenol as the sole source of carbon; reduce nitrates with the liberation of gas, presumably nitrogen

Mycoplana p. *118*
M p. 204
Not as above...................... **121**
121. Colonies yellow to greenish yellow
122
Colonies not as above.............. **126**
122. Agar hydrolyzed

Agarbacterium p. *145*
(*A. amocontactum*)
M p. 322
Flavobacterium (in Prévot)
Chromobacterium (in Krass.)

Cellulose hydrolyzed
Cellulomonas (in Prévot)
(See *C. ferruginea*, *C. flava*, and *C. rossica* in Prévot and *Chromobacterium ferrugineum* in Krassilnikov and *Pseudomonas lasia* in the *Manual*.)
Note: See also **Cellfalcicula** *viridis*.
Not as above...................... **123**
123. Organisms grow in a mineral salts base, using CO_2 as the sole source of carbon and oxidizing hydrogen

Hydrogenomonas p. *108*
M p. 75
Hydrogenomonas (in Prévot)
(*H. flava*)
Pseudobacterium (in Krass.)
(See also *Chromobacterium lentulum* in Krassilnikov and *Pseudomonas saccharophila* in Doudoroff, Enzymologia, *9*, 1940, 59, and note to Section H, **117**.)
Not as above...................... **124**
124. Flagella polar

Xanthomonas p. *113*
M p. 152
Xanthomonas (in Prévot)
Pseudomonas (in Krass.)
Note: a. This includes species 12, 23, 41, 46, 50, and 53 and *X. albilineans* in the *Manual* and *X. fici*, *X. glycines*, *X. itoana*, *X. lactucae*, *X. lactucae-scariolae*, and *X. suberfaciens* in Prévot.
(See also *P. cerevisiae*, *P. caudata*, *P. levistici*, *P. ochracea*, and *P. panicimilicei* in the *Manual* and *P. chrysea*, *P. herbicola*, and *P. turcosa* in Krassilnikov and *Flavobacterium aestumarinum* and *F. xanthochrum* in Prévot.)
b. Starr and Stephens (J. Bacteriol., *87*, 1964, 293) state that species of *Xanthomonas* are characterized by the presence of a distinctive carotenoid alcohol with absorption maxima at 418, 437, and 463 mμ in petroleum ether.
Flagella peritrichous............... **125**
125. Litmus milk strongly alkaline

Alcaligenes p. *143*
(*A. bookeri*)
M p. 297
Achromobacter (in Prévot)

Bacterium (in Krass.)
(*B. recti* var. *bookeri*)
(See also *Flavobacterium harrisonii* in the *Manual*, and *Chromobacterium chlorinum* and *C. rheni* in Krassilnikov and *Erwinia edgeworthiae* in Prévot.)
Litmus milk acid or unchanged
Flavobacterium p. *144*
M p. 309
Flavobacterium (in Prévot)
Chromobacterium (in Krass.)
Flavobacterium (in T and W, 5th ed.)
(This includes the *Manual* species 18, 19, 22 to 24, and 26. Krassilnikov lists species 18 and 19 under *C. neptunium*, species 22 under *C. matzooni*, species 23 under *C. flavum*, and species 24 under *C. denitrificans*. See also *C. aquatile*, *C. halophilum*, and *C. naphthalani* in Krassilnikov and *Flavobacterium vadosum* in Prévot.)
126. Pleomorphic rods; do not grow on meat infusion agar; grow well in semisolid media containing horse, rabbit, or human blood or other complex substances; rods and coccoid forms predominate in culture; flagella polar; pathogenic to man; multiply on erythrocytes and in fixed tissue cells; transmitted through the sandfly, *Phlebotomus verrucarum*......**Bartonella** p. *211*
M p. 969
Bartonella (in Prévot)
Bartonella (in Krass.)
Colonies mucoid, small, circular, and translucent; organisms cause conjunctival folliculosis in rabbits......**Noguchia** p. *133*
M p. 421
Noguchia (in Prévot)
Bacterium (in Krass.)
Small, smooth, raised, entire, pearly colonies on meat infusion agar; medium discolored; litmus milk alkaline in one to two days; cause bronchopneumonia in rodents and sometimes associated with canine distemper............**Bordetella** p. *128*
M p. 402
Bordetella (in Prévot)
Bacterium (in Krass.)
Bordetella (in T and W, 5th ed.)

Not as above...................... **127**
127. Agar digested................ **128**
Agar not digested................. **129**
128. Alginates are metabolized; flagella polar............ **Alginomonas** p. *118*
(*A. alginovora*)
M p. 202
Pseudomonas (in Prévot)
Bacterium (in Krass.)
(*B. pastinator*)
(See also *Pseudomonas gelatica* and *P. atlantica*)
Alginate metabolism not recorded
Agarbacterium p. *145*
M p. 322
(Includes *A. mesentericum* and *A. rhodomelae*. Prévot lists only the latter, as *Flavobacterium*, and Krassilnikov lists the former under *Bacterium granii* and the latter as a variety of *Chromobacterium amocontactum*. See also note b. in H, **130**.)
129. Obligate halophiles, requiring 20 to 30 per cent salt for growth
Halobacterium p. *119*
M p. 207
Serratia (in Prévot)
Pseudomonas (in Krass.)
(*P. carnea*)
(See also *Pseudomonas halestorga*.)
Not as above...................... **130**
130. Alginates metabolized; flagella polar
Alginomonas p. *118*
M p. 202
Pseudomonas (in Prévot)
Note: a. This entry includes *A. nonfermentans*, *A. alginica*, and *A. terrestralginica*. Krassilnikov lists *A. alginica* as a variety of *Bacterium pastinator* and *A. terrestralginica* under *Chromobacterium*.
b. Adams, Williams, and Payne (J. Bacteriol., *81*, 1961, 162) claim that *A. alginica* is peritrichous and should be removed from the genus *Alginomonas*.
Not as above...................... **131**
131. Organisms found growing in water among decomposing plant tissue; produce a characteristic lobed gelatinous zoogloea, in which the cells are well isolated

from one another; produce cartilaginous colonies on agar....... **Zoogloea** p. *118*
(*Z. ramigera*)
M p. 206
Zoogloea (in Prévot)
Bacterium (in Krass.)
(See also *B. burgeri* in Krassilnikov.)
Note: Lackey and Lackey (J. Gen. Microbiol., *26*, 1961, 29) described a colorless sulfur-depositing organism, forming zoogloeal masses resembling those of *Zoogloea*, under the name of **Thiodendron.**
Not as above..................... **132**
132. Bioluminescent...**Photobacterium**
(This entry covers *P. balticum, P. indicum,* and *P. issatchenkoi* listed by Krassilnikov but for which the type of flagellation was not known.)
Not bioluminescent............... **133**
133. Motile with polar flagella....... **134**
Peritrichate flagella............... **138**
Note: Bacterium apisepticum, B. galophilum, and *B. halophilum,* listed by Krassilnikov, and *Achromobacter sewerini* (in Prévot) are listed as motile, but the type of flagellation is not stated.
134. Cells deposit sulfur internally when growing in the presence of hydrogen sulfide
Thiospira p. *110*
M p. 82
Thiospira (in Prévot)
Thiospira (in Krass.)
Note: It is doubtful whether this genus should appear under aerobic organisms.
Not as above..................... **135**
135. Organisms will grow in a mineral salts medium, using CO_2 as the sole source of carbon, and will oxidize hydrogen
Hydrogenomonas p. *108*
(*H. facilis* and *H. pantotropha*),
M p. 75
Hydrogenomonas (in Prévot)
Pseudomonas (in Krass.)
Note: Krassilnikov lists only *P. pantotropha.* See also *H. ruhlandii* (Packer and Vishniac, J. Bacteriol., *70*, 1955, 216). *H. pantotropha* is reported to have peritrichous flagella.

Rods 0.5 by 1 to 2 μ; gelatin liquefied; nitrites and gas produced from nitrates; starch hydrolyzed; lipolytic; will grow autotrophically, oxidizing thiosulfate to sulfate and tetrathionate with an increase in pH. Sulfur is not precipitated
Thiobacillus p. *110*
M p. 83
Thiobacillus (in Prévot)
Thiobacillus (in Krass.)
Not as above..................... **136**
136. Organisms cause disintegration of filter paper when growing in 0.5 per cent peptone water....**Cellulomonas** p. *177*
M p. 601
(See also *Pseudomonas mira* and *P. effusa* in the *Manual* and *P. miniscula* in Krassilnikov.)
Not as above..................... **137**
137. No action on carbohydrates; alkaline reaction in the Hugh and Leifson test; indole negative; cholera red negative; methyl red and Voges-Proskauer tests negative; gelatin not liquefied; citrate not utilized; no growth in the presence of KCN; phenylalanine deaminase and Moeller's lysine, arginine, and ornithine tests negative; urease, catalase, and oxidase tests positive; no pigment or fluorescence under ultraviolet light; lophotrichous flagella................. **Comamonas**
(See Davis and Park, J. Gen. Microbiol., *27*, 1962, 101, and Hugh, Intern. Bull. Bacteriol. Nomen. Taxon., *12*, 1962, 33.)
Not as above.... **Pseudomonas** p. *111*
M p. 89
Pseudomonas (in Krass.)
Note: a. This includes the colorless *Manual* species 33 to 36, 38, 42, 43, 46 to 48, 50, 52, 56, 56a, 143, and 146, which are not listed as plant pathogens. In addition, the following species of plant pathogens will terminate here if not known to be pathogenic: 119, 130, 132, 134, 135, 148, and 149. Of these, Prévot lists 42, 43, 46, 48, 49, 52, and 56a in the genus *Achromobacter* and 130, 132, 134, 143, 146, and 148 in the genus *Phytobacterium.* Krassilnikov

does not list the *Manual* species 34, 48, and 56a and lists the *Manual* species 35, 36, 38, 42, 46, 49, 52, 143, and 146 under other species in the genus *Pseudomonas* and species 43 (*P. stutzeri*) under *Bacterium agile*, and *P. polygoni* in *Pseudobacterium*. He also lists the following species not found in the *Manual: Pseudomonas atlantica, P. epsteinii, P. flagellata,* and *P. sinuosa.*

b. See also *P. neritica* and *Phytobacterium destructans* in Prévot; *Pseudomonas maltophilia* in Hugh and Ryschenkov (J. Gen. Microbiol., *26*, 1961, 123); and *P. citronellolis* in Seubert (J. Bacteriol., *79*, 1960, 426).

c. Colorless mutants of the following *Manual* species of *Pseudomonas* would also terminate here: 1, 8, 9, 11, 14, 15, 17, 20 to 22, 24 to 27, 102, 104 to 106, 118, and 120. See also *P. cyanoides* and *P. viscosum* (in Prévot) and *P. manilae, P. spongiosa,* and *P. zelinski* (in Krassilnikov).

d. The following *Manual* species of plant pathogens may also terminate here if pathogenicity has not been noted: *Agrobacterium stellulatum, Xanthomonas panici, X. rubrisubalbicans, X. cannae, X. zingiberi,* and *Rhizobium japonicum.*

e. Polar flagellated forms of *Alcaligenes faecalis* will terminate here.

138. Litmus milk alkaline

Alcaligenes p. *143*
M p. *297*
Achromobacter (in Prévot)
Bacterium (in Krass.)

(This includes *A. faecalis* and *A. recti.* See also *Bacterium apisepticum, B. cajae,* and *B. pectinophorae* in Krassilnikov, *Erwinia ixiae* in Prévot, and *Agrobacterium radiobacter* and *Rhizobium* spp. in the *Manual.*)
Litmus milk acid or unchanged

Achromobacter p. *143*
M p. *300*
Achromobacter (in Prévot)
Bacterium (in Krass.)

(This includes *Manual* species 1, 3, 4, 9, and 10. Krassilnikov regards the *Manual*

species 9 and 10 as varieties of *B. album,* species 4 as a variety of *B. liquefaciens,* and *A. liquefaciens* as *Pseudomonas liquida.* See also *B. album, B. aliphaticum, B. agile, B. galophilum, B. halophilum, B. leucogloeum,* and *B. nitrificans* in Krassilnikov and *Achromobacter sewerini* and *Erwinia araliavora* in Prévot.)

SECTION I

1. Endospores produced.............. **2**
No endospores produced.............. **6**
2. Curved rods that reduce either sulfate or nitrate while oxidizing a variety of organic substances and, in one species, also reduce iron. Motile with polar flagella

Sporovibrio (in Prévot)

Note: a. Three species included by Prévot in this genus—*S. desulfuricans, S. desulfuricans* var. *aestuari, S. rubentschickii*—are described as nonsporing in the *Manual* and placed in the genus *Desulfovibrio.* Adams and Postgate (J. Gen. Microbiol., *20,* 1959, 252) describe a new species under the name of *Desulphovibrio orientis,* which Prévot has included in the genus *Sporovibrio.*

b. Campbell, Frank, and Hall (J. Bacteriol., *73,* 1957, 516) indicate that curved sporulating Gram negative rods growing at 55° C. and referred to as *Sporovibrio desulfuricans* by Starkey (1938) belong to *Clostridium nigrificans.* These should not be confused with nonsporulating curved rods growing at 30° C., which Campbell *et al.* (1957) regarded as *Desulfovibrio desulfuricans.*

c. Campbell and Postgate (Bacteriol. Revs., *29,* 1965, 359) have recently revised the classification of the sulfate-reducing bacteria and have separated the sporulating organisms into the genus **Desulfotomaculum** with *D. nigrificans* as the type species. The nonsporulating organisms are retained in the genus **Desulfovibrio.**
Long, thin rods, oxidizing primary alcohols to acids and secondary alcohols to ketones, while reducing CO_2 quantitatively to methane; glucose is not metabolized

Methanobacterium   p. *125*
(*M. omelianski*)
M p. *250*
Terminosporus (in Prévot)
Bacterium (in Krass.)
Not as above...................... **3**
3. Spores central or subterminal....... **4**
Spores terminal..................... **5**
4. Motile........ **Clostridium**   p. *180*
M p. *634*
Endosporus (in Prévot)
Bacillus (in Krass.)
Nonmotile........ **Clostridium**   p. *180*
M p. *634*
Paraplectrum (in Prévot)

Note: a. *Manual* species included in *Endosporus* here are *C. belfantii, C. cylindrosporum, C. propionicum,* and *C. venturellii*. Prévot lists six additional species, which the sixth edition of the *Manual* lists as possible synonyms of *C. belfantii*; three others, which are listed as species of *Clostridium* in the sixth edition of the *Manual*, and one, *E. utriculus,* which cannot be traced. Krassilnikov lists only three of the above species (*C. belfantii, C. venturelli,* and *C. lustigii,* which he regards as synonymous with *C. belfantii*).

b. Only two species of *Paraplectrum, P. malenominatum* (recorded as a species in the sixth edition of the *Manual*) and *P. papulum* (appendix to *Clostridium* in the sixth edition of the *Manual*), are recorded by Prévot.

5. Motile........ **Clostridium**   p. *180*
M p. *634*
Terminosporus (in Prévot)
Bacillus (in Krass.)
(Includes *Manual Clostridium* species 51, 57, 58, 61, 81, 84, 87, and 88.)
Nonmotile........ **Clostridium**   p. *180*
M p. *634*
Caduceus (in Prévot)
Bacillus (in Krass.)
(Includes *Manual* species 82, 83, and 86.)

Note: Prévot lists 11 species of *Terminosporus,* only 8 of which are recognized as species of *Clostridium* in the seventh edition

of the *Manual*. Krassilnikov lists 4 of these in his genus *Bacillus*. Prévot lists 5 species in the genus *Caduceus,* of which only 2 are recorded by the seventh edition of the *Manual,* and 1 by Krassilnikov. The majority of the others of both genera are to be found in appendices of the sixth edition of the *Manual*.

6. Motile........................ **7**
Nonmotile........................ **12**
7. Curved rods with a bunch of flagella inserted at or near the center of the concave side of the rod; recorded from the alimentary canal of ruminants and guinea pigs and from the buccal cavity of man
Selenomonas   p. *127*
M p. *258*
Selenomonas (in Prévot)

Note: Prévot lists only three species, two regarded as *species incertae sedis*.

Curved rods that reduce sulfates, sulfites, sulfur, thiosulfate, and hyposulfites to hydrogen sulfide, using a wide range of organic substances and possibly hydrogen as hydrogen donors; motile by means of polar flagella ....**Desulfovibrio**   p. *124*
M p. *248*
Vibrio (in Krass.)

Note: See note to *Sporovibrio* at I **2.**

Curved rods depositing sulfur internally when growing in the presence of hydrogen sulfide; motile by means of polar flagella
Thiospira   p. *110*
M p. *82*
Thiospira (in Prévot)
Thiospira (in Krass.)
Not as above...................... **8**
8. Curved rods; polar flagella; monotrichous; ferment glucose, producing large quantities of butyric acid, a little acetic acid, CO_2, and H_2. Catalase negative
Butyrivibrio (in Prévot)
(See Bryant and Small, J. Bacteriol., *72,* 1956, 16, and Blackburn and Hobson, J. Gen. Microbiol., *29,* 1962, 69.)
Curved rods; polar flagella; ferment glucose, producing predominantly succinic acid, with formic and acetic acid
Succinovibrio (in Prévot)

(See Bryant and Small, J. Bacteriol., *72*, 1956, 22.)

Curved rods other than the above
>   **Vibrio** p. *122*
>   M p. *229*
>   **Vibrio** (in Prévot)
>   **Vibrio** (in Krass.)

(See *Manual* species *V. coli*—microaerophile—*V. niger*, and *V. sputorum*. Prévot lists ten additional species not recorded in the seventh edition of the *Manual:* see also *V. stomatitis* in Krassilnikov.

Not as above......................... **9**

9. Organisms that ferment glucose with the production of large quantities of ethyl alcohol plus other by-products, including CO_2.............. **Zymomonas** p. *117*
>   M p. *199*
>   **Zymomonas** (in Prévot)

Not as above...................... **10**

10. Straight or irregular very pleomorphic rods; ovoid with bipolar staining; filamentous inflated ramified forms; presence of spheroids of variable size, which are free or sessile, containing masses of nuclear substance; metachromases in the elongated forms; nonsporing Gram negative
>   **Sphaerophorus** p. *157*
>   M p. *441*
>   **Sphaerocillus** (in Prévot)

Note: The above forms part of Prévot's definition of the genus. He further states that the spheroids result from fusion of nuclear material from adjacent cells and that new rods are produced from the spheroids.

Not as above...................... **11**

11. Rods tapered at the ends with metachromatic granules and spheroids of small size............. **Fusocillus** (in Prévot)

Rods with rounded or tapered ends without granules or spheroids
>   **Zuberella** (in Prévot)

Note: The precise difference between *Zuberella* and *Fusocillus* is not clear from the definition given by Prévot for the genera. Placed in the genus *Zuberella* are the *Manual* species *Bacteroides serpens*, *Bacteroides variegatus*, and *Fusobacterium praeacutum*.

12. Rods straight or slightly curved: occur in liquids in long chains, frequently in parallel bundles; produce methane from acetate and *n*-butyrate (*Methanobacterium soehngenii*) or from formate and CO_2 (*M. formicicum*) **Methanobacterium** p. *125*
>   M p. *250*
>   **Ristella** (in Prévot)
>   **Bacterium** (in Krass.)

(For *M. formicicum* see Mylroie and Hungate, Can. J. Microbiol., *1*, 1954, 55.)

Minute rod-shaped cells growing only in media containing sterile fresh tissue or ascitic fluid; found in the upper respiratory tract of man.......... **Dialister** p. *157*
>   M p. *440*
>   **"Bacterium"** *pneumosintes*
>   (in T and W, 5th ed.)
>   **Dialister** (in Prévot)
>   **Bacterium** (in Krass.)

Not as above...................... **13**

13. Acid and gas produced from glucose or acid from glucose and gas produced in peptone water...................... **14**

Acid but no gas or no acid or gas produced from glucose....................... **20**

Note: No sugar reactions are given for the following *Manual* species: *Sphaerophorus gonidiaformans, S. mortiferus, S. floccosus, S. influenzaeformis*, and *S. pyogenes;* and *Bacteroides distillationis, B. viscosus*, and *B. glutinosus*. They have been treated here as producing no acid or gas.

14. Lactose fermented.............. **15**

Lactose not fermented.............. **19**

15. Gas produced in peptone......... **16**

Not as above...................... **18**

16. Straight or irregular very pleomorphic rods; ovoid with bipolar staining; filamentous inflated ramified forms; presence of spheroids of variable size, which are free or sessile, containing masses of nuclear substance; metachromases in the elongated forms; nonsporing Gram negative
>   **Sphaerophorus** p. *157*
>   M p. *441*

Sphaerophorus (in Prévot)
Pseudobacterium (in Krass.)
(*S. ridiculosis, S. necroticus,* and *S. inequalis.*)
Not as above...................... 17
17. Capsulated rods
Capsularis (in Prévot)
Not capsulated..... **Bacteroides** p. *155*
(*B. fragilis*)
M p. 424
Pseudobacterium (in Krass.)
Ristella (in Prévot)
Note: Prévot lists three additional species, which terminate here. See also *Pseudobacterium thermophilum* in Krassilnikov.
18. Rods 5 to 14 μ long; often in chains of 2 to 8 elements; terminal swellings and metachromatic granules common; obligate serophile; acid and gas from glucose, fructose, galactose, lactose, sucrose, maltose, inulin, dextrin, raffinose, and mannose
Leptotrichia (in Prévot)
(*L. innominata*)
Note: Gilmour, Howell, and Biddy (Bacteriol. Revs., *25*, 1961, 131) list this organism as a synonym of *Leptotrichia buccalis* (Trevisan). Their description does not include gas formation.
Not as above...... **Bacteroides** p. *155*
M p. 424
Pseudobacterium (in Krass.)
a. Capsulated
Capsularis (in Prévot)
b. Not capsulated
  i. Bipolar stain
Pasteurella (in Prévot)
  ii. Not as above
Ristella (in Prévot)
(See also *Sphaerophorus gulosus.*)
Note: Prévot lists *Bacteroides thetaiotamicron* in the genus *Sphaerocillus; B. ovatus, B. vulgatus,* and *B. convexus* in *Pasteurella; B. variabilis* in *Capsularis;* and the *Manual* species 3, 4, 7, 8, and 16 in *Ristella.*
19. Straight or irregular very pleomorphic rods; ovoid with bipolar staining; filamentous inflated ramified forms; presence of spheroids of variable size, which are free or sessile, containing masses of nuclear sub-

stance; metachromases in the elongated forms; nonsporing; Gram negative. Produce gas from peptone (except *Sphaerophorus freundii*)....... **Sphaerophorus** p. *157*
M p. 441
Sphaerophorus (in Prévot)
Pseudobacterium (in Krass.)
(*S. freundii, S. necrogenes, S. necrophorus, S. pyogenes, S. siccus,* and *S. varius* of the *Manual* and *S. pseudonecrophorus* and *S. peritonitis* in Prévot. Krassilnikov places all these in *Pseudobacterium* except *S. necrophorus,* which is placed in *Proactinomyces,* and *S. pyogenes,* which is placed in *Bacteroides.*)
Not as above...... **Bacteroides** p. *155*
M p. 424
Ristella (in Prévot)
Pseudobacterium (in Krass.)
(*Bacteroides halosmophilus, B. furcosus,* and *Ristella clostridiiformis* in Prévot and *B. ruminicola* in Bryant *et al.,* J. Bacteriol., *76,* 1958, 15.)
20. Straight or irregular very pleomorphic rods; ovoid with bipolar staining; filamentous inflated ramified forms; presence of spheroids of variable size, which are free or sessile, containing masses of nuclear substance; metachromases in the elongated forms; nonsporing Gram negative
Sphaerophorus p. *157*
M p. 441
Sphaerophorus (in Prévot)
Pseudobacterium (in Krass.)
(See *Manual* species 4, 9, 10, and 13 to 17. Species 15 and 17 are not listed in Krassilnikov.)
Long fusiform cells; nonpleomorphic; do not grow well on peptone agar: not capsulated.......... **Fusobacterium** p. *156*
M p. 436
Fusiformis (in Prévot)
Fusobacterium (in Krass.)
Note: a. See *Manual* species 1, 2, 4, 5, and 6. Krassilnikov lists all the *Manual* species except *F. vescum* under *F. plautivincenti. F. vescum* is placed in the genus *Pseudobacterium* as *P. ovatum.* See also *F. haemolyticus* (in Prévot).

b. These should be compared with *Leptotrichia* spp. in Prévot.

Not as above...................... **21**

21. Capsulated..... **Bacteroides** p. *155*
(*B. viscosus*)
M p. 424
Capsularis (in Prévot)
Bacterium (in Krass.)
(See also *Capsularis zoogleiformans* and *C. stabilis* in Prévot.)

Not capsulated.................... **22**

22. Bipolar staining. **Bacteroides** p. *155*
(*B. coagulans*)
M p. 424
Pasteurella (in Prévot)
Pseudobacterium (in Krass.)
(See also *Pasteurella serophila* in Prévot.)

Not as above...... **Bacteroides** p. *155*
M p. 424
Ristella (in Prévot)
Pseudobacterium (in Krass.)
(Includes species 5, 10, 11, 15, 17, 18, 19, and 21 to 26. Of these, Krassilnikov lists species 10 and 11 in the genus *Bacterium* and does not list species 24 to 26. Prévot lists four additional species: *R. haloseptica, R. lichenis-plani, R. naviformis,* and *R. nodosa.*)

SECTION J

1. Cells occur singly; motile by means of polar flagella; may be encapsulated and may form zoogloeae, but if so, do not oxidize hydrogen sulfide and do not deposit sulfur internally..................... **2**

Cells occur singly, in pairs, or in short chains; nonmotile; individual cells encapsulated and usually contain two pseudovacuoles per cell, which make them buoyant and which may give them a polygonal appearance; sulfur is deposited internally
Rhodothece p. *100*
M p. 50
Rhodothece (in Prévot)
Rhodothece (in Krass.)

Cells occur in the natural habitat arranged radially to form rosettes and reassemble in this form after mechanical dispersion. In peptone-yeast extract and other media they occur singly or in small groups. Rosettes may be 15 to 17 μ in diameter; individual cells, 1 by 4 to 6 μ; motile; do not deposit sulfur internally..... **Vannielia** p. *105*

Note: This genus is not listed in the *Manual*. See Pringsheim, J. Gen. Microbiol., *13*, 1955, 285.

Cells occur in well-defined aggregates. When growing in the presence of hydrogen sulfide, sulfur is deposited internally.... **4**

2. Hydrogen sulfide is not oxidized. Sulfur is not deposited internally; do not aggregate in rosettes
Rhodopseudomonas p. *103*
M p. 53
Rhodopseudomonas (in Prévot)
Rhodopseudomonas (in Krass.)

Hydrogen sulfide is not oxidized; sulfur is not deposited internally; cells occur in their natural habitat arranged radially to form rosettes and reassemble in this form after mechanical dispersion. In peptone-yeast extract and other media they occur singly or in small groups. Individual cells may be 1 by 4 to 6 μ; motile. **Vannielia** p. *105*
(For reference, see Section J, **1.**)

Hydrogen sulfide is oxidized, and globular sulfur is deposited internally........... **3**

3. Cells of uneven width and length; often swollen, spindle-shaped, and filamentous
Rhabdomonas p. *101*
M p. 48
Rhabdomonas (in Prévot)
Rhabdochromatium (in Krass.)

Note: Krassilnikov recognizes *R. minus* and *R. fusiforme*, which the *Manual* regards as synonyms of *R. gracilis* and *R. rosea*, respectively. The *Manual* includes *Rhodocapsa suspensa* (in Krassilnikov) in *Rhabdomonas gracilis*.

Cells of uniform width; spherical to cylindrical, the latter sometimes slightly curved
Chromatium p. *100*
M p. 50
Chromatium (in Prévot)
Chromatium (in Krass.)

Note: a. Krassilnikov does not list *C.*

molischii. He cites *C. cuculliferum* as *C. warmingii* forma *minus.*

b. Single cells of *Thiothece, Thiocystis,* and *Lamprocystis* resemble *Chromatium* very closely. Also, cells of *Thiospirillum violaceum* are indistinguishable from curved cylindrical forms of *Chromatium.*

4. Cells occur in cubical packets

Thiosarcina p. *97*

M p. 39

Thiosarcina (in Prévot)

Thiosarcina (in Krass.)

Cells in young colonies appear as flat sheets, in which cells are arranged in parallel rows embedded in a capsular material. In an unfavorable position or environment, irregular clumping of cells may occur

Thiopedia p. *97*

M p. 40

Thiopedia (in Prévot)

Thiopedia (in Krass.)

Other than above.................... 5

5. Individual cells or cell masses embedded in conspicuous capsules or zoogloea..... 6
Individual cells or cell masses apparently devoid of capsular material, although cells within the mass may be clearly separated in space........................... 7

6. Cells spherical, occurring in large numbers, well separated in a conspicuous common slime capsule. In dry conditions the capsular material forms a double, contoured membrane around the cells. On moistening, the mass slowly swells and bursts. As the liberated cells divide, they form a flat, spreading colony, in which the cells are no more than three layers deep but are separated from one another by capsular material............ **Thiocapsa** p. *97*

M p. 41

Thiocapsa (in Prévot)

Thiocapsa (in Krass.)

Cells spherical and encapsulated. In the early stages of growth of the colony, cells form in tetrads,* resembling those of *Thio-*

---

* Winogradsky considered that cells that form tetrads divide in *three* directions, the result being a four-pointed group rather than a flat group of four.

cystis. Further division of the cells gives rise to a compact, opaque mass of cocci embedded in a large slime capsule. This is followed by formation of arched fragments similar in appearance to sections of a hollow sphere, the fragments being arranged as if on the surface of a sphere within the capsule. Continued growth of the arched fragments results in their edges touching but not coalescing. Infolding of the arched pieces takes place, finally almost filling the internal cavity and producing a network resembling a sponge. The enveloping capsule eventually ruptures, liberating fragments of the zoogloeal network, which reorganize into small groups interlinked by single cocci. Under unfavorable conditions, the cocci are vacuolated, and sulfur is confined to the peripheral cytoplasm. Free cells are motile (*cf. Chromatium*). The total transformation occurs in 40 days

Lamprocystis p. *99*

M p. 43

Lamprocystis (in Prévot)

Lamprocystis (in Krass.)

Note: Krassilnikov lists the following species, whose position in the seventh edition of the *Manual* is shown in parentheses: *L. gelatinosa* (*Thiothece gelatinosa*) and *L. rosea* and *L. rubra* (*Amoebobacter bacillosus*). *L. violacea* appears in the appendix to *Thiochodaceae* in the sixth edition of the *Manual* under the name of *Thiosphaerion violaceum.* A further species, *L. symbiotica,* whose *Manual* equivalent cannot be traced is also listed.

Cells spherical to cylindrical. Develop in small clusters, the compact clusters of 4 to 20 cells being widely separated in an almost spherical and seemingly cartilaginous capsule, the outer layer of which is neither sharply differentiated nor obviously deliquescent. As each cluster proliferates, it eventually separates into a number of smaller clusters *within the zoogloea.* Single cells are rare. At some stage individual clusters leave the mass as a result of either swelling and dispersion of the whole mass or a softening of the mass at one or more points. After separation, the cluster becomes motile. The process of separation of clusters requires three weeks. Generation time is approximately two days

Thiocystis p. *98*
M p. 42

Cells spherical to cylindrical; heavily encapsulated, with the capsules remaining attached to form zoogloea. The individual capsules are very thick. After division the cells become separated in space by the developing capsules and are eventually arranged at an obtuse angle to one another. Swarming is preceded by a softening of the capsule and an irregular rearrangement of the cells. Individual cells separate by a slow rotatory action and once free are actively motile (*cf. Chromatium*). Cells are pale gray. Sulfur granules are small and confined to the peripheral layer of cytoplasm

Thiothece p. *98*
M p. 42
Thiothece (in Prévot)
Thiothece (in Krass.)

7. Cells spindle-shaped; 1.5 to 1.7 by 2.5 to 5.0 μ. Cell families may consist of a long, irregular body made up of cells two to three layers thick, arranged in parallel fashion. When separated from other cell masses, the cells rearrange to form an open pyramidal network, in which the cells meet only at their tips. Colonies may be several hundred microns across and resemble *Hydrodictyon* of the green algae. Small cell groups detached from the mass are motile; compact masses form under unfavorable conditions. Individual cells contain an elongated vacuole and are pale in color; sulfur is confined to the peripheral cytoplasm

Thiodictyon p. *98*
M p. 41
Thiodictyon (in Prévot)
Thiodictyon (in Krass.)

Note: Thiodictyon minus (in Krassilnikov) is a synonym of *T. elegans* in the *Manual.*

Cells compressed into a compact mass; colored rose red; surrounded by a capsule composed of an inner, poorly refracting layer and an outer, strongly refracting layer. Placed in a favorable environment, the cyst cracks, and the cell mass slowly creeps out (one to two days). The empty cyst remains unchanged for some time. The group of cells does not disperse but grows in an irregularly contoured mass. Whole families are motile. Most cells are spherical. Division occurs in only one direction. Cells may be compressed or may be freely separated in the nonencysted state. There are rarely more than two to four within a group in the colony. They are continually changing position and proximity in the colony. Internal colonial movement can occur without much lateral movement. Coordinated lateral movement is amoeboid. Single cells occasionally become isolated from the mass and then are drawn back. Masses ultimately may separate into smaller groups. No capsular material can be discerned in the families. Families can be penetrated by small, motile bacteria with ease. Winogradsky considered that the connection was via plasma threads, but he was unable to demonstrate them. He considered the dense, compact masses to occur in the presence of O_2 and the open structure in the presence of hydrogen sulfide

Amoebobacter p. *99*
M p. 44
Amoebobacter (in Prévot)
Amoebobacter (in Krass.)

Note: Schlegel and Pfennig (Arch. Mikrobiol., *38*, 1961, 1) describe the isolation of cultures resembling *Amoebobacter roseus*, which under other conditions of culture also resemble *Rhodothece pendens.*

Shapeless, thick aggregates of small, spherical, vividly colored cells; nonmotile; do not form hollow spherical structures. The extremely smooth surface of the colony suggests a limiting capsular material, but no obvious capsule is visible. Eventually, growth, in the form of threads and flaps, appears on the surface, and the cells become separated...... **Thiopolycoccus** p. *100*
M p. 45

Thiopolycoccus (in Prévot)
Thiopolycoccus (in Krass.)

SECTION K

The keys of this Section have been reproduced and modified in this form with the permission of the publishers and authors, Dr. C. B. Philip, Dr. C. W. Rake, and Dr. D. Weinman.

1. Parasites, intracellular or intimately associated with tissue cells other than erythrocytes or with certain organs in arthropods; rarely extracellular in arthropods.............................. 2
Parasites, intracellular or facultatively extracellular; found characteristically in or on the erythrocytes of vertebrates, exceptionally in fixed-tissue cells........... 13
2. Frequently cause diseases of vertebrates. Transmitted by arthropod vectors..... 3
Intracellular parasites found in tissues of vertebrates. Not known to be transmitted by arthropod vectors................. 9
3. Adapted to existence in arthropods; vertebrate hosts include man; cells rod-shaped, ellipsoidal, coccoid, and diplococcoid; rarely filamentous................... 4
Only a few species adapted to invertebrate existence; pathogenic for certain mammals but not for man; cells spherical, occasionally pleomorphic.................... 5
Adapted to existence in arthropods as symbiotes but not in vertebrates as highly pathogenic parasites; cells pleomorphic, coccoid to short or long and curved rods, or even filamentous.................... 7
4. Nonfilterable; produce typhus-like rash and usually *Proteus X* (Weil-Felix) agglutinins in man........ **Rickettsia** p. *209*
Filterable; produce neither rash nor Weil-Felix agglutinins in man.. **Coxiella** p. *209*
M p. *947*
5. Transmitted by ticks.............. 6
Transmitted by parasitic trematodes; pathogenic principally for canines
Neorickettsia p. *210*
6. Transmitted transovarially; parasites of circulating monocytes of vertebrate hosts

Ehrlichia p. *209*
M p. *949*
Not transmitted transovarially; parasites of endothelial cells of vertebrate hosts
Cowdria p. *210*
M p. *950*
7. No known filterability; no reported association with intracellular crystalline inclusions............................. 8
Filterable; cause blue disease of beetle larvae; associated with intracellular, crystalline inclusions; reportedly invade cell nuclei........... **Rickettsiella** p. *210*
M p. *957*
8. Symbiotic to highly pathogenic; no mycetomes produced in hosts
Wolbachia p. *210*
M p. *953*
Symbiotic to the point that special mycetomes are developed for harboring the organisms, which are not pathogenic, in the host................**Symbiotes** p. *210*
M p. *956*
9. Noncultivable in chicken embryonic tissues........................... 10
Cultivate in chicken embryonic tissues
Miyagawanella p. *211*
M p. *961*
10. Organisms coccoid; do not exhibit pleomorphism...........**Chlamydia** p. *210*
M p. *958*
Organisms usually coccoid or ellipsoidal; exhibit marked pleomorphism........ 11
11. Pleomorphic forms small (200 mμ to 2 μ); pathogenic.................... 12
Pleomorphic forms large (2 μ). Apparently nonpathogenic; may be saprophytic
Colettsia p. *211*
M p. *961*
12. Occur intracytoplasmically as prominent colonies......... **Colesiota** p. *211*
M p. *959*
Occur intracytoplasmically as scattered growth.............. **Ricolesia** p. *211*
M p. *959*
13. Small, rod-shaped, bacteria-like cells. At least one species, when cultured, may show a single, polar flagellum. Arthropod

transmission established for some species
14
Very small, virus-like particles occurring in
the erythrocytes of vertebrates. Transmitted by arthropods
Anaplasma   p. *212*
M p. 981
14. Multiply on erythrocytes and within
fixed-tissue cells. Usually possess a single,
polar flagellum when cultivated in or on
nonliving media. Provoke a progressive
anemia or a cutaneous eruption, usually
both in succession, not both coincidentally.
Found in man and *Phlebotomus* spp.
Bartonella   p   *11*
M p   69
Not known to multiply in fixed-tissue cells;
parasitize erythrocytes and may multiply
there. Flagella not demonstrated. Occur in
mammals and possibly in other vertebrates,
but not known from man **15**
15. Usually parasitize less than 5 per cent
of the total erythrocytes, rarely more.
Relatively monomorphic in erythrocytes.
Nonpathogenic or only slightly so. Affected
little, if at all, by splenectomy. Cultivable
on nonliving media. Occur within the red
blood cells; epierythrocytic forms are prob-
lematical . . . . **Grahamella**   p. *211*
M p. 971
Parasitized cells may constitute more than
90 per cent of the total erythrocytes at the
peak of infection. Polymorphism is marked
when in or on red blood cells. May or may
not be pathogenic. Marked increase in
numbers after splenectomy. Cultivation on
nonliving media not confirmed. Occur on
the red blood cells; situation within red
cells possible but not proved **16**
16. Extremely polymorphic; however, rods
of varying sizes almost invariably occur,
often in chains. Habitat predominantly
epierythrocytic. Usually pathogenic, pro-
voking a progressive, sometimes fatal,
anemia . . . . . . **Haemobartonella**   p. *212*
M p. 972
Fundamental morphological type is ring-
or disc-shaped. Rods are one disc or ring
diameter in length; composite rods are

made of these units. Occur in great numbers
in the blood plasma as well as on the
erythrocytes. Usually nonpathogenic
Eperythrozoon   p. *212*
M p. 977

SECTION L

The keys in this section have been reproduced and modified in this form with the
permission of the publishers and the author,
Dr. R. Y. Stanier.
1. Neither fruiting bodies nor resting cells
produced . . . . **Cytophaga**   p. *201*
M p. 858
Resting cells produced **2**
2. Resting cells cylindrical, not spherical or
ellipsoidal. Fruiting bodies produced **3**
Resting cells (microcysts) spherical or el
lipsoidal, surrounded by a distinct wall.
Fruiting bodies formed except in the genus
Sporocytophaga **9**
3. Resting cells not contained in cysts.
Fruiting bodies consist of mesenteric masses
or finger-like aggregations of resting cells
4
Resting cells contained in cysts of definite
shape borne on the fruiting bodies **5**
4. Fruiting body depressed, usually irregularly delimited, the interior usually consisting of swollen or intestine-like twisted or
intertwined masses, the windings of which
may be constricted or may jut out (project)
as free ends . . . . **Archangium**   p. *202*
M p. 863
Archangium (in Prévot)
Archangium (in Krass.)
Fruiting body consists of single (separate)
columnar or finger-like structures arising
from the substrate . . **Stelangium**   p. *202*
M p. 866
Stelangium (in Prévot)
Stelangium (in Krass.)
5. Cysts angular. Vegetative cells always
thick and short, with blunt, rounded ends
Sorangium   p. *202*
M p. 866
Sorangium (in Prévot)
Sorangium (in Krass.)

Cysts rounded. Vegetative cells usually long and thin, with tapering ends.......... **6**
6. Cysts embedded in slime; sessile, occurring singly or as loose aggregates

Polyangium   p. *203*
M p. 870
Polyangium (in Prévot)
Polyangium (in Krass.)

Cysts never embedded in slime; either borne on stalks or arranged in tight clusters joined together at the base........... **7**
7. Many cysts united at base to form a large disc or rosette; either sessile or stalked

Synangium   p. *203*
M p. 877
Synangium (in Prévot)
Synangium (in Krass.)

Cysts not united at base; borne singly or in large numbers on stalks.............. **8**
8. Cysts borne singly on a stalk

Podangium   p. *203*
M p. 877
Podangium (in Prévot)

Numerous cysts on a stalk

Chondromyces   p. *204*
M p. 879
Chondromyces (in Prévot)
Chondromyces (in Krass.)

9. Definite fruiting bodies formed..... **10**
No definite fruiting bodies

Sporocytophaga   p. *206*
M p. 890
Sporocytophaga (in Prévot)
Sporocytophaga (in Krass.)

10. Microcysts not enclosed in larger cysts
11
Microcysts enclosed in larger cysts

Angiococcus   p. *205*
M p. 889
Angiococcus (in Prévot)
Angiococcus (in Krass.)

11. Fruiting bodies deliquescent

Myxococcus   p. *204*
M p. 883
Myxococcus (in Prévot)
Myxococcus (in Krass.)

Fruiting bodies firm, not deliquescent.. **12**
12. Cysts grouped in a fruiting body resembling *Boletus*

Melittangium (in Krass.)
Chondrococcus   p. *205*
M p. 886
Chondrococcus (in Prévot)

Not as above... **Chondrococcus**   p. *205*
M p. 886
Chondrococcus (in Prévot)
Chondrococcus (in Krass.)

DIGEST OF GENERA

PHOTOSYNTHETIC BACTERIA

RED AND PURPLE SULFUR BACTERIA

GENERAL NOTES: The following genera are all colored *red* or *purple* or, if they contain large quantities of sulfur, may be peach-colored. The color is due to carotenoid pigments, which predominate over the green *bacteriochlorophyll*. In their natural habitat these genera have been found in waters containing H_2S, and so far as is known from the isolated species, namely, of *Chromatium*, they develop only under anaerobic conditions, exposed to light in the presence of H_2S or other suitable hydrogen donor. The H_2S (HS^-) is oxidized to S^0, which is deposited internally.

Those species which are motile, with the exception of *Amoebobacter*, have polar flagella.

When examined spectroscopically, they show bands of absorption for bacteriochlorophyll at 375 and 590 mμ in the visible spectrum and 800, 850, and 890 mμ in the infrared region. These peaks are due to different components, the presence and quantities of which vary from species to species. They also show peaks for carotenoid pigments between 400 and 600 mμ, often obscuring the 590 mμ band for bacteriochlorophyll. Upon extraction with alcohol, the band at 590 mμ disappears and is replaced by another at approximately 774 mμ. The shift is possibly due to the dissociation of the chromoprotein.

The spectrogram for *Thiospirillum je-*nense is shown in Figure 3 (see Schlegel and Pfennig, Arch. Mikrobiol., *38*, 1961, 1).

Sulfur can be extracted with acetone or pyridine.

Most of the genera have been described from slide cultures of crude material by Winogradsky, and generic differences lie mainly in the state of aggregation of the cells. Observations by van Niel (Bacteriol. Revs., *8*, 1944, 1) suggest that at least some of the genera may represent only different environmental reactions of a single genus *Chromatium*. Others, because of their particular mode of division, are quite distinct. Single cells of *Thiothece*, *Thiocystis*, and *Lamprocystis* resemble *Chromatium* very closely. Also, cells of *Thiospirillum violaceum* are indistinguishable from the curved forms of *Chromatium*.

Van Niel found that *Thiocystis*-like purple bacteria varied in size from 7 μ at pH 7.2 to 1.5 μ at pH 9.0 in the presence of 0.02 per cent H_2S. They also varied in size, with increase within limits, in the sulfide concentration. At high pH, forms resembling *Thiothece*, *Thiocystis*, and *Thiocapsa* were unmistakable. At low pH, forms similar to *Thiosarcina* and *Thiopedia* were produced.

This group of genera is morphologically heterogeneous and does not, in the author's opinion, form a true taxonomic group. These genera are placed in the family *Thiorhodaceae* in the *Manual*.

96

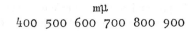

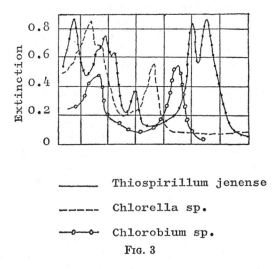

_____ Thiospirillum jenense

_ _ _ _ _ Chlorella sp.

—o—o— Chlorobium sp.

FIG. 3

In the following genera all those attributed to Winogradsky were described in Zur Morphologie und Physiologie der Bakterien, I. Schwefelbacterien, Leipzig, 1888.

Thiosarcina (Thi.o.sar.ci′na) Winogradsky, 1888. *M p. 39.*

DIFFERENTIATING CHARACTERS: Unicellular, spherical organisms, 2 to 3 μ in diameter, occurring in cubical packets. They contain bacteriochlorophyll and carotenoid pigments with predominance of the latter so that the cell masses are colored various shades of red or purple. When growing in the presence of H₂S they deposit sulfur internally.

Type species: *Thiosarcina rosea* (Schroeter) Winogradsky.

NOTES: Only one species is described. (See also general notes, p. *96.*)

Thiopedia (Thi.o.ped′ia) Winogradsky, 1888. *M p. 40.*

DIFFERENTIATING CHARACTERS: Unicellular, spherical organisms, 1 to 2 μ in diameter. Under optimal conditions the cells in young colonies are arranged in chains, which occur in parallel bundles in flat sheets and are embedded in a capsular material. These forms resemble *Merismopedia* of the blue-green algae. Under unfavorable conditions this typical arrangement may be lost. The organisms contain bacteriochlorophyll and carotenoid pigments, and the latter predominate to color the cell masses various shades of red or purple. When growing in the presence of H₂S they deposit sulfur internally.

Type species: *Thiopedia rosea* Winogradsky.

NOTES: Only one species has been described. (See also general notes, p. *96.*)

Thiocapsa (Thi.o.cap′sa) Winogradsky, 1888. *M p. 41.*

DIFFERENTIATING CHARACTERS: Unicellular, spherical organisms, 2.5 to 3.0 μ in diameter, occurring in large numbers, well separated in a conspicuous common slime capsule. In dry conditions the capsular material forms a double, contoured membrane around the cells. Upon moistening, the mass slowly swells and bursts. As the liberated cells divide they form a flat, spreading colony in which the cells are no more than three layers deep but are separated from one another by a capsular material. Individual cells or cell masses are embedded in conspicuous capsules or zoogloea. Contain bacteriochlorophyll and carotenoid pigments and the latter predominate to color the cell masses various shades of red or purple. When growing in the presence of H₂S they deposit sulfur internally.

Type species: *Thiocapsa roseopersicina* Winogradsky.

NOTES: Only one species has been described. (See also general notes, p. *96*.)

Thiodictyon (Thi.o.dic′ty.on) Winogradsky, 1888. *M p. 41.*

DIFFERENTIATING CHARACTERS: Unicellular, spindle-shaped organisms, 1.5 to 1.7 μ by 2.5 to 5.0 μ. Cell families may consist of a long, irregular body made up of cells 2 to 3 layers thick, arranged in parallel fashion. When separated from other cell masses, the cells rearrange to form an open pyramidal net in which the cells meet only at their tips. Colonies may be several hundred microns across and resemble *Hydrodictyon* of the green algae. Small cell groups detached from the mass are motile. Compact masses form under favorable conditions. Individual cells contain an elongated vacuole and are pale in color, and sulfur is confined to the peripheral cytoplasm. Individual cells or cell masses are apparently devoid of capsular material, although cells within the mass may be clearly separated in space. The organisms contain bacteriochlorophyll and carotenoid pigments; the latter predominate to color the cell masses various shades of red or purple. When growing in the presence of H₂S they deposit sulfur internally.

Type species: *Thiodictyon elegans* Winogradsky.

NOTES: Only one species is described. (See also general notes, p. *96*.)

Thiothece (Thi.o.the′ce) Winogradsky, 1888. *M p. 42.*

DIFFERENTIATING CHARACTERS: Unicellular, spherical to cylindrical organisms, 4 to 6 μ by 4 to 7 μ, heavily capsulated, with the capsules remaining attached to form zoogloea. The individual capsules are very thick. After division, the cells become separated in space by the developing capsules and are eventually arranged at an obtuse angle to one another, in a manner similar to *Aphanothece* of the blue-green algae. Swarming is preceded by a softening of the capsule and an irregular rearrangement of the cells. Individual cells separate by a slow rotatory action and, once free, are actively motile with polar flagella (*cf. Chromatium*). Cells are pale gray to a dirty yellow. Sulfur globules are small and confined to the peripheral layer of cytoplasm. Bacteriochlorophyll and carotenoid pigments are contained; the latter predominate to color the cell masses various shades of red or purple. When growing in the presence of H₂S they deposit sulfur internally.

Type species: *Thiothece gelatinosa* Winogradsky.

NOTES: Only one species is described. (See also general notes, p. *96*.)

Thiocystis (Thi.o.cys′tis) Winogradsky, 1888, *M p. 42.*

DIFFERENTIATING CHARACTERS: Unicellular, spherical to cylindrical organisms. They develop in small clusters, the compact clusters of 4 to 20 cells being widely separated in an almost spherical and seemingly cartilaginous capsule, the outer layer of which is neither sharply differentiated nor obviously deliquescent. As each cluster proliferates, it eventually separates into a number of smaller clusters within the zoogloeum. The 4-cell stage of development is similar in appearance to the early stages in the development of *Lamprocystis*. Single cells are rare but resemble *Chromatium*. At some stage, individual clusters leave the mass either as a result of swelling and dispersion of the whole mass or of softening of the mass at one or more points. After separation, the cluster becomes motile. The process of separation of clusters observed by Winogradsky took 3 weeks. The generation time is approximately 2 days. The organisms contain bacteriochlorophyll and carotenoid pigments, with the latter predominating to color the cell masses various shades of red or purple. When growing in the presence of H₂S they deposit sulfur internally.

Type species: *Thiocystis violacea* Winogradsky.

NOTES: Two species have been described, one with a diameter of 2.5 to 5.5 μ and the other less than 1 μ. (See also general notes, p. *96*.)

Lamprocystis (Lam.pro.cys'tis) Schroeter, 1888. *M p. 43*. (Die Pilze Schlesiens, in Cohn, Kryptogamen-Flora von Schlesien, *3*, 1, 1886, 151.)

DIFFERENTIATING CHARACTERS: Unicellular, spherical organisms, 2.0 to 2.5 μ in diameter; capsulated. In the early stages of growth of the colony, cells form in tetrads resembling *Thiocystis*. (Winogradsky considered that cells which form tetrads divide in three directions, the result being a 4-pointed group rather than a flat group of 4.) Further division of the cells gives rise to a *compact* opaque mass of cocci embedded in a large slime capsule. This is followed by the formation of arched fragments, similar in appearance to sections of a hollow sphere, arranged as if on the surface of a sphere within the capsule. Continued growth of the arched fragments results in their edges touching but not coalescing. Infolding of the arched pieces takes place, and finally the internal cavity is almost filled, and a network resembling a sponge is produced. The enveloping capsule eventually ruptures and liberates fragments of the zoogloeal network, which reorganize into small groups interlinked by single cocci. Under unfavorable conditions the cocci are vacuolated, and sulfur is confined to the peripheral cytoplasm. Free cells are motile (*cf. Chromatium*). The total transformation observed by Winogradsky occurred in 40 days. The organisms contain bacteriochlorophyll and carotenoid pigments, and the latter predominate to color the cell masses various shades of red or purple. When growing in the presence of H_2S they deposit sulfur internally.

Type species: *Lamprocystis roseopersicina* (Kutzing) Schroeter.

NOTES: Only one species is described. (See also general notes, p. *96*.)

Amoebobacter (A.moe.bo.bac'ter) Winogradsky, 1888. *M p. 44*.

DIFFERENTIATING CHARACTERS: Unicellular, spherical, or rod-shaped organisms. At one stage of development cells are compressed into a compact mass, colored rose red, surrounded by a capsule composed of an inner, poorly refracting layer and an outer, strongly refracting layer. Placed in a favorable environment, the cyst cracks, and the cell mass slowly creeps out (1 to 2 days). The empty cyst remains unchanged for some time. The group of cells does not disperse but grows in an irregular, contoured mass. Whole families are motile. Most cells are spherical. Division occurs in only one direction. Cells may be compressed or freely separated in the nonencysted state. There are rarely more than 2 to 4 within a group in the colony. They are continually changing position and proximity in the colony. Internal colonial movement can occur without much lateral movement. Coordinated lateral movement is amoeboid. Single cells occasionally become isolated from the mass and then are drawn back. Masses ultimately may separate into smaller groups. No capsular material can be discerned in the families. Families can be penetrated by small motile bacteria with ease. Winogradsky considered the connection was via plasma threads but was unable to demonstrate them. He considered the dense, compact masses to occur in the presence of O_2, and the open structure, in the presence of H_2S. Individual cells or cell masses are apparently devoid of capsular material, although cells within the mass may be clearly separated in space. Bacteriochlorophyll and carotenoid pigments are contained, with the latter predominating to color the cell masses various shades of red or purple. When growing in the presence of H_2S they deposit sulfur internally.

Type species: *Amoebobacter roseus* Winogradsky.

NOTES: Three species have been described, two of which are spherical and one rod-shaped. Cell width varies from 0.5 to

3.5 μ, depending on the species. (See also general notes, p. *96*.)

Thiopolycoccus (Thi.o.po.ly. coc'cus) Winogradsky, 1888. *M p. 45.*

DIFFERENTIATING CHARACTERS: Unicellular, spherical, nonmotile organisms, approximately 1.2 μ in diameter. Growth occurs in the form of shapeless thick aggregates of small, spherical, vividly colored cells. They do not form hollow, spherical structures. The extremely smooth surface of the colony suggests a limiting capsular material, but no obvious capsule is visible. Eventually, growth, in the form of threads and flaps, appears on the surface, and cells become separated. Individual cells or cell masses are apparently devoid of capsular material, although cells within the mass may be clearly separated in space. Contain bacteriochlorophyll and carotenoid pigments, the latter predominating to color the cell masses various shades of red or purple. When growing in the presence of H_2S the organisms deposit sulfur internally.

Type species: *Thiopolycoccus ruber* Winogradsky.

NOTES: Only one species is described. (See also general notes, p. *96*.)

Thiospirillum (Thi.o.spi.ril'lum) Winogradsky, 1888. *M p. 46.*

DIFFERENTIATING CHARACTERS: Unicellular, spirally twisted* organisms, actively motile, with polar flagella. The width of the cells lies within the limits of 1 to 40 μ, depending on the species. Bacteriochlorophyll and carotenoid pigments are contained, with the latter predominating to color the cell masses various shades of red or purple. When growing in the presence of H_2S they deposit sulfur internally.

Type species: *Thiospirillum jenense* (Ehrenberg) Winogradsky.

NOTES: Five species are described, separated on the basis of size and color of the cell mass. None has been isolated. (See also general notes, p. *96*.)

---

* *Thiospirillum violaceum* is rarely more than a slightly bent rod and is indistinguishable from some forms of *Chromatium*.

Rhodothece (Rho.do.the'ce) Molisch, 1907. *M p. 50.* (Die Purpurbakterien, Jena, 1907, 19.)

DIFFERENTIATING CHARACTERS: Unicellular, spherical organisms, 1.8 to 2.5 μ in diameter, occurring singly, in pairs, or in short chains; nonmotile. Individual cells are capsulated and usually contain two gas vacuoles (aerosomes) per cell, which makes them buoyant and may give them a polygonal appearance. The organisms contain bacteriochlorophyll and carotenoid pigments; the latter predominate to color the cell masses various shades of red or purple. When growing in the presence of H_2S they deposit sulfur internally.

Type species: *Rhodothece pendens* Molisch.

NOTES: Only one species has been described. (See also general notes, p. *96*.)

Chromatium (Chro.ma'ti.um) Perty, 1852. *M p. 50.* (Zur Kenntniss kleinster Lebensformen, Bern, 1852, 174.)

DIFFERENTIATING CHARACTERS: Unicellular spherical to cylindrical organisms, the latter occasionally being curved. Rod-shaped cells are of uniform width throughout. The cells occur singly and are motile with polar flagella. They may be capsulated but do not form zoogloea. They contain bacteriochlorophyll and carotenoid pigments, the latter predominating to color the cell masses various shades of red or purple. When growing in the presence of H_2S they deposit sulfur internally.

Type species: *Chromatium okenii* Perty.

NOTES: Twelve species are described, the only differentiating feature being size. Width of the cells lies within the limits of 1 to 10 μ. In view of the effect of the environmental conditions on the size of such cells, the differentiation appears invalid. Although they are described as occurring singly, they form sheets over the surface of glass containers in which they are grown, particularly on the side exposed to light. The organisms can be cultured quite readily (see method of isolation for *Chromatium*). (See also general notes, p. *96*.)

Some recent papers on the physiology of

Chromatium, to which the reader is referred for further references, follow; see also under *Chlorobium:*

Bartsch, R. G., and Kamen, M. D., J. Biol. Chem., *235*, 1960, 825.

Fuller, R. C., and Kornberg, H. L., Biochem. J., *79*, 1961, 8–9P.

Fuller, R. C., Smillie, R. M., Sissler, E. C., and Kornberg, H. L., J. Biol. Chem., *236*, 1961, 2140.

Hurlbert, R. E., and Lascelles, J., J. Gen. Microbiol., *33*, 1963, 445.

Pfennig, N., Naturw., *5*, 1961, S. 136, 1.

Schlegel, H. G., Dtsch. Bot. Ges. Neue Folge, Nr. 1, 1961.

Schlegel, H. G., Arch. Mikrobiol., *42*, 1962, 110.

Schlegel, H. G., and Gottschalk, G., Angew. Chemie., *74*, 1962, 342.

Schlegel, H. G., and Pfennig, N., Arch. Mikrobiol., *38*, 1961, 1.

Taylor, J. J., Exp. Cell Res., *17*, 1959, 533.

Truper, H., Arch. Mikrobiol., *49*, 1964, 23.

Truper, H., Antonie van Leeuwenhoek, *30*, 1964, 385.

Truper, H., and Schlegel, H. G., Antonie van Leeuwenhoek, *30*, 1964, 225.

Rhabdomonas (Rhab.do.mo′nas) Cohn, 1875. *M p. 48.* (Beitr. Biol. Pflanz., *1*, Heft 3, 1875, 167.)

DIFFERENTIATING CHARACTERS: Unicellular, rod-shaped organisms of uneven width and length, often swollen, spindle-shaped, and filamentous. Cells occur singly. They are motile with polar flagella and contain bacteriochlorophyll and carotenoid pigments, with the latter predominating to color the cell masses various shades of red or purple. When growing in the presence of H₂S they deposit sulfur internally.

Type species: *Rhabdomonas rosea* Cohn.

NOTES: Three species have been described. They are differentiated on cell width and the presence or absence of calcium carbonate crystals in the cells. The organisms may be variants of *Chromatium*. The calcium carbonate may be only an environmental characteristic. (See also general notes, p. *96*.)

GREEN SULFUR BACTERIA

The following genera are all green or yellowish green and do not show the characteristic absorption band for bacteriochlorophyll at 590 mμ. They contain, so far as they have been examined, *chlorobium chlorophyll*, which has an absorption band in the infrared region at approximately 750 mμ. They grow under strictly anaerobic conditions in the presence of sulfide and with exposure to light. The sulfide is oxidized to sulfur, which is deposited *externally* (except with *Clathrochloris*). So far only one of these genera, *Chlorobium*, has been isolated.

Chlorobium (Chlo.ro′bi.um) Nadson, 1912. *M p. 62.* (Bull. Jard. Impér. Botan., St. Pétersburg, *12*, 1912, 64, Russian, 83, German.)

DIFFERENTIATING CHARACTERS: Unicellular, ovoid organisms, 0.7 to 0.9 μ by 1.5 μ, occurring singly or in chains and frequently embedded in mucus. They do not form characteristic aggregates. Nonmotile. Gram negative. Cell masses green because of the presence of chlorobium chlorophyll. (See p. *97* for the absorption spectrum of *Chlorobium*.) Oxidize H₂S, depositing sulfur outside the cell.

Type species: *Chlorobium limicola* Nadson.

NOTES: There are two species described in the *Manual* that are indistinguishable morphologically. Sulfur is oxidized to sulfate by both species. *Chlorobium thiosulfatophilum* Larsen will also oxidize thiosulfate, tetrathionate, and molecular hydrogen.

These organisms occur in marine and fresh water muds. Mass development of *Chlorobium limicola* occurs under conditions of high sulfide concentration and low pH.

The reader is referred to the following recent contributions on *Chlorobium* for other references:

Bicknell, A. K., J. Bacteriol., *63*, 1952, 145.

Cohen-Bazire, G., Pfennig, N., and Kunisawa, R., J. Cell Biol., *22*, 1964, 207.

Gibson, J., Biochem. J., *79*, 1960, 151.

Hughes, D. E., Conti, S. F., and Fuller, R. C., J. Bacteriol., *85*, 1963, 577.

Hulcher, F. H., and Conti, S. F., Biochem. Biophys. Res. Comm., *3*, 1960, 497.

Hoare, D. S., and Gibson, J., Biochem. J., *91*, 1964, 546.

Larsen, H., J. Bacteriol., *64*, 1952, 187.

Mandel, M., Bergendahl, J. C., and Pfennig, N., J. Bacteriol., *89*, 1965, 917.

Pelodictyon (Pe.lo.dic'ty.on) Lauterborn, 1913. *M p. 63*. (Allgem. botan. Z., *19*, 1913, 98.)

DIFFERENTIATING CHARACTERS: Unicellular, capsulated, spherical, or rod-shaped organisms, 0.5 to 1.5 by 2.4 μ, which may aggregate into characteristic net-like structures or in two or three dimensional masses in which the cells are arranged irregularly or in parallel strands. Nonmotile. Cell masses are yellowish green and contain a photosynthetic pigment, which is not plant chlorophyll or bacteriochlorophyll. The organisms are found in mud and stagnant water containing high concentrations of H_2S and exposed to light.

Type species: *Pelodictyon clathratiforme* (Szafer) Lauterborn.

NOTES: Three species are described in which differentiation is based on the arrangement of cells in the masses. Pleomorphic forms appear to be common.

AUTHOR'S NOTE: The difference between *P. aggregatum* and the mucoid growth of *Chlorobium limicola* is not obvious from the descriptions.

Clathrochloris (Clath.ro.chlo'ris) Geitler, 1925. *M p. 64*. (In Pascher, Die Süsswasserflora Deutschlands, Österr. u. Schweiz, Jena, *12*, 1925, 457.)

DIFFERENTIATING CHARACTERS: Unicellular, spherical organisms, 0.5 to 0.7 μ in diameter, occurring in loose, trellis-like aggregates. Nonmotile. Sulfide is oxidized and

sulfur is deposited inside the cells. Cell masses are yellowish green and contain a photosynthetic pigment.

Type species: *Clathrochloris sulphurica* (Szafer) Geitler.

NOTES: There is only one described species found in mud and stagnant water containing high concentrations of sulfide. The nature of the green pigment has not been described.

Chlorobacterium (Chlo.ro.bac.te'-ri.um) Lauterborn, 1915. *M p. 65*. (Verhandl. naturhist.-medizin. Ver., Heidelberg, N. F., *13*, 1915, 429.)

DIFFERENTIATING CHARACTERS: Unicellular, rod-shaped organisms, 0.5 by 2 to 5 μ, often slightly curved. Nonmotile. Found forming a covering over certain protozoan cells. Cells and cell masses are green and contain a photosynthetic pigment.

Type species: *Chlorobacterium symbioticum* Lauterborn.

NOTES: There is only one described species. Such an association between a green cell and a protozoan hardly constitutes valid grounds for the designation of a genus.

Found in pond water in Germany. No mention is made of H_2S in these ponds.

Chlorochromatium (Chlo.ro.chro.-ma'ti.um) Lauterborn, 1906. *M p. 65*. (Allgem. botan. Z., *19*, 1906, 196.)

DIFFERENTIATING CHARACTERS: Unicellular, rod-shaped organisms, 0.5 to 1.0 μ by 1 to 2.5 μ, attached in 4 to 6 rows to the surface of an actively motile, polar-flagellated bacterial cell to form a barrel-shaped aggregate. The aggregate measures 2.5 to 5 μ by 7 to 12 μ. Cells are green and contain a photosynthetic pigment, which is not plant chlorophyll or bacteriochlorophyll. They grow in the presence of H_2S, depositing sulfur outside the cells.

Type species: *Chlorochromatium aggregatum* Lauterborn.

NOTES: There is only one species. Unless it can be proved that the symbiosis (?) is obligatory, there appears little justification for recognition of this genus.

Found in mud and stagnant water.

Schlegel and Pfennig (Arch. Mikrobiol., *38*, 1961, 1) note the growth of *Chlorochromatium aggregatum* in raw cultures of Reyershauser lake water.

Cylindrogloea (Cyl.in.dro.gloe′a) Perfiliev, 1914. *M p. 66.* (Zhur. Mikrobiol., Epidemiol., Immunobiol., *1*, 1914, 223.)

DIFFERENTIATING CHARACTERS: Unicellular, rod-shaped organisms, 0.5 to 1.0 μ by 2 to 4 μ, forming a layer on the surface of a slime capsule surrounding a colorless, cylindrical, bacterial cell. The aggregate may measure 7 to 8 μ wide and up to 50 μ long and is surrounded by another layer of slime. Nonmotile. Cells are green and contain a photosynthetic pigment, which is not plant chlorophyll or bacteriochlorophyll. They grow in the presence of H_2S, depositing sulfur outside the cells.

Type species: *Cylindrogloea bacterifera* Perfiliev.

NOTES: There is only one species. Perfiliev emphasizes that the species designation is only a provisional one.

Found in mud and stagnant water.

RED, PURPLE, AND BROWN NON-SULFUR BACTERIA

The following genera contain bacteriochlorophyll and carotenoid pigments. The former gives an absorption band at 590 mμ in the intact cells and 774 mμ in alcoholic extracts.

They are all capable of growth anaerobically in the presence of suitable hydrogen donors and when *exposed to light*. Some species grow in the dark but only aerobically.

They do not oxidize H_2S (SH^-) and therefore do not deposit sulfur internally or externally.

Rhodopseudomonas (Rho.do.pseu.-do.mo′nas) Kluyver and van Niel, 1937, and van Niel, 1944. *M p. 53.* (Kluyver and van Niel, in Czurda and Maresch, Arch. Mikrobiol., *8*, 1937, 119; and van Niel, Bacteriol. Revs., *8*, 1944, 86.)

DIFFERENTIATING CHARACTERS: Unicellular, rod-shaped, or spherical organisms less than 2 μ wide; motile with polar flagella.

They do not aggregate in the form of radial colonies. Gram negative. They contain bacteriochlorophyll and carotenoid pigments, the latter predominating. They do not oxidize H_2S.

Type species: *Rhodopseudomonas palustris* (Molisch) van Niel.

NOTES: Four species, *R. palustris*, *R. gelatinosa*, *R. capsulata*, and *R. spheroides*, have been described in the *Manual*.

R. spheroides is predominantly spherical in all media.

R. capsulata is rod-shaped in media above pH 7.0 and spherical in more acid media. The other species are rod-shaped. All species show a considerable degree of pleomorphism, with the shape varying with the pH and the substrate. Pleomorphic forms are frequently nonmotile.

The width of cells varies from 0.5 μ up to 4 μ (*R. spheroides*). Capsulated forms are common. Growth occurs over a pH range of 6.0 to 8.5.

The color of the colonies varies with the conditions of growth and is affected by light, oxygen, and the nature of the carbon substrate. Anaerobic cultures of *R. capsulata*, *R. spheroides*, and *R. palustris* are yellowish brown, greenish brown, or reddish brown. All three of these species can be adapted to aerobic growth when colonies are distinctly red. Most cultures of *R. gelatinosa* will not grow aerobically. Anaerobic growth is pinkish.

Species other than *R. capsulata* may produce a water-soluble, bluish-red pigment, which is not a carotenoid.

Although capable of photosynthetic metabolism, the species are not autotrophic, being dependent on growth factors and usually on organic hydrogen donors.

Differentiation is based on morphological and nutritional characteristics.

(See also methods of isolation.)

The following are some recent papers on *Rhodopseudomonas*, to which the reader is referred for further references:

Burnham, B. F., and Lascelles, J., Biochem. J., *87*, 1963, 462.

Clayton, R. K., J. Bacteriol., *82*, 1961, 314.

Clayton, R. K., and Smith, C., Biochem. Biophys. Res. Comm., *3*, 1960, 143.

Cooper, R., Biochem. J., *89*, 1963, 100.

Gibson, K. D., Neuberger, A., and Tait, G. H., Biochem. J., *88*, 1963, 325.

Gibson, K. D., Biochem. J., *93*, 1964, 21P.

Gibson, K. D., J. Bacteriol., *90*, 1965, 1059.

Griffiths, M., J. Gen. Microbiol., *27*, 1962, 427.

Hoare, D. S., and Heath, H., Biochem. J., *73*, 1959, 679.

Jones, O. T. G., Biochem. J., *86*, 1963, 429.

Jones, O. T. G., Biochem. J., *88*, 1963, 335.

Jones, O. T. G., Biochem. J., *89*, 1963, 182.

Jones, O. T. G., Biochem. J., *91*, 1964, 572.

Lascelles, J., J. Gen. Microbiol., *23*, 1960, 487.

Lascelles, J., J. Gen. Microbiol., *23*, 1960, 499.

Neuberger, A., and Tait, G. H., Biochem. J., *90*, 1964, 607.

Siegel, J. M., J. Biol. Chem., *228*, 1957, 41.

Sistrom, W. R., J. Gen. Microbiol., *22*, 1960, 778.

Willard, J. M., Schulman, M., and Gibbs, M., Nature, London, *206*, 1965, 4980.

Rhodospirillum (Rho.do.spi.ril'lum) Molisch, 1907, emend. van Niel 1944. *M* p. *58*. (Molisch, Die Purpurbakterien, Jena, 1907, 24; van Niel, Bacteriol. Revs., *8*, 1944, 86.)

DIFFERENTIATING CHARACTERS: Unicellular, spiral-shaped organisms less than 2 μ wide; motile with polar flagella. Gram negative. Contain bacteriochlorophyll and carotenoid pigments, the latter predominating. They do not oxidize H_2S.

Type species: *Rhodospirillum rubrum* (Esmarch) Molisch.

NOTES: Four species have been described, *R. rubrum*, *R. fulvum*, *R. molischianum*, and *R. photometricum*.

The depth and amplitude of the spirals vary with the species and conditions of growth. Half spirals are frequently produced. A cyclic development similar to that described by Williams and Rittenberg (Intern. Bull. Bacteriol. Nomen. Taxon., *7*, 1957) for the genus *Spirillum* has not yet been reported for the genus *Rhodospirillum*.

The colonies of *R. rubrum* are a deep red. In addition to the band at 590 mμ for the bacteriochlorophyll, this species shows another band at 550 mμ for spirilloxanthin, which is absent from the other species, which have bands at 520 mμ and 485 mμ for carotenoids. The colonies of other species are reddish brown to orange.

Gelatin is not liquified.

Thiosulfate is not oxidized.

Except for *R. fulvum*, glucose and other carbohydrates and polyalcohols are *not* suitable substrates.

All species oxidize ethanol and certain fatty and hydroxy acids and amino acids.

None of the species is capable of strictly autotrophic growth.

They are all strict anaerobes with the exception of *R. rubrum*.

The following are recent papers relevant to the systematics of *Rhodospirillum:*

Boatman, E. S., J. Cell Biol., *20*, 1964, 297.

Cohen-Bazire, G., and Kunisawa, R., J. Cell Biol., *16*, 1963, 401.

Giesbrecht, P., and Drews, G., Arch. Mikrobiol., *43*, 1962, 152.

Hickman, D. D., and Frenkel, A. N., J. biophys. biochem. Cytol., *6*, 1960, 277.

Oda, T., and Horio, T., Exp. Cell Res., *34*, 1964, 414.

Pijper, A., and Steynberg, A. L., Path. Microbiol., *26*, 1963, 274.

Vernon, L. P., J. Biol. Chem., *234*, 1959, 1883.

Pfennig, N., Eimhjellen, K. E , and Jensen, S. L., Arch. Mikrobiol., *51*, 1965, 258.

Vannielia (Van.ni.el′i.a or Van.-niel′i.a) Pringsheim, 1955. (J. Gen. Microbiol., *13*, 1955, 285.)

This genus does not appear in the seventh edition of the *Manual*. It has recently been described as a pink polar flagellate, which, in natural media, aggregates into small radial colonies. Pringsheim failed, however, to obtain such colonies in peptone media. This is possibly another species of *Rhodopseudomonas*.

Type species: *Vannielia aggregata* Pringsheim.

Rhodomicrobium (Rho.do.mi.cro′-bi.um) Duchow and Douglas, 1949. *M p. 277*. (J. Bacteriol., *58*, 1949, 409.)

DIFFERENTIATING CHARACTERS: Oval to rod-shaped cells, which reproduce by producing a long, thin (0.1 to 0.2 μ), tubular process, from which a new cell is produced. The tubular process may branch. Individual cells are motile with polar flagella. Gram negative. They contain bacteriochlorophyll and carotenoid pigments, with the latter predominating. They do not oxidize H_2S.

Type species: *Rhodomicrobium vannielii* Duchow and Douglas.

NOTES: Only one species has been recorded. The mature cells are ovoid and measure 1.2 by 2.8 μ. One to three daughter cells may be produced by branching of the tubular outgrowths. A thickening appears in the tube between the mother and the daughter cell.

Colonies are a dark orange-red.

Growth occurs anaerobically in the light and in the presence of a suitable organic hydrogen donor, such as ethanol, propanol, butanol, acetate, propionate, butyrate, valerate, caproate, lactate, and malate.

Glucose, mannose, fructose, mannitol, citrate, tartrate, formate, thiosulfate, and sulfide are not utilized.

The optimal temperature is 25° to 31° C.

The genus *Rhodomicrobium* has a counterpart in the colorless *Hyphomicrobium*. (It should be noted that Griffiths and Stanier, J. Gen. Microbiol., *14*, 1956, 698, have produced colorless, nonphotosynthetic variants of *Rhodopseudomonas* by exposure to ultraviolet light.)

The following are some recent papers on *Rhodomicrobium* to which the reader is referred for further references:

Boatman, E. S., and Douglas, H. C., J. Biophys. Biochem. Cytol., *11*, 1961, 469.

Conti, S. F., and Hirsch, P., Arch. Mikrobiol., *48*, 1964, 358.

Conti, S. F., and Hirsch, P., J. Bacteriol., *89*, 1964, 503.

Douglas, H. C., and Wolfe, R. S., J. Bacteriol., *78*, 1959, 597.

Hirsch, P., and Conti, S. F., Arch. Mikrobiol., *48*, 1963, 339.

Zavarsin (Mikrobiologia, *30*, 1961, 954) reviews the stalked bacteria and records a genus **Pedomicrobium** having a morphology similar to *Rhodomicrobium* but found heavily encrusted with manganese.

NONPHOTOSYNTHETIC ORGANISMS

Hyphomicrobium (Hy.pho.mi.cro′-bi.um) Stutzer and Hartleb, 1898. *M p. 277*. (Mitt. Landwirtsch. Inst. d. k. Univ. Breslau, 1898.)

DIFFERENTIATING CHARACTERS: Colorless, spherical to ovoid organisms, 0.5 by 1.0 μ when mature; motile with a single polar flagellum; reproduce by the produc-

tion of a tubular outgrowth, 0.2 to 0.3 μ wide, on the end of which a daughter cell is formed. The tubular outgrowths may be simple or branched. Daughter cells are initially spherical but later become ovoid.

Type species: *Hyphomicrobium vulgare* Stutzer and Hartleb, 1898.

NOTES: A single species is described. The

predominant growth habit is a dense group of cells from which filaments radiate outwards.

The organism grows well on a formate-nitrate agar but poorly on gelatin or peptone agar.

Formate, formaldehyde, methanol, acetate, and lactate are suitable carbon sources.

Aerobic; optimal temperature 25° C. Found in soil.

For recent references see *Rhodomicrobium* and Hirsch and Conti (Arch. Mikrobiol., *48*, 1963, 339, and *48*, 1964, 358). These papers give an excellent description of the mode of growth and nutrition of *Hyphomicrobium.* Leifson (Antonie van Leeuwenhoek, *30*, 1964, 249) describes a new species, *H. neptunium.*

Nitrosomonas (Ni.tro.so.mon'as) Winogradsky, 1890. *M p. 68.* (Ann. inst. Pasteur, *4*, 1890, 257.)

DIFFERENTIATING CHARACTERS: Unicellular, colorless, ovoid to rod-shaped organisms less than 2 μ wide; motile with a single polar flagellum; not capsulated; Gram negative; *aerobic;* do not oxidize ferrous iron or deposit iron oxides in or on the cells; do not grow on meat extract agar or other complex organic media; strict autotrophs, which use carbon dioxide as the sole source of carbon and derive their energy from the oxidation of ammonia to nitrite.

Type species: *Nitrosomonas europea* Winogradsky.

NOTES: Two species have been described (*N. europea* and *N. monocella*). The optimal pH is approximately 8.0 to 9.0, with little or no growth below pH 7.0.

Found in soils.

The following are some recent papers on *Nitrosomonas* to which the reader is referred for further references. For comments on the validity of the other nitrifying genera, see particularly the paper by Engel:

Anderson, J. H., Biochem. J., *91*, 1964, 8.

Anderson, J. H., Biochem. J., *92*, 1964, 1c.

Burge, W. D., Malavolta, E., and Delwiche, C. C., J. Bacteriol., *85*, 1963, 106.

Engel, M. S., J. Bacteriol., *81*, 1961, 833.

Schoberl, P., and Engel, H., Arch. Mikrobiol., *48*, 1964, 393.

Yoshida, T., and Alexander, M., Can. J. Microbiol., *10*, 1964, 923.

Nitrosococcus (Ni.tro.so.coc'cus) Winogradsky, 1892. *M p. 69.* (Arch. sci. biol., St. Pétersburg, *1*, 1892, 127.)

DIFFERENTIATING CHARACTERS: Unicellular, colorless, spherical organisms less than 2 μ in diameter; Gram positive; *aerobic;* do not deposit oxides of iron in or on the cells; strict autotrophs, which will not grow in organic media but use carbon dioxide as the sole source of carbon and obtain their energy from the oxidation of ammonia to nitrite.

Type species: *Nitrosococcus nitrosus* (Migula) Buchanan.

NOTES: Only one species is described. Cells measure 1.5 to 1.7 μ in diameter and are surrounded by a thick cell membrane. Motility has not been demonstrated. Small, turbid, yellowish colonies are produced on silica gel.

See notes to *Nitrosomonas.*

Nitrosospira (Ni.tro.so.spi'ra) S. Winogradsky, 1931. *M p. 70.* (Compt. rend., *192*, 1931, 1004.)

DIFFERENTIATING CHARACTERS: Rigid, unicellular, colorless, spiral-shaped organisms less than 2 μ wide; *aerobic;* autotrophic, with carbon dioxide used as the sole source of carbon and energy obtained by the oxidation of ammonia to nitrite.

Type species: *Nitrosospira briensis* S. Winogradsky and H. Winogradsky, 1933.

NOTES: Two species are described. In both species the spirals are very closely wound and may be up to 20 μ long. Motility is not recorded but is presumably by means of flagella. Optimal pH 7.0 to 7.2.

Found in soil.

See notes to *Nitrosomonas.*

Nitrosocystis (Ni.tro.so.cys'tis) S. Winogradsky, 1931. *M p. 70.* (Compt. rend., *192*, 1931, 1003.)

DIFFERENTIATING CHARACTERS: Unicellular, colorless, rod-shaped organisms less than 2 μ wide; capsulated and aggregated in zoogloea, which become encysted; motile with polar flagella or nonmotile; *aerobic;* strict autotrophs, which will not grow on meat infusion agar or other complex organic media; carbon dioxide used as the sole source of carbon and energy obtained from the oxidation of ammonia to nitrite; do not oxidize ferrous iron or deposit iron oxide in or on the cells.

Type species: *Nitrosocystis javanensis* (Winogradsky) Starkey.

NOTES: Two species are described. Motility is not described for one species (*N. coccoides*).

Winogradsky differentiated *Nitrosomonas* from *Nitrosocystis* on the formation of soft (or clear) colonies by the former and hard (or dark) colonies by the latter. Considerable doubt has been cast on the validity of this differentiation by Meikeljohn (Nature, *16*, 1951, 56, and J. Soil Sci., *4*, 1953, 62), who states that the nature of the colonies is largely determined by conditions of culture. Kingma Boltjes (Arch. Mikrobiol., *6*, 1935, 69) claims to have obtained both types from single cell isolates of *Nitrosomonas*. Imsenecki (Nature, *157*, 1946, 877) and Grace (Nature, *168*, 1951, 117) suggest that the organisms are myxobacteria or cultures are contaminated with myxobacteria.

For a recent study on the structure of *Nitrosocystis* see Murray and Watson (J. Bacteriol., *89*, 1965, 1954).

Both species were isolated from soils.

See notes to *Nitrosomonas*.

Nitrosogloea (Ni.tro.so.gloe'a) H. Winogradsky, 1935. *M p. 71.* (Compt. rend., *200*, 1935, 1887.)

DIFFERENTIATING CHARACTERS: Unicellular, colorless, coccoid to rod-shaped organisms less than 2 μ wide; capsulated and aggregated into zoogloeae, which do not become encysted; *aerobic;* strict autotrophs, which will not grow on meat infusion agar or other complex organic media; use carbon dioxide as the sole source

of carbon and obtain their energy by the oxidation of ammonia to nitrite. Do not oxidize ferrous iron or deposit iron oxides in or on the cells.

Type species: *Nitrosogloea merismoides* H. Winogradsky.

NOTES: Three species are recorded, differentiated apparently on morphology and colonial characters. Motility is not stated. Cells may be arranged in chains or at random in the zoogloea.

These may also be only a growth form of *Nitrosomonas*.

See notes to *Nitrosomonas*.

Nitrobacter (Ni.tro.bac'ter) Winogradsky, 1892. *M p. 72.* (Arch. sci. biol., St. Pétersburg, *1*, 1892, 127.)

DIFFERENTIATING CHARACTERS: Unicellular, colorless, rod-shaped organisms less than 2 μ wide; do not form zoogloea; motile by means of a single polar flagellum or nonmotile; *aerobic;* strict autotrophs, which do not grow on meat infusion agar or other complex organic media; use carbon dioxide as the sole source of carbon and obtain their energy by the oxidation of nitrite to nitrate. Do not oxidize ferrous iron or deposit oxides of iron on or in the cells.

Type species: *Nitrobacter winogradskyi* Winslow *et al.*

NOTES: Two species are described. The Gram stain is variable. On silica gel or washed agar media the colonies are minute and take 7 to 10 days to develop. They are, on the surface of media, frequently only one cell deep and are clear to slightly brownish. Growth is inhibited by organic substances (particularly of a nitrogenous nature) and by ammonium ions in an alkaline medium (*N. winogradskyi*). Limits of growth, pH 6.6 to 10.0 (*N. agilis*). Optimal temperature range 25° to 28° C.

Found in soils.

The following are some recent papers on *Nitrobacter* to which the reader is referred for further references:

Aleem, M. I. H., and Alexander, M., App. Microbiol., *8*, 1960, 80.

Butt, W. D., and Lees, H., Biochem. J., *76*, 1960 425.

Laudelot, H., and L. van Tichelen, J. Bacteriol., *79*, 1960, 39.

Malavolta, E., Delwiche, C. C., and Burge, W. D., Biochem. Biophys. Res. Comm., *2*, 1960, 445.

Schöberl, P., and Engel, H., Arch. Mikrobiol., *48*, 1964, 393.

Nitrocystis (Ni.tro.cys'tis) H. Winogradsky, 1935. *M p. 73.* (Trans. Third Cong. Intern. Soil Sci., Oxford, *1*, 1935, 139.)

DIFFERENTIATING CHARACTERS: Unicellular, colorless, rod-shaped organisms less than 2 μ wide; capsulated and aggregated into zoogloea; motility is not recorded; *aerobic;* strict autotrophs, which will not grow on meat infusion agar or other complex organic media; use carbon dioxide as the sole source of carbon and obtain their energy from the oxidation of nitrite to nitrate; do not oxidize ferrous iron or deposit oxides of iron on or in the cells.

Type species: *Nitrocystis sarcinoides* H. Winogradsky.

NOTES: Two species are recorded. Cells of the type species are grouped in sarcina-like packets. Colonies on silica gel are amber to yellow and wart-like. Old colonies shrink to hard sand-like grains. Both species have been isolated from activated sludge. The strictly autotrophic nature stated above is presumed. No mention of it is made in the *Manual*.

Methanomonas (Me.tha.no.mo'nas) Orla-Jensen, 1909. *M p. 74.* (Zentr. Bakteriol. Parasitenk., Abt. II, *22*, 1909, 311.)

DIFFERENTIATING CHARACTERS: Unicellular, nonphotosynthetic, rod-shaped organisms, 0.6 by 1.0 μ; motile with a polar flagellum; Gram negative; *aerobic;* grow autotrophically in a mineral salts medium with ammonia nitrogen and under an atmosphere containing methane, oxygen, and carbon dioxide, oxidizing the methane to carbon dioxide and water. Methane and methanol the only carbon compounds used.

Type species: *Methanomonas methanica* (Sohngen) Orla-Jensen.

NOTES: The above information is taken from a paper by Dworkin and Foster (J. Bacteriol., *72*, 1956, 646). According to these authors, Sohngen's isolates used a number of organic substrates, all of which failed to support growth of their isolates. Foster* points out, however, that the claims made for growth factor requirements in the paper cited above are invalid. The organisms will grow in a purely mineral medium. See Methods, p. *217*.

The optimal gas phase is one containing methane, 10 to 90 per cent; oxygen, 15 per cent; and CO_2, 0.3 per cent.

The organism produces a pink pellicle on liquid media. The pigment is insoluble in water, soluble in *n*-hexane, chloroform, and ether. The absorption spectrum of a chloroform extract has a clear maximum at 503 mμ and has properties of carotenoids.

See also Harrington and Kallio, Can. J. Microbiol., *6*, 1960, 1; and Kallio and Harrington, J. Bacteriol., *80*, 1960, 321.

Hydrogenomonas (Hy.dro.ge.no.mon'as) Orla-Jensen, 1909. *M p. 75.* (Zentr. Bakteriol. Parasitenk., Abt. II, *22*, 1909, 311.)

DIFFERENTIATING CHARACTERS: Unicellular, straight, rod-shaped organisms less than 2 μ in width; colorless or yellowish but not photosynthetic; motile by means of polar flagella† or nonmotile; *aerobic;* Gram negative; facultative autotrophs, which grow readily on organic media but are able to grow in a mineral medium with carbon dioxide as the sole source of carbon and energy obtained by oxidizing hydrogen to water.

Type species: *Hydrogenomonas pantotropha* (Kaserer, 1906) Orla-Jensen, 1909.

NOTES: Four species are described in the *Manual*. Rods are 0.3 to 0.5 μ by 1 to 2 μ. Two of the four species are recorded as Gram negative. Two species are capsulated. Colonies on inorganic media are butyrous

---

* Personal communication.

† *H. pantotropha* and *H. eutropha* have recently been shown to be peritrichously flagellated (Report of the Pseudomonas Subcommittee of the ICNB, Moscow, 1966).

or mucoid, depending on the species, and are colorless (one species) or slightly yellowish (three). In liquid mineral salts media pellicles are formed by three of the four species.

Hydrogen is oxidized, but CO_2 is not fixed when organic hydrogen donors have been used in respiration experiments with *H. facilis*. There are numerous bacteria that can oxidize hydrogen in respiratory experiments but are incapable of autotrophic growth at the expense of H_2 and CO_2 in mineral media. Growth and not hydrogen oxidation is therefore the cardinal characteristic.

The two species that have been described more fully have failed to produce acid from carbohydrates, are indole negative and H_2S negative, and produce slight alkalinity in litmus milk.

Lack of acid formation in carbohydrates and production of alkalinity in protein media are general characteristics of the polar flagellate heterotrophs. There are exceptions.

Found in soil and water. Optimal temperature, 28° C. The optimal gas ratio for growth is approximately 10 per cent CO_2, 30 per cent air, and 60 per cent hydrogen.

For information on *Hydrogenomonas* see the following:

Crouch, D. J., and Ramsey, H. H., J. Bacteriol., *84*, 1962, 1340.

De Cicco, B. T., and Umbreit, W., J. Bacteriol., *88*, 1964, 1590.

Gottschalk, G., Arch. Mikrobiol., *49*, 1964, 96.

Hirsch, P., Georgiev, G., and Schlegel, H., Nature, London, *197*, 1963, 313.

McFadden, B. A., and Homann, H. R., J. Bacteriol., *86*, 1963, 971.

Packer, L., and Vishniac, W., J. Bacteriol., *70*, 1955, 216.

Schindler, J., and Schlegel, H., Biochem. Zeitschr., *339*, 1963, 154.

Schindler, J., Arch. Mikrobiol., *49*, 1964, 236.

Schlegel, H. G., Kaltwasser, H., and Gottschalk, G., Arch. Mikrobiol., *38*, 1961, 209.

Schlegel, H. G., Gottschalk, G., and von Bartha, R., Nature, London, *191*, 1961, 463.

Schlegel, H. G., and von Bartha, R., Zeitschr. Naturforschung, *16*, 1961, 777.

Carboxydomonas (Car.box.y.do.-mon'as) Orla-Jensen, 1909. *M p. 77.* (Zentr. Bakteriol. Parasitenk., Abt. II, *22*, 1909, 311.)

DIFFERENTIATING CHARACTERS: Unicellular, colorless, straight, rod-shaped organisms less than 2 μ wide; nonmotile; capable of growth in a mineral salts medium with *carbon monoxide* used as the sole source of carbon.

Type species: *Carboxydomonas oligocarbophilus* (Beijerinck and van Delden, 1903) Orla-Jensen, 1909.

NOTES: There is considerable doubt about the identity of this organism. Kistner (Koninkl. Ned. Akad. Wetenschap., Proc. Ser. C, *56*, 1953, No. 4) has shown that species of *Hydrogenomonas* can oxidize carbon monoxide. (For more detailed comments see the *Manual.*)

Thiobacterium (Thi.o.bac.te'ri.um) Janke, 1924. *M p. 79.* (Allgem. Tech. Mikrobiol., Teil I, 1924, 68.)

DIFFERENTIATING CHARACTERS: Unicellular, rod-shaped organisms, 0.3 to 15 μ by 2 to 5 μ, which grow in colonies on the surface of water containing sulfide and deposit sulfur either inside or outside the cells. One species produces a bladder-like colony with cells embedded in the surface. Motility has not been observed.

Type species: *Thiobacterium bovista* Janke.

NOTES: Three species have been described. Colonies floating on water are white by reflected light and black by transmitted light.

AUTHOR'S NOTE: These organisms need closer examination. Oxidation of sulfide at the water surface may account for the appearance of sulfur in the colonies but not in the cells.

Macromonas (Mac.ro.mo'nas) Utermöhl and Koppe, 1923. *M p. 80.* (Verhandl.

Intern. Ver. f. Theoret, u. angew. Limnologie, 1923, 86.)

DIFFERENTIATING CHARACTERS: Large, unicellular, cylindrical, pear-shaped or slightly curved rods, 3 to 14 μ wide. Actively motile with a single polar flagellum. They contain large spherules of calcium carbonate and possibly oxidize sulfide, depositing sulfur inside the cells.

The presence of $CaCO_3$ may be dependent upon an environment rich in Ca^{++}.

Type species: *Macromonas mobilis* (Lauterborn) Utermöhl and Koppe.

NOTES: Two species are described, which differ mainly in size. Found in a fresh water environment containing sulfide and calcium.

Thiovulum (Thi.o'vu.lum) Hinze, 1913. *M p. 81*. (Ber. deut. botan. Ges., *31*, 1913, 195.)

DIFFERENTIATING CHARACTERS: Unicellular, spherical to ovoid organisms, 5 to 20 μ in diameter, with the cytoplasm compressed in one end of the cell. Sulfur is deposited in the cytoplasm. The cells have an extremely rapid darting motion in liquids suggestive of flagella. They are found in sea water over decomposing organic matter liberating H_2S, where growth occurs in the form of a tenacious web in a zone of critical H_2S-O_2 concentration.

Type species: *Thiovulum majus* Hinze.

NOTES: There is only one described species.

E. Fauré-Fremiet and C. Rouiller (Exptl. Cell Research, *14*, 1958, 29) gave some excellent micrographs of sections of *Thiovulum*, which confirmed its bacterial nature, but no flagella could be found. Instead, a peculiar fibrillar polar apparatus was discovered; its true function is not understood.

De Boer, la Rivière, and Houwink (Antonie van Leeuwenhoek, *27*, 1961, 447) succeeded in demonstrating peritrichous flagella and provide further evidence of the fine structure of the cells. La Rivière (in Symposium on Marine Microbiology, edited by C. H. Oppenheimer, Charles C Thomas, Publisher) describes the cultivation and properties of *Thiovulum majus*. Sulfur inclusions in the cells are orthorhombic.

Thiospira (Thi.o.spi'ra) Vislouch, 1914. *M p. 82*. (J. Microbiologie, *1*, 1914, 50.)

DIFFERENTIATING CHARACTERS: Rigid, unicellular, curved organisms, 6 to 50 μ long, actively motile with a polar flagellum. Sulfur is deposited inside the cells.

Type species: *Thiospira winogradskyi* (Omelianski) Vislouch.

NOTES: Two species are described. They differ in size and distribution of the sulfur granules. Although the name suggests a spiral axis, there is little evidence of this in the descriptions or illustrations, which suggest only a curvature in the rods. They are probably anaerobic.

Found in curative muds and sea water.

Thiobacillus (Thi.o.ba.cil'lus) Beijerinck, 1904. *M p. 83*. (Zentr. Bakteriol. Parasitenk., Abt. II, 11, 1904, 593.)

DIFFERENTIATING CHARACTERS: The genus is divisible into two groups, the strict autotrophs and facultative autotrophs.

The *strict autotrophs* are unicellular, colorless, straight, rod-shaped organisms; motile with polar flagella or nonmotile; Gram negative; *aerobic;* will not grow on meat extract agar or other complex organic media; carbon dioxide used as the sole source of carbon, and their energy is obtained by the oxidation of thiosulfate.

The *facultative autotrophs* differ from strict autotrophs in their ability to grow on organic media.

Type species: *Thiobacillus thioparus* Beijerinck.

NOTES: Nine species are recorded. The Gram stain is not recorded for two species. Cells measure 0.5 by 1 to 3 μ except *T. coprolyticus* (which measures 0.1 to 0.2 μ by 6 to 8 μ); some species are motile with polar flagella, others are nonmotile.

Five species are acknowledged as strict autotrophs; three are facultative. The facultative autotrophs give a moderate to copious growth on nutrient agar. No acid production from carbohydrates is reported.

All species oxidize thiosulfate with sulfate as one of the end products and can utilize CO_2 as the sole source of carbon. Species differentiation is based on the nature of sulfur compounds oxidized and the products of thiosulfate oxidation.

Those species which oxidize S^0 are all strict autotrophs, and the end product is only sulfuric acid. The oxidation of S^0 is associated with a fall in pH, the extent of which is determined by the pH tolerance of the cells.

H_2S is oxidized by several but not all species. Species that oxidize H_2S will tolerate 200 p.p.m. H_2S mixed with air. One per cent H_2S in air is toxic. The H_2S is oxidized to sulfuric acid with an associated fall in pH.

Pellicle formation in liquid thiosulfate media is usually associated with the production of sulfur.

Oxidation of thiosulfate follows four different pathways as either one- or two-step reactions.

A. $6 Na_2S_2O_3 + 5 O_2 \rightarrow$

$$4 Na_2SO_4 + 2 Na_2S_4O_6$$

$2 Na_2S_4O_6 + 6 H_2O + 7 O_2 \rightarrow$

$$2 Na_2SO_4 + 6 H_2SO_4$$

Tetrathionate is formed and reoxidized. Curiously, two of the organisms that do this, *T. concretivorus* and *T. thiooxidans*, cannot oxidize tetrathionate alone. *T. neapolitanus* will oxidize the tetrathionate.

There is a fall in pH

B. $5 Na_2S_2O_3 + H_2O + 4 O_2 \rightarrow$

$$5 Na_2SO_4 + H_2SO_4 + 4 S$$

$2 S + 3 O_2 + 2 H_2O \rightarrow 2 H_2SO_4$

brought about by *T. thioparus*. There is a fall in pH

C. $Na_2S_2O_3 + 2 O_2 + H_2O \rightarrow$

$$Na_2SO_4 + H_2SO_4$$

brought about by *T. novellus*—a faculta-

tive autotroph. There is a fall in pH

D. $2 NA_2S_2O_3 + H_2O + \frac{1}{2} O_2 \rightarrow$

$$Na_2S_4O_6 + 2 NaOH$$

brought about by some facultative autotrophs. There is a rise in pH, sometimes followed by a slight fall to the original value.

Ammonia nitrogen is used by all organisms. Nitrate nitrogen is either used, not used, or is toxic. NO_3 is reduced to N_2 by *T. denitrificans*.

Colonies on silica gel or washed thiosulfate agar are small and colorless, or, with species precipitating S^0 from the oxidation of thiosulfate, they may be yellowish or white.

T. ferrooxidans on media containing ferrous iron becomes dark brown from the oxidation of the ferrous to ferric iron at low pH. Other species do not deposit iron about the cells.

Pseudomonas (Pseu.do′mo.nas or Pseu.do.mo′nas) Migula, 1894. *M p. 89.* (Arb. bakteriol. Inst. Karlsruhe, *1*, 1894, 237.)

DIFFERENTIATING CHARACTERS: Unicellular, nonphotosynthetic, nonsporing, rod-shaped organisms less than 2 μ wide; arranged singly; motile with polar flagella or nonmotile (rare); Gram negative; aerobic; heterotrophic; oxidative; acid only produced from carbohydrates.

They do not oxidize ethanol to acetic acid, oxidize thiosulfate autotrophically, produce alcohol from glucose, or metabolize alkylamines.

Type species: *Pseudomonas aeruginosa* (Schroeter) Migula.

NOTES: The genus is the subject of intensive re-examination, and amended descriptions have appeared for several species (see references). Species that have been retained in the genus have a DNA base composition (GC%) of 60 to 67.

In the *Manual* 149 species are described, most of which are ovoid to short rods, motile with a single polar flagellum or having lophotrichous flagella. Only 6 species are recorded as nonmotile.

The majority of species will grow in a mineral salts medium with ammoniacal nitrogen and a simple carbon source. Only a few require aminonitrogen or growth factors (*e.g.*, *P. pseudomallei*). They usually grow well on peptone media, producing entire, translucent, butyrous low convex to umbonate colonies 1 to 3 mm. in diameter in 24 hours.

A large number of species produce water-soluble and sometimes fluorescent pigments (*e.g.*, pyocyanin, fluorescin, chlororaphin), which diffuse into the medium and leave the colonies an off-white in color. Pigmentation is not a constant feature and varies with the medium. *P. iodinum* produces a purple pigment, whereas *P. indoloxidans* produces blue crystals of indigotin from indole. Soluble red pigments are occasionally produced.

Pyocyanin is a "redox" indicator, which becomes colorless in the reduced state. In liquid media only the upper layer may appear bluish green. On shaking, the dye re-oxidizes.

For a recent paper on pigments, see Wasserman (App. Microbiol., *13*, 1965, 175).

The genus is essentially oxidative. Species examined all oxidize glucose to gluconic acid, 2-ketogluconic acid, and other derivatives. In liquid media the limited oxygen supply results in a slow acid production, which in peptone media may be obscured by a more rapid production of ammonia.

Among substances attacked are cellulose (by six species), agar (by one), hexoses, pentoses, mono-, di-, and tri-carboxylic acids, hydroxy acids, and various hydrocarbons, including kerosene and gasoline. Lactose is rarely attacked (27/132).* Gas is not produced except by *P. petasitis*.

The majority actively attack amino acids, peptones, and some proteins, particularly gelatin, which is hydrolyzed by

* The number of species positive over the number tested.

99/148 species. Coagulated blood serum is liquefied by 9/11 species.

Indole is produced by 24/125.
Starch is hydrolyzed by 36/91.
Fats are hydrolyzed by 15/35.

Marine species require about 3 per cent added salt but are not strongly halophilic.

Nitrite is produced from nitrate by 60/127 and nitrogen by 5/127.

The organisms are essentially oxygen dependent, although this is not obligatory. Alternative hydrogen acceptors, such as nitrate and malate, are reduced by some species in the absence of oxygen, the former giving rise via nitrite to ammonia, nitrous oxide, or nitrogen gas.

At least half the species in the genus and possibly all of them are found in soil or water. Ninety of the 149 recorded species are pathogenic to plants. Two species, *P. aeruginosa* and *P. pseudomallei*, are animal pathogens. *P. aeruginosa* is also a plant pathogen and occurs in water and soils.

The heterogenous nature of the genus is indicated by no fewer than 22 entries in the key.

Extensive reviews of *Pseudomonas* and related genera were published by De Ley (Ann. Rev. Microbiol., *18*, 1964, 17) and by Stanier *et al.* (1966), Mandel (1966), and Redfearn *et al.* (1966), to which the reader is referred. The following are papers omitted from, or more recent than, De Ley's publication, which are of systematic interest. Numerous other papers have been published:

Alford, J. A., J. Bacteriol., *79*, 1960, 591.

Anthony, C., and Zatman, L. J., Biochem. J., *92*, 1964, 609.

Anthony, C., and Zatman, L. J., Biochem. J., *92*, 1964, 614.

Ayers, W. A., and Papavizas, G. C., App. Microbiol., *11*, 1963, 533.

Buck, J. D., Meyers, S. P., and Leifson, E., J. Bacteriol., *86*, 1963, 1125.

Colwell, R. R., Intern. Bull. Bacteriol. Nomen. Taxon., *15*, 1965, 87.

Davey, B. B., and Turner, M., J. App. Bacteriol., *24*, 1961, 78.

Frank, H., J. Bacteriol., *84*, 1962, 68.

Hansen, A. J., Weeks, O. B., and Colwell, R. R., J. Bacteriol., *89*, 1965, 752.

Lautrop, H., and Jensen, O., Acta Path. Microbiol., Scand., *60*, 1964, 588.

Liston, J., Wiebe, W., and Colwell, R. R., J. Bacteriol., *85*, 1963, 1061.

Málek, I., Radochová, M., and Lysenko, O., J. Gen. Microbiol., *33*, 1963, 349.

Mandel, M., J. Gen. Microbiol., *43*, 1966, 273.

Moore, H. B., and Pickett, M. J., Can. J. Microbiol., *6*, 1960, 35.

Palleroni, N. J., and Doudoroff, M., J. Bacteriol., *89*, 1965, 264.

Redfearn, M. S., Palleroni, N. J., and Stanier, R. Y., J. Gen. Microbiol., *43*, 1966, 293.

Stanier, R. Y., Palleroni, N. J., and Doudoroff, M., J. Gen. Microbiol., *43*, 1966, 159.

Tomlinson, G. A., and Campbell, J. J. R., J. Bacteriol., *86*, 1963, 434.

Xanthomonas (Xan.tho′mo.nas or Xan.tho.mo′nas) Dowson, 1939. *M p. 152.* (Zentr. Bakteriol. Parasitenk., Abt. II, *100*, 1939, 187.)

DIFFERENTIATING CHARACTERS: Unicellular, yellow-pigmented, nonphotosynthetic, nonsporing, straight rods less than 2 μ wide; arranged singly; motile with polar flagella; heterotrophic organisms; *aerobic;* Gram negative; pathogenic to plants causing necrotic infections.

Type species: *Xanthomonas hyacynthi* (Wakker) Dowson.

NOTES: Sixty species are described. They are all Gram negative rods, usually 1 to 3 μ long.

The majority of species grow well on ordinary nutrient agar and produce colonies that have a nondiffusible pigment, which is some shade of yellow. Colonies are usually opaque.

Starr and Stephens (J. Bacteriol., *87*, 1964, 293) have shown that the pigment is a unique "*Xanthomonas*—carotenoid" with absorption maxima in petroleum ether of 418, 437, and 463 mμ.

Fifty-five out of 58 tested species liquefy gelatin, and 52/60 cause an alkaline peptonization of milk. Six are reported to liquefy coagulated serum.

Thirty-seven out of 50 species tested produce acid from glucose and lactose and frequently from other carbohydrates. Three species produce gas.

Nitrates are reduced to nitrite by 14/59, and 8/46 produce indole.

H_2S is produced by 44/50.

Starch is hydrolyzed by 48/51.

Of 25 species 19 are lipolytic, and 15 out of 26 cause a liquefaction of pectate media.

The foregoing data has been abstracted from the *Manual* descriptions. Dye (New Zealand J. Sci., *5*, 1962, 393) states that species of *Xanthomonas* are all Gram negative rods with monotrichous flagella; strict aerobes; oxidative; produce small quantities of acid but no gas from a range of carbohydrates; utilize acetate, citrate, malate, propionate, and succinate; usually methyl red negative; Voges-Proskauer negative; catalase positive; show marked proteolysis of milk; indole negative; urease negative: do not reduce nitrates to nitrite and produce H_2S from cysteine. Several other tests were variable.

Dye suggests that the many species of *Xanthomonas* could be considered as special forms of one species. Colwell and Liston (J. Bacteriol., *82*, 1961, 913) examined 16 species of *Xanthomonas* by Adansonian methods and detected 2 subgroups. For other recent papers on *Xanthomonas* see Dye (New Zealand J. Sci., *3*, 1960, 61; *6*, 1963, 146, 179, 313, 483, 495, and *7*, 1964, 261). See also Hayward and Hodgkiss (J. Gen. Microbiol., *26*, 1961, 133). See also Stolp and Starr (Ann. Rev. Phytopathol., *3*, 1965, 231).

Acetobacter (A.ce.to.bac′ter) Beijerinck, 1898. *M p. 183.* (Quoted from Kral's Sammlung v. Mikroorg., Prague, 1898, 7.) Emend. Leifson, 1954. (Antonie van Leeuwenhoek, *20*, 1954, 102).

TABLE 10

Group	Catalase	CO_2 from acetate and lactate	Ketogenic*	Oxidation of glucose to gluconate
Peroxydans	−	+	− or (+)	−
Oxydans	+	+	− or (+)	+ (except A. ascendens)
Mesoxydans	+	+	+	+
Suboxydans	+	−	++	++

* Oxidation of glycerol to dihydroxyacetone; mannitol to fructose; glucose to 5-keto-gluconate. The following signs are used: −, negative; + positive; and (+), very weak positive.

DIFFERENTIATING CHARACTERS: Unicellular, nonsporing, nonphotosynthetic, rod-shaped organisms; motile with peritrichous flagella or nonmotile; Gram negative; aerobic; oxidize ethanol to acetic acid and then oxidize the acetic acid to CO_2 and H_2O.

Type species: Acetobacter aceti (Beijerinck) Beijerinck.

NOTES: The genus Acetobacter as it appears in the Manual has been shown by Leifson and others to be composed of two distinct groups of organisms. One of these is peritrichously flagellated and oxidizes ethanol to acetic acid and thence to CO_2 and water. The other consists of polarly flagellated, nonmotile organisms, which oxidize ethanol only to acetic acid. For the latter, Leifson proposed the genus Acetomonas (vide infra).

Frateur (La Cellule, 53, 1950, 287) surveyed the genus Acetobacter (sensu Bergey) on the basis of five criteria: (a) catalase; (b) "over oxidation" of ethanol through acetic acid to CO_2 and H_2O; (c) oxidation of lactate to carbonate; (d) ketogenic power, particularly production of dihydroxyacetone from glycerol; and (e) the production of gluconic acid from glucose. On this basis he recognized four groups: the peroxydans, oxydans, mesoxydans, and suboxydans groups. The properties of these groups are summarized in Table 10 (after De Ley, J. Gen. Microbiol., 24, 1961, 31). These groupings have been severely criticized by Shimwell (Antonie van Leeuwenhoek, 25, 1959, 49), who cites intergrading forms throughout the peroxydans, oxydans, and mesoxydans groups.

De Ley (Antonie van Leeuwenhoek, 24, 1958, 281), on the other hand, presents evidence for the formal recognition of A. peroxydans (not included in the Manual).

Of Frateur's groups, the suboxydans group constitutes the genus Acetomonas Leifson, whereas the others belong to Acetobacter (sensu Leifson).

The properties of the two genera quoted by Carr and Shimwell (1961) are given in Table 11.

The oxidation of glucose to gluconate by members of the acetic acid bacteria (other than Frateur's peroxydans group) does not yield any useful energy.

The oxidation of alcohols has been investigated by De Ley and Kersters (Biochim. Biophys. Acta, 71, 1963, 311) and Kersters and De Ley (Bacteriol. Revs., 28, 1964, 164), to which the reader is referred for the extensive range of substances oxidized.

TABLE 11

	Acetobacter	Acetomonas
Ethanol oxidized to acetate	+	+
Acetate oxidized to $CO_2 + H_2O$	+	−
Lactate oxidized to carbonate	+	−
Nutritional type	lactophilic	glycophilic
Oxidize amino acids	+	−
Citric acid cycle	+	−
Flagella (if present)	peritrichous	polar

In general, primary alcohols are oxidized to corresponding acids. Oxidation of secondary alcohols depends on the distance between both groups in the molecule. When they are adjacent, only the secondary alcohol function is oxidized to a ketone. When they are separated by a —CH_2— group as in 1,3-butanediol, the primary alcohol function is oxidized to the corresponding acid.

In the case of 1,2-propanediol, the oxidation of the secondary alcohol function proceeds more rapidly with the D (−) form than the L (+) form, although both occur. (This is contrary to the statement made in the first edition of the *Guide*.)

NOTES: Carr and Shimwell (Antonie van Leeuwenhoek, *27*, 1961, 386) reviewed the developments in the classification of the acetic acid bacteria from 1941 to 1961. The reader is referred to this paper for references prior to 1961. There is a difference of opinions expressed by Shimwell and his associate and De Ley's group, of Gent, Belgium. The reader should consult the relevant papers and, as Shimwell suggests, form his own opinion.

More recent papers relevant to the systematics of the acetic acid bacteria are:

Benziman, M., and Burger-Rachamimov, H., J. Bacteriol., *84*, 1962, 625.

Benziman, M., and Abeliovitz, A., J. Bacteriol., *87*, 1964, 270.

Benziman, M., and Heller, N., J. Bacteriol., *88*, 1964, 1678.

Claus, G. W., and Roth, L. E., J. Cell Biol., *20*, 1964, 217.

De Ley, J., Antonie van Leeuwenhoek, *24*, 1958, 281.

De Ley, J., and Schell, J., J. Gen. Microbiol., *29*, 1962, 589.

De Ley, J., Antonie van Leeuwenhoek, *29*, 1963, 177.

De Ley, J., *Ibid.*, *29*, 1963, 305.

De Ley, J., and Kersters, K., Bacteriol. Revs., *28*, 1964, 164.

Hodgkiss, W., Shimwell, J. L., and Carr, J. G., Antonie van Leeuwenhoek, *28*, 1962, 357.

Kersters, K., and De Ley, J., Biochim. Biophys. Acta, *71*, 1962, 311.

Kerwar, S. S., Chelderin, V. H., and Parks, L. W., J. Bacteriol., *88*, 1964, 179.

Kimmitt, M. R., and Williams, P. J. le B., J. Gen. Microbiol., *31*, 1963, 447.

Ohad, I., Danon, D., and Hestrin, S., J. Cell Biol., *12*, 1962, 31.

Schell, J., and De Ley, J., Antonie van Leeuwenhoek, *28*, 1962, 445.

Scopes, A. W., J. Gen. Microbiol., *28*, 1962, 69.

Shimwell, J. L., and Carr, J. G., Nature, London, *201*, 1964, 1051.

Shimwell, J. L., and Carr, J. G., Antonie van Leeuwenhoek, *27*, 1961, 65.

Webb, T. E., and Colvin, J. R., Can. J. Microbiol., *8*, 1962, 841.

White, G. A., and Wang, C. H., Biochem. J., *90*, 1964, 408, 424.

Acetomonas (A.ce.to.mo'nas) Leifson, 1954. (Antonie van Leeuwenhoek, *20*, 1954, 102.)

DIFFERENTIATING CHARACTERS: Unicellular, nonsporing, nonphotosynthetic, rod-shaped organisms; motile with polar flagella or nonmotile; oxidize ethanol to acetic acid only. Gram negative; *aerobic;* heterotrophic.

Type species: *Acetomonas suboxydans* (Kluyver and de Leeuw) Leifson.

NOTES: For discussion on the differentiation of this genus from *Acetobacter*, see Notes to *Acetobacter*.

The species placed in the genus by various authors include *A. suboxydans, A. melanogenus, A. industrium,* and *A. capsulatum.* Shimwell and Carr (Antonie van Leeuwenhoek, *25*, 1959, 353) regard all these as synonymous and recommend that they be recognized as the single species *Acetomonas oxydans* (Henneberg) Shimwell and Carr.

Differentiation of *Pseudomonas* from *Acetomonas* has been studied by Shimwell, Carr, and Rhodes (J. Gen. Microbiol., *23*, 1960, 283). They recommend four criteria: (a) production of acid on ethanol + Ca CO₃ plates; (b) oxidation of calcium lactate to carbonate; (c) production and accumulation of dihydroxyacetone in glycerol media; and (d) growth at an initial pH of 4.5.

For these, *Acetomonas* is positive for (a), (c), and (d) and *Pseudomonas* only for (b).

De Ley (J. Gen. Microbiol., *24*, 1961, 31) prefers the use of the name **Gluconobacter** Asai to *Acetomonas* Leifson with the definition modified to exclude from it polar flagellates that fail to oxidize alcohol. For further discussion see references to *Acetobacter*.

Aeromonas (A.e.ro.mo′nas) Kluyver and van Niel, 1936. *M p. 189.* (Zentr. Bakteriol. Parasitenk., Abt. II, *94*, 1936, 398.)

DIFFERENTIATING CHARACTERS: Unicellular, colorless, nonsporing, straight, rod-shaped organisms, less than 2 μ wide, occurring singly or in pairs; motile with polar flagella or nonmotile; Gram negative; *aerobic;* heterotrophic; liquefy gelatin; acidify, coagulate, and peptonize milk; reduce nitrates to nitrite and produce acid and gas from glucose. Pathogenic to fish, eels, and frogs.

Type species: *Aeromonas liquefaciens* (Beijerinck) Kluyver and van Niel.

NOTES: Four species are described. They are rods 0.5 to 1.0 μ by 1 to 3 μ, not capsulated. Three of the four species are motile with polar flagella.

The organisms grow well on nutrient agar. The ability to grow in a mineral medium with ammonium salts as the sole source of nitrogen is not recorded. *A. salmonicida* requires methionine and arginine.

Colonies on nutrient agar are 1 to 2 mm. in diameter in 24 hours, circular, entire, and translucent.

H₂S and indole are produced and starch is hydrolyzed by three of the four species.

Acid is produced from lactose by one species.

The organisms occur in fresh and polluted water and are pathogenic for fish, eels, and frogs. They cause a fatal bacteremia in some laboratory animals. The optimal temperature varies with the species.

Some bioluminescent organisms with essentially the same characteristics have been placed in the genus *Photobacterium*.

Smith (J. Gen. Microbiol., *33*, 1963, 263) notes that *Aeromonas salmonicida* does not produce gas from glucose and this and other properties should exclude it from the genus. She suggests a new genus **Necromonas.**

See also **Fergusonia** (in the Key).

For other references see:

Bullock, G. L., App. Microbiol., *9*, 1961, 587.

Clement, M. T., and Gibbons, N. E., Can. J. Microbiol., *6*, 1960, 591.

Krantz, G. E., Reddecliff, J. M., and Heist, C. E., J. Immunol., *91*, 1963, 757.

Liu, P. V., J. Gen. Microbiol., *24*, 1961, 145.

Photobacterium (Pho.to.bac.te′-ri.um) Beijerinck, 1889, emend. Breed and Lessel, 1954. *M p. 193.* (Beijerinck, Arch. néerl. sci., *23*, 1889, 401; Breed and Lessel, Antonie van Leeuwenhoek, *20*, 1954, 60.)

DIFFERENTIATING CHARACTERS: Unicellular, colorless, nonsporing organisms less than 2 μ in width; Gram negative; *aerobic;* heterotrophic; *bioluminescent* on media made from sea water or containing 3 per cent salt.

Type species: *Photobacterium phosphoreum* (Cohn) Ford.

NOTES: Four species are described. They may be coccoid or straight or curved rods. Rudimentary branching may occur in asparagine media. Motile species have polar flagella.

Despite the lengthy descriptions of species given in the *Manual*, there has been insufficient uniformity in the method of description to merit enumeration of reactions, and there is little other than bioluminescence upon which to base a general description. See Spencer (J. Gen. Microbiol., *13*, 1955, 111) for discussion on the classification of the luminescent bacteria.

The organisms are found on fresh and decaying fish. One species was isolated from the photogenic organ of the cephalopod *Rondeletia minor*.

Azotomonas (A.zo.to.mo'nas) Stapp, 1940. *M p. 198*. (Zentr. Bakteriol. Parasitenk., Abt. II, *102*, 1940, 18.)

DIFFERENTIATING CHARACTERS: Unicellular, colorless, straight, nonsporing, rod-shaped organisms less than 2 μ in width; motile with polar flagella; heterotrophic; *fix atmospheric nitrogen when growing in a mineral salts medium with a suitable carbon source*. Gram negative. *Aerobic*.

Type species: *Azotomonas insolita* Stapp.

NOTES: Only two species are described. They are rods 0.6 to 1.2 μ by 0.6 to 5.0 μ.

Good growth occurs on meat infusion agar. Colonies are whitish and entire and may be iridescent (*A. insolita*) or produce a diffusible yellow or violet pigment (*A. fluorescens*).

The only other common characteristic is the hydrolysis of starch. *A. insolita* shares with *Aeromonas* spp. the characteristic of gas production from glucose and lactose, which is rarely found in polar flagellates.

Acid is produced from alcohol by *A. fluorescens*, but the extent is not stated (*cf. Acetobacter*).

Found in soil.

Zymomonas (Zy.mo.mo'nas) Kluyver and van Niel, 1936. *M p 199*. (Zentr. Bakteriol. Parasitenk., Abt. II, *94*, 1936, 399.)

DIFFERENTIATING CHARACTERS: Unicellular, colorless, straight, nonsporing, rod-shaped organisms up to 2 μ in width; motile with polar flagella; heterotrophic; grow poorly on organic media devoid of yeast extract and carbohydrates; *ferment glucose with the production of up to 10 per cent ethyl alcohol*, some lactic acid, and carbon dioxide; anaerobic to microaerophilic; Gram negative.

Type species: *Zymomonas mobilis* (Lindner) Kluyver and van Niel.

NOTES: Only two species are described. They are rather thick rods, 1 to 2 μ by 2 to 5 μ, occurring in pairs or small clumps.

Colonies on glucose yeast extract malt wort are approximately 1 mm. in diameter, circular, convex, and creamy to white by reflected light and brownish by transmitted light.

Gelatin is not liquefied.

The optimal temperature is 30° C.

Found in fermenting plant juices.

See also:

Dawes, E. A., Ribbons, D. W., and Large, P. J., Biochem. J., *98*, 1966, 795.

Dawes, E. A., Ribbons, D. W., and Rees, D. A., Biochem. J., *98*, 1966, 804.

Protaminobacter (Pro.ta.mi.no.-bac'ter) den Dooren de Jong, 1926. *M p. 200*. (Bijdrage tot de Kennis van het Mineralisatieproces. Thesis, Rotterdam, 1926, 159.)

DIFFERENTIATING CHARACTERS: Unicellular, nonsporing, nonphotosynthetic, rod-shaped organisms less than 2 μ wide; motile with polar flagella or nonmotile; heterotrophic; capable of using alkylamines as the sole source of carbon and nitrogen. *Aerobic;* catalase positive; Gram negative.

Type species: *Protaminobacter alboflavus* den Dooren de Jong, 1926.

NOTES: Only two species are described. Both grow on meat infusion agar and alkylamine agar, producing opaque colonies, which may be white, yellow, or red. The pigment produced is not prodigiosin.

Ability to use alkylamines may be lost in cultures maintained for long periods on meat infusion media.

Although no appreciable amount of acetic acid is produced from ethyl alcohol (?), the latter is used as a carbon source. A wide range of fatty and hydroxy acids can be metabolized when ammonia is used as a nitrogen source.

The optimal temperature is 30° C.

Found in soil and water.

Alginomonas (Al.gi.no.mo′nas) Thjøtta and Kåss, 1945. *M p. 202.* (Avhandl. Norske Videnskaps-Akad., Oslo. I. Mat.-Naturv. Kl., No. 5, 1945, 17.)

DIFFERENTIATING CHARACTERS: Unicellular, nonsporing, colorless (or black), straight, rod-shaped organisms less than 2 μ wide; motile with polar flagella; heterotrophic; capable of hydrolyzing and metabolizing alginates. *Aerobic.* Gram negative.

Chitin hydrolysis is not mentioned in descriptions. One local isolate was found to hydrolyze both alginates and chitin.

Type species: *Alginomonas nonfermentans* Thjøtta and Kåss, 1945.

NOTES: Five species are described, three of which are of marine origin and require seawater media for growth.

They are rods 0.5 to 1.0 μ by 1 to 2 μ. Two species are capsulated.

Gelatin is liquefied by 4/5 species.

Agar is liquefied by 2/5 species.

Carbohydrates are stated to be "not utilized," although the fact is not mentioned in descriptions of 4 out of 5 species, and *A. terrestralginica* is reported to produce acidity in milk.

Optimal temperature 20°, 30°, or 37° C.

Found in soil and fresh sea water.

Eller and Payne (J. Bacteriol., *80,* 1960, 193) redescribe *A. alginica.* In addition to characters given in the *Manual,* they cite the following: acid but no gas produced from glucose, fructose, mannose, galactose, mannitol, *l*-arabinose, maltose, and sucrose, but not from lactose, *d*-arabinose, xylose, glycerol, or adonitol. They describe a new, unnamed alginate hydrolyzing organism.

Mycoplana (My.co.pla′na) Gray and Thornton, 1928. *M p. 204.* (Zentr. Bakteriol. Parasitenk., Abt. II, *73,* 1928, 82.)

DIFFERENTIATING CHARACTERS: Unicellular, nonsporing, colorless or buff, straight or curved, rod-shaped organisms, which may exhibit rudimentary branching; less than 2 μ wide; motile with polar flagella; heterotrophic; *capable of using phenol as a sole source of carbon* in the presence of a suitable nitrogen source; reduce nitrates, liberating nitrogen; no acid is produced from glucose or other carbohydrates; *aerobic,* facultative; Gram negative.

Type species: *Mycoplana dimorpha* Gray and Thornton.

NOTES: There are only two species, differentiated on gelatin liquefaction. They are rods, 0.5 to 1.0 μ by 1.5 to 4.5 μ, showing a tendency towards rudimentary branching. This is possibly a pleomorphic state.

Good growth of circular, smooth, glistening, buff-colored colonies is produced on meat extract agar.

The optimal temperature is below 30° C.

Found in soil.

Zoogloea (Zo.o.gloe′a) Cohn, 1854. *M p. 206.* (Nov. Act. Acad. Caes. leop.-carol. Nat. Cur., *24,* 1854, 123.)

DIFFERENTIATING CHARACTERS: Unicellular, colorless, nonsporing, straight, rod-shaped organisms, less than 2 μ wide, which characteristically develop in large numbers in a firm, gelatinous matrix; Gram negative; free cells motile with polar flagella or nonmotile; *aerobic;* heterotrophic.

Type species: *Zoogloea ramigera* Itzigsohn.

NOTES: Two species are described. They are rods 0.8 to 1.0 μ by 1 to 4 μ. In their natural environment they usually develop as a lobate gelatinous growth; that of *Z. ramigera* is broadly lobate, whereas that of *Z. filipendula* is made up of long, narrow fingers. On agar media, small hemispherical, cartilaginous colonies are produced. The natural formation is difficult to reproduce even when growth occurs under water and is almost certainly due to injury to the mass during development.

Found in water and sewage and activated sludge.

Dugan and Lundgren (App. Microbiol., *8,* 1960, 357) have given a recent redescription of *Zoogloea ramigera*, to which the reader is referred for other references.

See also:

Crabtree, K., McCoy, E., Boyle, W. C., and Rohlich, G. A., Appl. Microbiol., *13*, 1965, 218.

Halobacterium (Ha.lo.bac.te′ri.um) Elazari-Volcani, 1940. *M p. 207.* (Studies on the Microflora of the Dead Sea. Thesis, Hebrew Univ., Jerusalem, 1940.)

DIFFERENTIATING CHARACTERS: Unicellular, nonsporing nonphotosynthetic, spherical to rod-shaped organisms; motile with polar flagella or nonmotile; heterotrophic; obligate halophiles, which require 12 to 30 per cent salt for growth. Gram negative; *aerobic*.

Type species: *Halobacterium salinarium* Elazari-Volcani.

NOTES: Five species are described. They are normally rods 0.5 to 1.0 μ by 1 to 8 μ; extremely pleomorphic, with the shape varying with the medium and the specific salt content. Spherical cells are common, particularly with variation in magnesium content. Gas vacuoles occur in *Halobacterium halobium* (Houwink, J. Gen. Microbiol., *15*, 1956, 146).

The spherical cells are not motile.

Growth occurs on peptone media only when the salt content exceeds 16 per cent. Better growth occurs with some species with 24 per cent salt. Colonies range in diameter from 1 to 6 mm. and are orange, yellow, red, or purple. The pigments of three species have been tested and yield a blue color with sulfuric acid, suggesting carotenoids.

Gelatin is liquefied by 2/5.

Indole is not produced.

H₂S production is recorded as positive for 2/5 species.

Acid is produced from glucose by *H. marismortui*.

Lactose is not fermented.

Starch is not hydrolyzed (4/5).

Nitrates are reduced by three species, two of which produce gas.

The optimal temperature is 30° C. (for one species) or 37° (for four).

The organisms are responsible for the production of discoloration in hides, fish, and salt. Their natural habitat is sea water and brines.

The following is a list of some recent publications on *Halobacterium* to which the reader is referred for further references:

Baxter, R. M., Can. J. Microbiol., *6*, 1960, 417.

Bayley, S. T., and Kushner, D. J., J. Mol. Biol., *9*, 1964, 654.

Boring, J., Kushner, D. J., and Gibbons, N. E., Can. J. Microbiol., *9*, 1963, 143.

Dundas, I. D., Srinivasan, V. R., and Halvorson, H. O., Can. J. Microbiol., *9*, 1963, 619.

Holmes, P. K., and Halvorson, H. O., Can. J. Microbiol., *9*, 1963, 904.

Kushner, D. J., and Bayley, S. T., Can. J. Microbiol., *9*, 1963, 53.

MacLeod, R. A., and Matula, T. I., Can. J. Microbiol., *8*, 1962, 883.

Mohr, V., and Larsen, H., J. Gen. Microbiol., *31*, 1963, 267.

Mohr, V., and Larsen, H., Acta Chem. Scand., *17*, 1963, 888.

Onishi, H., McCance, M. E., and Gibbons, N. E., Can. J. Microbiol., *11*, 1965, 365.

Sehgal, S. N., and Gibbons, N. E., Can. J. Microbiol., *6*, 1960, 165.

Siderocapsa (Si.de.ro.cap′sa) Molisch, 1909. *M p. 218.* (Ann. Jard. bot. Buitenz. 2 Sér., Supp., 3, 1909, 29.)

DIFFERENTIATING CHARACTERS: Unicellular, colorless, nonsporing, spherical* organisms 1 to 2 μ wide; 2 to 60 or more cells occur at random in a primary capsule 10 to 20 μ wide; secondary capsules unite to form a mucilaginous colony; iron or manganese compounds are stored in the secondary capsule. Heterotrophic.†

* *Siderocapsa major* is described as a rod-shaped cell. It would be more logical to place it in the genus *Sideromonas*.
† None has been isolated. The heterotrophic nature is only an assumption.

Type species. *Siderocapsa treubii* Molisch.

NOTES: Six species differentiated on morphological and ecological characters are described. The type species is found only in alkaline waters—a condition under which the true iron oxidizer like *Ferrobacillus* does not flourish.

Found mainly on the surfaces of growing plants in iron-bearing waters.

GENERAL NOTES: This genus and a number of the following genera are at best of doubtful significance. When surface scums from natural waters and decaying plant material are examined, isolated bacterial cells or groups of cells heavily encrusted with iron are frequently encountered. Iron encrustation is common also to numerous algae and some loricate and testate protozoa. Inorganic salts of ferrous iron are insoluble above pH 5.5, and inorganic salts of ferric iron are insoluble above a pH of approximately 2.3. In the neutral and alkaline environment of most natural waters, the only iron salts that occur in solution are organic. A typical salt is ferrous ammonium citrate.

Halliday and Grau (Nature, *179*, 1957, 733) have shown that, when ferrous sulfate and citric acid are mixed, ferrous citrate is formed and the citrate catalyzes the oxidation of the ferrous iron to the ferric state while undergoing decarboxylation. Thus ferrous ammonium citrate, commonly used as a source of reduced iron, remains so for only a short period (less than one hour), so that in normal circumstances it is completely oxidized to the ferric state before the medium is inoculated. Further *oxidation* cannot occur. It would appear that in neutral and alkaline waters the iron-depositing organisms release the iron by metabolizing the organic substance with which it is chelated. The free ferric ion is either converted to the hydroxide or chelates with a component of the cell. Baas Becking suggests that pectin is one such substance, which he claims occurs in the sheath of *Sphaerotilus*.

Almost any cell that metabolizes the citrate will deposit iron around itself in a ferric ammonium citrate medium. Hence, the validity of the genus *Siderocapsa* or the following iron-depositing genera is in doubt.

Siderosphaera   (Si.de.ro.sphae′ra) Beger, 1944. *M p. 220.* (Ber. deut. botan. Ges., *62*, (1944) 1950, 7.)

DIFFERENTIATING CHARACTERS: Unicellular, colorless, nonsporing, spherical cells, occurring in pairs, with one or more pairs embedded in a common capsule. Oxides of iron are deposited on the surface of the capsules.

Type species: *Siderosphaera conglomerata* Beger.

NOTES: Only one species has been described. It has not been isolated. Found on the surface of mud in bogs of the Austrian Alps.

See also general notes to *Siderocapsa*, p. *120*.

Sideronema (Si.de.ro.ne′ma) Beger, 1941. *M p. 220.* (Zentr. Bakteriol. Parasitenk., Abt. II, *103*, 1941, 321.)

DIFFERENTIATING CHARACTERS: Unicellular, colorless, nonsporing, ovoid to rod-shaped cells, 4.8 to 5.0 μ by 6.5 μ, forming short chains embedded in a thin mucilaginous capsule. Iron or manganese is deposited in the surface membrane of the cells rather than in the capsules.

Type species: *Sideronema globuliferum.*

NOTES: Only one species is described. It has not been isolated. The organism is nonmotile and was found on a glass slide submerged in spring water near Magdeburg, Germany.

See also general notes to *Siderocapsa*, p. *120*.

Ferribacterium (Fer.ri.bac.te′ri.um) Brussoff, 1916. *M p. 221.* (Zentr. Bakteriol. Parasitenk., Abt. II, *45*, 1916, 547.)

DIFFERENTIATING CHARACTERS: Unicellular, colorless, rod-shaped organisms less than 2 μ wide, arranged in pairs or in chains; capsulated; oxides of iron or manganese are deposited in the capsule, but a torus is not formed. Heterotrophic.

Type species: *Ferribacterium duplex* Brussoff.

NOTES: Two species have been described. One species has been cultivated on peat infusion agar, in iron ammonium citrate broth, and in iron peptone broth, but only morphological and cultural data have been given.

Found forming a pellicle on iron-bearing waters.

See also general notes to *Siderocapsa*, p. 120.

Sideromonas (Si.de.ro.mo′nas) Cholodny, 1922. *M p. 222.* (Ber. deut. botan. Ges., *40*, 1922, 326.)

DIFFERENTIATING CHARACTERS: Unicellular, colorless, rod-shaped organisms less than 2 μ wide; capsulated and arranged at random, in pairs or in chains in zoogloeal masses; the primary capsules are impregnated with iron or manganese oxides. Heterotrophic.*

Type species: *Sideromonas confervarum* Cholodny.

NOTES: Four species are described in the *Manual*. In two the cells are distinctly listed as occurring in pairs or in chains, and in the other two, as occurring at random. The genus *Ferribacterium* is differentiated from *Sideromonas* in the *Manual* keys (p. 217) on the formation of chains and pairs. Some rearrangement is obviously needed unless there exists a more suitable differentiating character, which is not obvious from the *Manual* descriptions unless zoogloeae are not formed by the genus *Ferribacterium*.

See also general notes to *Siderocapsa*, p. 120.

Naumanniella (Nau.man.ni.el′la) Dorff, 1934. *M p. 223.* (Die Eisenorganis-

men, Pflanzenforschung, Jena, Heft 16, 1934, 19.)

DIFFERENTIATING CHARACTERS: Unicellular, colorless, nonsporing, rod-shaped organisms, which may exceed 2 μ in width, around which iron is deposited in the form of a solid ring or *torus*, which gives the cell the appearance of a link in a chain; heterotrophic.*

Type species: *Naumanniella neustonica* Dorff, 1934.

NOTES: Five species are described, which are differentiated on morphology, size, and arrangement of the cells.

Found in surface films and bottom muds of iron-bearing waters.

See also general notes to *Siderocapsa* p. 120.

Ochrobium (O.chro′bi.um) Perfiliev, 1921. *M p. 225.* (In Wislouch, Bull. Inst. Hydrobiol., Russia, 1921.)

DIFFERENTIATING CHARACTERS: Unicellular, colorless, ovoid to rod-shaped, nonsporing organisms, which may exceed 2 μ in width; partially surrounded by a solid ring or *torus* of iron, giving the cell the appearance of an open link in a chain; motile with two flagella of unequal length, which emerge from the "open" end of the torus. Heterotrophic.†

Type species: *Ochrobium tectum* Perfiliev.

NOTES: Only one species is described. It has not been isolated. The cells measure 0.5 to 3.0 μ by 1.5 to 5.0 μ. It resembles the alga *Pteromonas* and, because of the unusual type of flagellation, may, in fact, be an algal cell.

See also general notes to *Siderocapsa*, p. 120.

Siderococcus (Si.de.ro.coc′cus) Dorff, 1934. *M p. 225.* (Die Eisenorganismen, Pflanzenforschung, Jena, Heft 16, 1934, 9.)

---

* It is suggested that some species are autotrophs or facultative autotrophs. Since no information on the pH of the waters is given, it is difficult to comment, but should they be acid tolerant and autotrophic, the relationship to *Ferrobacillus* needs examination.

* No indication is given of the autotrophic or heterotrophic nature of these organisms, and none has been isolated. Forms that bear a striking resemblance to illustrations of *Naumanniella* have been observed by Grau in the author's laboratory in cultures of *Sphaerotilus* grown in a peptone medium containing an iron nail.

† Heterotrophism is assumed.

DIFFERENTIATING CHARACTERS: Colorless, unicellular, spherical organisms less than 2 μ in diameter; not capsulated; oxides of iron or manganese deposited on the cells.

Type species: *Siderococcus limoniticus* Dorff.

NOTES: Two species are described. The cells are small, 0.2 to 1.0 μ in diameter, and occur singly or in chains. Neither species has been isolated in pure culture. In Dorff's original description of *S. limoniticus*, objects immersed in water overlayering slime from bog ore deposits became coated with a deposit of iron in a zone about equidistant from the slime and the surface of the water in the container.

S. communis is frankly described as heterotrophic; it deposits iron through the metabolism of citrate from ferric ammonium citrate. It seems likely that *S. limoniticus* is also heterotrophic.

See also general notes to *Siderocapsa*, p. *120*.

Siderobacter (Si.de.ro.bac'ter) Naumann, 1922. *M p. 226*. (Kgl. Svenska Vetenskapsakad. Handl., *62*, No. 4, 1922, 55.)

DIFFERENTIATING CHARACTERS: Unicellular, colorless, nonsporing, rod-shaped organisms, which may exceed 2 μ in width; not capsulated; deposit oxides of iron directly on the cells; heterotrophic.

Type species: *Siderobacter linearis* Naumann.

NOTES: Five species are described, none of which has been isolated. Only one species, *S. latus*, has cells exceeding 1.0 μ in width. Differentiation is based solely on morphology and arrangement.

Found as surface growths on *Zoogloea filipendula* and on other submerged objects.

See also general notes to *Siderocapsa*, p. *120*.

Ferrobacillus (Fer.ro.ba.cil'lus) Leathen and Braley, 1954. *M p. 227*. (Bacteriol. Proc., 54th General Meeting, Soc. Am. Bacteriologists, 1954, 44.)

DIFFERENTIATING CHARACTERS: Unicellular, colorless, straight, rod-shaped organisms less than 2 μ wide; motile with polar flagella; obligate autotrophs, which will not grow on meat infusion agar or other complex organic media; CO_2 used as a source of carbon and energy obtained from the oxidation of ferrous to ferric iron. Thiosulfate is not oxidized. *Aerobic.*

Type species: *Ferrobacillus ferrooxidans*, Leathen and Braley.

NOTES: A single species is described. The organism is a rod 0.6 to 1.0 μ by 1.0 to 1.6 μ; Gram negative. It has been isolated in pure culture. It is a strict autotroph, which oxidizes ferrous iron at a pH of 2.2 to 4.6, in which range ferrous, but not ferric, iron is soluble. The ferric iron produced by the oxidation is precipitated on the cells and in the medium.

It differs from *Thiobacillus ferrooxidans* in its inability to oxidize thiosulfate.

Kinsel (J. Bacteriol., *80*, 1960, 628) isolated and described a new species, *Ferrobacillus sulfooxidans*, which oxidizes elemental sulfur. It seems to be similar to an unnamed isolated culture described at the same time by Beck (J. Bacteriol., *79*, 1960, 502). For other information on *Ferrobacillus*, see the following:

Blaylock, B. A., and Nason, A., J. Biol. Chem., *238*, 1963, 3453.

Dugan, P. R., and Lundgren, D. G., J. Bacteriol., *89*, 1965, 825.

Kinsel, N. A., and Umbreit, W. W., J. Bacteriol., *87*, 1964, 1243.

Silverman, M. P., and Lundgren, D. G., J. Bacteriol., *77*, 1959, 642.

Silverman, M. P., and Lundgren, D. G., J. Bacteriol., *78*, 1959, 326.

See also general notes to *Siderocapsa*, p. *120*.

Vibrio (Vib'ri.o) Muller, 1773. *M p. 229*. (Vermium terrestrium et fluviatilum, *1*, 1773, 39.)

DIFFERENTIATING CHARACTERS: Unicellular, nonsporing, nonphotosynthetic, rod-shaped organisms with a curved (not spiral) axis; motile with polar flagella; Gram negative; heterotrophic.

They *do not or are not known* to deposit sulfur internally; hydrolyze cellulose (except *V. agarliquefaciens* and *V. fuscus*); oxidize thiosulfates autotrophically; utilize phenol (except *V. cyclosites*); produce water-soluble (except *V. fuscus*) or other pigments (except *V. extorquens* and *V. hyphalus*); oxidize ethyl alcohol quantitatively to acetic acid; produce alcohol from glucose; fix gaseous nitrogen; reduce sulfates to sulfides or deposit iron oxides on the cells.

Type species: *Vibrio comma* (Schroeter) Winslow *et al.*

NOTES: Thirty-four species have been described. They are differentiated on oxygen tolerance, acid production from carbohydrates, bioluminescence (four species),* liquefaction of gelatin, indole production, reduction of nitrates, coagulation of milk, pigment production (three species), salt tolerance (four), hydrolysis of cellulose (two) and agar (five), metabolism of naphthalene (one) and oxalates (two), pathogenicity to animals, and temperature of growth.

Most of the organisms grow well on meat infusion agar, and many tolerate an unusually high pH. The type species will grow at a pH of 9.0.

Four of the five anaerobic species are pathogenic to man and animals. They cause foul-smelling infections of the alimentary and urogenital tracts and other deep-seated infections. They require the addition of blood or ascitic fluid.

Six of the aerobic species cause diseases in man, animals, and insects. *V. comma* is the etiologic agent of Asiatic cholera.

The failure of many cultures of *Vibrio* to produce rods with a curved axis and the recurrent habit of many "straight" rods to do so have led to a search for other means of identification. Shewan and Hodgkiss

* Spencer (J. Gen. Microbiol., *13*, 1955, 111) draws attention to curved forms in the genus *Photobacterium*.

(Nature, *173*, 1954, 108) proposed the use of antibiotic sensitivity and sensitivity to 2,4-diamino-6,7-di-isopropyl pteridine (0/129). Vibrios tested were inhibited by Terramycin (10 μg./ml.) and by 0/129 but not by penicillin (2.5 I.U.). *Pseudomonas* species were not affected by any of these. These tests are useful when positive, but the 0/129 reagent is not marketed, and the general use of the tests presupposes a knowledge of the parameters of the genus *Vibrio*.

Davis and Park (J. Gen. Microbiol., *27*, 1962, 101) proposed the removal of *V. percolans*, *V. cyclosites*, *V. neocistes*, and *V. alcaligenes* into the genus **Comamonas** (see Key, Section H, 33a). This proposal was supported by Sebald and Véron (Ann. inst. Pasteur, *105*, 1963, 897), who stated that the DNA base composition (GC%) is 64. They also proposed the separation of *V. fetus* and *V. bubulus* into a genus **Campylobacter** with a GC% of 30 to 34. Both the above groups have expressed the opinion that the genus *Vibrio* should be restricted to curved, usually pleomorphic rods with a single polar flagellum, which *ferment* carbohydrate without gas production. Colwell and Mandel (*vide infra*) quote the DNA base composition (GC%) for some vibrios as ranging from 39 to 49. For other papers see:

Beam, W. E., J. Bacteriol., *77*, 1959, 328.

Colwell, R. R., and Mandel, M., J. Bacteriol., *88*, 1964, 1816.

Colwell, R. R., and Morita, R. Y., J. Bacteriol., *88*, 1964, 831.

Hugh, R., Intern. Bull. Bacteriol. Nomen. Taxon, *15*, 1965, 13.

Hugh, R., Bacteriol. Proc., G6, 1961.

Hugh, R., Bacteriol. Proc., G70, 1961.

Mashimo, P. A., and Ellison, S. A., J. Bacteriol., *78*, 1959, 636.

Park, R. W. A., J. App. Bacteriol., *24*, 1961, 23.

Reich, C. V., Heist, C. E., and Dunne, H. W., J. Bacteriol., *82*, 1961, 210.

Ringen, L., and Frank, F. W., J. Bacteriol., *86*, 1963, 344.

Smibert, R. M., J. Bacteriol., *85*, 1963, 394.

Wolin, M. J., Wolen, E. A., and Jacobs, N. J., J. Bacteriol., *81*, 1961, 911.

Bdellovibrio (Bdel.lo.vib′ri.o) Stolp and Starr, 1963. (Antonie van Leeuwenhoek, *29*, 1963, 217.)

DIFFERENTIATING CHARACTERS: Usually curved rods 0.3 μ wide with a single, stout, ensheathed flagellum. Forcibly attack Gram negative host cells fixing themselves by the flagellated end and bringing about a final dissolution of the cell. On bacterial lawns they produce plaques superficially like those of bacteriophages, but they appear first after 24 to 48 hours and increase in size.

Type species: *Bdellovibrio bacteriovorus* Stolp and Starr.

NOTES: Nonpredatory cultures have been obtained that produce colonies on nutrient media.

Desulfovibrio   (De.sul.fo.vib′ri.o) Kluyver and van Niel, 1936. *M p. 248.* (Zentr. Bakteriol. Parasitenk., Abt. II, *94*, 1936, 369.)

DIFFERENTIATING CHARACTERISTICS: Unicellular, colorless, nonsporing,* rod-shaped organisms with curved axes (not spiral); less than 2 μ wide; motile with a single polar flagellum; Gram negative; *anaerobic;* heterotrophic; reduce sulfates, sulfites, sulfur, thiosulfates, and hyposulfites to H_2S with the use of a wide range of organic substances and possibly hydrogen as the hydrogen donor; do not deposit iron oxides.

Type species: *Desulfovibrio desulfuricans* (Beijerinck, 1895) Kluyver and van Niel, 1936.

NOTES: Three species are described. They are differentiated on salt tolerance and the nature of the organic hydrogen donors.

The organisms are strict anaerobes, which are capable of reducing sulfates with liberation of hydrogen sulfide. In media

---

* Spore formation in *Desulfovibrio desulfuricans* has been reported, but the statement has since been withdrawn.

---

containing iron salts this results in the production of black iron sulfide.

Primary isolation has been most successful in a peptone-yeast extract-lactate medium deoxygenated with a little sodium sulfide. Claims have been made that the organisms will grow under strictly autotrophic conditions with oxidation of H_2 for energy.

The three species recorded do not liquefy gelatin or reduce nitrates. No record is made of acid production, but all species utilize glucose, ethanol, propanol, butanol, glycerol, lactate, malate, and several amino acids as hydrogen donors when reducing the inorganic sulfur compounds.

Jean Le Gall (J. Bacteriol., *86*, 1963, 1120) reports the isolation of a new species, *Desulfovibrio gigas*, which uses lactate and pyruvate but not glucose nor acetate: contains cytochrome and desulphoviridin (common to most strains of *Desulfovibrio*) and hydrogenase.

Although enrichment cultures are easily maintained, subculture has proved very difficult.

Two reviews on *Desulfovibrio* have been published by Postgate (Ann. Rev. Microbiol., *13*, 1959, 505) and Starkey (Lecture: University of Maryland, Dept. of Microbiol., 1960 to 1961). For more recent papers see the following:

Akagi, J. M., and Campbell, L. L., J. Bacteriol., *86*, 1963, 563.

Alico, R. K., and Liegey, F. W., J. Bacteriol., *91*, 1966, 1112.

Campbell, L. L., and Postgate, J. R., Bacteriol. Rev., *29*, 1965, 359.

Iverson, W. P., Appl. Microbiol., *14*, 1966, 529.

Krasna, A. I., Riklis, E., and Rittenberg, D., J. Biol. Chem., *235*, 1960, 2717.

MacPherson, R., and Miller, J. D. A., J. Gen. Microbiol., *31*, 1963, 365.

Mechalas, B. J., and Rittenberg, S. C., J. Bacteriol., *80*, 1960, 501.

Miller, J. D. A., and Saleh, A. M., J. Gen. Microbiol., *37*, 1964, 419.

Miller, J D. A., and Wakerley, D. S., J. Gen Microbiol., *43*, 1966, 101.

Peck, H. D., J. Biol. Chem., *235*, 1960, 2734.

Postgate, J. R., Bacteriol. Revs., *29*, 1965, 425.

Saunders, G. F., Campbell, L. L., and Postgate, J. R., J. Bacteriol., *87*, 1964, 1093.

Methanobacterium (Me. tha. no.-bac. te'ri. um) Kluyver and van Niel, 1936. *M p. 250.* (Zentr. Bakteriol. Parasitenk., Abt. II, *94*, 1936, 399.)

INTRODUCTORY NOTE: Two organisms appear in the *Manual* with the generic designation *Methanobacterium*. One, *M. soehngenii* Barker, has been listed as the sole species of the genus *Methanobacterium*. The other, *M. omelianski*, has been listed in an appendix to the genus *Clostridium* (p. 693). Both organisms occur in soil, sewage, and fresh water *or* marine muds.

The characteristics of both are given. (See also P. H. Smith and R. E. Hungate, J. Bacteriol., *75*, 1958, 713.)

1. Methanobacterium soehngenii

DIFFERENTIATING CHARACTERS: Unicellular, colorless, nonsporing, rod-shaped organisms less than 2 μ wide with a straight or slightly curved axis; occur in chains in liquid media; nonmotile; Gram negative; *anaerobic;* heterotrophic; acetate and *n*-butyrate fermented with the production of CO_2 and methane; ethyl alcohol, *n*-butyl alcohol, and glucose not fermented.

Type species: *Methanobacterium soehngenii* Barker, 1936.

2. Methanobacterium omelianski

DIFFERENTIATING CHARACTERS: Unicellular, colorless, unbranched, rod-shaped organisms less than 2 μ wide; *endospores produced; anaerobic;* heterotrophic; oxidize primary alcohols, including ethyl alcohol and *n*-butyl alcohol, to the corresponding fatty acids and secondary alcohols to ketones, while reducing CO_2 quantitatively to methane; sulfate is not reduced and sulfur is not deposited internally. Buchanan and Rabinowitz (J. Bacteriol., *88*, 1964,

806) report on the reisolation of, and study of, the highly reducing electron carrier ferredoxin from *Methanobacterium omelianski*.

Cellvibrio (Cell. vib'ri. o) Winogradsky, 1929. *M p. 250.* (Ann. inst. Pasteur, *43*, 1929, 577.)

DIFFERENTIATING CHARACTERS: Unicellular, nonphotosynthetic, nonsporing, rod-shaped organisms with a curved (not spiral) axis; less than 2 μ wide; Gram negative; *aerobic;* grow moderately well on mineral salts agar containing starch; produce a yellow, ochre, or colorless growth on cellulose strips on a mineral salts agar and oxidize* the cellulose to oxycellulose; do not produce a clearing around colonies on precipitated cellulose agar nor cause disintegration of filter paper in 0.5 per cent peptone water.

Type species: *Cellvibrio ochraceus* Winogradsky.

NOTES: Four species are described. They are differentiated on their ability to grow on glucose and starch agars and on pigmentation. Optimal temperature, 20° C.

Found in decaying vegetable matter and soils.

For recent papers on *Cellvibrio* see the following:

Love, S. H., and Hulcher, F. H., J. Bacteriol., *87*, 1963, 39.

Storvick, W. O., and King, K. W., J. Biol. Chem., *235*, 1960, 303.

Tuckett, J. D., and Moore, W. E. C., J. Bacteriol., *77*, 1959, 227.

Cellfalcicula (Cell. fal. ci'cu. la) Winogradsky, 1929. *M p. 252.* (Ann. inst. Pasteur, *43*, 1929, 616.)

DIFFERENTIATING CHARACTERS: Unicellular, nonphotosynthetic, nonsporing, sickle-shaped or curved rods less than 2 μ wide; motile with a single polar flagellum; Gram negative; heterotrophic; *aerobic;* do not grow on a mineral salts medium containing starch; grow on cellulose strips layered on a mineral salts agar, oxidizing the cellulose

---

* See the discussion of the validity of this statement in Methods, p. *229.*

to oxycellulose* and producing a green, cream, or brownish growth; do not cause disintegration of cellulose strips in peptone water.

Type species: *Cellfalcicula viridis* Winogradsky.

NOTES: Three species are described.

Microcyclus (Mic.ro.cyc'lus) Ørskov, 1928. *M p. 253.* (Zentr. Bakteriol. Parasitenk., Abt. I, Orig., *107*, 1928, 180.)

DIFFERENTIATING CHARACTERS: Unicellular, colorless, curved, rod-shaped organisms about 1 μ long. During growth they produce closed rings, 2.0 to 3.0 μ in diameter, which later change to two horseshoe-shaped halves fastened together without any evidence of divisional lines. These divide into separate rods, which reproduce the cycle; capsulated; nonmotile; Gram negative; *aerobic;* heterotrophic; grow well in 0.5 per cent peptone water.

Type species: *Microcyclus aquaticus* Ørskov.

NOTES: Only one species has been described.

It does not produce acid from hexoses out produces slight acid from pentoses.

Gelatin is not liquefied and indole is not formed.

Temperature range, 5° to 30° C.

Found in lake water and soil.

Spirillum (Spi.ril'lum) Ehrenberg, 1832. *M p. 253.* (Physik. Abhandl. Akad. Wiss., Berlin, 1832, 38.)

DIFFERENTIATING CHARACTERS: Unicellular, nonsporing, nonphotosynthetic, rod-shaped organisms with a spiral axis and a relatively rigid cell wall; less than 2 μ wide; motile with polar flagella; Gram negative; heterotrophic; do not deposit sulfur internally.

Type species: *Spirillum undula* (Müller) Ehrenberg.

NOTES: Nine species have been described in the *Manual.* They are differentiated on morphological and cultural characteristics. The spirilla are common in putrid and

* See comment on the validity of this statement in Methods, p. *229.*

stagnant waters. One species, *S. minus,* is considered to be a cause of rat-bite fever.

The genus *Spirillum* has been redescribed in a monograph by Williams and Rittenberg (Intern. Bull. Bacteriol. Nomen. Taxon., *7*, 1957, 49). They note that species of *Spirillum* are capable of changing from the characteristic spiral form to a coccoid body in aging cultures. These coccoid bodies germinate in a fresh medium to give the normal spiral forms. The cultures are very sensitive to Na⁺. This claim has been verified in the author's laboratory. Four cultures supplied by Williams have grown well on a Difco peptone-yeast extract agar without the usual 0.5 per cent salt.

The suggested relationship between *Spirillum* and the myxobacteria seems unlikely. The formation of flagella by the species of *Spirillum* sets them aside from the nonflagellated creeping myxobacteria.

For recent papers on the genus *Spirillum* see the following:

Becking, J. H., Abstracts VIIIth International Congress for Microbiology, 1962.

Canale-Parola, E., Rosenthal, S. L., and Kupfer, D. G., Antonie van Leeuwenhoek, *32*, 1966, 113.

Houwink, A. L., Biochim. Biophys. Acta, *10*, 1953, 360.

MacDonald, J. B., Madlener, E. M., and Socransky, S. S., J. Bacteriol., *77*, 1959, 559.

Martinez, R. J., Biochim. Biophys. Res. Comm., *12*, 1963, 180.

Martinez, R. J., and Rosenberg, E., J. Mol. Biol., *8*, 1964, 702.

Murray, R. G. E., Can. J. Microbiol., *9*, 1963, 381.

Pijper, A., and Steynberg, A. L., Zentr. Bakteriol., Abt. II, *118*, 1964, 349.

Pretorius, W. A., J. Gen. Microbiol., *32*, 1963, 403.

Rittenberg, B. T., and Rittenberg, S. C., Arch. Mikrobiol., *42*, 1962, 138.

Williams, M. A., J. Gen. Microbiol., *21*, 1958, 109.

Williams, M. A., Intern. Bull. Bacteriol. Nomen. Taxon., *9*, 1959, 35; *9*, 1959, 137.

Williams, M. A., J. Bacteriol., *78*, 1959, 374.

Williams, M. A., and Chapman, G. B., J. Bacteriol., *81*, 1961, 195.

MacDonald *et al.* (*vide supra*) have examined the properties of *Spirillum sputigenum* and compare them with *Selenomonas*, into which Lessel and Breed (Bacteriol. Revs., *18*, 1954, 165) recommended the species should be placed. They disagree with the recommendation and suggest the rejection of the genus *Selenomonas*.

Paraspirillum (Pa.ra.spi.ril′lum) Dobell, 1912. *M p. 257.* (Arch. Protistenk., *24*, 1912, 97.)

DIFFERENTIATING CHARACTERS: Unicellular, colorless, nonsporing organisms with a spiral axis; rather sharply angulated; cells 1.5 to 2.0 μ wide at the center and tapering towards both ends. In the center of the cell is an oval to rounded body almost as wide as the cell and clearly visible without staining. It stains deeply with neutral red in killed cells and with Heidenhain's iron-hematoxylin or Giemsa stain in fixed cells and is considered by Dobell to be a nucleus; motile with polar flagella; when attached to an object by one end the cells are capable of contraction to a more angulated spiral; do not deposit sulfur internally.

Type species: *Paraspirillum vejdovskii* Dobell.

NOTES: A single species is described. Cells are 8 to 15 μ long. The "well defined nucleus" described by Dobell is a most unusual character for a bacterial cell. Similar cells have been found in local waters, in which the central "nucleus" looked like a pale-green chloroplast. It may be an algal cell (author's note). It has not been isolated.

Selenomonas (Se.le.no.mo′nas) von Prowazek, 1913. *M p. 258.* (Zentr. Bakteriol. Parasitenk., Abt. I, Orig., *70*, 1913, 36.)

DIFFERENTIATING CHARACTERS: Unicellular, colorless, curved, rod-shaped organisms, which may exceed 2 μ in width; motile by means of a bunch of flagella inserted in the concave side of the cell; nonsporing; Gram negative; heterotrophic; *anaerobic;* do not deposit sulfur or calcium carbonate internally or iron externally.

Type species: *Selenomonas palpitans* Simons.

NOTES: The organisms occur in the rumen, cecum, and buccal cavities. Only one species has been isolated (from the buccal cavity of man). It requires enriched media and produces on blood agar a smooth, convex, grayish-yellow colony less than 0.5 mm. in diameter. It produces acid from glucose and sucrose and acidifies and coagulates milk. It does not produce H_2S or indole or reduce nitrates.

Several authors have claimed that *Selenomonas* belongs to the *Protozoa*. Electron micrographs of flagella should resolve this question. See notes to *Spirillum*.

Myconostoc (My.co.nos′toc) Cohn, 1875. *M p. 260.* (Beitr. Biol. Pflanz., *1*, Heft 3, 1875, 183.)

DIFFERENTIATING CHARACTERS: Unicellular, colorless, nonsporing, curved rods less than 2 μ wide; arranged in chains wound into a ball inside a nearly spherical capsule; polar flagellated swarm cells are produced. Gram negative (?); heterotrophic (?).

Type species: *Myconostoc gregarium* Cohn, 1875.

NOTES: Only one species is described. It has been found in the surface scum of sulfur water in a jar of decomposing algae and in peat bogs. Not isolated.

Pasteurella (Pas.teu.rel′la) Trevisan, 1887. *M p. 395.* (Rend. reale ist. lombardo sci., 1887, 94.)

DIFFERENTIATING CHARACTERS: Unicellular, colorless, ovoid to straight, rod-shaped organisms less than 2 μ wide; nonmotile or motile with flagella; nonsporing; Gram negative; *aerobic;* heterotrophic; no gas from carbohydrates. Parasitic on man, animals, and birds.

Type species: *Pasteurella multocida*

(Lehmann and Neumann) Rosenbusch and Merchant.

NOTES: Organisms 0.1 to 0.7 μ by 0.3 to 1.7 μ, generally ellipsoidal, often showing a bipolar stain. Nonmotile except for *P. pseudotuberculosis*, which is motile below 30° C. and has peritrichous flagella.

All species except *P. tularensis* and *P. novicida* grow on meat infusion agar; the colonies are small (1 mm.) in diameter, circular, translucent, and colorless to slightly yellowish in 24 hours at 37° C. Colonies of some species spread on further incubation and may have a draughtsman-like appearance.

P. tularenis grows on blood agar and *P. novicida* on yeast extract agar, both with colonies similar to the above.

Gelatin is slowly liquefied by 3/7 species.

Litmus milk remains unchanged or is slightly alkaline.

H_2S is produced by all species except *P. pfaffii*.

Indole is produced by only one species.

Acid but no gas is produced from glucose by all species except *P. anatipestifer*.

No acid is produced from lactose (except *P. haemolytica*).

Optimal temperature, 37° C. except for *P. pseudotuberculosis* (30° C.).

PATHOGENICITY: The organisms are responsible for septicemic conditions characterized by the production of multiple small hemorrhages (petechiae) throughout the body.

P. multocida: a cause of chicken cholera and hemorrhagic septicemia in warm-blooded animals.

P. septicaemiae: fatal septicemia of young geese.

P. haemolytica: pneumonia of sheep and cattle.

P. pestis: bubonic and pneumonic plague in man.

P. pfaffii: epidemic septicemia in canaries.

P. pseudotuberculosis: causes pseudotuberculosis in a wide range of hosts.

P. tularensis: tularemia in man.

P. novicida: tularemia-like disease of rodents.

Some recent papers pertinent to the systematics of *Pasteurella* are:

Heyl, J. G., Antonie van Leeuwenhoek, *29*, 1963, 1.

Hoogendijk, J. L., Antonie van Leeuwenhoek, *28*, 1962, 315.

Talbot, J. M., and Sneath, P. H. A., J. Gen. Microbiol., *22*, 1960, 303.

The papers by Heyl and Hoogendijk discuss the characteristics of *P. ureae* and *P. pneumotropa*, species not listed in the *Manual*.

Bordetella (Bor.de.tel′la) Moreno-López, 1952. *M p. 402.* (Microbiol. españ., *5*, 1952, 177.)

DIFFERENTIATING CHARACTERS: Unicellular, colorless, ovoid to rod-shaped organisms less than 2 μ in diameter; nonmotile or motile with flagella; Gram negative; heterotrophic; no acid or gas produced from glucose or lactose; litmus milk made alkaline in 1 to 2 days; organisms produce whooping cough or related diseases in children or bronchopneumonia in rodents.

Type species: *Bordetella pertussis* (Holland) Moreno-López.

NOTES: Minute, rod-shaped organisms, 0.2 to 0.3 μ by 1 μ. Gram negative. Of the three species only one, *Bordetella bronchiseptica*, is motile. It has peritrichous flagella.

B. parapertussis and *B. bronchiseptica* will grow on first isolation on meat infusion agar, but the type species will not. It requires a different medium. The potato-blood-glycerol medium of Bordet and Gengou has proved most suitable. It has been replaced by a charcoal agar, which suggests that the unsuitability of meat infusion agar may be due to a toxic component adsorbed on the charcoal rather than a deficiency of some essential metabolite.

Colonies are colorless, circular, convex, and entire and are about 1 mm. in diameter in 24 hours.

Gelatin is not hydrolyzed.

Litmus milk turns alkaline very slowly. Indole is not produced.

Nitrite is produced from nitrate by *B. bronchiseptica.*

No acid or gas is produced from glucose or lactose.

Citrate is used as a sole source of carbon and urease is produced by *B. parapertussis* and *B. bronchiseptica.*

Catalase positive.

Aerobic; optimal temperature, 37° C.

B. pertussis and *B. parapertussis* have been isolated from cases of whooping cough and related infections in man. *B. bronchiseptica* is isolated from dogs affected with distemper.

A review of *Bordetella pertussis* was published in 1957 by Rowatt (J. Gen. Microbiol., *17*, 1957, 297). Sutherland and Wilkinson (J. Gen. Microbiol., *30*, 1963, 105) have described the presence of Azurin, a copper protein in cells and culture fluids of *Bordetella pertussis*, *B. parapertussis*, and *B. bronchiseptica*. It is a water-soluble autoxidizable protein of high oxidation potential ($+$ 395 mV.). Several other papers, concerned mainly with antigenic constituents of *Bordetella*, have been published. Rauch and Pickett (Can. J. Microbiol., *7*, 1961, 126) have isolated phages of *B. bronchiseptica* that lyse strains of *B. parapertussis.*

Brucella (Bru.cel'la) Meyer and Shaw, 1920. *M p. 404.* (J. Infectious Diseases, *27*, 1920, 173.)

DIFFERENTIATING CHARACTERS: Unicellular, colorless, nonsporing, straight to ovoid, rod-shaped organisms less than 2 μ in width; nonmotile; Gram negative; heterotrophic. The organisms grow well on liver extract or tryptose-phosphate agar; no *apparent* acid or gas is produced from glucose or lactose in peptone water; litmus milk turns alkaline; Loeffler's inspissated serum is not liquefied.

The organisms cause *brucellosis* in man and animals and may cause abortion in animals.

Type species: *Brucella melitensis* (Hughes) Meyer and Shaw.

NOTES: Three species are described in the *Manual.* Two other species, *Brucella neotomae* and *B. intermedia,* have appeared in more recent literature. They have been differentiated on tolerance to the dyes thionin and basic fuchsin, production of H_2S, and antigenic pattern (*vide infra*).

Organisms are 0.2 to 0.3 μ by 0.5 to 1.0 μ.

Growth occurs on meat infusion agar but is improved by liver extract. An increased CO_2 concentration favors isolation of *B. abortus,* but the optimal oxygen concentration is still 20 per cent.

Colonies are 1 mm. in diameter.

Gelatin is not liquefied.

Litmus milk becomes slowly alkaline.

Indole is not produced.

Nitrite is produced from nitrate.

No visible acid is produced from carbohydrates in peptone water, although glucose and other carbohydrates are reported to be oxidized. This is due to neutralization of the acid by the ammonia liberated.

Aerobic. Optimal temperature, 37° C. Optimal pH, 7 to 7.2. No growth below pH 6.0.

Brucella abortus causes contagious abortion in cattle and undulant fever in man. It also affects swine. *Brucella melitensis* causes abortion in goats and undulant fever in man. It may affect swine. *Brucella suis* causes abortion in swine and undulant fever in man. It also affects chickens, horses, dogs, cows, and monkeys.

Meyer and Cameron and Meyer have investigated speciation in the genus by a study of metabolic characteristics compared with the more conventional tests. The results of their investigations have been reproduced in Table 12.

Strains of *Brucella intermedia* (Renoux) were found to belong to *B. melitensis, B. abortus,* and *B. suis* on metabolic patterns. For other references, see the following:

Cameron, H. S., and Meyer, M. E., J. Bacteriol., *76*, 1958, 546.

TABLE 12*

	Brucella melitensis	Brucella abortus	Brucella suis			Brucella neotomae
Production of H₂S	−	++	++++			++++
CO₂ for isolation	−	+	−			−
Resistance to						
Basic fuchsin						
10 µg./ml.	+	+	−			−
20 µg./ml.	+	+	−			−
40 µg./ml.	−	+	−			−
Thionine						
10 µg./ml.	+	−	+			−
20 µg./ml.	+	−	+			−
40 µg./ml.	−	−	+			−
			Type I	Type II	Type III	
Oxidation of:						
L-alanine	+	+	+	+	+	+
L-glutamic	+	+	∓	+	+/−	+
L-asparagine	+	+	−	−	−/+	+
D-asparagine						+
L-arginine	−	−	+	+	+	−
L-citrulline	−	−	+	+	+	−
DL-ornithine	−	−	+	+	+	−
L-lysine	−	−	+	−	+	+
L-arabinose	−	+	+	+	−	+
D-galactose	−	+	+	+	+	+
D-ribose	−	+	+	+	+	+/−
D-xylose	−	−	+	+	+	−
Sensitivity to B. abortus phage	−	+	−	−	−	−

* The following signs are used: +, growth or oxidation; ∓, weak to strong; +/−, variable strain reactions. Many strains of B. abortus and to a lesser extent other species fail to conform to the conventional H₂S-CO₂-dye resistance patterns but conform to the metabolic and phage sensitivity patterns.

Meyer, M. E., and Cameron, H. S., J. Bacteriol., *82*, 1961, 387 and 396.

Meyer, M. E., J. Bacteriol., *82*, 1961, 401 and 950.

Stoenner, H. G., and Lackman, D. B., Amer. J. Vet. Research, *18*, 1957, 947.

Redfearn and Berman (Bull. Wld. Hlth. Org., *23*, 1960, 133) have described a gel-diffusion technique for typing *Brucella* species.

Moreira-Jacob (J. Bacteriol., *86*, 1963, 599) recommends the use of safranin sensitivity. Strains of B. *suis* but not B. *meliten-sis* or B. *abortus* were inhibited by concentrations ranging from 50 to 200 µg of safranin per ml.

Haemophilus (Hae.mo′phi.lus) Winslow *et al.*, 1917. *M p. 406*. (J. Bacteriol., *2*, 1917, 561.)

DIFFERENTIATING CHARACTERS: Unicellular, colorless, nonsporing, straight, rod-shaped organisms less than 2 µ in width; nonmotile; Gram negative; heterotrophic; fastidious organisms, which will not grow on meat infusion agar but require the addition of X- or V-factor (or both) or diphosphothiamine to support growth. No gas is produced from carbohydrates; acid may be produced from glucose but only rarely from lactose; not halophilic; parasitic.

Type species: *Haemophilus influenzae* (Lehmann and Neumann) Winslow.

NOTES: Fifteen species are described with differentiation on pathogenicity and dependence on X- and V-factors. Although normally rod-shaped, the cells may become very pleomorphic, especially in pathological material.

The organisms do not grow on meat infusion agar except after adaptation. Individual species require the addition of hemin (X-factor) and phosphopyridine nucleotide (V-factor) for growth. X-factor is contained in blood and the V-factor in yeast extract. The only exception is *Haemophilus piscium*, which requires neither but does require diphosphothiamine or adenosine.

In practice a medium (known as Levinthal base) devoid of X- and V-factors is employed, upon which these organisms will *not* grow. The addition of X- or V-factor or X- + V-factors determines their growth requirements. It should be remembered that when an organism will not grow on a meat infusion base it is useless to employ *peptone* as a base in media for biochemical tests. Careful examination must be made to check for growth before any assessment of activity is made.

Colonies on suitable media vary from tiny colorless colonies 0.5 mm. in diameter to iridescent colonies 2 to 3 mm. in diameter with different species. Colonies of *H. citreus* are lemon yellow.

Gelatin is not suitable for growth.

Indole is rarely produced (4/15).

Nitrite is produced from nitrate by all species.

Acid but no gas is produced from glucose by strains of all species, although strains frequently occur that will not produce acid from any sugars.

Acid is produced from lactose by three species, which also produce a slight acidity in litmus milk.

Blood is hemolyzed by only 3/15 species. Hemolysis may be either of an α (green) or β (colorless) type.

Optimal temperature is 37° C. for all but *H. piscium*, which has an optimum between 20° and 25° C. It causes ulcers in trout.

PATHOGENICITY: Obligate parasites of animals; not always pathogenic. Diseases caused are listed below.

H. influenzae: purulent meningitis and conjunctivitis in man.

H. hemolyticus: subacute endocarditis.

H. aegyptius: acute and subacute conjunctivitis.

H. ducreyi: Soft chancre.

H. citreus: genital vesicular eruptions in cattle.

H. piscium: ulcers of trout.

H. haemoglobinophilus: respiratory tract of man and preputial secretions of dogs.

H. parahemolyticus: pharyngitis.

H. parainfluenzae: nonpathogenic.

H. gallinarum: fowl coryza.

H. suis: associated with a virus in swine influenza.

H. putoriorum: respiratory tract of ferrets.

Recent literature on *Haemophilus* has been concerned primarily with fundamental research on nutrition and antigenic patterns. Some papers more pertinent to systematics are:

Biberstein, E. L., and Gills, M., J. Bacteriol., *81*, 1961, 380.

Biberstein, E. L., Mini, P. D., and Gills, M. G., J. Bacteriol., *83*, 1963, 814.

Nickel, L., and Goodgal, S. H., J. Bacteriol., *88*, 1964, 1538.

Redmond, D. L., and Kotcher, E., J. Gen. Microbiol., *33*, 1963, 89.

Actinobacillus (Ac.ti.no.ba.cil'lus) Brumpt, 1910. *M p. 414.* (Précis de Parasitologie, 1st ed., Paris, 1910, 849.)

DIFFERENTIATING CHARACTERS: Unicellular, colorless, nonsporing, rod-shaped organisms less than 2 μ in width; nonmotile; Gram negative; *aerobic;* heterotrophic; no gas produced from carbohydrates; production of acid from lactose and glucose varies with the species. Animal parasites.

Type species: *Actinobacillus lignieresii* Brumpt.

NOTES: Often occur in clumps in tissue and cultures. Growth occurs on meat infusion agar without enrichment. The colony form varies with the species from small (0.5 to 1 mm.), smooth, entire, butyrous colonies, which may increase in size on further incubation to small mucoid or cartilaginous colonies, which adhere to the agar. Most species produce a granular growth adherent to the walls of the tubes in liquid media.

Granules obtained from lesions may have to be crushed before primary isolation can be achieved.

Gelatin is not liquefied.

Litmus milk may be turned slightly acid over a period of weeks.

Slight acid production occurs in glucose and also in lactose with 4/5 species but may not be evident in 24 to 48 hours. No gas is produced.

Optimal temperature, 37° C.

PATHOGENICITY: Diseases caused in animals are listed below.

A. lignieresii: actinobacillosis in cattle; causes lesions mainly in soft tissues, particularly in lymph nodes and muscles of the tongue.

A. equuli: causes joint ill and purulent nephritis in foals.

A. actinomycetocomitans: found associated with *Actinomyces hominis* in actinomycosis.

A. actinoides: chronic pneumonia in calves.

A. mallei: glanders in horses.

Calymmatobacterium (Ca.lym.ma.-to.bac.te'ri.um) Aragão and Vianna, 1913. *M p. 418.* (Mem. inst. Oswaldo Cruz, *5*, 1913, 221.)

DIFFERENTIATING CHARACTERS: Unicellular, colorless, nonsporing, straight, rod-shaped organisms less than 2 μ wide; nonmotile; Gram negative; *aerobic;* heterotrophic; isolated from cases of *granuloma inguinale;* growth does not occur on meat infusion agar on primary isolation; may be cultivated in the yolk sac of the developing chick embryo or in the condensation water of a sloped medium prepared by adding 50 per cent unheated embryonic yolk to melted and cooled nutrient agar.

Type species: *Calymmatobacterium granulomatis* Aragão and Vianna.

NOTES: There is only one species. Rod-shaped, pleomorphic, unicellular organisms 0.8 to 1.4 μ by 1.5 to 4.5 μ. Smaller cell types 0.5 to 0.7 μ by 1.4 to 1.5 μ occur. Single cells may be slightly curved. Encapsulated.

On primary isolation the organism will grow only on a medium containing unheated embryonic egg yolk but can later be adapted to Levinthal basal medium + X-factor (Rake and Oskay, J. Bacteriol., *55*, 1948, 667). Adapted forms produce a shiny translucent colony, which grows to 1.5 mm. in diameter and turns gray, then brown. Colonies take 4 days to appear. Spasmodic growth occurs in beef heart broth without blood extract.

Good growth occurs in the yolk sac of the developing chick embryo.

Optimal temperature, 37° C. No further information on cultural and biochemical reactions is available.

The organisms are found in granulomatous lesions in man and are considered to be the cause of *granuloma inguinale.*

Moraxella (Mo.rax.el'la) Lwoff, 1939. *M p. 419.* (Ann. inst. Pasteur, *62*, 1939, 168.)

DIFFERENTIATING CHARACTERS: Unicellular, colorless, nonsporing, straight, rod-shaped organisms less than 2 μ wide; motile*; Gram negative; *aerobic;* heterotrophic; *liquefy Loeffler's inspissated serum;* no acid or gas produced from glucose or lactose. Species cause ophthalmia (pink eye) of cattle, angular conjunctivitis in man, monkeys, and apes, and possibly trachoma in man.

* See note on motility in the Key in Section F 20.

Type species: *Moraxella lacunata* (Eyre) Lwoff.

NOTES: Three species are described, differentiated in the *Manual* by their action on gelatin and litmus milk.

They are rod-shaped organisms, 0.4 to 0.5 μ by 1.5 to 2.0 μ.

Growth on meat infusion agar is poor. It is improved by the addition of serum or ascitic fluid.

Litmus milk does not support growth of 2/3 species. The third one turns it slightly alkaline.

Loeffler's inspissated serum is liquefied.

No acid is produced from carbohydrates, although it is stated that *M. lacunata* "attacks various carbohydrates and mannitol."

Optimal temperature, 37° C.

Catlin (J. Gen. Microbiol., *37*, 1964, 353 and 369) reports genetic transformation between *Moraxella nonliquefaciens* and *Mima polymorpha* and also *Neisseria catarrhalis*. According to Murray and Traunt (J. Bacteriol., *67*, 1954, 13), *Moraxella* species divide in only one plane, yielding chains, whereas *Neisseria* divides in two planes. Mitchell and Burrell (J. Bacteriol., *87*, 1964, 900) report on a study of serological relationships between *Moraxella*, *Mima*, *Herellea*, and *Bacterium anitratum*.

For further information see:

Henderson, A., Antonie van Leeuwenhoek, *31*, 1965, 395.

Lwoff, A., Ann. Inst. Pasteur, *106*, 1964, 483.

Piéchaud, M., Ann. Inst. Pasteur, *104*, 1961, 291.

Steel, K. J., and Cowan, S. T., Ann. Inst. Pasteur, *106*, 1964, 479.

Noguchia (No.gu'chi.a) Olitsky *et al.*, 1934. *M p. 421*. (J. Exptl. Med., *60*, 1934, 382.)

DIFFERENTIATING CHARACTERS: Unicellular, colorless, straight, rod-shaped organisms less than 2 μ wide; motile with flagella; Gram negative; heterotrophic; *aerobic;* no gas is produced from carbohydrates; acid production from glucose and lactose varies with the species; parasitic on warm-blooded animals, producing granular conjunctival folliculosis in rabbits.

Type species: *Noguchia granulosis* (Noguchi) Olitsky *et al.*

NOTES: Three species are described. They are differentiated in the *Manual* on acid production from glucose, raffinose, maltose, and salicin.

Rod-shaped organisms, 0.2 to 0.3 μ by 0.5 to 1.2 μ. Motile with peritrichous flagella. (Flagellation is considered to be peritrichous, although in some instances only a single flagellum may be produced, located either laterally or at the pole.)

Two out of three tested species grow on meat infusion agar and the third on blood agar. Colonies are small, grayish, and translucent and may be mucoid with capsulated organisms.

Litmus milk is not changed.

Gelatin is not liquefied.

Acid but no gas is produced from glucose and lactose by two species. *N. cuniculi* does not produce acid from sugars.

Nitrite is not produced from nitrate.

Indole is not produced.

Aerobic. Optimal temperature is between 28° and 30° C. with all three species. Motility may not be present in cultures grown at higher temperatures.

Species are serologically homogeneous.

PATHOGENICITY: All species are pathogenic and cause the following diseases.

N. granulosis: considered to cause trachoma in man.

N. simiae: conjunctival folliculosis in monkeys.

N. cuniculi: conjunctival folliculosis in rabbits.

Mima (Mi'ma) de Bord, 1942. (Iowa State Coll. J. Sci., *16*, 1942, 471.)

DIFFERENTIATING CHARACTERS: Unicellular, colorless, nonsporing organisms less than 2 μ wide, which occur predominantly as diplococci on solid media on primary isolation but as a mixture of cocci and rods in liquids with the rod form increasing in proportion as the culture ages; encapsulated; nonmotile; Gram negative; *aerobic;* heterotrophic; grow well on meat infusion agar; no acid or gas produced from glucose or lactose.

Type species: *Mima polymorpha* de Bord.

NOTES: This genus is not listed in the *Manual.*

Only one species has been described. The rod form of the organism is 0.5 to 0.7 μ by 1.0 to 3.0 μ; the cocci are 0.5 to 0.7 μ in diameter.

Colonies on meat extract agar are white, glistening, smooth, moist, and viscid.

Methyl red negative.

Voges-Proskauer negative.

Citrate negative.

Indole negative.

Nitrites are not produced from nitrate.

Catalase positive.

Oxidase negative.

Found in the normal vagina.

See note to *Moraxella.* Catlin and Cunningham (J. Gen. Microbiol., *37*, 1964, 353) refer to the use of oxidase negative strains of *Mima polymorpha.*

Herellea (He.rel'le.a) de Bord, 1942. (Iowa State Coll. J. Sci., *16*, 1942, 471.)

DIFFERENTIATING CHARACTERS: Unicellular, colorless, nonsporing organisms less than 2 μ wide, which occur predominantly as diplococci on solid media on primary isolation but as a mixture of cocci and rods in liquids, with the rod form increasing in proportion as the culture ages; encapsulated; nonmotile; Gram negative; *aerobic;* heterotrophic; grow well on meat extract agar; acid but no gas produced from glucose; lactose not fermented.

Type species: *Herellea vaginicola* de Bord.

NOTES: This genus is not listed in the *Manual.* Only one species is described.

Rod forms are 0.5 to 0.7 μ by 1.0 to 3.0 μ; cocci are 0.5 to 0.7 μ in diameter. Colonies on meat extract agar are white, glistening, smooth, moist, and viscid.

Acid is produced from glucose, mannitol, and dulcitol.

Methyl red negative.

Voges-Proskauer negative.

Nitrites not produced from nitrate.

Citrate is utilized.

Catalase positive.

Oxidase negative.

Found in the normal vagina and in cases of conjunctivitis.

See note to *Moraxella.*

Colloides (Col.loi'des or Col.lo.i'des) de Bord, 1942. (Iowa State Coll. J. Sci., *16*, 1942, 471.)

DIFFERENTIATING CHARACTERS: Unicellular, colorless, nonsporing organisms, less than 2 μ wide, which occur predominantly as diplococci on solid media on primary isolation but as a mixture of cocci and rods in liquids, with the rod form increasing in proportion as the culture ages; encapsulated; nonmotile; Gram negative; *aerobic;* heterotrophic; grow well on meat extract agar; acid and gas produced from glucose and lactose; methyl red positive; Voges-Proskauer negative; not luminescent.

Type species: *Colloides anoxydana* de Bord.

NOTES: This genus is not listed in the *Manual.* Only one species is described. Rod forms are 0.5 to 0.7 μ by 1.0 to 3.0 μ; cocci are 0.5 to 0.7 μ in diameter. Colonies on meat extract agar are white, glistening, smooth, moist, and viscid.

Acid and gas produced from glucose, maltose, lactose, mannitol, and dulcitol. Sucrose, salicin, and dextrin are not fermented.

Indole positive.

Nitrites produced from nitrates.

Catalase positive.

Oxidase negative.

Found in the normal vagina and in cases of conjunctivitis.

Sphaerotilus (Sphae.ro'til.us) Kützing, 1833. *M p. 263.* (Linnaea, *8*, 1833, 385.)

DIFFERENTIATING CHARACTERS: Unicellular, colorless, straight, rod-shaped organisms, which may exceed 2 μ in width. Occur in chains enclosed in a sheath of uniform width attached by means of a conspicuous holdfast; free cells motile with subpolar flagella.

Type species: *Sphaerotilus natans* Kützing.

NOTES: Three species have been described. They are rod-shaped cells, 2 by 3 to 6 μ and motile with subpolar flagella. Gram negative. In the living cells of *S. natans* under dark ground illumination there seems to be only one flagellum of wide amplitude. In stained specimens this "flagellum" is found to separate into at least seven individual flagella.

Cells develop sudanophilic granules, which have been shown to be poly-β-hydroxy butyrate. These, whilst they have an optical resemblance to the sulfur globules described by Skerman *et al.* (*vide infra*), are quite distinctly different. The sulfur globules deposit rapidly in cells virtually devoid of the poly-β-hydroxy butyrate within a few minutes of exposure to hydrogen sulfide.

Motile cells secrete a gum that fixes them to a surface, usually at the liquid-air junction. The cell is usually fixed with the long axis in a vertical position. Division is followed by further secretion of the capsular material, which is composed of polysaccharide containing galactose, fucose, glucose, and glucuronic acid. This is followed by the development of a tubular sheath, which is produced continuously as the chain of cells grows. The sheath is a protein-polysaccharide-lipid complex, which is chemically and anatomically distinct from the capsule (Romano and Peloquin). A cell liberated from the tip or by rupture will start a new colony. Occasionally it adheres to the sheath of the original chain, and the new chain gives the appearance of a false branch. The cells and sheath are colorless in substrates free of organic iron compounds. In the presence of the latter, iron is deposited in the sheath and the organisms become indistinguishable from *Leptothrix*. Pringsheim (Phil. Trans. Roy. Soc. London, Ser. B, *233*, 1949, 605; and Biol. Revs., Cambridge Phil. Soc., *24*,

1949, 200) considers the genera identical. Beger (Zentr. Bakteriol. Parasitenk., Abt. II, *107*, 1953, 318) claims that the sheaths are of different composition. More recently, Mulder and his associates (*vide infra*) have reinvestigated the *Sphaerotilus-Leptothrix* group. They disagree with Pringsheim's views considering *Leptothrix*. They claim that *Sphaerotilus natans* does deposit iron and resembles *Leptothrix* but that it is incapable of oxidizing manganous salts—a property that they attribute to *Leptothrix* species.

During the deposition of the iron, the sheaths become thickened and hard and brittle. The cells within the basal portion of the sheath become progressively thinner and disappear (author's note).

Growth occurs readily on 0.1 per cent peptone in the form of filamentous colonies, the projecting edges of which show organisms within a clearly defined sheath. The organisms require cyanocobalamin for growth. In the denser regions the sheath disappears. On richer media the organism may produce yeast-like colonies in which cells occur at random in a mucilaginous mass.

Skerman, Dementjeva, and Carey (J. Bacteriol., *73*, 1957, 504) demonstrated that *Sphaerotilus natans*, when exposed to H_2S, deposits sulfur internally.

Some recent papers published on the *Sphaerotilus-Leptothrix* group are as follows:

Dondero, N. C., Phillips, R. A., and Heukelekian, H., App. Microbiol., *9*, 1961, 219.

Gaudy, E., and Wolfe, R. S., App. Microbiol., *9*, 1961, 580.

Johnson, A. H., and Stokes, J. L., Antonie van Leeuwenhoek, *31*, 1965, 165.

Johnson, A. H., and Stokes, J. L., J. Bacteriol., *91*, 1966, 1543.

Mandel, M., Johnson, A., and Stokes, J. L., J. Bacteriol., *91*, 1966, 1657.

Mulder, E. G., Deinema, M. H., Van Meen, W. L., and Zevenhuizen, L. P.

T. M., Recl. Trav. chim. Pays-Bas Belg., *81*, 1962, 797.

Mulder, E. G., and Van Veen, W. L., Antonie van Leeuwenhoek, *28*, 1962, 236.

Mulder, E. G., and Van Veen, W. L., Antonie van Leeuwenhoek, *29*, 1963, 121.

Okrend, H., and Dondero, N. C., J. Bacteriol., *87*, 1964, 286.

Pijper, A., Zentral. Bakt., I. Orig., *186*, 1962, 205.

Romano, A. H., and Peloquin, J. P., J. Bacteriol., *86*, 1963, 252.

Rouf, M. A., and Stokes, J. L., J. Bacteriol., *83*, 1962, 343.

Rouf, M. A., and Stokes, J. L., Arch. Mikrobiol., *49*, 1964, 132.

Stokes, J. L., and Powers, M. T., Antonie van Leeuwenhoek, *31*, 1965, 157.

Stokes, J. L., and Johnson, A. H., Antonie van Leeuwenhoek, *31*, 1965, 175.

Leptothrix (Lep'to.thrix) Kützing, 1843. *M p. 264.* (Phycologia Generalis, 1843, 198.)

DIFFERENTIATING CHARACTERS: Unicellular, colorless, rod-shaped organisms less than 2 μ wide; occur in chains within a sheath that does not increase in width *from the base to the tip;* divide by transverse division only; extruded cells are of the same dimensions as those in the sheath; deposit oxides of iron or manganese within the sheath.

Type species: *Leptothrix ochracea* Kützing.

NOTES: Twelve species, differentiated purely on morphological grounds, have been described in the *Manual.*

The essential characteristic of species within this genus is their ability to oxidize iron, depositing the latter within the sheath. Apart from this character, they do not differ from *Sphaerotilus* (see notes on *Sphaerotilus*).

AUTHOR'S NOTE: The form of motility and the general morphology of some species placed in this genus are very vague. There is a suggestion that some may show gliding

motility. It should be noted in this regard that, when *Sphaerotilus natans* is grown in 0.1 per cent peptone water containing ferric ammonium citrate, the width of individual cells within the sheath varies very considerably with the amount of iron deposited in the sheath. If a very long sheathed filament is examined, the cells toward the tip, where the sheath has recently been formed and is still colorless, are fully developed and at least 2.0 μ wide. The cells become progressively smaller in width towards the older portion of the sheath and are reduced to thin rods only 0.5 μ wide in the region where the sheath has become quite brown and brittle. Microscopic examination of filaments in this region has frequently revealed the sudden disappearance of individual cells within the chain, followed by a very sharp movement of the rest of the chain along the rigid tube. This could quite easily be confused with the gliding movement characteristic of *Beggiatoa*. The normal terminal cells, however, are actively motile when free and have clearly defined flagella. For recent discussions on *Leptothrix* see the statement on *Sphaerotilus*.

Toxothrix (Tox'o.thrix) Molisch, 1925. *M p. 269.* (Sci. Repts. Tôhoku Imp. Univ. Fourth Ser., 1925, 144.)

DIFFERENTIATING CHARACTERS: Unicellular, colorless, rod-shaped organisms less than 2 μ in width, arranged in chains within a sheath. With further development, arched, fan-shaped groups of sheathed organisms are formed; iron is deposited in the sheath. Multiplication of the cells is by transverse division only, and sheaths do not increase in width from the base to the tip.

Type species: *Toxothrix trichogenes* (Molisch) Beger.

NOTES: There are two described species. There is a difference of opinion regarding the mode of formation of the arched groups. In one species, *T. gelatinosa*, several sheathed chains of cells appear to arise from approximately the same point, and false branching is common. The branches tend to arch outwards.

In the other species, *T. trichogenes*, it is

suggested that splitting of the original sheath, followed by continued development of the chain of cells, results in the formation of the arched groups.

Peloploca (Pe.lo'plo.ca) Lauterborn, 1913. *M p. 270.* (Allgem. botan. Z., *19*, 1913, 99.)

DIFFERENTIATING CHARACTERS: Multicellular, colorless, organisms 2 μ or less in width, in which each of the individual cells is rod-shaped and contains a gas vacuole (aerosome), which emits a reddish gleam in transmitted light. Trichomes are arranged in bundles; nonmotile; do not deposit iron oxides; do not oxidize sulfides to sulfur.

Type species: *Peloploca undulata* Lauterborn.

NOTES: Two species are recorded. No mention is made in descriptions of a sheath on either species, although this is a character employed for their differentiation in the Key to families of the order *Chlamydobacteriales.*

Individual cells are 3 to 10 μ in length.

The descriptions in the *Manual* leave some doubt whether the organisms of this genus and that of *Pelonema* are chains of unicellular organisms or simply multicellular organisms like *Beggiatoa.* The formation of "trichomes" without sheaths, as described for *Peloploca,* may indicate a multicellular form, although it can well be argued that the same should apply to *Streptococcus.*

Pending clarification of this, the organisms of the genera *Pelonema* and *Peloploca* have been considered as multicellular.

Pelonema (Pe.lo.ne'ma) Lauterborn, 1915. *M p. 271.* (Verhandl. naturhist.-medizin. Ver., Heidelberg, N. F., *13*, 1915, 408.)

DIFFERENTIATING CHARACTERS: Multicellular, colorless organisms, 2 μ or less in width, in which each of the individual cells is rod-shaped and contains a gas vacuole (aerosome), which emits a reddish gleam in transmitted light. Trichomes occur singly and are enclosed in a thin sheath;* do not

deposit iron oxides; do not oxidize sulfides to sulfur.

Type species: *Pelonema tenue* Lauterborn.

NOTES: Four species are described, which are differentiated on morphological characteristics. Individual cells range from 4 to 12 μ long. Trichomes may exceed 200 μ in length.

Found on the surface of waters that contain decomposing algae and that are poorly aerated.

See also note to *Peloploca.*

Crenothrix (Cre'no.thrix) Cohn, 1870. *M p. 272.* (Beitr. Biol. Pflanz., *1*, Heft 1, 1870, 108.)

DIFFERENTIATING CHARACTERS: Colorless, unicellular,* rod-shaped organisms arranged in chains within a sheath, which increases in width from the base to the tip; cells in the basal portion of the sheath are longer than wide. Cells within the sheath vary in size and may exceed 2 μ in width. They divide transversely and longitudinally near the tip to yield a mass of coccoid elements, which are nonmotile. When growing in iron- or manganese-bearing waters, they deposit large quantities of iron or manganese within the sheath.

Type species: *Crenothrix polyspora* Cohn.

NOTES: Only one species is described. It has not been isolated.

Phragmidiothrix (Phrag.mi'di.o.-thrix) Engler, 1883. *M p. 273.* (Vierter Ber. d. Commission z. wissensch. Unters. d. deutsch. Meere in Kiel für 1877 bis 1881, I Abt., 1883, 187.)

DIFFERENTIATING CHARACTERS: Unicellular,† colorless, disc-shaped organisms arranged in chains within a sheath, which increases in width from the base to the tip.

---

* It is not clear from descriptions whether *Crenothrix* is a chain of separated cells enclosed in a sheath or a multicellular organism in a sheath. The Comprehensive Key avoids a decision on this point, which needs clarification.

† It is not clear whether this species is a multicellular organism or a group of unicellular organisms arranged in a chain. The name suggests multicellularity. The Comprehensive Key avoids the issue, which needs clarification.

---

* The presence of a sheath, indicated in the description of the genus in the *Manual,* is not mentioned in any of the species descriptions.

Cells in the basal portion of the sheath are much wider than long and may exceed 2 μ in width. They divide longitudinally and transversely near the tip to produce a mass of nonmotile coccoid elements; do not deposit iron in the sheath.

Type species: *Phragmidiothrix multiseptata* Engler.

NOTES: There is only one species, which has not been isolated.

Found on seaweed in polluted water of the northern Adriatic.

Clonothrix (Clo'no.thrix) Roze, 1896. M p. 274. (J. de Botanique, 10, 1896, 325.)

DIFFERENTIATING CHARACTERS: Unicellular,* colorless, rod-shaped organisms, 2 μ in width, arranged in chains within a sheath; divide by transverse division only and produce at the tip spherical, nonmotile cells, which are extruded singly or in chains. The sheath becomes heavily impregnated with iron or manganese and becomes wide at the base and tapers towards the tip; attached by a holdfast; false branching is common.

Type species: *Clonothrix putealis* (Kirchner 1878) Beger.

NOTES: Only one species is recorded. It has not been isolated.

Found in iron- and manganese-bearing waters.

Caulobacter (Cau.lo.bac'ter) Henrici and Johnson, 1935. M p. 213. (J. Bacteriol., 29, 1935, 4; also 30, 1935, 83.)

DIFFERENTIATING CHARACTERS: Unicellular, colorless, nonsporing, vibrioid, limonoid, subvibrioid, fusiform or bacteroid, rod-shaped organisms, less than 2 μ wide, attached to a substrate by means of a stalk produced as a continuation of the cell wall parallel to the long axis of the cell; reproduction by transverse fission of the cell, with the daughter cell separating from the

---

* It is not clear whether this organism is a unicellular form occurring in chains, as indicated above, or multicellular like *Beggiatoa*. That Roze should have considered it a blue-green alga suggests multicellularity. The Comprehensive Key avoids the issue, which should be clarified.

free end and developing a single polar flagellum. The daughter cell breaks away and produces a stalk from the end of the cell at which the flagellum is located. Reproduction can only occur after the organism has formed its stalk. *Aerobic;* heterotrophic; Gram negative.

Type species: *Caulobacter vibrioides* Henrici and Johnson.

NOTES: The genus **Caulobacter** has recently been subjected to a painstaking reexamination by Jeanne Stove Poindexter (Bacteriol. Revs., 28, 1964, 231), to which the reader is referred. Poindexter has erected a new genus **Asticcacaulis** to cover organisms that develop an excentric stalk (see Key, Section F, 3).

For further information see:

Cohen-Bazire, G., Kunisawa, R., and Poindexter, J. S., J. Gen. Microbiol., 42, 1966, 301.

Schmidt, J. M., and Stanier, R. Y., J. Cell Biol., 28, 1966, 423.

Poindexter, J. L., and Cohen-Bazire, G., J. Cell Biol., 23, 1964, 587.

Gallionella (Gal.li.o.nel'la) Ehrenberg, 1838. M p. 214. (Die Infusionsthierchen, 1838, 166.)

NOTE: Woutera van Iterson (1958) has written a monograph entitled "*Gallionella ferruginea* Ehrenberg in a Different Light," published by N. V. Noord-Hollandsche Uitgevers Maatschappij, Amsterdam, pp. 185. The monograph merits very thoughtful consideration. In van Iterson's own words (p. 116):

"The study has led to the conception that the basic structure of *Gallionella ferruginea* is the ferruginous band to which are ascribed properties of a form of presumably autotrophic life. In or on the bands are variously shaped regions of dense material, and in organic continuity with the ferruginous structures cells may develop. The cells are sometimes flagellated and can also be observed free; many or all of them are apparently capable of a fully heterotrophic way of life. Apart from this mode of development, under some conditions the species may perpetuate by the formation of 'the sporangia of *Gallionella*' or by means of the 'primordial plasm.' Prolonged study of the ferruginous ribbons may disclose further new aspects of fundamental problems connected with life."

Should this study receive confirmation, the insertion in *Bergey's Manual* will be completely outmoded. Readers are therefore asked to treat the *Manual's* descriptions with caution.

See also Vatter and Wolfe (J. Bacteriol., *72*, 1956, 248).

DIFFERENTIATING CHARACTERS: Unicellular, colorless, curved, rod-shaped organisms, less than 2 μ wide, which are attached by means of a stalk originating from the concave side of the cell. The stalk, which is ribbon-like and usually twisted, is composed of or impregnated with oxides of iron and dissolves completely in dilute mineral acid.

Type species: *Gallionella ferruginea* Ehrenberg.

NOTES: Five species have been described in the *Manual*. They are curved to rounded cells, 0.6 by 1.2 to 5.0 μ, which secrete a ribbon-like stalk, dumbbell-shaped in cross section from the concave side. The stalk is reputed to be composed solely of ferric hydroxide, although this is doubtful. It is possibly of an organic nature and impregnated with iron. It dissolves completely in dilute mineral acids. The stalk is usually characteristically twisted. This is attributed in the *Manual* to a slow rotatory motion of the cells, a most unlikely suggestion. Van Iterson (1958) has published electron photomicrographs showing polar flagella on most of the cells.

Found in iron-bearing waters in cool climates. They have been found in local Brisbane (Australia) waters in the middle of winter. The iron-encrusted stalks minus the terminal cells are quite commonly encountered among the hardened sheaths of *Leptothrix*.

Sharply (App. Microbiol., *9*, 1961, 380) describes a marine species of *Gallionella*.

Siderophacus (Si.de.ro'pha.cus) Beger, 1944, *M p. 216*. (Ber. deut. botan. Ges., *61*, 1944, 12.)

DIFFERENTIATING CHARACTERS: Unicellular, colorless, curved or straight, rod-shaped organisms, less than 2 μ wide, *attached* at right angles to the axis of the cell by means of a horn-shaped stalk, circular in cross section and not twisted. The stalk is impregnated with ferric hydroxide.

Type species: *Siderophacus corneolus* (Dorff) Beger.

NOTES: Only one species has been described. Cells are 0.6 to 1.0 μ by 2.5 to 3.0 μ. The stalks, broader at the base than at the top, are 15 to 30 μ long.

Found in iron-bearing waters.

Nevskia (Nev'ski.a) Famintzin, 1892. *M p. 216*. (Bull. Acad. Imp. Sci., St. Pétersburg, Sér. IV, *34*, (N. S. 2), 1892, 484.)

DIFFERENTIATING CHARACTERS: Unicellular, colorless, rod-shaped organisms, 2 μ wide; attached, at right angles to the long axis of the cell, to the ends of lobose, dichotomously branched stalks composed of gum. Iron is not deposited in the stalk.

Type species: *Nevskia ramosa* Famintzin.

NOTES: A single species has been described. Cells are 2.0 by 6 to 12 μ and contain a number of highly refractile globules of fat or sulfur. Colonies are globular, bushlike or plate-like, and float on the surface of water.

It is possible that there is some relationship between these organisms and those of the genus *Thiobacterium* Janke. Neither has been isolated (author's note).

Pasteuria (Pas.teu'ri.a) Metchnikoff, 1888. *M p. 279*. (Ann. inst. Pasteur, *2*, 1888, 166.)

DIFFERENTIATING CHARACTERS: Unicellular, colorless, pear-shaped cells, 1 to 2 μ wide; *attached* to one another or to a firm substrate by holdfasts secreted at the narrow end; multiplication by longitudinal fission or by terminal budding.

Type species: *Pasteuria ramosa* Metchnikoff.

NOTES: Only one species is described. Cells are 1 to 2 μ by 4 to 5 μ. They form cauliflower-like masses. The cells and method of reproduction resemble those of *Chamaesiphon*, a blue-green alga.

Parasitic on fresh water crustacea (*Daphnia* spp.) Forms resembling them have been found on submerged glass slides.

Blastocaulis (Blas.to.cau'lis) Henrici and Johnson, 1935 *M p. 279.* (J. Bacteriol., *30*, 1935, 84.)

DIFFERENTIATING CHARACTERS: Unicellular, colorless, pear-shaped to spherical organisms, 2 μ in width, borne on the end of a long, slender stalk attached to a holdfast; reproduce by budding from the free end of the cell.

Type species: *Blastocaulis sphaerica* Henrici and Johnson, 1935.

NOTES: There is only a single species described. It has not been isolated. During budding the bud stains intensely and uniformly, whereas the mother cell shows differentiation. The former is usually Gram positive and the latter Gram negative. The organisms described were from waters of Lake Alexander, Minnesota, where the temperature did not exceed 23° C.

Azotobacter (A.zo.to.bac'ter) Beijerinck, 1901. *M p. 283.* (Zentr. Bakteriol. Parasitenk., Abt. II, *7*, 1901, 567.)

DIFFERENTIATING CHARACTERS: Unicellular, colorless, nonsporing, spherical to rod-shaped organisms, which may exceed 2 μ in width; motile or nonmotile; Gram negative; *aerobic;* heterotrophic; fix gaseous nitrogen in the absence of a leguminous host; do not deposit iron about the cells or sulfur internally.

Type species: *Azotobacter chroococcum* Beijerinck.

NOTES: The genus as described in the *Manual* has three species. *A. chroococcum* and *A. agilis* are large rods, 2 to 3 μ by 3 to 6 μ. *A. indicus* is much smaller, 0.5 to 1.2 μ by 1.7 to 2.7 μ. Motile by means of peritrichous flagella. *A. insigne* Derx and *A. macrocytogenes* Jensen (see Baillie, Hodgkiss, and Norris, J. App. Bacteriol., *25*,

1962, 116) have polar flagella (*A. insigne*) or a polar phase (*A. macrocytogenes*).

A. chroococcum during the development of the colonies changes from a uniformly staining rod to a lozenge-shaped cell and finally to a spherical cell with a marked reticulate stain. Colonies during this change turn from transparent to milky or opalescent. Finally, the cells deposit a melanin pigment and cell walls become considerably thickened—the so-called "arthrospore" or "cyst" stage—and colonies turn black.

The process of cyst formation has been studied with the electron microscope in *A. chroococcum* by Tchan, Birch-Andersen, and Jensen (Arch. Mikrobiol., *43*, 1962, 50); in *A. agilis* by Socolofsky and Wyss (J. Bacteriol., *81*, 1961, 946) and Layne and Johnson (J. Bacteriol., *87*, 1964, 684); and in *A. vinelandii* by Wyss, Neumann, and Socolofsky (J. Biochem. Biophys. Cytol., *10*, 1961, 555), to which the reader is referred for details.

Vela and Wyss (J. Bacteriol., *87*, 1964, 476) describe a new staining method for visualization of the cysts by light microscopy.

A. agilis produces slightly yellowish colonies with a pigment—not fluorescin—that fluoresces a bluish green under ultraviolet light. Cells are nearly spherical. Tchan (Proc. Linnean Soc. N. S. W., *78*, 1953, 85) places this organism in the genus *Azotococcus*. The capsular polysaccharide of *A. agilis* strain 132 is composed of a polymer of galactose and rhamnose at a molar ratio of approximately 1.0:0.7. A component similar to sialic acid is also present (Cohen and Johnson, J. Bacteriol., *88*, 1964, 1695).

A. indicus appears to be bicellular, although it is described in the *Manual* as having two highly refractile bodies in the ends of a unicellular form. It is very acid-tolerant.

Derx (Koninkl. Ned. Akad. Wetenschap., Proc. Sect. Sci., *53*, 1950, 145; and Ann. Bogoriensis, *1*, 1950, 1) has made this species the type species of a new genus,

Beijerinckia. His opinion is strongly supported by Tchan (Proc. Linnean Soc. N. S. W., *78*, 1953, 85).

All three species grow poorly on peptone but slowly and copiously on a glucose- or mannitol-mineral salts agar, fixing atmospheric nitrogen.

Some other papers of systematic interest are the following:

Becking, J. H., Plant and Soil, *16*, 1962, 171.

De Ley, J., and Park, I. W., Antonie van Leeuwenhoek, *32*, 1966, 6.

Goldschmidt, M. C., and Wyss, O., J. Bacteriol., *91*, 1966, 120.

Jensen, H. L., Petersen, E. J., De, P. K., and Bhattacharya, R. A., Arch. Mikrobiol., *36*, 1960, 182.

Layne, J. S., and Johnson, E. J., J. Bacteriol., *87*, 1964, 684.

Layne, J. S., and Johnson, E. J., J. Bacteriol., *88*, 1964, 956.

Parker, L. T., and Socolofsky, M., D. J. Bacteriol., *91*, 1966, 297.

Sen, M., and Sen, S. P., J. Gen. Microbiol., *41*, 1965, 1.

Stevensen, L. H., and Socolofsky, M. D., J. Bacteriol., *91*, 1966, 304.

Stockdale, H., Ribbons, D. W., and Dawes, E. A., J. Gen. Microbiol., *41*, (1965) XVIII, Proceedings.

Tomlinson, G. A., and Campbell, J. J. R., J. Bacteriol., *86*, 1963, 1165.

Van Schreven, D. A., Antonie van Leeuwenhoek, *28*, 1962, 97.

Rhizobium (Rhi.zo'bi.um) Frank, 1889. *M p. 285.* (Ber. deut. Botan. Ges., *7*, 1889, 380.)

DIFFERENTIATING CHARACTERS: Unicellular, colorless, nonsporing, rod-shaped organisms, less than 2 μ wide; motile with peritrichous flagella* or nonmotile; Gram negative; heterotrophic; *aerobic;* capable of forming nodules on, and fixing nitrogen in association with, leguminous plants under specified conditions.

Type species: *Rhizobium leguminosarum* Frank.

NOTES: Six species have been described. Differentiation is based on host specificity and acid formation in, or peptonization of, litmus milk. Some practical results have been achieved by application of serological tests.

In the host plant the bacterial cells undergo pleomorphic changes into T- and Y-shaped "bacteroids" generally considered to be degenerate. For a review on the subject of bacteroids, see Jordan (Bacteriol. Revs., *26*, 1962, 119).

Away from the host they will not fix nitrogen.

Acid production from sugars is very slight.

Milk is peptonized by several host species.

The organisms are easy to identify if isolated from the host. If they are isolated from soil, identification may be exceedingly difficult.

If nodule formation is ignored and species are compared with those of other genera, they may key out to the genera *Pseudomonas, Alcaligenes,* and *Paracolobactrum.*

A detailed survey of strains of *Rhizobium* and *Agrobacterium* has recently been made by Graham (J. Gen. Microbiol., *35*, 1964, 511; Antonie van Leeuwenhoek, *29*, 1963, 281; *30*, 1964, 68) and by Graham and Parker (Plant and Soil, *20*, 1964, 383). For other papers of systematic interest see the following:

Balassa, G., Bacteriol. Revs., *27*, 1963, 228.

Cook, F. D., and Quadling, C., Can. J. Microbiol., *8*, 1962, 934.

---

* Leifson and Erdman (Antonie van Leeuwenhoek, *24*, 1958, 97) have examined the flagellation of 82 strains of *Rhizobium* and describe two types of flagellation. In one, flagella are single and subpolar with a wave length of 1.9 to 2.2μ. The other type shows peritrichous flagellation with usually one flagellum or, less often, several flagella with a wave length of 1.3 to 1.6 μ. The former grow slowly on peptone media and the latter relatively rapidly.

In view of this report, the classification of the group needs re-examination.

Dart, P. J., and Mercer, F. V., Arch. Mikrobiol., *47*, 1963, 1.

Dart, P. J., and Mercer, F. V., J. Bacteriol., *85*, 1963, 951.

Dart, P. J., and Mercer, F. V., J. Bacteriol., *91*, 1966, 1314.

Date, R. A., and Morris Decker, A., Can. J. Microbiol., *11*, 1965, 1.

De Ley, J., and Rassel, A., J. Gen. Microbiol., *41*, 1965, 85.

Dudman, W. F., J. Bacteriol., *88*, 1964, 782.

Ellis, N. J., Kalz, G. G., and Doncaster, J. J., Can. J. Microbiol., *8*, 1962, 836.

Graham, P. H., J. Gen. Microbiol., *30*, 1963, 245.

Graham, P. H., Antonie van Leeuwenhoek, *31*, 1965, 349.

Gupta, B. M., and Kleczkowska, J., J. Gen. Microbiol., *27*, 1962, 473.

Hertogh, A. A., Mayeux, P. A., and Evans, H. J., J. Bacteriol., *8*, 1964, 239.

Humphrey, B., and Vincent, J. M., J. Gen. Microbiol., *29*, 1962, 557.

Humphrey, B. A., and Vincent, J. M., J. Gen. Microbiol., *41*, 1965, 109.

Jordan, D. C., Can. J. Microbiol., *3*, 1957, 911.

Jordan, D. C., and Grinyer, I., Can. J. Microbiol., *11*, 1965, 721.

Lange, R. T., Antonie van Leeuwenhoek, *25*, 1959, 272.

Means, U. M., Johnson, H. W., and Date, R. A., J. Bacteriol., *87*, 1964, 547.

Mosse, B., J. Gen. Microbiol., *36*, 1964, 49.

Norris, D. O., Aust. J. Agr. Res., *10*, 1959, 651.

Norris, D. O., Plant and Soil, *22*, 1965, 143.

Vincent, J. M., J. Gen. Microbiol., *28*, 1962, 653.

Vincent, J. M., Humphrey, B., and North, R. J., J. Gen. Microbiol., *29*, 1962, 551.

Agrobacterium (Ag.ro.bac.te'ri.um) Conn, 1942. *M p. 288.* (J. Bacteriol., *44*, 1942, 359.)

DIFFERENTIATING CHARACTERS: Unicellular, nonphotosynthetic, nonsporing, straight, rod-shaped organisms, less than 2 μ wide; motile with flagella or nonmotile; Gram negative; *aerobic;* heterotrophic; acid production from glucose and lactose varies with the species; no gas produced in peptone sugars; five of the seven species are pathogenic to plants and produce hyperplastic diseases.

Type species: *Agrobacterium tumefaciens* (Smith and Townsend) Conn.

NOTES: Rods 0.2 to 0.8 μ by 1 to 3.0 μ. Generally motile, although the location of flagella is in doubt. Some cells have a single flagellum in a polar or lateral position. Others have several and are peritrichous. This may vary, as in *Chromobacterium*, with the medium.

Grow well on nutrient agar and frequently also in mineral salts media with a suitable carbon source. Acid production from carbohydrates is very weak and may be overshadowed by ammonia liberated from the peptone. Litmus milk is turned alkaline and is peptonized by some species.

Most species are pathogenic to plants and produce hyperplastic diseases, such as galls and hairy root. When isolated directly from soil, the organisms may be difficult to identify. They may key sub to the genera *Pseudomonas, Alcaligenes, Achromobacter,* and *Flavobacterium.*

For further information see:

De Ley, J., Bernaerts, M., Rassel, A., and Guilmot, J., J. Gen. Microbiol., *43*, 1966, 7.

Chromobacterium* (Chro.mo.bac.te'ri.um) Bergonzini, 1881. *M p. 292.* (Ann. Soc. Naturalisti in Modéna, Ser. 2, *14*, 1881, 153.)

DIFFERENTIATING CHARACTERS: Unicellular, nonsporing, nonphotosynthetic, rod-shaped organisms, less than 2 μ wide, with

---

* The papers by P. H. A. Sneath and his associates (J. Gen. Microbiol., *15*, 1956, 70 and 99; *20*, 1959, 284 and 414; and Iowa State Coll. J. Sci., *34*, 1960, 243) should be consulted for this genus.

a deep purple color due to the pigment violacein; motile with peritrichous or polar flagella; Gram negative; heterotrophic.

Type species: *Chromobacterium violaceum* (Schroeter) Bergonzini.

NOTES: Four species are described. They are differentiated in the *Manual* on cultural characteristics.

Rods, 0.4 to 0.8 μ by 1.0 to 5.0 μ, motile by polar or peritrichous flagella. Gram negative. Leifson (J. Bacteriol., *71*, 1956, 393) states that two different types of flagella are produced, the polar being quite different from the lateral flagella. Some cultures produce only polar and others produce both.

The organisms grow well on nutrient agar, producing a violet pigment, which is not soluble in water. It has been identified as violacein, chemically related to indigo. Colorless variants are not uncommon.

Cultures are difficult to maintain, apparently because of high sensitivity to peroxides.

Leifson has recently re-examined 28 strains of purple organisms from different sources and gives the following information:

All strains produced acid from glucose and fructose.

None of them produced acid from lactose, dulcitol, or salicin; none hydrolyzed urea or produced indole.

Gelatin was liquefied by all but three strains, and nitrates were reduced by all but one strain.

Sixteen of the 28 strains fermented glucose, fructose, and inulin and grew at 37° C.

Six oxidized glucose and fructose, and several other sugars and did *not* grow at 37° C.

The *Manual* records four species, *C. violaceum, C. amethystinum, C. janthinum,* and *C. marismortui.*

Leifson's strains probably cover *C. violaceum* and possibly *C. janthinum* and one new species.

C. marismortui is halophilic.

Alcaligenes   (Al.ca.li'ge.nes)   Castel-

lani and Chalmers, 1919. *M p. 297.* (Manual Trop. Med., 3rd ed., 1919, 936.)

DIFFERENTIATING CHARACTERS: Unicellular, nonphotosynthetic, nonsporing, straight, rod-shaped bacteria, less than 2 μ wide; do not form zoogloea; nonmotile or motile with flagella; Gram negative; *aerobic;* heterotrophic; grow well on meat extract agar without the addition of growth factors; no acid or gas produced from glucose or lactose; litmus milk turned strongly alkaline.

Type species: *Alcaligenes faecalis* Castellani and Chalmers.

NOTES: Six species are described, separated in the *Manual* on motility, gelatin liquefaction and growth in milk.

Straight, rod-shaped, unicellular organisms, 0.5 to 1.0 μ by 1 to 3 μ. Three of six species are motile. Although recorded in the *Manual* as peritrichous, other texts record polar flagellation. Frequently capsulated.

Grow quite well on meat infusion agar, producing translucent, grayish colonies or white, opaque colonies (depending on species), which are frequently viscid with the capsulated forms. Gelatin is liquefied by three species.

Litmus milk is made alkaline and is also peptonized by two of the gelatin-liquefying species.

No acid or gas is produced from carbohydrates.

Indole is not produced.

Nitrate reduction is variable.

Optimal temperature, 20° or 37° C. depending on origin.

Found in the intestinal canal, milk, and water.

For information relating to species of *Alcaligenes* see the following:

Moore, H. B., and Pickett, M. J., Can. J. Microbiol., *6*, 1960, 43.

Koontz, F. P., and Faber, J. E., *Ibid.*, *9*, 1963, 499.

Achromobacter   (A.chro.mo.bac'ter) Bergey *et al.*, 1923. *M p. 300.* (Bergey's

Manual of Determinative Bacteriology, 1st ed., 1923, 132.)

DIFFERENTIATING CHARACTERS: Unicellular, colorless, nonsporing, straight, rod-shaped organisms, less than 2 μ wide; nonmotile or motile with peritrichous flagella; Gram negative; *aerobic;* heterotrophic; grow well on meat infusion agar with or without 3 per cent salt added. No gas produced from carbohydrates; acid is produced by a few species from glucose or from glucose and lactose; litmus milk acid or unchanged.

They are not pathogenic to warm-blooded animals and bear no antigenic relationship, so far as is known, to organisms of the *Enterobacteriaceae.*

Type species: *Achromobacter liquefaciens* (Eisenberg) Bergey *et al.*

NOTES: Fifteen species have been described. They have been separated in the *Manual* on morphological and biochemical properties.

Ten species are motile and have peritrichous flagella.

Colonies are not pigmented but may be translucent to off-white.

Gelatin is liquefied by 8/15 species.

Litmus milk remains unchanged (12/15) or becomes alkaline (1/15) or acid (2/15).

Acid but no gas is produced from glucose by 6/11. Only one species (*A. delmarvae*) produces acid from lactose. No acid or gas is produced by 5/11.

Starch is hydrolyzed by 3/9 species.

Fat is hydrolyzed by 1/3.

Indole is not produced (11/11).

Nitrite is produced from nitrate by 10/14.

Urease is not produced by 4/4 species.

H_2S is produced by 2/7.

Naphthalene is utilized by 2/2 and citrate by 2/3.

Trimethylamine is produced from trimethylamine oxide by 1/7.

The organisms are principally of soil or water origin and have an optimal temperature of about 25° C.

For information relating to the species of *Achromobacter* see the following:

Bailey, L., J. Gen. Microbiol., *31*, 1963, 147.

Citarella, R. V., and Colwell, R. R., Can. J. Microbiol., *12*, 1966, 418.

Goerz, R. D., and Pengra, R. M., J. Bacteriol., *81*, 1961, 568.

Tulecke, W., Orenski, S. W., Taggart, R., and Colavito, L., J. Bacteriol., *89*, 1965, 905.

Ingram, M., and Shewan, J. W., J. App. Bacteriol., *23*, 1960, 373.

Flavobacterium (Fla.vo.bac.te′ri.um) Bergey *et al.*, 1923. *M p. 309.* (Bergey's Manual of Determinative Bacteriology, 1st ed., 1923, 97.)

DIFFERENTIATING CHARACTERS: Unicellular, nonsporing, nonphotosynthetic, straight, rod-shaped organisms less than 2 μ wide; nonmotile or motile with peritrichous flagella; Gram negative; *aerobic;* heterotrophic; with the appropriate salt concentration, they all grow on meat infusion and other media and produce colonies with yellow or orange pigments, which are not soluble in water; no gas produced from carbohydrates; acid *may* be produced from glucose and lactose; litmus milk may be rendered acid or alkaline or not change. Starch may be hydrolyzed and nitrates may be reduced to nitrite.

Type species: *Flavobacterium aquatile* (Frankland and Frankland) Bergey *et al.*

NOTES: Twenty-six species are described. They are separated on motility, pigmentation, action on litmus milk, reduction of nitrate, growth on potato, fermentation of glucose, production of indole, liquefaction of gelatin, and ecological characters.

Straight, rod-shaped, unicellular organisms, 0.5 to 1.0 μ by 0.8 to 3.0 μ. Gram negative. Fifteen of the 26 recorded species are motile and have peritrichous flagella.

In the presence of the required amount of salt (some species are marine), growth occurs on nutrient agar with the production of an insoluble yellow pigment.

Nineteen out of 26 tested species liquefy gelatin.

Litmus milk remains unchanged or becomes slightly alkaline. Slight acidity is recorded for only two species, which do not produce acid from lactose.

Indole is produced by only 1/23 species (*F. suaveolens*). Nitrate is reduced by only 9/23.

Acid but *no gas* is produced from glucose by 9/12 species, three of which also ferment lactose.

H₂S is produced by 5/14 species.

Urease is not produced (7/7).

Fat is not hydrolyzed (5/5).

Coagulated serum is liquefied by 1/5 species.

Ammonia is produced from peptone by 5/5.

Casein is hydrolyzed by 2/4.

The organisms have been isolated from water, soil, dairy wastes, sea water, sea mud, and fish. *F. piscicida* is highly pathogenic to fish. Hansen, Ingebritsen, and Weeks (J. Bacteriol., *86*, 1963, 602) report that this species produces no carotenoid pigments and is a polar flagellate. It should be removed from the genus *Flavobacterium*.

For some recent papers on the systematics of *Flavobacterium* see the following:

Hayes, P. R., J. Gen. Microbiol., *30*, 1963, 1.

Twarog, R., and Cleverdon, R. C., Antonie van Leeuwenhoek, *27*, 1961, 316.

Agarbacterium (A.gar.bac.te′ri.um) Angst, 1929. *M p. 322.* (Publs. Puget Sound Biol. Sta., Univ. Wash., *7*, 1929, 52.)

DIFFERENTIATING CHARACTERS: Unicellular, nonphotosynthetic, nonsporing, straight, rod-shaped organisms, less than 2 μ wide; nonmotile or motile with peritrichous flagella; Gram negative; *aerobic;* heterotrophic. With the appropriate salt concentration, all species will grow on meat infusion agar and cause a liquefaction of the agar. The growth is buff, yellow, or orange; no gas is produced from carbohydrates; acid produced from glucose or lactose by only a few species.

Type species: *Agarbacterium aurantiacum* Angst.

NOTES: Twelve species are described. Organisms 0.5 to 1.0 μ by 1 to 4 μ. One species (*A. uliginosum*) is described as slightly curved. Six of the twelve recorded species are nonmotile. Of the others, two have peritrichous flagella, and for four the type of flagellation is not recorded.

Gelatin is liquefied by all species except *A. pastinator.*

Litmus milk remains unchanged except with *A. pastinator*, which turns it slightly acid.

No acid or gas is produced from glucose or lactose by 8 of the 12 species. Acid is produced by *A. pastinator* and *A. uliginosum* from both sugars. Four species are reported to produce acid from mannitol and not from glucose.

Starch is hydrolyzed by 8/12 species.

Indole is not produced (10/10).

H₂S is produced by 2/7 species.

Eleven of the 12 species are of marine origin. The optimal temperature is between 20° and 28° C.

Beneckea (Be.neck′e.a) Campbell, 1957. *M p. 328.* (Bergey's Manual of Determinative Bacteriology, 7th ed., 1957, 328.)

DIFFERENTIATING CHARACTERS: Unicellular, nonsporing, nonphotosynthetic, straight, rod-shaped organisms; motile with peritrichous flagella; Gram negative; *aerobic;* heterotrophic; acid but no gas produced from glucose; no acid from lactose; chitin is hydrolyzed.

Type species: *Beneckea labra* (Campbell and Williams) Campbell.

NOTES: Six species are listed. They are separated in the *Manual* on gelatin liquefaction and production of nitrite from nitrate and acid from sucrose.

The organisms grow well on nutrient agar. Only one of the six species recorded is pigmented (yellow-orange).

Gelatin is liquefied by 4/6 species.

Litmus is rendered slightly acid after 2 to 6 days by 4 species, although all fail to produce acid from lactose in peptone water (?).

Acid but no gas is produced from glucose but not from lactose by 6/6 species.

Starch is hydrolyzed by 5/5.

Chitin is hydrolyzed—the significant generic character.

Casein is hydrolyzed by 3/5.

Fat is hydrolyzed by 1/4 species.

Indole is produced by 1/5.

Nitrite is produced from nitrate by 3/6.

Ammonia is produced from peptone by 6/6.

Urease is produced by 1/5.

H₂S is produced by 5/5 species.

Trimethylamine is not produced from trimethylamine oxide (5/5).

All recorded species are of marine origin, principally from sea mud.

The optimal temperature for growth lies between 20° and 30° C.

Alginobacter (Al.gi′no.bac.ter) Thjøtta and Kåss, 1945. *M p. 348.* (Avhandl. Norske Videnskaps-Akad., Oslo. I Mat.-Naturv. Kl., No. 5, 1945, 17.)

DIFFERENTIATING CHARACTERS: Unicellular, colorless, nonsporing, straight, rod-shaped organisms; motile with peritrichous flagella; Gram negative; *aerobic;* heterotrophic; acid and gas are produced from glucose and lactose; gelatin not liquefied; *alginates fermented with the production of acid and gas;* hydrogen sulfide produced; methyl red positive; Voges-Proskauer weak; citrate utilized; nitrite produced from nitrate.

Type species: *Alginobacter acidofaciens* Kåss, Lid, and Molland.

NOTES: There is only one species; found in soil. Optimal temperature, 30° C.

Erwinia (Er.wi′ni.a) Winslow *et al.*, 1917. *M p. 349.* (J. Bacteriol., *2*, 1917, 560.)

DIFFERENTIATING CHARACTERS: Unicellular, nonphotosynthetic, nonsporing, straight, rod-shaped organisms less than 2 μ wide; motile with peritrichous flagella. Gram negative (except for two species); *aerobic;* heterotrophic; produce acid or acid and gas from glucose; produce wilts and necrotic diseases of plants.

Species differ considerably on other characters, of which the more commonly described are presented in the Notes.

Type species: *Erwinia amylovora* (Burrill) Winslow *et al.*

NOTES: Seventeen species are recorded. They are separated in the *Manual* on the type of lesion produced; color; hydrolysis of starch; coagulation of milk; utilization of ethyl alcohol, dulcitol, malonate, and hippurate; gelatin liquefaction and growth in Uschinsky's solution.

Rods 0.4 to 0.9 μ by 0.8 to 2.5 μ. Fifteen out of seventeen species are Gram negative. Two (*E. carnegieana* and *E. citrimaculans*) are described variously as Gram positive and Gram negative.

Grow well on meat infusion agar, producing colonies that are a grayish white, yellowish, brown, or red (*Erwinia rhapontica*). The red pigment is not prodigiosin.

Gelatin is liquefied by 13/17 species.

Starch is hydrolyzed by 2/15 species.

Blood serum is not liquefied by species tested on it.

Indole is produced by three species.

H₂S is produced by 7/13 species.

Nitrite is produced from nitrates by 15/17.

Citrate is utilized by all of four species tested.

Acid is produced from glucose by all species. Gas is produced by *E. chrysanthemi, E. carnegieana, E. dissolvens, E. nimipressuralis, E. carotovora,* and *E. atroseptica.*

E. carotovora produces acid from 5 per cent ethyl alcohol.

Acid is produced from lactose by 13 of the 16 species for which it is recorded. Gas is also produced by the species listed under glucose.

Litmus milk is turned acid and clotted by most lactose fermenters.

The methyl red and Voges-Proskauer reactions are not recorded for all species. Of the nine recorded, eight are methyl red negative and Voges-Proskauer positive. *E. carotovora* is methyl red positive and Voges-Proskauer negative.

Species are noted for the production of diseases in plants. Six species, all of which produce acid but no gas from glucose, are responsible for dry rots, galls, and wilts in plants but *not* soft rot. All other species are responsible for the production of soft rots of various plants. The soft rot is caused by the breakdown of the middle lamella of the plant parenchyma by the enzyme protopectinase.

The fermentative action of *Erwinia* species and their other reactions suggest that they may well be integrated into groups within the *Enterobacteriaceae*. This awaits a comparative study. Some recent papers on the *Erwinia* group are the following:

Billing, E., Baker, L. A. E., Crosse, J. E., and Garrett, C. M. E., J. App. Bacteriol., *24*, 1961, 195.

Billing, E., and Baker, L. A. E., J. App. Bacteriol., *26*, 1963, 58.

Grula, E. A., J. Bacteriol., *80*, 1960, 369, 375.

Grula, E. A., J. Bacteriol., *83*, 1962, 981.

Grula, M. M., and Grula, E. A., J. Bacteriol., *83*, 1962, 989.

Grula, E. A., and Grula, M. M., Biochem. Biophys. Res. Comm., *17*, 1964, 341.

Kilgore, W. W., and Starr, M. P., J. Biol. Chem., *234*, 1959, 2227.

Lockhart, W. R., and Koenig, K., J. Bacteriol., *90*, 1965, 1638.

Sutton, D. D., and Starr, M. P., J. Bacteriol., *78*, 1959, 427.

Sutton, D. D., Ark, P. A., and Starr, M. P., Phytopathol., *50*, 1960, 182.

Sutton, D. D., and Starr, M. P., J. Bacteriol., *78*, 1959, 427.

Sutton, D. D., and Starr, M. P., J. Bacteriol., *80*, 1959, 104.

Salmonella (Sal.mo.nel′la) Lignières, 1900. *M p. 368.* (Rec. méd. vétér., Sér. 8, *7*, 1900, 389.)

DIFFERENTIATING CHARACTERS: Unicellular, colorless, nonsporing, straight, rod-shaped organisms, less than 2 μ wide; motile with peritrichous flagella or nonmotile (*S. pullorum* and *S. gallinarum*); Gram negative; *aerobic;* heterotrophic; grow well on meat infusion agar, producing discrete, colorless colonies on firm media; produce acid and gas from glucose (except *S. typhi* and *S. gallinarum*); no acid from lactose; Voges-Proskauer negative; gelatin not liquefied; indole not produced; urease negative.

Pathogenic; contain antigens assigned to the genus *Salmonella*.

Type species: *Salmonella choleraesuis* (Smith) Weldin.

NOTES: These represent only commonly encountered species. The genus as presented in the *Manual* has 10 described species.

Serotypes are separated into groups on the basis of the smooth, somatic antigens and serotypes on the flagellar antigens.

In addition to the differentiating characteristics, the following should be noted:

Litmus milk turns slightly alkaline or remains unchanged.

H_2S production is variable.

Acid and gas are produced from glucose by all but two important species, *S. typhi* and *S. gallinarum,* which produce only acid. *Lactose, sucrose,* and *salicin* are not fermented.

Nitrite is produced from nitrate.

Citrate is utilized by most species.

Optimal temperature, 37° C.

All species cause disease in man or animals, usually of an alimentary nature. *S. typhi* causes typhoid fever. *S. paratyphi* and *S. schottmuelleri* cause typhoid-like fevers. Other species cause gastroenteritis.

The literature on *Salmonella* is voluminous. Only four papers dealing with unusual aspects of the genus are quoted. As with other members of the family *Enterobacteriaceae*, the group is under constant review by the Subcommittee on the *Enterobacteriaceae*. Their definition of the genus follows:

The group (genus) *Salmonella* consists of motile or nonmotile nonsporing Gram negative rods, which may or may not have fimbriae; grow on ordinary media, reduce nitrates to nitrites, give a negative oxidase reaction and break down carbohydrates by a fermentative reaction that distinguishes them from other families in which the reaction is oxidative.

Gas from glucose* .... +
Lactose (acid) .... −
Sucrose (acid) .... −
Mannitol (acid) .... +
Dulcitol (acid) .... d
Salicin (acid) .... −
Adonitol (acid) .... −
Inositol (acid) .... d
Indole .... −
Methyl red .... +
Voges-Proskauer .... −
Ammonium citrate .... +
H₂S .... +
Urease .... −
Gelatin liquefaction .... d
Growth in KCN medium .... −
Phenylalanine deaminase .... −
Sodium malonate .... −
Lysine decarboxylase .... +
Arginine dehydrolase .... +
Ornithine decarboxylase .... +

For further details see Intern. Bull. Bacteriol. Nomen. Taxon., *13*, No. 2, 1963, 69.

For other information see the following:
Asakura, S., Eguchi, G., and Iino, T., J. Mol. Biol., *10*, 1964, 42.
Iino, T., and Lederberg, J., in The World Problem of Salmonellosis, Monographiae Biological, *13*, 1964, Uitgeverij, Dr. W. Junk, Dur Haag.
Leistner, L., Deibel, R. H., Johantges, J., and Niven, C. F., Jr., Amer. Meat Inst. Foundation Bull., *56*, 1963.
Silliker, J. H., Deibel, R. H., and Chiu, J. Y., App. Microbiol., *12*, 1964, 395.

Arizona Group

The definition for the genus given by the Subcommittee on the *Enterobacteriaceae* of the I C N B is as follows:
The *Arizona* group (genus) consists of motile, nonsporing, Gram negative rods; grow on ordinary media, reduce nitrates to nitrites, give a negative oxidase reaction, and break down carbohydrates by a fer-

* The following signs are used: +, positive; −, negative; d, different biochemical types.

mentative reaction that distinguishes them from other families in which the reaction is oxidative.

Gas from glucose† .... +
Lactose .... d
Sucrose .... −
Mannitol .... +
Dulcitol .... −
Salicin .... −
Adonitol .... −
Inositol .... −
Indol .... −
Methyl red .... +
Voges-Proskauer .... −
Ammonium citrate .... +
Hydrogen sulfide .... +
Urease .... −
Gelatin liquefaction .... (+)
Growth in KCN medium .... −
Phenylalanine deaminase .... −
Sodium malonate .... +
Lysine decarboxylase .... +
Arginine dihydrolase .... (+)
Ornithine decarboxylase .... +

For further details see Intern. Bull. Bacteriol. Nomen. Taxon., *13*, No. 2, 1963, 69.

Citrobacter Group

The definition for the genus given by the Subcommittee on the *Enterobacteriaceae* of the I C N B is as follows:
The *Citrobacter* group (genus) consists of motile, nonsporing, Gram negative rods: grow on ordinary media, reduce nitrates to nitrites, give a negative oxidase reaction, and break down carbohydrates by a fermentative reaction that distinguishes them from other families in which the reaction is oxidative.

Gas from glucose‡ .... +
Lactose .... + or ×
Sucrose .... d
Mannitol .... +
Dulcitol .... d

† The following signs are used: +, positive; −, negative; d, different biochemical types; (+), rare strains positive.
‡ The following signs are used: +, positive; −, negative; ×, delayed; d, different biochemical types; (+), rare strains positive.

ILLUSTRATIONS

The following illustrations have been compiled from several sources for the purpose of showing the cardinal features of genera mentioned in the Keys and in the *Manual*. A large number of them are original photomicrographs from slide cultures prepared by the techniques described in Methods.

With the following exceptions, all organisms photographed by phase contrast have been cultured on peptone yeast extract agar containing 0.5 per cent sodium chloride:

Chlorobium: Chlorobium medium.

Acetobacter, Diplococcus, Streptococcus, Pediococcus, Leuconostoc, Lactobacillus, Propioni-
bacterium: peptone yeast extract agar + 1 per cent glucose.

Caulobacter: 0.1 per cent peptone water.

Spirillum. Williams and Rittenberg's *Spirillum* medium.

Halobacterium: Gibbons' halophile agar.

Photobacterium: Peptone yeast extract agar + 3 per cent NaCl.

Sphaerotilus: 0.1 per cent peptone water.

Haemophilus: Levinthal + X- and V-factor agar.

Streptomyces: Nitrosomonas mineral salts agar. (The growth of the *Streptomyces* was flodded with acetone and immediately covered with a coverslip before being photographed.)

All borrowed illustrations are reproduced with the permission of the author or publisher, or both, and their courtesy is very gratefully acknowledged.

There have been a few omissions caused mainly by lack of suitable cultures for the illustrations.

It is hoped that these illustrations will help materially in the interpretation of the Keys.

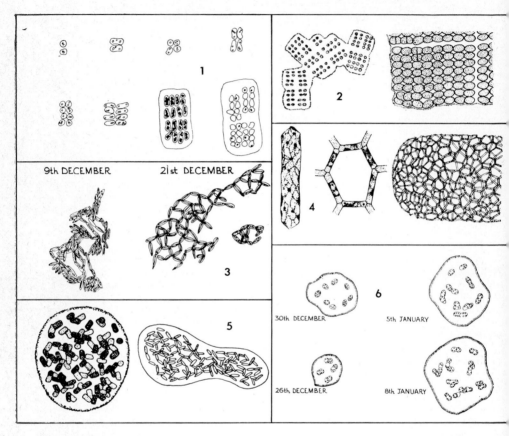

PLATE 1

1. *Thiopedia rosea*. Reproduced by permission from Winogradsky, Microbiologie du Sol, Masson et Cie, Paris. × 1000. 2. *Merismopedia* sp. Reproduced by permission from G. M. Smith, Freshwater Algae of the United States, McGraw-Hill Book Company. × 300. 3. *Thiodictyon elegans*. Reproduced by permission from Winogradsky, Microbiologie du Sol, Masson et Cie, Paris. × 450. 4. *Hydrodictyon* sp. Reproduced by permission from G. M. Smith, Freshwater Algae of the United States, McGraw-Hill Book Company. × 200. 5. *Aphanothece* sp. Reproduced by permission from G. M. Smith, Freshwater Algae of the United States, McGraw-Hill Book Company. × 430. 6. *Thiothece gelatinosa*. Reproduced by permission from Winogradsky, Microbiologie du Sol, Masson et Cie, Paris. × 320.

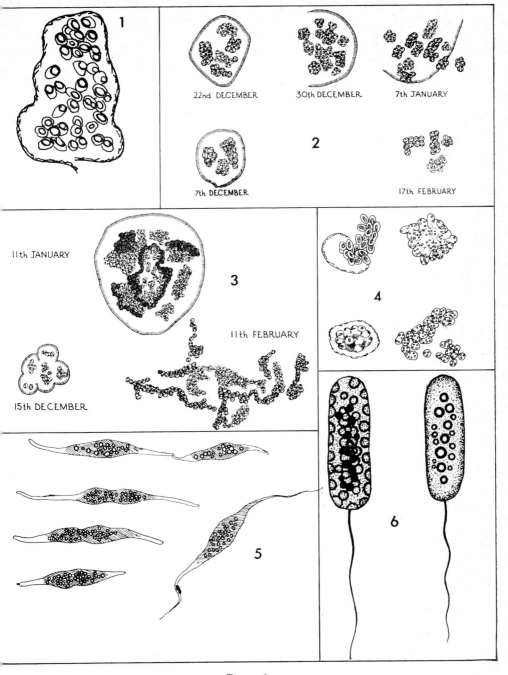

PLATE 2

1. *Thiocapsa roseo-persicina*. Reproduced by permission from Winogradsky, Microbiologie du Sol, Masson et Cie, Paris. × 1050. **2.** *Thiocystis violacea*. Reproduced by permission from Winogradsky, Microbiologie du Sol, Masson et Cie, Paris. × 420. **3.** *Lamprocystis roseo-persicina*. Reproduced by permission from Winogradsky, Microbiologie du Sol, Masson et Cie, Paris. × 420. **4.** *Amoebobacter roseus*. Reproduced by permission from Winogradsky, Microbiologie du Sol, Masson et Cie, Paris. × 700. **5.** *Rhabdomonas roseum*. Reproduced by permission from Winogradsky, Microbiologie du Sol, Masson et Cie, Paris, × 700. **6.** *Chromatium linsbaueri*. From Gicklhorn. Ber. deut. botan. Ges., *39*, 1921, 312. Courtesy of Gustav Fischer, Stuttgart. × 2550.

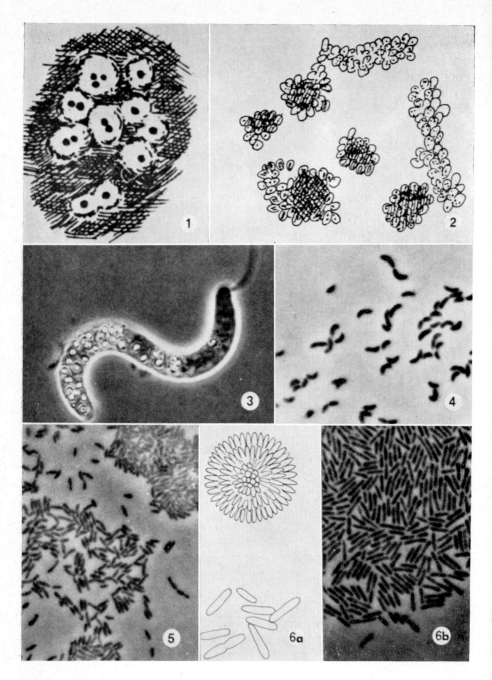

1. *Rhodothece pendens*. Reproduced by permission from Ellis, The Sulphur Bacteria, Longmans, Green and Co., Limited. × 1000. 2. *Thiopolycoccus ruber*. Reproduced by permission from Winogradsky, Microbiologie du Sol, Masson et Cie, Paris. × 1400. 3. *Thiospirillum* sp. Original. × 1800. 4. *Rhodospirillum rubrum*. Slide culture. Original. × 1800. 5. *Rhodopseudomonas sphaeroides*. Slide culture. Original. × 1800. 6. *Vannielia aggregata*. *a*, Reproduced by permission from Pringsheim, J. Gen. Microbiol., *13*, 1955, 289. × 1000. *b*, Slide culture. Original. × 1800.

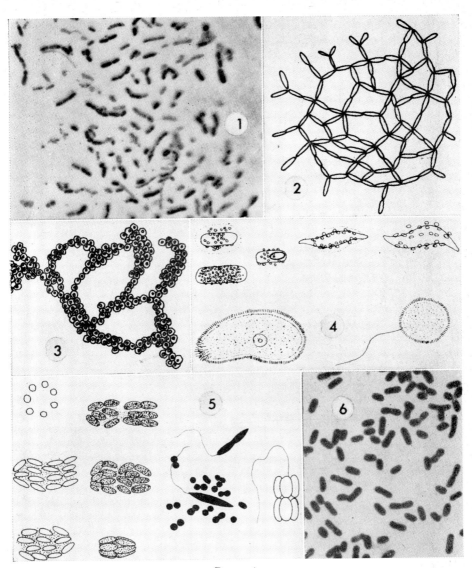

PLATE 4

1. *Chlorobium* sp. Flask culture. Original. × 1800. 2. *Pelodictyon* sp. From Geitler and Pascher, Die Süsswasserflora Deutschlands, Österreichs und der Schweiz, Jena, *12*, 1925, 457. Courtesy of Gustav Fischer, Stuttgart. × 1000. 3. *Clathrochloris sulphurica*. From Geitler and Pascher, Die Süsswasserflora Deutschlands, Österreichs und der Schweiz, Jena, *12*, 1925, 457. Courtesy of Gustav Fischer, Stuttgart. × 2000. 4. *Chlorobacterium symbioti-cum*. From Geitler and Pascher, Die Süsswasserflora Deutschlands, Österreichs und der Schweiz, Jena, *12*, 1925, 462. Courtesy of Gustav Fischer, Stuttgart. × 1000. 5. *Chlorochro-matium aggregatum*. After Lauterborn and after Buder, from Geitler and Pascher, Die Süsswasserflora Deutschlands, Österreichs und der Schweiz, Jena, *12*, 1925, 459. Courtesy of Gustav Fischer, Stuttgart. × 1000. 6. *Nitrosomonas* sp. Reproduced by permission from Winogradsky, Microbiologie du Sol, Masson et Cie, Paris. × 1800.

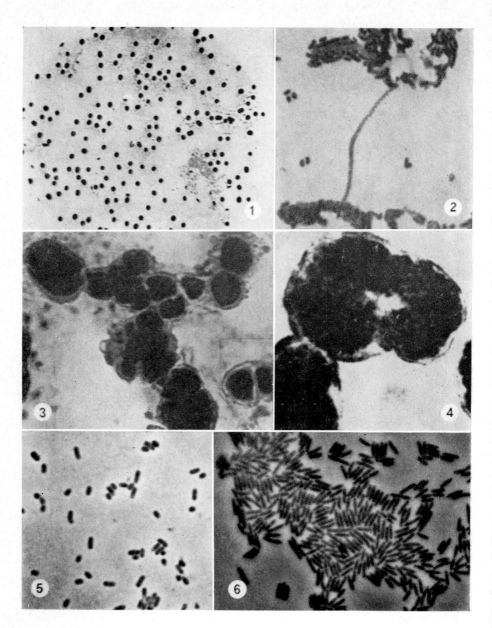

PLATE 5
1. *Nitrosococcus nitrosus*. Reproduced by permission from Winogradsky, Microbiologie du Sol, Masson et Cie, Paris. × 1800. 2. *Nitrosospira* sp. Reproduced by permission from Winogradsky, Microbiologie du Sol, Masson et Cie, Paris. × 1800. 3. *Nitrosocystis* sp. Reproduced by permission from Winogradsky, Microbiologie du Sol, Masson et Cie, Paris. × 1800. 4. *Nitrosogloea* sp. Reproduced by permission from Winogradsky, Microbiologie du Sol, Masson et Cie, Paris. × 1800. 5. *Nitrobacter* sp. Liquid culture. Original. × 1800. 6. *Hydrogenomonas* sp. Slide culture. Original. × 1800.

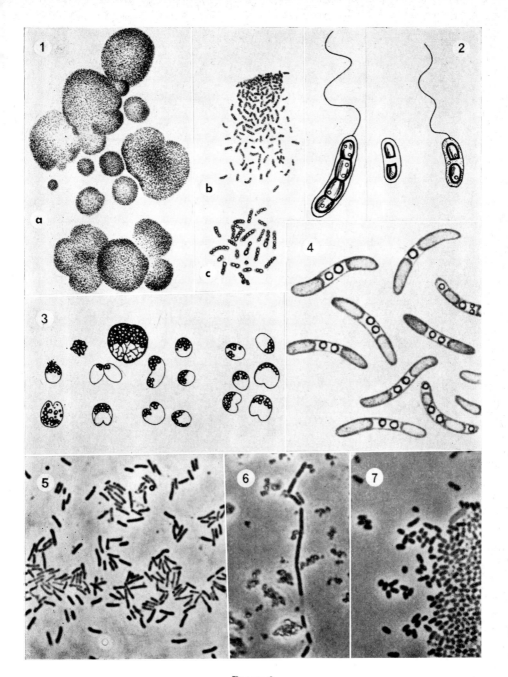

PLATE 6

1. *Thiobacterium bovista*. From Molisch, Zentr. Bakteriol. Parasitenk., Abt. II, *33*, 1912, 55. Courtesy of Gustav Fischer, Stuttgart. *a*, × 20; *b*, × 500; *c*, × 1000. 2. *Macromonas mobilis*. From Ellis, The Sulphur Bacteria, Longmans, Green and Co., Limited. × 1000. 3. *Thiovulum majus*. From Hinze, Ber. deut. botan. Ges., *31*, 1913, 195. Courtesy of Gustav Fischer, Stuttgart. × 750. 4. *Thiospira bipunctatum*. From Molisch, Zentr. Bakteriol. Parasitenk., Abt. II, *33*, 1912, 55. Courtesy of Gustav Fischer, Stuttgart. × 1500. 5. *Thiobacillus thiooxidans*. Liquid culture. Original. × 1800. 6. *Ferrobacillus ferrooxidans* amongst precipitated iron. Original. × 1800. 7. *Pseudomonas aeruginosa*. Slide culture. Original. × 1800.

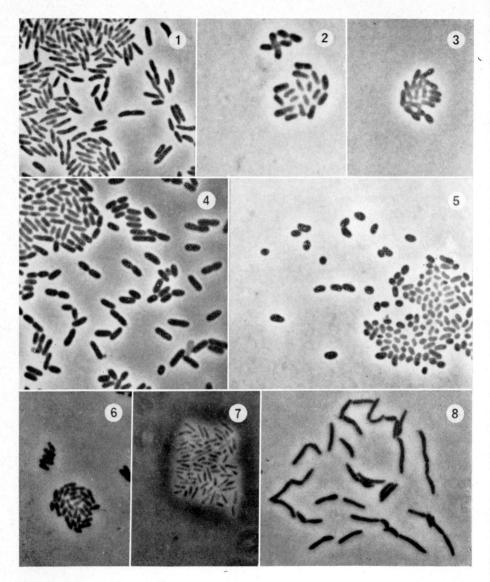

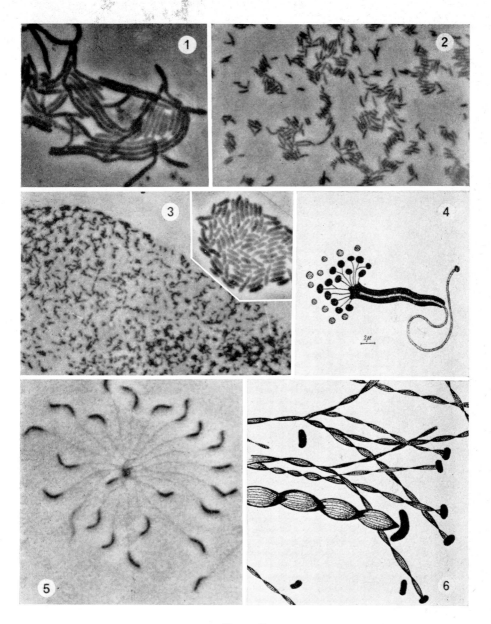

PLATE 8

1. *Halobacterium* sp. From 16 per cent salt agar. Original. × 1800. 2. *Mycoplana bullata.* Slide culture. Original. × 1800. 3. *Zoogloea ramigera.* Lobe from natural growth showing dispersed bacterial cells. Original. × 840. *Inset,* Growth on slide culture peptone-yeast extract agar. Original. × 1800. 4. *Krassilnikovia capsulata.* Line drawing by courtesy of Zavarsin, Mikrobiologia, *30,* 1961, 969. 5. *Caulobacter* sp. From 0.1 per cent peptone. Original. × 1800. 6. *Gallionella* sp. Line drawing from photomicrograph by Cholodny, taken from Dorff, Die Eisenorganismen, Pflanzenforschung, Heft 16, 1934, 25. Courtesy of Gustav Fischer, Stuttgart. × 1950.

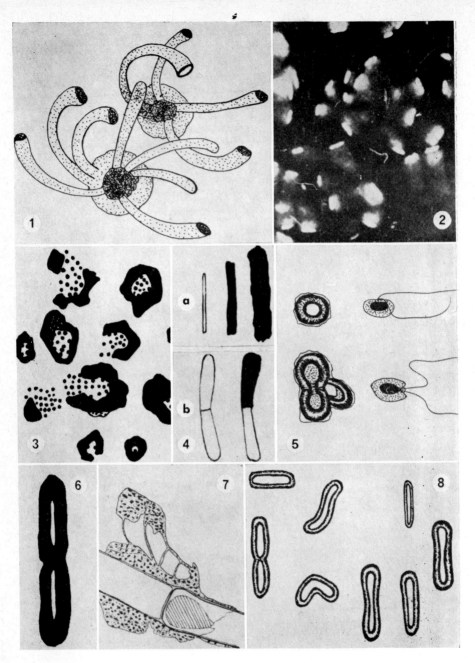

PLATE 9

1. *Siderophacus corneolus*. × 2000. 2. *Nevskia ramosa*. Photomicrograph reproduced by permission from Henrici and Johnson, J. Bacteriol., *30*, 1935, 63. × 500. 3. *Siderocapsa major*. From Molisch, taken from Dorff, Die Eisenorganismen, Pflanzenforschung, Heft 16, 1934, 15. Courtesy of Gustav Fischer, Stuttgart. × 2000. 4. *Siderobacter* sp. *a, S. lineare. b, S. duplex*. × 2000. 5. *Ochrobium tectum*. × 2000. 6. *Ferribacterium rectangulare*. From Naumann, taken from Dorff, Die Eisenorganismen, Pflanzenforschung, Heft 16, 1934, 15. Courtesy of Gustav Fischer, Stuttgart. × 3000. 7. *Sideromonas confervarum* on Oedogonium × 900. 8. *Naumanniella neustonica*. × 2000. Figures 1, 4, 5, 7, and 8 from Dorff, Die Eisenorganismen, Pflanzenforschung, Heft 16, 1934. Courtesy of Gustav Fischer, Stuttgart.

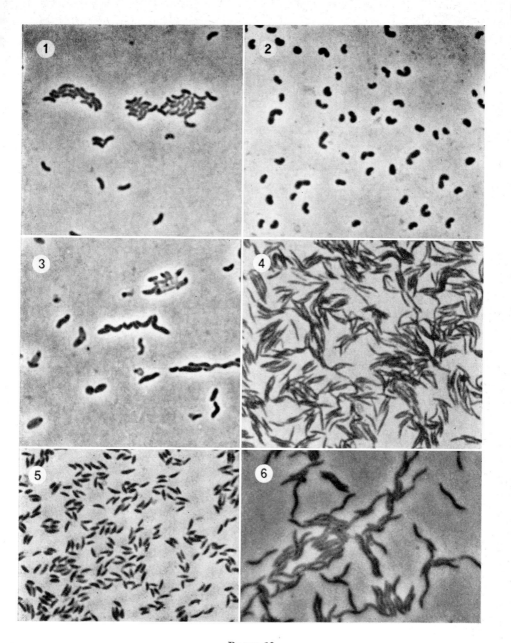

PLATE 10

1. *Desulfovibrio desulfuricans.* Slide culture. Original. × 1800. 2. *Microcyclus aquaticus.*
Original. × 1800. 3. *Vibrio metschnikovii.* Slide culture. Original. × 1800. 4. *Cellvibrio
flavescens.* Reproduced by permission from Winogradsky, Microbiologie du Sol, Masson et
Cie, Paris. × 1850. 5. *Cellfalcicula fusca.* Reproduced by permission from Winogradsky,
Microbiologie du Sol, Masson et Cie, Paris. × 1850. 6. *Spirillum itersonii.* Slide culture.
Original. × 1800.

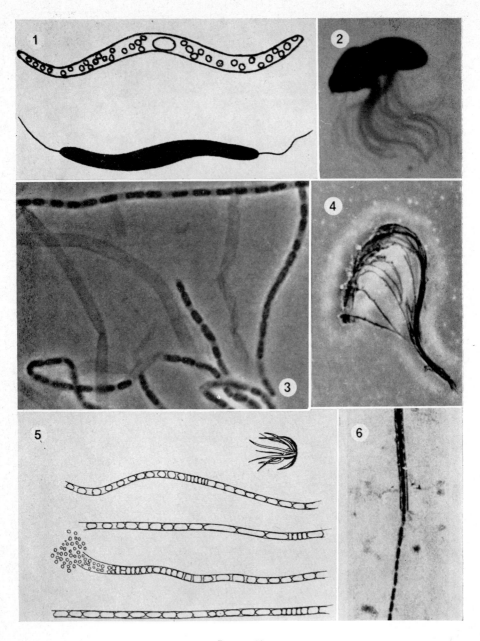

PLATE 11

1. *Paraspirillum vejdovkii*. From Dobell, Arch. Protistenk., *24*, 1912, 97. Courtesy of Gustav Fischer, Stuttgart. × 4000. 2. *Selenomonas* sp. Courtesy of C. F. Robinow. × 3600. 3. *Sphaerotilus natans*. From 0.1 per cent peptone water. Original. × 1800. 4. *Toxothrix trichogenes*. Original. × 1800. 5. *Crenothrix polyspora*. From Dorff, Die Eisenorganismen, Pflanzenforschung, Heft 16, 1934, 40. Courtesy of Gustav Fischer, Stuttgart. × 1100. 6. *Leptothrix ochracea*. From Cholodny, Die Eisenbakterien, Pflanzenforschung, Heft 16, 1934, Table 4, Fig. 20. Courtesy of Gustav Fischer, Stuttgart. × 1000.

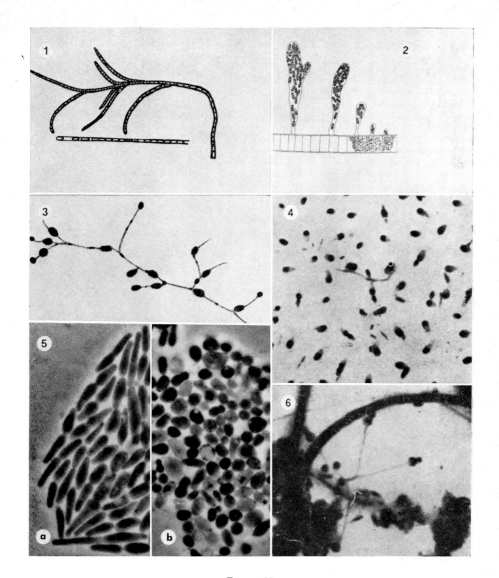

PLATE 12

1. *Clonothrix fusca*. From Molisch, taken from Dorff, Die Eisenorganismen, Pflanzen-forschung, Heft 16, 1934, 41. Courtesy of Gustav Fischer, Stuttgart. × 750. 2. *Thiodendron mucosum*. Photomicrograph reproduced by permission from Lackey and Lackey, J. Gen. Microbiol., *26*, 1961, 29. × 1600. 3. *Rhodomicrobium vannielii*. Line drawing of photomicrograph reproduced by permission from Duchow and Douglas, J. Bacteriol., *58*, 1949, 409. × 850. 4. *Pasteuria ramosa*. Photomicrograph reproduced by permission from Henrici and Johnson, J. Bacteriol., *30*, 1935, 93. × 850. 5. *Azotobacter chroococcum*. *a*, Early rod lozenge stage; *b*, early spherical stage. Originals. × 1500. 6 *Blastocaulis sphaerica*. Photomicrograph reproduced by permission from Henrici and Johnson, J. Bacteriol., *30*, 1935, 93. × 1260.

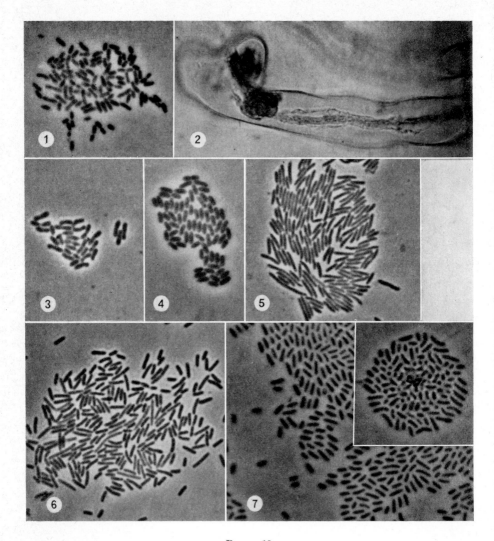

PLATE 13

1. *Rhizobium* sp. Slide culture. Original. × 1620. 2. Infection thread of *Rhizobium* in the root hair of a legume. Courtesy of Gösta Fåhraeus. × 1620. 3. *Agrobacterium radiobacter*. Slide culture. Original. × 1800. 4. *Chromobacterium violaceum*. Slide culture. Original. × 1620. 5. *Flavobacterium* sp. Slide culture. Original. × 1800. 6. *Alcaligenes faecalis*. Slide culture. Original. × 1800. 7. *Agarbacterium* sp. Dispersed cells. *Inset*, microcolony. Original. × 1620.

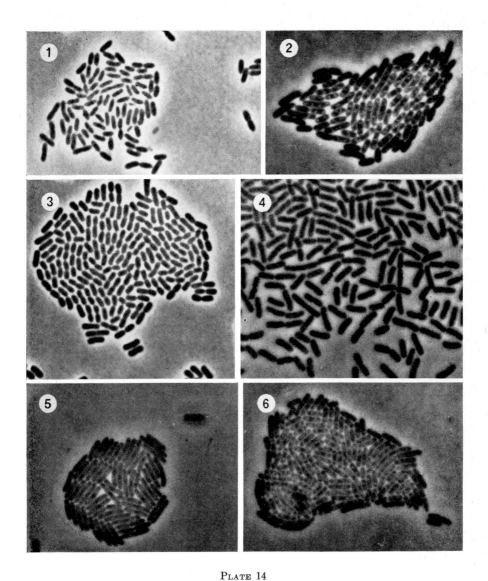

PLATE 14

1. *Beneckea hyperoptica*. Slide culture. Original. × 1800. 2. *Escherichia coli*. Slide culture. Original. × 1800. 3. *Aerobacter aerogenes*. Slide culture. Original. × 1800. 4. *Klebsiella pneumoniae*. Slide culture. Original. × 1800. 5. *Paracolobactrum intermedium*. Slide culture. Original. × 1800. 6. *Erwinia carotovora*. Slide culture. Original. × 1800.

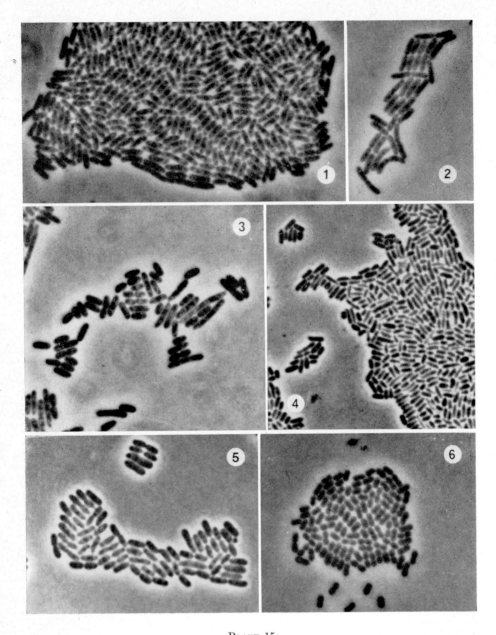

PLATE 15

1. *Serratia marcescens.* Slide culture. Original. × 1800. 2. *Salmonella stanley.* Slide culture. Original. × 1800. 3. *Proteus morganii.* Slide culture. Original. × 1800. 4. *Shigella flexneri.* Slide culture. Original. × 1800. 5. *Pasteurella multocida.* Slide culture. Original. × 1800. 6. *Bordetella pertussis.* Slide culture. Original. × 1800.

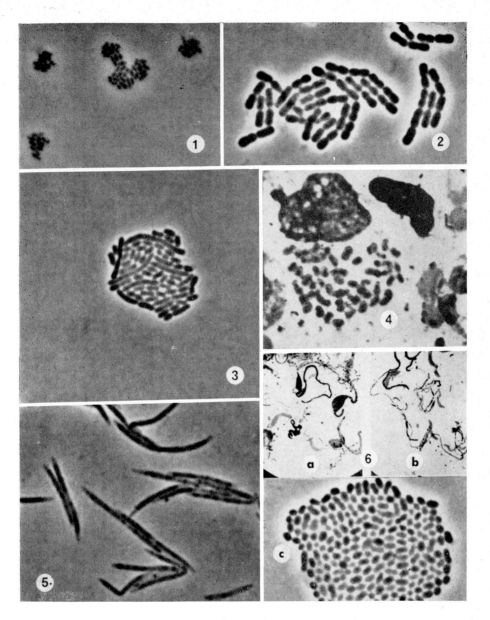

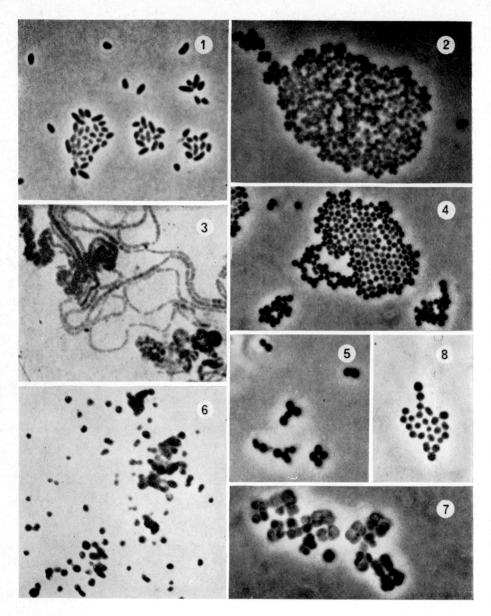

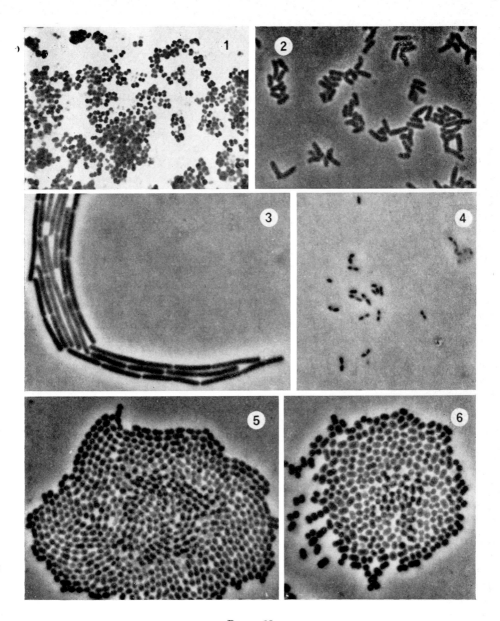

PLATE 18

1. *Neisseria catarrhalis*. Slide culture. Original. × 900. 2. *Brevibacterium linens*. Slide culture. Original. × 1800. 3. *Kurthia zopfii*. Fringe of microcolony on slide culture. Original. × 1800. 4. *Diplococcus pneumoniae*. Slide culture. Original. × 1800. 5. *Streptococcus pyogenes*. Slide culture. Original. × 1800. 6. *Pediococcus cerevisiae*. Slide culture. Original. × 1800.

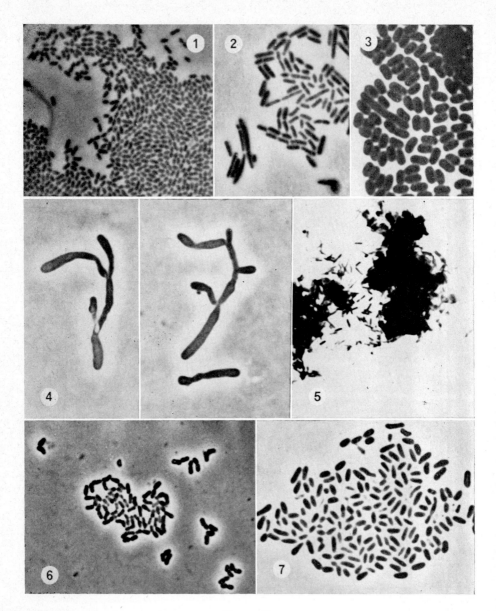

PLATE 19

1. *Leuconostoc mesenteroides.* Slide culture. Original. × 1800. **2.** *Lactobacillus plantarum.*
Slide culture. Original. × 1800. **3.** *Eubacterium* sp. Slide culture. Original. × 1800. **4.** *Lepto-trichia dentium.* Slide culture. Original. × 1800. **5.** *Ramibacterium* sp. Smear. Original.
× 1800. **6.** *Propionibacterium rubrum.* Slide culture. Original. × 1800. **7.** *Butyribacterium rettgeri.* Slide culture. Original. × 1800.

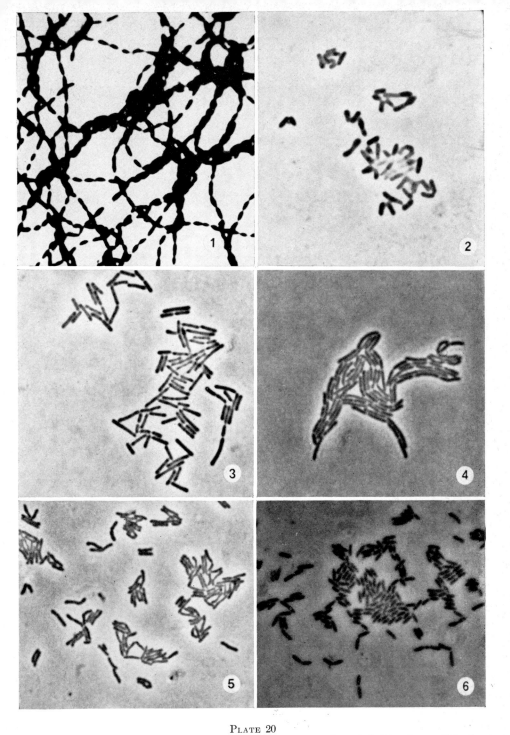

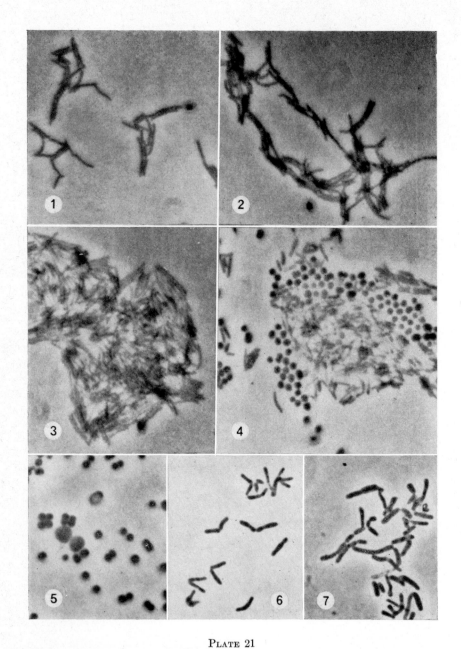

PLATE 21

1, 2, and 3. *Arthrobacter* sp. Development of microcolony. 4. Transference to cocci. 5. Cocci and cystites. Original. × 1800. 6. *Myobacterium phlei*. Original. × 1800. 7. *Jensenia canicruria*. Original. × 1800.

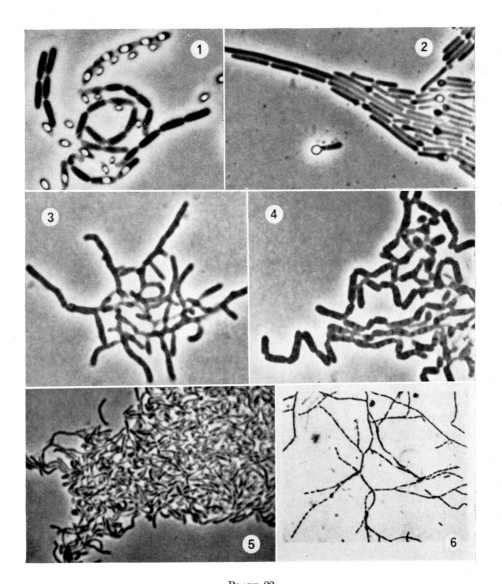

PLATE 22

1. *Bacillus megaterium.* Smear. Original. × 1800. 2. *Clostridium tetani.* Slide culture. Original. × 1800. 3 and 4. *Nocardia salmonicolor.* Slide culture showing initial branching with later disintegration. Original. × 1800. 5. *Actinomyces.* Original. × 1800. 6. *Pseudonocardia thermophila.* Photomicrograph reproduced by permission from Henssen, Arch. Mikrobiol., *26*, 1957, 373.

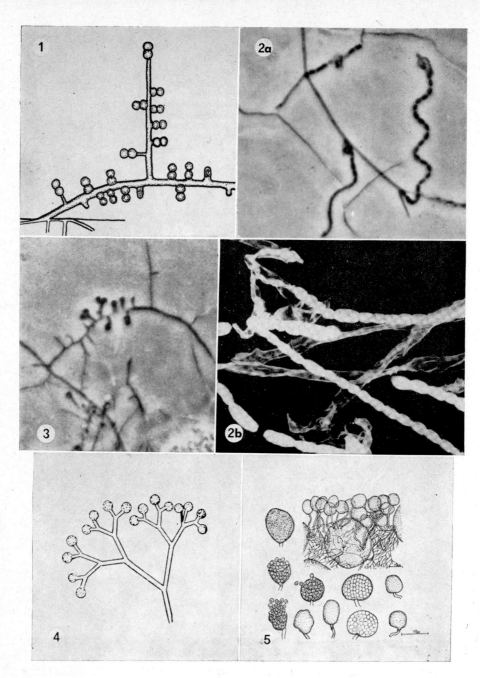

PLATE 23

1. *Microbispora*, (*Waksmania*) sp. Reproduced by permission from Lechevalier and Lechevalier, J. Gen. Microbiol., *17*, 1957, 104. × 1700. 2. *Streptomyces* sp. *a*, Slide culture. Original. × 1440. *b*, Electron photomicrograph of chains of aerial conidia of *Streptomyces* showing clearly that these "conidia" are formed intracellularly in the aerial hypha and not by constriction of the aerial hypha. Photograph by courtesy of T. R. Vernon, Plant Disease Division, D.S.I.R., Private Bag, Auckland. 3. *Micromonospora* sp. Slide culture. Original. × 1440. 4. *Actinobifida* sp. After Krassilnikov, Mikrobiologia, *33*, 1964, 935. 5. *Actinoplanes utahensis*. Reproduced by permission from Couch, J. Elisha Mitchell Sci. Soc., *79*, 1963, 68.

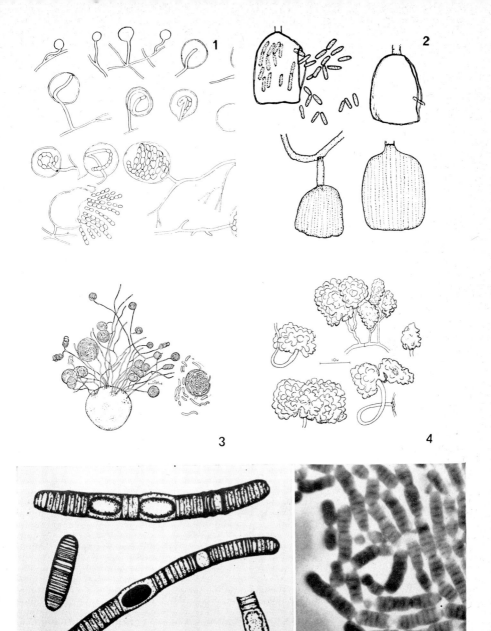

PLATE 24

1. *Streptosporangium* sp. Reproduced by permission from Brummelen and Went, Antonie van Leeuwenhoek, *23*, 1957, 385. × 820. 2. *Ampullariella*. Reproduced by permission from Couch, J. Elisha Mitchell Sci. Soc., *79*, 1963, 62. 3. *Spirillospora albida*. × 800. 4. *Amorphosporangium auranticolor*. Figures 3 and 4 reproduced by permission from Couch, J. Elisha Mitchell Sci. Soc., *79*, 1963, 66. 5. *Oscillospira guillermondii*. From Chatton and Pérard, Compt. rend. soc. Biol., Paris, *74*, 1913, 1159. Courtesy of Masson et Cie. × 1000. 6. *Caryophanon latum*. Slide culture. Original. × 1440.

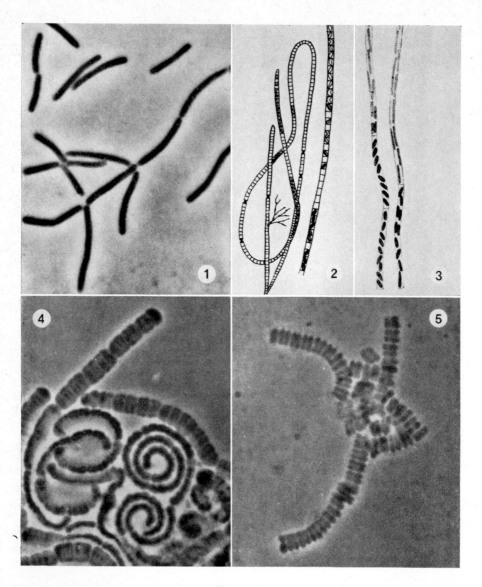

PLATE 25

1. *Lineola* sp. Slide culture. Original. × 900. 2. *Arthromitus cristatus*. Reproduced by permission from "Flora and Fauna within Living Animals" by J. Leidy in Smithsonian Inst. Publs. Contrib. to Knowledge, *5*, 1851. × 1850. 3. *Coleomitus pruvotii*. Reproduced by permission from Duboscq and Grassé, Arch. zool. exptl. gén., *68*, 1929, Notes and Revue, 14. × 1800. 4. *Simonsiella*. Original. × 1800. 5. *Alysiella*. Original. × 1800.

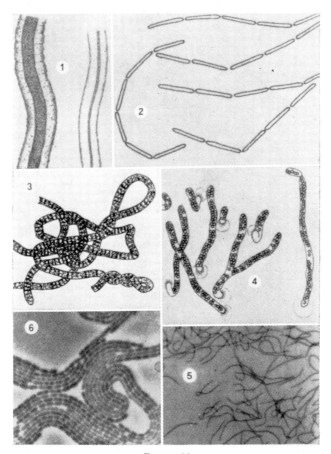

PLATE 26

1. *Thioploca schmidlei.* From Lauterborn, Ber. deut. botan. Ges., *25*, 1907, 238. Courtesy of Gustav Fischer, Stuttgart. × 120. **2.** *Bactoscilla mobilis.* Reproduced by permission from Pringsheim, J. Gen. Microbiol., *5*, 1951, 124. × 1700. **3.** *Beggiatoa mirabilis.* From Cohn, Hedwigia, No. 6, 1865, facing p. 184. × 200. **4.** *Thiothrix nivea.* Reproduced by permission from Winogradsky, Microbiologie du Sol, Masson et Cie, Paris. × 800. **5.** *Microscilla* sp. Slide culture. Original. × 340. **6.** *Vitreoscilla* sp. Slide culture. Original. × 1530.

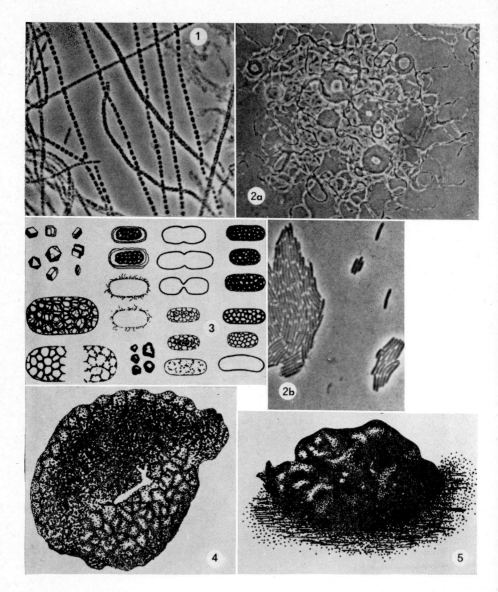

PLATE 27

1. *Leucothrix* sp. Slide culture. Original. × 1800. 2. *Cytophaga* sp. *a*, Growth on agar showing migration of cells and slime trails. × 360. *b*, Cells migrating from the margin of the colony. × 1300. Originals. 3. *Achromatium oxaliferum*. Reproduced by permission from West and Griffiths, Proc. Roy. Soc. London, B, *81*, 1909, Plate 9. × 360. 4. *Sorangium sorediatum*. From Quehl, Zentr. Bakteriol. Parasitenk., Abt. II, *16*, 1906, Plate I, Fig. 2. Courtesy of Gustav Fischer, Stuttgart. × 210. 5. *Archangium gephyra*. From Quehl, Zentr. Bakteriol. Parasitenk., Abt. II, *16*, 1906, Plate I, Fig. 7. Courtesy of Gustav Fischer, Stuttgart. × 50.

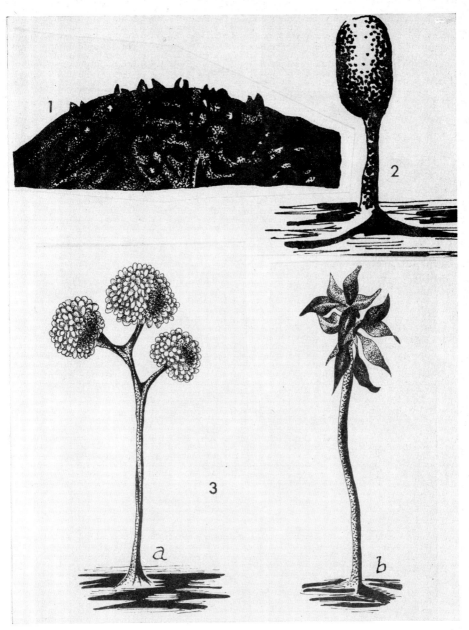

PLATE 28

1. *Polyangium fuscum*. From Quehl, Zentr. Bakteriol. Parasitenk., Abt. II, *16*, 1906,
Plate I, Fig. 16. Courtesy of Gustav Fischer, Stuttgart. × 25. 2. *Podangium gracilipes*. From
Quehl, Zentr. Bakteriol. Parasitenk., Abt. II, *16*, 1906, Plate I. Courtesy of Gustav Fischer,
Stuttgart. × 700. 3. *Chondromyces* sp. *a, C. crocatus* (Plate I, Fig. 10). × 190. *b, C. apiculatus*
(Plate I, Fig. 13.) × 220. From Quehl, Zentr. Bakteriol. Parasitenk., Abt. II, *16*, 1906.
Courtesy of Gustav Fischer, Stuttgart.

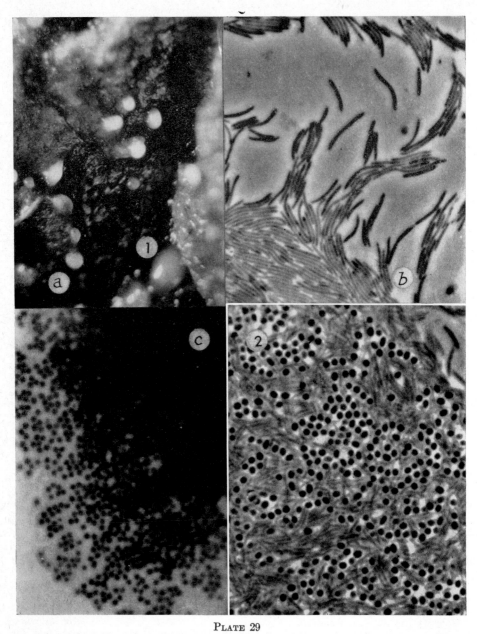

PLATE 29

1. *Myxococcus* sp. Originals. *a*, Fruiting bodies on rabbit dung. × 2. *b*, Migrating cells from the margin of a colony. × 1530. *c*, Crushed fruiting body. × 1530. 2. *Sporocytophaga* sp. Microcysts among the flexible rods. Original. × 1530.

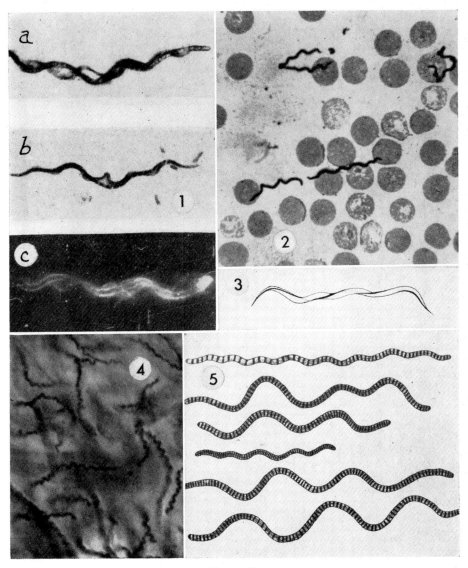

PLATE 30

1. *Cristispira* sp. Reproduced by permission from Noguchi, J. Exptl. Med., *27*, 1918, Plate 29. *a*, *C. veneris*. × 1200. *b*, *C. balbianii*. × 1200. 2. *Borrelia* sp. Blood smear. Original. × 900. Prepared from a slide from Turtox Biological Supplies. 3. *Spirochaeta* sp. From Holling, Arch. Protistenk. Bd. XXIII. Courtesy of Gustav Fischer, Stuttgart. × 750. 4. *Treponema pallidum*. Photomicrograph. × 2500. Courtesy of Turtox Biological Supplies. 5. *Saprospira grandis*. Reproduced by permission from Dimitroff, J. Bacteriol., *12*, 1926, 171. × 1000.

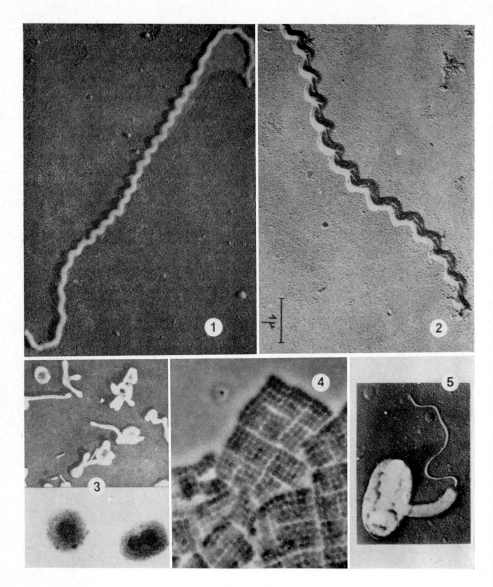

PLATE 31

1. *Leptospira canicola.* Reproduced by permission from Gsell, Leptospirosen, Hans Huber, Bern, Switzerland. × 9000. 2. *Leptospira hebdomalis.* Courtesy of Dr. Elisabeth Mölbert. × 12,000. 3. *Mycoplasma* sp. Reproduced by permission from Klieneberger-Nobel and Cuckow, J. Gen. Microbiol., *12*, 1955, 98, Fig. 5. × 6600. 4. *Lampropedia hyalina.* Slide culture. Original. × 1800. 5. *Bdellovibrio bacteriovorus.* Electron micrograph. Reproduced by permission from Stolp and Starr, Antonie van Leeuwenhoek, *29*, 1963, 217. × 26,200.

Salicin............................. d
Adonitol........................... −
Inositol........................ − or ×
Indol........................... − or ×
Methyl red........................ +
Voges-Proskauer................... −
Ammonium citrate.................. +
Hydrogen sulfide.................. +
Urease...................... − or (+)
Gelatin liquefaction................ −
Growth in KCN medium............. +
Phenylalanine deaminase........... −
Sodium malonate................... −
Lysine decarboxylase.............. −
Arginine dihydrolase.............. (+)
Ornithine decarboxylase......... − or +

For further details see Intern. Bull. Bacteriol. Nomen. Taxon., *13*, No. 2, 1963, 69.

Escherichia (Esch.er.ich′i.a) Castellani and Chalmers, 1919. *M p. 335.* (Manual Trop. Med., 3rd ed., 1919, 941.)

DIFFERENTIATING CHARACTERS: Unicellular, nonphotosynthetic, nonsporing, straight, rod-shaped organisms, less than 2 μ wide; motile with peritrichous flagella or nonmotile; Gram negative; *aerobic;* heterotrophic; acid and gas produced from glucose and lactose within 48 hours; methyl red positive; Voges-Proskauer negative; gelatin liquefied by one species.

Type species: *Escherichia coli* (Migula) Castellani and Chalmers.

NOTES: Four species are described in the *Manual.* They are differentiated on pigmentation, utilization of citrate, and production of hydrogen sulfide.

Growth occurs readily on meat infusion agar, typical colonies being 2 to 3 mm. in diameter in 24 hours at 37° C.; circular, low convex, entire, smooth and glistening, butyrous, and easily emulsified. Colonies are normally an off-white color and translucent. Fecal odor.

This type of colony is often called a *coliform* colony. It is characteristic of many Gram negative rods, particularly those of intestinal origin.

Escherichia aurescens produces a reddishbrown pigment, which is not prodigiosin (*cf. Serratia*).

The organisms of this genus will use ammonia nitrogen and hence can be grown in a variety of mineral salts media containing a suitable carbon source.

Gelatin is not hydrolyzed except by some strains of *E. freundii.*

Litmus milk is rendered acid and usually clots. The litmus may be reduced.

Nitrites are produced from nitrates.

Indole may be produced.

H$_2$S may be produced.

Acid and gas are produced from glucose and lactose and many other sugars and sugar alcohols. Acid production from lactose occurs within 48 hours.

Methyl red positive.

Voges-Proskauer negative.

Citric acid is utilized as the sole source of carbon by 2/4 species but *not* by the type species.

Catalase positive.

Facultative anaerobes with a pH range of 4.5 to 8.5 and optimal temperature of approximately 37° C.

Found in the alimentary tract of man and animals and in soil and waters.

The literature on *Escherichia*, particularly *E. coli*, is voluminous. Since the systematics of this group and others of the family *Enterobacteriaceae* is the subject of continuous review by the Subcommittee on the *Enterobacteriaceae*, no attempt is made to cite specific papers other than the reports of the Subcommittee. The following is their definition of the *Escherichia* group:

The *Escherichia* group consists of motile or nonmotile, nonsporing, Gram negative rods; grow on ordinary media, reduce nitrates to nitrites, give a negative oxidase reaction and break down carbohydrates by a fermentative reaction that distinguishes them from other families in which the reaction is oxidative.

Gas from glucose*................... +
Lactose...................... + or x
Sucrose........................... d

---

* The following signs are used: +, positive; −, negative; d, different biochemical types; ×, delayed.

Mannitol	+
Dulcitol	d
Salicin	d
Adonitol	−
Inositol	−
Indol	+
Methyl red	+
Voges-Proskauer	−
Ammonium citrate	−
Hydrogen sulfide	−
Urease	−
Gelatin liquefaction	−
Growth in KCN medium	−
Phenylalanine deaminase	−
Sodium malonate	−

For further details see Intern. Bull. Bacteriol. Nomen. Taxon., *8*, 1958, 25.

Shigella (Shi.gel′la) Castellani and Chalmers, 1919. *M p. 384.* (Manual Trop. Med., 3rd ed., 1919, 936.)

DIFFERENTIATING CHARACTERS: Unicellular, colorless, nonsporing, straight, rod-shaped organisms, less than 2 μ wide; nonmotile; Gram negative; *aerobic;* heterotrophic; grow well on meat infusion agar, producing discrete colonies; acid, but no gas is produced from glucose; no acid from lactose or lactose fermentation delayed. Enteric pathogens, which agglutinate with *Shigella* antisera. (See Intern. Bull. Bacteriol. Nomen. Taxon., *4*, 1953.)

Type species: *Shigella dysenteriae* (Shiga, 1898) Castellani and Chalmers, 1919.

NOTES: Eight species are described. They are separated on the production of acid from mannitol, lactose, arabinose, rhamnose, xylose, and dulcitol; production of indole and trimethylamine; and on serological reactions.

Gelatin is not liquefied.

H₂S is not produced.

Nitrite is produced from nitrate.

Litmus milk turns alkaline except with the slow lactose-fermenting *Shigella dispar* and *Shigella sonnei.*

Indole production is variable.

Optimal temperature, 37° C.

Cause of enteric bacillary dysentery in man.

The definition for the *Shigella* group

given by the Subcommittee on the *Enterobacteriaceae* of the I C N B is as follows:

The *Shigella* group consists of nonmotile, nonsporing, Gram negative rods; grow on ordinary media, reduce nitrates to nitrites, give a negative oxidase reaction, and break down carbohydrates by a fermentative reaction that distinguishes them from other families in which the reaction is oxidative.

Gas from glucose*	−
Lactose	−
Sucrose	−
Mannitol	d
Dulcitol	d
Salicin	−
Adonitol	−
Inositol	−
Indol	d
Methyl red	+
Voges-Proskauer	−
Ammonium citrate	−
Hydrogen sulfide	−
Urease	−
Gelatin liquefaction	−
Growth in KCN medium	−
Phenylalanine deaminase	−
Sodium malonate	−

Some biotypes of *Shigella flexneri* 6 are known to produce small volumes of gas from glucose and other fermentable substrates. For further details see Intern. Bull. Bacteriol. Nomen. Taxon., *8*, No. 1, 1958, 25.

Klebsiella (Kleb.si.el′la) Trevisan, 1885. *M p. 344.* (Atti accad. Fisio-Medico-Statistica in Milano, Ser. 4, *3*, 1885, 105.)

DIFFERENTIATING CHARACTERS: Unicellular, colorless, nonsporing, straight, rod-shaped organisms less than 2 μ wide; capsulated; nonmotile; Gram negative; heterotrophic; grow well on meat infusion agar; acid and gas usually produced from glucose; acid usually produced from lactose in 48 hours; methyl red negative; Voges-Proskauer positive. Virulent forms pathogenic, producing diseases principally of respiratory origin.

Type species: *Klebsiella pneumoniae* (Schroeter) Trevisan.

* The following signs are used: +, positive; −, negative; d, different biochemical types.

NOTES: Three species are described. They are separated in the *Manual* on pathogenicity and action on glucose. Rod-shaped microorganisms, 0.3 to 0.5 μ by 2 to 5 μ.

Capsule formation is a variable character, and noncapsulated avirulent forms resemble *Aerobacter*. In addition, some *Aerobacter* strains are virulent and some are capsulated.

Colonies produced are often slimy as a result of capsule formation.

Nitrite is produced from nitrate.

H₂S is not produced.

Acid is produced from glucose.

Gas is produced also by 2/3 species.

Acid and gas from glucose and acid from lactose are normal for the group.

Lactose may or may not be fermented and may, if fermented, be fermented very slowly.

Litmus milk becomes acid without coagulation or remains unchanged.

The methyl red and Voges-Proskauer tests vary with the species.

Citrate is utilized by 1/3 species.

The organisms are aerobic and facultatively anaerobic. The optimal temperature is 37° C.

They are pathogenic and have been isolated from cases of pneumonia and other infections of the respiratory tract.

Some recent papers on systematics of the genus *Klebsiella* are as follows:

Benjamin, M. A., de Guzman, B. C., and Weil, A., J. Bacteriol., *87*, 1964, 234.

Centifanto, Y. M., and Silver, W. S., J. Bacteriol., *88*, 1964, 776.

Cowan, S. T., Steel, K. J., Shaw, C., and Duguid, J. P., J. Gen. Microbiol., *23*, 1960, 601.

Hugh, R., Can. J. Microbiol., *5*, 1959, 251.

Thornley, M. J., and Horne, R. W., J. Gen. Microbiol., *28*, 1962, 51.

The paper by Cowan *et al.* is particularly pertinent in its measure of disagreement with the Subcommittee on the *Enterobacteriaceae* on the definition of *Klebsiella*, which Cowan *et al.* use to cover the *Kleb-*

siella and *Enterobacter* groups. In view of these differences, the species as defined by Cowan *et al.* have been incorporated in the Keys in parallel with those of the Subcommittee.

The definition for the genus given by the Subcommittee on the *Enterobacteriaceae* of the I C N B is as follows:

The *Klebsiella* group (genus) consists of nonmotile, encapsulated, nonsporing, Gram negative rods; grow on ordinary media, reduce nitrates to nitrites, give a negative oxidase reaction, and break down carbohydrates by a fermentative reaction that distinguishes them from other families in which the reaction is oxidative.

Gas from glucose*	+
Lactose	+
Sucrose	+
Mannitol	+
Dulcitol	d
Salicin	+
Adonitol	+
Inositol (gas)	+
Glycerol (gas)	+
Cellobiose (gas)	+
Insoluble starch (gas)	+
Indol	−
Methyl red	−
Voges-Proskauer	+
Ammonium citrate	+
Hydrogen sulfide	−
Urease	(+)
Gelatin liquefaction	−
Growth in KCN medium	+
Phenylalanine deaminase	−
Sodium malonate	+
Lysine decarboxylase	+
Arginine dihydrolase	−
Ornithine decarboxylase	−

For further details see Intern. Bull. Bacteriol. Nomen. Taxon., *13*, No. 2, 1963.

Aerobacter (Ae.ro.bac′ter) Beijerinck, 1900. *M p. 341.* (Zentr. Bakteriol. Parasitenk., Abt. II, *6*, 1900, 193.)

DIFFERENTIATING CHARACTERS: Unicellular, colorless, nonsporing, straight, rod-

* The following signs are used: +, positive; −, negative; d, different biochemical types; (+), rare strains positive.

shaped organisms, less than 2 μ wide; non-motile or motile with peritrichous flagella; Gram negative; *aerobic;* heterotrophic; acid and gas produced from glucose and lactose in 48 hours; methyl red negative; Voges-Proskauer positive; gelatin may or may not be liquefied.

Type species: *Aerobacter aerogenes* (Kruse) Beijerinck.

NOTES: Only two species are described; they are separated in the *Manual* on glycerol fermentation and gelatin liquefaction.

Straight, rod-shaped, unicellular organisms. Nonmotile or motile with peritrichous flagella. Gram negative. Species are frequently capsulated, particularly when grown at 25° C. in the presence of fermentable carbohydrates.

Grow well on meat infusion agar and also in mineral media containing ammonium sulfate and a suitable carbon source. Colonies are usually more opaque than those of *Escherichia* and are mucoid with the capsulated types.

Gelatin is liquefied slowly by *A. cloacae* but not by *A. aerogenes.*

Litmus milk is acidified and coagulated. It is slowly peptonized by *A. cloacae.*

Nitrite is produced from nitrates.

Indole production is variable.

Acid and gas are produced from glucose and lactose and several other sugar alcohols. Acid production from lactose occurs within *48 hours.*

Methyl red negative.

Voges-Proskauer positive.

Citrate is used as the sole source of carbon.

Catalase positive.

Facultative anaerobes with a pH range of approximately 4.5 to 8.5.

The optimal temperature is between 30° and 37° C.

Found mainly on grain and plant tissue and in feces, soil, and water.

There have been repeated and well-substantiated reports of nitrogen fixation by *Aerobacter.*

The *Manual* differentiates between the genus *Aerobacter* and *Klebsiella* on the basis of capsule formation and pathogenicity of the latter. These are not valid criteria.

The species in this genus have been reallocated to the genus *Klebsiella* (nonmotile strains) and the genus *Enterobacter* (motile strains). See I C N B definitions for these genera.

The definition for the *Enterobacter* group given by the Subcommittee on the *Enterobacteriaceae* of the I C N B as is follows:

The *Enterobacter* (*Cloaca*) group (genus) consists of motile, nonsporing, Gram negative rods; grow on ordinary media, reduce nitrates to nitrites, give a negative oxidase reaction and break down carbohydrates by a fermentative reaction that distinguishes them from other families in which the reaction is oxidative.

	A	B	C
Gas from glucose*...	+	+	+
Lactose.............	+	+	(+)
Sucrose.............	+	+	+
Mannitol...........	+	+	+
Dulcitol............	−	−	−
Salicin.............	+	+	+
Adonitol...........	d	+	
Inositol (gas).......	−	+	(+)
Glycerol (gas)......	−	+	+
Cellobiose (gas).....	+	+	(+)
Rhamnose...........	+	+	−
Raffinose...........	+	+	+
Arabinose..........	+	+	+
Xylose.............	+	+	+
Sorbitol............	+	+	+
Insoluble starch (gas)	−	−	(+) or −
Indol...............	−	−	−
Methyl red.........	−	−	d
Voges-Proskauer.....	+	+	d
Ammonium citrate...	+	+	+
Hydrogen sulfide....	−	−	−
Urease.............	−	−	−
Gelatin liquefaction..	(+)	d	+
Growth in KCN medium.............	+	+	+
Sodium malonate....	+	+	−

* The following signs are used: +, positive; −, negative; d, different biochemical types; (+), rare strains positive.

Phenylalanine deaminase..............	−	−	−
Lysine decarboxylase.	−	+	(+)
Arginine dihydrolase.	+	−	−
Ornithine decarboxylase..............	+	+	+

For further details see Intern. Bull. Bacteriol. Nomen. Taxon., *13*, No. 2, 1963, 69.

Hafnia Group

The definition for the group given by the Subcommittee on the *Enterobacteriaceae* of the I C N B is as follows:

The *Hafnia* group consists of motile, nonsporing, Gram negative rods; grow on ordinary media, reduce nitrates to nitrites, give a negative oxidase reaction, and break down carbohydrates by a fermentative reaction that distinguishes them from other families in which the reaction is oxidative.

	37° C.	22° C.
Gas from glucose*	d	+
Lactose...............	− or x	− or x
Sucrose...............	x	x
Mannitol..............	+	+
Dulcitol..............	−	−
Salicin...............	d	d
Adonitol..............	−	−
Inositol..............	−	−
Indol.................	−	−
Methyl red............	+	−
Voges-Proskauer........	d	+
Ammonium citrate.....	d	+
Hydrogen sulfide.......	−	(+)
Urease...............	−	−
Gelatin liquefaction....	−	−
Growth in KCN medium.	+	+
Phenylalanine deaminase.................	−	−
Sodium malonate.......	d	d

For further details see Intern. Bull. Bacteriol. Nomen. Taxon., *8*, No. 1, 1958, 25.

Serratia (Ser.ra′ti.a) Bizio, 1823. *M p. 359.* (Polenta porporina, Biblioteca ital. o sia Giorn. lettera, sci., arti, *30*, 1823, 288.)

* The following signs are used: +, positive; −, negative; ×, delayed; d, different biochemical types; (+), rare strains positive.

DIFFERENTIATING CHARACTERS: Unicellular, nonphotosynthetic, rod-shaped organisms less than 2 μ wide; motile with peritrichous flagella; Gram negative; *aerobic;* heterotrophic; grow well on meat infusion agar *producing a red pigment, prodigiosin,* which is insoluble in water.

Type species: *Serratia marcescens* Bizio.

NOTES: Five species are described. They are separated in the *Manual* on solubility of the pigment in water and alcohol; production of gas from glucose; production of acetoin; and growth in broth.

Very small organisms, 0.5 by 0.6 to 2.0 μ.

Grow well on meat infusion agar. Colonies on various media are rose red to a deep magenta red because of the production of the pigment, prodigiosin, which distinguishes these organisms from other red-pigmented bacteria. The pigment is readily soluble in alcohol and some other organic solvents but not in water.

Pigment production is variable, and numerous colorless mutants are produced; in some instances pigmentation is completely lost.

Gelatin is liquefied by all species.

Litmus milk is rendered acid and coagulated.

Acid is produced from glucose and lactose. Gas is produced but may not always be visible because of solubility.

Voges-Proskauer positive for 3/5 species.

Nitrates are reduced to nitrites.

Trimethylamine is produced by most species.

Aerobic and facultatively anaerobic.

The optimal temperature is between 25° and 30° C.

Found in water, soil, and milk.

Some recent publications relevant to the systematics of *Serratia* are as follows:

Belser, W. L., and Bunting, M. I., J. Bacteriol., *72*, 1956, 582.

Bishop, D. G., and Still, J. L., J. Bacteriol. *82*, 1961, 370.

Colwell, R. R., and Mandel, M., J. Bacteriol., *89*, 1965, 454.

Ewing, W. H., Johnson, J. G., and Davis,

B. R., The Occurrence of *Serratia marcescens* in Nosocomial Infections. U. S. Department of Health, Education and Welfare Public Health Service Publication, 1962.

Ewing, W. H., Davis, B. R., and Johnson, J. G., Intern. Bull. Bacteriol. Nomen. Taxon., *12*, 1962, 47.

Fulton, M., Forney, C. E., and Leifson, E., Can. J. Microbiol., *5*, 1959, 269.

Green, J. A., and Williams, R. P., J. Bacteriol., *78*, 1959, 336.

Hearn, W. R., Worthington, R. E., Burgus, R. C., and Williams, R. P., Biochem. Biophys. Res. Comm., *17*, 1964, 517.

Lewis, S. M., and Corpe, W. A., App. Microbiol., *12*, 1964, 13.

Rizki, M. T. M., J. Bacteriol., *80*, 1960, 305.

Williams, R. P., Goth, C. L., and Green, J. A., J. Bacteriol., *81*, 1961, 376.

The definition for the *Serratia* group given by the Subcommittee on the *Enterobacteriaceae* of the I C N B is as follows:

The *Serratia* group consists of motile, nonsporing, Gram negative rods; grow on ordinary media, reduce nitrates to nitrites, give a negative oxidase reaction, and break down carbohydrates by a fermentative reaction that distinguishes them from other families in which the reaction is oxidative.

Gas from glucose* .... d
Lactose .... −
                    (or + weak and delayed)
Sucrose .... +
Mannitol .... +
Dulcitol .... −
Salicin .... +
Adonitol .... d
Inositol .... d
Indol .... −
Methyl red .... −
Voges-Proskauer .... +
Ammonium citrate .... +
Hydrogen sulfide .... −
Urease .... −

* The following signs are used: +, positive; −, negative; d, different biochemical types.

Gelatin liquefaction .... +
Growth in KCN medium .... +
Phenylalanine deaminase .... −
Sodium malonate .... −

For further details see Intern. Bull. Bacteriol. Nomen. Taxon., *8*, No. 1, 1958, 25.

Proteus (Pro′te.us) Hauser, 1885. *M p. 364.* (Manual Trop. Med., 3rd ed., 1919, 932.)

DIFFERENTIATING CHARACTERS: Unicellular, colorless, nonsporing, straight, rod-shaped organisms, less than 2 μ wide; motile with peritrichous flagella; Gram negative; *aerobic;* heterotrophic; grow well and often produce a swarming growth on meat infusion agar; acid and gas produced from glucose. No acid produced from lactose; gelatin liquefied *or* indole produced *or* both; urease positive.

Type species: *Proteus vulgaris* Hauser.

NOTES: Five species are described in the *Manual.* Rods 0.5 to 1.0 μ by 1 to 3 μ.

Grow well on meat infusion agar, usually with a thin, moist, spreading colony, which frequently covers the whole plate.

Gelatin is liquefied by 2/5 species.

Indole is produced by 4/5 species.

Litmus milk usually becomes alkaline.

Acid and gas are produced from glucose.

Lactose is not fermented.

Nitrite is produced from nitrate.

Citrate is utilized by 4/5 species.

All species produce phenyl pyruvic acid from phenylalanine.

Optimal temperature, 37° C.

Found in putrefying materials and often associated with intestinal disorders, especially in children, and in urinary tract infections.

Strains of the type species *Proteus vulgaris* have been found to have antigenic characters similar to the *Rickettsia* of typhus fever.

Some recent papers relevant to the systematics of *Proteus* are as follows:

Annear, D. I., Aust. J. Exp. Biol. Med. Sci., *42*, 1964, 723.

Bergquist, L. M., and Searcy, R. L., J. Bacteriol., *85*, 1963, 954.

Coetzee, J. N., and Sacks, T. G., J. Gen. Microbiol., *23*, 1960, 209, 445.

Coetzee, J. N., J. Gen. Microbiol., *29*, 1962, 455.

Coetzee, J. N., J. Gen. Microbiol., *31*, 1963, 219, *33*, 1963, 1.

Crisley, F. D., J. Bacteriol., *86*, 1963, 346.

Ewing, W. H., Suassuna, I., and Suassuna, I. R., The Genus Proteus, U. S. Department of Health, Education and Welfare Publication, 1960.

Ewing, W. H., Intern. Bull. Bacteriol. Nomen. Taxon., *12*, 1962, 93.

Hatch, M. H., and Stuart, C. A., J. Bacteriol., *83*, 1962, 1119.

Haughton, B. G., and King, H. H., Biochem. J., *80*, 1961, 268.

Hoeniger, J. F. M., Can. J. Microbiol., *10*, 1964, 1.

Rauss, K., Intern. Bull. Bact. Nomen. Taxon., *12*, 1962, 53.

The definition for the *Proteus-Providence* group given by the Subcommittee on *Enterobacteriaceae* of the I C N B is as follows:

The *Proteus-Providence* group consists of motile, nonsporing, Gram negative rods; grow on ordinary media, reduce nitrates to nitrites, give a negative oxidase reaction, and break down carbohydrates by a fermentative reaction that distinguishes them from other families in which the reaction is oxidative.

Lactose*	−
Dulcitol	−
Growth in KCN	+
Phenylalanine deaminase	+
Sodium malonate	−
Lysine decarboxylase	−
Arginine dihydrolase	−

For further details see Intern. Bull. Bacteriol. Nomen. Taxon., *13*, No. 2, 1963, 69.

The *Proteus-Providence* group is divided into four subgroups. All four subgroups

* The following signs are used: +, positive; −, negative.

produce phenylalanine deaminase. The *Proteus*, *Morganella*, and *Rettgerella* groups deaminate urea but *Providencia* does not. Swarming at 37° C. on nutrient agar is characteristic of the majority of strains of the *Proteus* and *Morganella* subgroups. This phenomenon is less easily demonstrable in the *Rettgerella* and *Providence* subgroups, but many strains of these subgroups will swarm under special conditions of media and temperature.

Paracolobactrum (Pa . ra . co . lo . - bac′trum) Borman *et al.*, 1944, *M p. 346*. (J. Bacteriol., *48*, 1944, 361.)

DIFFERENTIATING CHARACTERS: It is possible to frame only a quasidefinition of this genus. The organisms are related biochemically to most of the recognized genera of the *Enterobacteriaceae*. They are colorless, unicellular, nonsporing, Gram negative, *aerobic*, heterotrophic organisms, which produce acid or acid and gas from glucose. Lactose fermentation is usually delayed.

The *Enterobacteriaceae* Subcommittee in its report to the Nomenclature Committee at the Seventh International Congress of Microbiology at Stockholm (1958) recommended that the genus *Paracolobactrum* not be recognized. In view of this, and the fact that these strains have, in the main, been redistributed amongst other consolidated groups in the family *Enterobacteriaceae*, there is little point in perpetuating the names. Since the Keys still make reference to the *Manual* (7th ed.), the names have been retained in the Keys at the appropriate points.

Type species: *Paracolobactrum aerogenoides* Borman *et al.*

Bacteroides (Bac. te . ro . i′des) Castellani and Chalmers, 1919. *M p. 424*. (Manual Trop. Med., 3rd ed., 1919, 959.)

DIFFERENTIATING CHARACTERS: Unicellular, nonphotosynthetic, nonsporing, rod-shaped organisms, less than 2 μ wide; nonmotile or motile with flagella; Gram negative; *anaerobic;* heterotrophic; do not ferment glucose with the production of large quantities of ethyl alcohol or ferment acetate and *n*-butyrate with the production of methane; do not require sterile fresh tissue or ascitic fluid for growth.

Further characters that provide a uniform differentiation of the genus *Bacteroides* from other genera of anaerobic, Gram negative rods are lacking. The separation of *Bacteroides* from *Fusobacterium* on the basis of the shape of cells (the former are round-ended and the latter pointed) is not supported by the descriptions of the species. Similarly, differentiation from other genera on the basis of pleomorphism is not supported by the species descriptions. The author has attempted a separation at the species level in the keys.

Type species: *Bacteroides fragilis* (Veillon and Zuber) Castellani and Chalmers.

NOTES: Thirty species are described. They are differentiated on morphological and biochemical characters.

Rod-shaped organisms, pleomorphic in old cultures, 0.5 to 1.0 μ by 2 to 6 μ. Only 2/30 species are motile and have peritrichous flagella. Gram negative.

The majority of species will grow on meat infusion agar. Two are favored by the addition of ascitic fluid. One species is halophilic. Colony types vary with the species.

Gelatin is liquefied by 10/28 species.

Litmus milk is turned acid and may be coagulated by 16/26. It is peptonized by two.

Production of nitrite from nitrate is negative for all species in which it is recorded (16).

Indole is produced by 9/19 species.

Gas is produced by 5/23 species from peptone water without added carbohydrates.

Acid or acid and gas are produced from glucose by 24/27 species. Acid is produced from lactose by 20/27.

H₂S is produced by 15/22 species only.

Coagulated serum is liquefied by 1/9.

Optimal temperature, 35° to 37° C.

Found in the alimentary canal and buccal cavity of man and animals, in abscesses, and in decomposing organic matter.

Some recent papers relevant to the systematics of *Bacteroides* are as follows:

Akkada, A. R. A., and Blackburn, T. H., J. Gen. Microbiol., *31*, 1963, 461.

Blackburn, T. H., and Hobson, P. N., J. Gen. Microbiol., *29*, 1962, 69.

Bladen, H. A., and Waters, J. F., J. Bacteriol., *86*, 1963, 1339.

Bryant, M. P., Small, N., Bouma, C., and Chu, H., J. Bacteriol., *76*, 1958, 15.

Gutierrez, J., Davis, R. E., and Lindahl, I. L., App. Microbiol., *7*, 1959, 303.

Gibbons, R. J., and MacDonald, J. B., J. Bacteriol., *80*, 1960, 164.

Goldberg, H. S., Barnes, E. M., and Charles, A. B., J. Bacteriol., *87*, 1964, 737.

Harrison, A. P., and Hansen, P. A., Antonie van Leeuwenhoek, *29*, 1963, 22.

Reeves, R., J. Bacteriol., *85*, 1963, 1197.

White, D. C., Bryant, M. P., and Caldwell, D. R., J. Bacteriol., *84*, 1962, 822.

Fusobacterium (Fu.so.bac.te'ri.um) Knorr, 1922. *M p. 436.* (Zentr. Bakteriol. Parasitenk., Abt. I, Orig., *87*, 1922, 536.)

DIFFERENTIATING CHARACTERS: Unicellular, colorless, nonsporing, rod-shaped organisms with pointed ends, less than 2 μ wide; nonmotile or motile with flagella; Gram negative; *anaerobic;* heterotrophic; acid but no gas produced from glucose; variable reaction on lactose; do not produce large quantities of ethyl alcohol from glucose or methane from acetate and *n*-butyrate.

Type species: *Fusobacterium fusiforme* (Veillon and Zuber) Hoffmann.

NOTES: Six species are described in the *Manual.* They are spindle-shaped rods with pointed ends, straight or slightly curved. Only one species is motile (*F. praeacutum*). Gram negative. Two species are 8 to 16 μ long. The remaining four do not exceed 4 μ. They will not pass through Chamberland L2 filters.

Growth of two species is favored by blood or serum. Others grow well on meat infusion agar but not on plain peptone agar.

Gelatin is not liquefied.

Litmus milk is not altered.

Indole is not produced.

Nitrite is produced by 1/6 species.

Acid is produced from glucose by all species. Three also produce acid from lactose.

No gas is produced from carbohydrates or from peptone.

Optimal temperature, 37° C.

Found in the buccal cavity and intestinal tract of man and animals.

An excellent method for the isolation of oral fusobacteria is described by Omata and Disraely, J. Bacteriol., *72*, 1956, 677.

For further information see the following:
de Araujo, W. C., Varah, E., and Mergenhagen, S. E., J. Bacteriol., *86*, 1963, 837.

Baird-Parker, A. C., J. Gen. Microbiol., *22*, 1960, 458.

Dialister (Di.a.lis'ter) Bergey *et al.*, 1923. *M p. 440.* (Bergey's Manual of Determinative Bacteriology, 1st ed., 1923, 271.)

DIFFERENTIATING CHARACTERS: Unicellular, colorless, nonsporing, rod-shaped organisms of such small size that they are capable of passing through the Chamberland L2 filter; nonmotile; Gram negative; *anaerobic;* heterotrophic; acid but no gas produced from glucose; lactose not fermented; found in the upper respiratory tract.

Type species: *Dialister pneumosintes* (Olitsky and Gates) Bergey *et al.*

NOTES: Two species are described. Very minute rods, 0.15 to 0.3 μ by 0.5 to 1.0 μ.

The type species will not grow on meat infusion agar but requires the addition of blood or fresh tissue fluids.

D. granuliformans grows on meat infusion agar.

Colonies are very small and colorless.

Litmus milk is not changed.

Indole is not produced.

Nitrite is not produced.

Acid but no gas is produced from glucose but not from lactose.

Optimal temperature, 37° C.

Found in the respiratory tract of man.

For further information see the following:
Chen, C. C., and Cleverdon, R. C., Life Sciences, No. 8, 1962, 401.

Chen, C. C., and Cleverdon, R. C., J. App. Bacteriol., *26*, 1963, 107.

Sphaerophorus (Sphae.ro'pho.rus) Prévot, 1938. *M p. 441.* (Ann. Inst. Pasteur, *60*, 1938, 297.)

DIFFERENTIATING CHARACTERS: Unicellular, colorless, nonsporing organisms, which may exhibit a marked degree of pleomorphism, the pleomorphic forms frequently exceeding 2 μ in width and occasionally branched; nonmotile (17/18) or motile with flagella (1/18); Gram negative; *anaerobic;* heterotrophic; do not produce ethyl alcohol from glucose or methane from acetate or *n*-butyrate; variable reactions on glucose and lactose.

Characters that will further differentiate the genus as a whole from other anaerobic Gram negative rods are lacking. The author has attempted differentiation at the species level.

Type species: *Sphaerophorus necrophorus* (Flügge) Prévot.

NOTES: Eighteen species are described. They are differentiated in the *Manual* on morphological, nutritional, and biochemical characteristics.

Straight or curved, rod-shaped organisms showing very marked pleomorphism. Filamentous and branching forms occur. All cells except swollen pleomorphic ones are less than 2 μ wide.

Only 1/18 species, *S. bullosus,* is motile and has peritrichous flagella.

Serum or ascitic fluid is required by seven species.

Coagulated serum or egg is not liquefied by 6/6.

Gelatin is slowly liquefied by only 2/18 species.

Litmus milk is acidified by 5/17 species and is peptonized by only two.

Indole is produced by 8/12 species.

H₂S is produced by 9/11.

Nitrite is produced from nitrate by 0/8.

Gas is produced from peptone by 8/13 species.

Acid or acid and gas are produced from glucose by 11/13 species. Lactose is fermented by five.

The DNA base composition of *Sphaerophorus necrophorus* was 31% G + C (Dowell, Loper, and Hill, J. Bacteriol., *88*, 1964, 1805, Notes).

Found in lesions in all parts of the human body, particularly where secondary invaders can establish the anaerobic conditions. Found also in the alimentary and urogenital canals.

Streptobacillus (Strep.to.ba.cil'lus) Levaditi *et al.*, 1925. *M p. 451.* (Compt. rend., *180*, 1925, 1188.)

DIFFERENTIATING CHARACTERS: Unicellular, colorless, nonsporing, rod-shaped organisms, normally less than 2 μ wide and occurring in chains up to 100 to 150 μ long; may exhibit a high degree of pleomorphism, particularly on primary isolation; homogeneous in young cultures but become granulated, beaded, and swollen in old cultures and tend to fragment into rods and cocci; large, spherical swellings packed with granules are common; cholesterol globules appear among the growth. In pathological material only rods and short filaments are observed; nonmotile; Gram negative; *aerobic;* heterotrophic; require blood or ascitic fluid for growth; acid but no gas produced from glucose; variable acid production from lactose; highly virulent for mice, causing polyarthritis.

Type species: *Streptobacillus moniliformis* Levaditi *et al.*

NOTES: Only one species is described in the *Manual.*

Pleomorphic, rod-shaped organism; homogeneous in young cultures; 0.1 to 0.5 μ by 2.0 μ; pleomorphic forms may be filamentous and bulbous and measure up to 15 μ across. The spherical swellings are frequently packed with granules. Cholesterol globules appear among the growth. In pathological material only rods and short filaments occur; nonmotile; Gram negative.

The organism will not grow on meat infusion agar but requires ascitic fluid or blood. Colonies are 1 to 2.5 mm. in diameter in 3 days on ascitic fluid; circular, low convex, and colorless. L-phase variants are common.

Gelatin is not liquefied.

Litmus milk is not altered.

Indole negative.

Nitrite is not produced from nitrate.

H₂S positive.

Methylene blue is reduced.

Urease, catalase, and oxidase negative.

Acid is produced from glucose and other carbohydrates. Lactose fermentation variable.

Optimal temperature, 35° to 38° C.

Highly virulent for mice; an intravenous injection causes sepsis and death in 24 to 48 hours or a chronic disease characterized by purulent polyarthritis, anemia, emaciation, diarrhea, conjunctivitis, and transient or permanent paralysis.

Causes Haverhill fever in man.

Micrococcus (Mi.cro.coc'cus) Cohn, 1872. *M p. 455.* (Beitr. Biol. Pflanz., *1*, Heft 2, 1872, 153.)

DIFFERENTIATING CHARACTERS: Unicellular, spherical, nonsporing, nonphotosynthetic organisms; occasionally exceed 2 μ in diameter; arranged singly, in pairs, and in irregular clusters from both liquid and solid media; *aerobic;* heterotrophic; oxidative. Gram positive

They *do not* produce at least 0.5 to 0.7 per cent of *optically inactive lactic acid* in yeast extract-glucose-tryptone-phosphate broth, lowering the pH below 4.0.

Type species: *Micrococcus luteus* (Schroeter) Cohn.

NOTES: Considerable difficulty may be encountered in differentiating between the genus *Micrococcus* and the genera *Staphylococcus* and *Pediococcus*.

The genus *Micrococcus*, as described in the seventh edition of the *Manual*, includes spherical, nonphotosynthetic, unicellular organisms, which aggregate in irregular clusters and are capable of growth in defined media, in which the sole nitrogen source is ammonium phosphate. Their acid production from carbohydrates is considered to be *oxidative*, although there is nothing in the descriptions given in the *Manual* to support the latter statement; the ability to use ammonia nitrogen is cited for only 12 of the 16 species, and, of these, 5 are recorded as negative.

The genus *Staphylococcus*, to which only two species, *S. aureus* and *S. epidermidis*, have been allocated, consists of spherical, nonphotosynthetic, unicellular organisms, which aggregate in irregular clusters and are dependent on amino nitrogen for growth. Acid production from glucose is considered to be *fermentative*, but again supporting evidence in the *Manual* appears to be lacking.

A Subcommittee on *Staphylococcus* and *Micrococcus* has been set up within the International Committee on Nomenclature of Bacteria to examine the problem of differentiation of the two genera. The Subcommittee has recommended the use of a modification of Hugh and Leifson's test for determining the mode of metabolism of glucose (see p. *246*), placing fermentative cultures in the genus *Staphylococcus* and oxidative cultures in *Micrococcus*.

The genus *Pediococcus*, which is placed in an entirely different family in the *Manual*, is prone to produce pairs and chains of cells but forms tetrads regularly in acid media. Its species produce a strong acid reaction in sugar solutions. The lactic acid produced is optically inactive. The titratable acidity is equivalent to at least 0.5 per cent lactic acid, and the pH falls as low as 4.0.

The use of a quantitative character, such as the percentage of acid produced, is not a sound taxonomic practice. Inevitably, weak, acid-producing strains will be encountered. The optical inactivity of the lactic acid produced is the more important character. Unfortunately, there is little information on the nature of the by-products produced by the genus *Staphylococcus* and the genus *Micrococcus*.

The foregoing points should be borne in mind when considering the differentiating characteristics for the three genera as they appear in the *Manual*.

Williams, Hirch, and Cowan (*vide infra*) have also proposed the separation of a fourth genus, *Aerococcus*, mainly on the basis of its tolerance of 40 per cent bile and 1:400,000 crystal violet. The genus is not listed in the *Manual*. See *p. 161*.

The following additional notes on the genus *Micrococcus* cover only those tests which have been uniformly applied over all the listed species. Other characters, such as chitin hydrolysis, starch hydrolysis, and deamination of urea, have been used in the species Keys but have not been uniformly applied to all species.

The majority of the 16 species in the genus *Micrococcus* are Gram positive, although Gram negative species have been described.

Four species have been reported as motile. They have single flagella or are peritrichously flagellated.

All species grow well on meat infusion agar, although two (*M. morrhuae* and *M. halodenitrificans*) require added salt. Colonies are usually opaque and are frequently pigmented white, yellow, orange, pink, or red.

Gelatin is liquefied by 8/16 species.

Growth on liquid media is uniformly turbid.

Acid but no gas is produced from carbohydrates.

Litmus milk is rendered acid by 9/16 species, four of which also peptonize it.

Indole is not produced.

Nitrite is produced from nitrate by 8/16 species, and two reduce it to *nitrogen*.

The optimal temperature is 20° to 28° C. The organisms occur mainly in soil, water, milk, and other foodstuffs. Marine species are isolated from fish.

Some recent papers relevant to the systematics of *Micrococcus* are as follows:

Anderson, J. I. W., J. App. Bacteriol., *25*, 1962, 362.

Auletta, A. E., and Kennedy, E. R., J. Bacteriol., *92*, 1966, 28.

Baird-Parker, A. C., J. Gen. Microbiol., *30*, 1963, 409.

Baird-Parker, A. C., Ann. N. Y. Acad. Sci., *128*, 1965, 4.

Baird-Parker, A. C., J. Gen. Microbiol., *38*, 1965, 363.

Campbell, J. N., Nichols, J. L., and Berry, S. A., Can. J. Microbiol., *10*, 1964, 659.

Eisenberg, R. C., and Evans, B. E., Can. J. Microbiol., *9*, 1963, 633.

Evans, J. B., Bradford, W. L., Jr., and Niven, C. F., Jr., Intern. Bull. Bacteriol. Nomen. Taxon., *5*, 1955, 61.

Finnerty, W. R., Hawtrey, E., and Kallio, R. E., Zeitschr. Allg. Mikrobiol., *2*, 1962, 169.

Finnerty, W. R., Kallio, R. E., Klimstra, P. E., and Wawzonek, S., Zeitschr. Allg. Mikrobiol., *2*, 1962, 263.

Grula, E. A., Can. J. Microbiol., *8*, 1962, 855.

Kitchell, A. G., J. App. Bacteriol., *25*, 1962, 416.

Kocur, M., and Martinec, T., Folia Biologia I, Prague, Vol. 3, No. 3, 1962.

Kocur, M., and Martinec, T., J. Gen. Microbiol., *32*, 1963, 185.

Pichinoty, F., and D'Ornano, L., Ann. Inst. Pasteur, *101*, 1961, 418.

Pohja, M. S., and Gyllenberg, H. G., J. App. Bacteriol., *25*, 1962, 341.

Rosypal, S., and Kocur, M., Antonie van Leeuwenhoek, *29*, 1963, 313.

Rosypalová, A., Boháček, J., and Rosypal, S., Antonie van Leeuwenhoek, *32*, 1966, 105 and 192.

Seto, J. T., and Wilson, J. B., Amer. J. Veterinary Research, *19*, 1958, 241.

Stewart, G. T., Ann. N. Y. Acad. Sci., *128*, 1965, 132.

Whiteley, H. R., and Ordal, E. J., J. Bacteriol., *74*, 1957, 331.

Staphylococcus (Staph.y.lo.coc′cus) Rosenbach, 1884. *M p. 464*. (Mikroorganismen bei den Wundinfektionskrankheiten des Menschen, Weisbaden, 1884, 27.)

DIFFERENTIATING CHARACTERS: Unicellular, spherical, nonsporing, nonphotosynthetic organisms; occasionally exceed 2 μ in diameter; arranged singly, in pairs, and in irregular clusters from both liquid and solid media; *aerobic;* heterotrophic; fermentative. Gram positive

They *do not* produce at least 0.5 to 0.7 per cent of *optically inactive lactic acid* in yeast extract-glucose-tryptone-phosphate broth, lowering the pH below 4.0.

Type species: *Staphylococcus aureus* Rosenbach.

NOTES: There are only two species recognized in the genus. Both are cocci, 0.8 to 1.0 μ in diameter, occurring in grape-like clusters. Gram positive and nonmotile.

They will not utilize ammonia nitrogen but grow quite well on meat infusion agar, producing circular, entire, low convex, smooth, shining, butyrous, opaque colonies. They may be white or pigmented a golden yellow. Catalase positive.

Gelatin is liquefied.

Growth in broth is uniformly turbid.

Litmus milk is acidified and may coagulate.

Acid only is produced from a range of carbohydrates, including lactose.

Indole is not produced.

Nitrite is produced from nitrate.

The optimal temperature is 37° C.

Aerobic, facultatively anaerobic.

Staphylococcus aureus is the common cause of boils, carbuncles, and various other purulent diseases. Colonies are usually a golden yellow, but white variants appear. The pathogenic strains are able to coagulate blood plasma (coagulase positive).

S. epidermidis, a white form, is a common inhabitant of human skin.

See also notes on *Micrococcus*.

The following are recent papers relevant to the systematics of *Staphylococcus:*

Baird-Parker, A. C., J. Gen. Microbiol., *30*, 1963, 409.

Baird-Parker, A. C., J. App. Bacteriol., *25*, 1962, 352.

Baird-Parker, A. C., Intern. Bull. Bacteriol. Nomen Taxon., *15*, 1965, 107, 109.

Blair, J. E., Bacteriol. Revs., *26*, 1962, 375.

Beining, P. R., and Kennedy, E. R., J. Bacteriol., *85*, 1963, 732.

Cohen, J. O., and Oeding, P., J. Bacteriol., *84*, 1962, 735.

Cowan, S. T., and Steel, K. J., J. Bacteriol., *88*, 1964, 804.

Hill, L. R., Silvestri, L. G., Ihm, R., Farchi, G., and Lanciani, P., J. Bacteriol., *89*, 1965, 1393.

Jones, D., Deibel, R. H., and Niven, J. C. F., J. Bacteriol., *85*, 1963, 62.

Kocur, M., and Martinec, T., J. Gen. Microbiol., *32*, 1963, 185.

Pike, E. B., J. App. Bacteriol., *25*, 1962, 448.

Rosypal, S., Kocur, M., and Hodak, K., J. Gen. Microbiol., *32*, 1963, 189.

Aerococcus (Aer.o.coc′cus) Williams, Hirch, and Cowan, 1953. (J. Gen. Microbiol., *8*, 1953, 475.)

The above authors give the following constant generic characteristics: Gram positive, nonmotile cocci occurring in pairs or irregular clusters, usually small. Aerobic and facultatively anaerobic; growth occurs on solid media at 22° C. almost as well as at 37° but not at 45°. Colonies on blood agar incubated aerobically at 37° for 18 to 24 hours are semitransparent and surrounded by a zone of green color. Grow well in peptone water. Growth is not inhibited by 40 per cent bile, or by 1:400,000 crystal violet. Arginine is not hydrolyzed.

The organisms survive heating to 60° C. for 30 minutes and grow at pH 9.6 but not in acid media; usually catalase positive. Acid and formamide extracts do not react with sera prepared against Lancefield Group D streptococci.

Type species: *Aerococcus viridans.*

NOTE: The organism is a common contaminant from laboratory air.

Gaffkya (Gaff′ky.a) Trevisan, 1885. *M p. 466.* (Atti accad. Fisio-Medico-Statistica in Milano, Ser. 4, *3*, 1885, 106.)

DIFFERENTIATING CHARACTERS: Unicellular, colorless, nonsporing, spherical organisms, less than 2 μ in diameter; characteristically arranged in tetrads and encapsulated in body fluids but occurring in pairs, tetrads, and irregular masses in culture media; heterotrophic; Gram positive; *aerobic.*

They *do not* produce at least 0.5 to 0.7 per cent optically inactive lactic acid in yeast extract-glucose-tryptone-phosphate broth, lowering the pH below 4.0.

Type species: *Gaffkya tetragena* (Gaffky) Trevisan.

NOTES: This genus contains only two species, *G. tetragena* and *G. homari.*

Morphology as above. In laboratory cultures the organisms occur as pairs and irregular clusters. Individual cells are usually 0.6 to 1.0 μ in diameter. Nonmotile.

Growth occurs on meat infusion agar; colonies are circular, smooth, glistening and entire, grayish white, and 1 to 2 mm. in diameter. The two species require growth factors (biotin, calcium pantothenate, thiamin, and nicotinic acid) and some amino acids for growth.

Growth in liquid media is usually in the form of a sediment.

Litmus milk is acidified.

Gelatin is not hydrolyzed.

Acid but no gas is produced from glucose and lactose and from some other carbohydrates.

Aerobic. Optimal temperature, 37° C.

Gaffkya tetragena, which gives a viscid white growth on potato, has been demonstrated in sputum and isolated from the skin and air.

Gaffkya homari, which does not grow on potato, causes a fatal disease of lobsters.

Deibel and Niven (J. Bacteriol., *79*, 1960, 175) have re-examined this species in relation to *Aerococcus viridans* and recommend that both be placed as one species in the genus *Pediococcus*. See also Kocur and Martinec (Intern. Bull. Bacteriol. Nomen. Taxon., *15*, 1965, 177) for validity of the genus.

Sarcina (Sar.ci'na) Goodsir, 1842. *M p. 467.* (Edinburgh Med. and Surg. J., *57*, 1842, 430.)

DIFFERENTIATING CHARACTERS: Spherical, nonphotosynthetic, unicellular organisms, which divide in three perpendicular planes to produce cubical packets of eight cells each.

They do not deposit sulfur internally (*cf. Thiosarcina*).

Type species: *Sarcina ventriculi* Goodsir.

NOTES: The genus is best treated in two parts.

Part 1, consisting of *S. ventriculi, S. maxima, S. methanica,* and *S. barkeri,* covers a group of *anaerobic* species in which the diameter of individual cells is 2.0 μ or more. *S. ventriculi* and *S. maxima* are both 3.5 to 4.5 μ in diameter.

S. ventriculi and *S. maxima* will grow only in sugar-containing peptone media. Both produce acid and gas from glucose, lactose, maltose, fructose, galactose, and sucrose. The gas is CO_2. Other byproducts include ethyl alcohol (*S. ventriculi*) and acetic and butyric acid (*S. maxima*).

S. methanica has been cultivated only in a medium containing calcium acetate or calcium butyrate, which it converts to CO_2, methane, and calcium carbonate.

S. barkeri can grow autotrophically on CO_2 or CO and heterotrophically on sodium acetate or methanol, from which it produces methane and CO_2.

Part 2 comprises the remaining six recognized species, all of which are *aerobic* and grow well on meat infusion agar (except *S. littoralis*, which is halophilic), producing off-white or distinctly yellow, orange, or coral-red colonies. Because of the structural units in the colonies, they usually have a matt surface.

Very little information of value is provided for the differentiation of these species. They occur in air and water and have an optimal temperature between 20° and 30° C.

Unusual among this group is *Sarcina ureae*, which is motile with a single polar flagellum and produces spherical endospores. It is active in the deamination of urea.

The following are recent papers relevant to the systematics of *Sarcina:*

Canale-Parola, E., and Wolfe, R. S., J. Bacteriol., *79*, 1960, 857, 860.

Canale-Parola, E., Borasky, R., and Wolfe, R. S., J. Bacteriol., *81*, 1961, 311.

Chapman, G. B., J. Bacteriol., *79*, 1960, 132.

Jandola, J. J., and Ordal, Z. J., J. Bacteriol., *87*, 1964, 235.

Kocur, M., and Martinec, T., Intern. Bull. Bacteriol. Nomen. Taxon., *13*, 1963, 201.

Methanococcus (Me.tha.no.coc'cus) Kluyver and van Niel, emend. Barker, 1936. *M p. 473.* (Kluyver and van Niel, Zentr. Bakteriol. Parasitenk., Abt. II, *94*, 1936, 400; Barker, Arch. Mikrobiol., *7*, 1936, 430.)

DIFFERENTIATING CHARACTERS: Unicellular, colorless, nonphotosynthetic, nonsporing, spherical cells, which may exceed 2 μ in diameter; pleomorphic; arranged singly and in masses; Gram positive; *anaerobic;* ferment certain organic compounds with the production of methane and carbon dioxide.

Type species: *Methanococcus mazei* Barker.

NOTES: There are only two species, *M. mazei* and *M. vannielii.* In the former the cells are small and may be aggregated in cysts. In the latter they vary in diameter from 0.5 to 4.0 μ. *M. vannielii* is motile.

M. mazei attacks acetate but not ethanol or butanol. It does not use organic nitrogen compounds.

M. vannielii attacks formate but not acetate, propionate, butyrate, succinate, ethanol, or methanol.

Both species occur in mud and have an optimal temperature between 20° and 37° C.

Foster and Davis (J. Bacteriol., *91*, 1966, 1924–1931) describe a new methane-dependent coccus, *Methylococcus capsulatus* gen. nov., sp. nov.

Peptococcus (Pep. to. coc′cus) Kluyver and van Niel, 1936. *M p. 474*. (Zentr. Bakteriol. Parasitenk., Abt. II, *94*, 1936, 400.)

DIFFERENTIATING CHARACTERS: Unicellular, nonphotosynthetic, spherical organisms less than 2.0 μ in diameter (except *P. glycinophilus*); arranged singly, in pairs, and in irregular clusters; nonmotile; Gram positive; *anaerobic;* heterotrophic.

Type species: *Peptococcus niger* (Hall) Kluyver and van Niel.

NOTES: Eleven species are recorded. They are differentiated on cultural and biochemical properties only.

The organisms grow on meat infusion agar. Three species may require added glycine. In deep agar cultures 5/11 species produce gas from the peptone and cause a splitting of the agar. One species (*P. niger*) produces a water-soluble black pigment, which should not be confused with blackening that occasionally takes place where H_2S is produced in iron- or lead-containing media.

P. glycinophilus has cells ranging in diameter from 0.7 to 2.5 μ. It is one of the species requiring glycine for growth and decomposes it to CO_2, NH_3, and acetic acid. For recent papers dealing with the organism see the following:

Klein, S. M., Sagers, R. D., J. Bacteriol., *83*, 1962, 121.

Sagers, R. D., and Gunsalus, I. C., J. Bacteriol., *81*, 1961, 541.

Good growth occurs on blood agar without any evidence of hemolysis.

Broth becomes uniformly turbid, with gas production occurring with 5/11 species. Gas results from the decomposition of amino acids with the liberation of CO_2, H_2, and NH_3.

Gelatin is liquefied by 3/11 species.

Litmus milk is unchanged (3/11) or rendered slightly acid (1/11) or the litmus is reduced without acid production (6/11).

Acid is produced from a limited range of carbohydrates, but lactose is fermented by only one species (*P. grigoroffi*).

Seven species are recorded as catalase positive.

The optimal temperature is 37° C.

The species have been isolated principally from infections of the natural body cavities of man, particularly from the alimentary, vaginal, and respiratory tracts. Some of these may be secondary invaders.

Neisseria (Neis. se′ri.a) Trevisan, 1885. *M p. 480*. (Atti accad. Fisio-Medico-Statistica in Milano, Ser. 4, *3*, 1885, 105.)

DIFFERENTIATING CHARACTERS: Unicellular, colorless, kidney-shaped, or hemispherical organisms occurring basically in pairs with the flat sides adjacent; animal parasites; Gram negative; *aerobic;* heterotrophic.

Type species: *Neisseria gonorrhoeae* Trevisan.

NOTES: The genus has 10 species, all of which are parasites of man or animals. With few exceptions they occur in the respiratory tract. Nonmotile.

Species differentiation is based on cultural and biochemical characters only. Pigmentation and production of acid from glucose, maltose, fructose, and sucrose are the main points of difference.

See also notes on the genera, *Mima, Herellea*, and *Colloides* and also:

La Macchia, E. H., and Pelczar, M. J., J. Bacteriol., *91*, 1966, 514.

Murray, R. G. E., Reyn, A., and Birch-

Andersen, A., Can. J. publ. Hlth., *54*, 1963, 46.

Veillonella (Veil.lo.nel'la) Prévot, 1933. *M p. 485*. (Ann. Sci. nat., Sér. Bot., *15*, 1933, 118.)

DIFFERENTIATING CHARACTERS: Unicellular, colorless, spherical organisms, 0.3 to 2.0 μ in diameter; arranged in pairs or in clusters; Gram negative; do not produce methane from acetate; *anaerobic;* heterotrophic.

Type species: *Veillonella parvula* (Veillon and Zuber) Prévot.

NOTES: Six species are described. All are nonmotile. It should be noted that the diameters of cells of individual species range from 0.3 to 2.0 μ and not 0.3 to 0.4 μ as indicated in the generic description in the *Manual* (*vide infra*).

The organisms grow well in meat extract media, with three of the six species producing gas from the proteins. Blood is hemolyzed by only 1/6 species.

Glucose is fermented with the production of acid and gas by the type species only (*vide infra*).

Broth cultures of 3/6 species are malodorous.

Anaerobic, obligatory.

Optimal temperature, 37° C.

Found in natural cavities in the human body. Their numbers appear to increase in certain diseases of these cavities, but they may not be associated therewith.

Since the publication of the seventh edition of the *Manual*, a thorough re-examination of the genus *Veillonella* has been undertaken by Rogosa *et al.* (J. Bacteriol., *76*, 1958, 455; *87*, 1964, 162 and 574; *88*, 1964, 37; Bacteriol. Proc., 1961, p. 127), to which the reader is referred for details and references to other work. The authors restate the characteristics of the genus as follows: "The genus *Veillonella* thus would comprise species which are anaerobic and nonmotile; are small, spherical, gram-negative cocci appearing as pairs, masses, and short chains; and are cytochrome-oxidase- and benzidine-negative. *Veillonella*

would be further characterized in that glucose or any other carbohydrate is not fermented; indole is not produced; gelatin is not liquefied; nitrate is reduced; H_2S is produced; propionic and acetic acids, CO_2, and H_2 are produced from lactate during growth; and pyruvic, oxaloacetic, malic, fumaric, and succinic acids are metabolized by resting cells, but citric, isocitric, and malonic acids are not." The species recommended for exclusion by the above authors are essentially those assigned to *Neisseria* by Prévot (see Key, D.21

The cell walls of *V. parvula* and *V. alcalescens* contain diaminopimelic acid (Cosenza and Cleverdon, J. Bacteriol., *77*, 1959, 118). See also J. N. Ladd, (Biochem. J., *71*, 1959, 16).

For further information see:

Bladen, H. A., and Mergenhagen, S. E., J. Bacteriol., *88*, 1964, 1482.

Graham, R. K., and May, J. W., J. Gen. Microbiol., *41*, 1965, 243.

Brevibacterium (Brev.i.bac.te'ri.um) Breed, 1953. *M p. 490*. (Riassunti delle Comunicazioni, 6th Cong. intern. microbiol., Rome, *1*, 1953, 13.)

DIFFERENTIATING CHARACTERS: Unicellular, nonphotosynthetic, nonsporing, unbranched, rod-shaped organisms less than 2 μ wide; occur singly or in pairs and short chains; nonmotile or motile with flagella; Gram positive; nonacid-fast; heterotrophic; acid with no gas *or* no reaction in glucose; no acid from lactose.

They *do not or are not known to:* produce propionic acid from lactic acid or alcohol from glucose.

Type species: *Brevibacterium linens* (Weigmann) Breed.

NOTES: Twenty-three species are described. They are separated in the *Manual* on color, motility, action on litmus milk, reduction of nitrate, liquefaction of gelatin, production of acid from maltose, and salt requirements.

It is not possible to define this genus clearly. It was introduced primarily to provide a grouping (taxon) into which an assemblage of Gram positive, nonsporing nonacid-fast rods, having no clear-cut affinities with other genera of Gram positive rods, could be placed. Only a general description of the genus can be given.

Unicellular, rod-shaped, unbranched organisms, averaging 0.5 to 1.0 μ by 2 to 5 μ. Gram positive, nonacid-fast. Of the listed species, 17/23 are nonmotile. Of the remaining six, four are listed as peritrichously flagellated, and two as polarly flagellated. The majority are arranged singly and at random. Pairs and short chains do occur. Nonsporing.

The organisms grow on meat infusion agar, four with a sea water base. Colonies range from 1 to 5 mm. in diameter. The type of colony varies with the species. They are either nonpigmented or are various shades of red or yellow. The pigment of *B. linens* turns an intense carmine red when treated with 5 N NaOH, 5 N KOH, or saturated Ba(OH)$_2$; salmon pink with glacial acetic acid; brick red with aniline; and green, turning blue with syrupy phosphoric acid (Crecz and Dack, J. Bacteriol., *82*, 1961, 241).

Gelatin is liquefied by 17/23 species.

Litmus milk is rarely acidified. In most cases litmus is reduced and peptonization occurs.

Indole negative (21/23).

Nitrite is produced from nitrate by 6/19 species.

Acid but no gas is produced from glucose by 14/23 species. Lactose is not fermented (only one species is listed as variable in this respect). Acid is produced from maltose by 8/16 species.

Optimal temperature, between 20° and 30° C.

Listed species have been isolated from dairy products, rumen contents, insects, fish, plants, and soil.

Kurthia (Kurth'i.a) Trevisan, 1885. *M p. 503.* (Atti accad. Fisio-Medico-Statistica in Milano, Ser. 4, *3*, 1885, 92.)

DIFFERENTIATING CHARACTERS: Unicellu-

lar, colorless, nonsporing, unbranched, rod-shaped organisms less than 2 μ wide and arranged in chains in liquid media; motile with peritrichous flagella; Gram positive; nonacid-fast; *aerobic;* heterotrophic; no acid from carbohydrates; nonpathogenic to plants and animals.

Type species: *Kurthia zopfii* (Kurth) Trevisan.

NOTES: Three species are described. They are rods 0.8 by 1 to 8 μ and are separated in the *Manual* on the basis of gelatin liquefaction and hydrogen sulfide production.

Grow well on meat infusion agar, producing circular or irregular colonies; not pigmented.

Growth in broth is turbid with a flocculent sediment. Broth cultures have a very unpleasant odor attributable to liberation of ammonia.

Gelatin is hydrolyzed by 1/3 species.

Litmus milk is unchanged (2/3) or made alkaline and peptonized (1/3).

No acid or gas is produced from any carbohydrates.

Indole negative.

Nitrites are not produced from nitrates.

Optimal temperature, 25° to 30° C.

Isolated from hen manure, feces, and putrefying organic matter.

Diplococcus (Dip.lo.coc'cus) Weichselbaum, 1886. *M p. 507.* (Weiner med. Jahrb., *82*, 1886, 483.)

DIFFERENTIATING CHARACTERS: Unicellular, colorless, spherical to lanceolate organisms occurring in pairs, particularly in animal tissues, where they are capsulated; chains are common in culture media; soluble in bile; parasitic; found in the respiratory tract of man. Lactic acid is produced from glucose in small amounts and is dextrorotatory; Gram positive; *aerobic;* heterotrophic.

Type species: *Diplococcus pneumoniae* Weichselbaum.

NOTES: There is only the one species. It is nonmotile. The organisms are found in sputum in cases of pneumococcal pneumonia. In sputum they occur in pairs in a common capsule, the organism being lanceolate and arranged end to end with flat sides adjacent. In liquids the capsules are frequently lost, and the organisms assume a more spherical form. [It is possible that the lanceolate shape is the result of heat fixation before staining (author's note).] Serological typing of the species is based on differences in the capsular polysaccharide.

The organism grows on meat infusion agar, producing colonies that are 0.5 to 1 mm. in diameter, circular, entire, high convex, smooth and transparent.

On blood agar a greening of the medium occurs around the colony because of a change in the blood pigment, without effect on the intact blood cells. This is called alpha (α) hemolysis.

A uniform turbidity is produced in liquid media.

Gelatin is not liquefied.

Litmus milk is acidified and clotted.

Acid only is produced from glucose, lactose, sucrose, and inulin.

The organisms are soluble in neutral solutions of 10 per cent bile. This is possibly attributable to acceleration of an autolytic process to which this organism is prone.

The optimal temperature is 37° C.

Found in various inflammatory conditions of man.

Kauffmann, Lund, and Eddy (Intern. Bull. Bacteriol. Nomen. Taxon, *10*, 1960, 31) recommend placing *D. pneumoniae* in the genus *Pneumococcus*.

Streptococcus (Strep.to.coc′cus) Rosenbach, 1884. *M p. 508.* (Mikroorganismen bei den Wundinfektionskrankheiten des Menschen, 1884, 22.)

DIFFERENTIATING CHARACTERS: Unicellular, colorless, spherical to ovoid organisms, less than 2 μ in diameter; arranged in pairs and chains in liquid media; not soluble in bile; produce dextrorotatory lactic acid, if any, from glucose; do not form gas in Eldredge tubes when growing in glucose-yeast-extract-tryptone-phosphate broth; *aerobic;* heterotrophic.

Type species: *Streptococcus pyogenes* Rosenbach.

NOTES: Nineteen species are described. The cocci rarely exceed 1.0 μ in diameter. Chain formation results from division in one plane only. In some species cells are ovoid, with the long axis at right angles to the direction of the chain or parallel to it. The latter, particularly during division, may resemble rod-shaped organisms. Motile strains of streptococci have been described by Hugh (Can. J. Microbiol., *5*, 1959, 351) and Langston, Gutierrez, and Bouma (J. Bacteriol., *80*, 1960, 714).

Transient capsule formation occurs in body fluids with some pathogenic species. Other species may produce a capsular material of the dextran type similar to *Leuconostoc* but differ from the latter in the type of acid produced.

Growth of most species will occur on meat infusion agar but is greatly improved by blood or carbohydrates. Colonies are rarely more than 1 mm. in diameter and are circular and entire. The surface may vary from mucoid to smooth to rough.

On blood agar colonies are often surrounded by a zone in which the blood pigments have undergone some form of alteration. These alterations are classed as follows:

Beta (β) hemolysis: a water-clear zone around the colony from which the blood pigment and cells have completely disappeared.

Alpha (α) hemolysis: a greenish zone around the colonies in which the red blood cells remain intact, but there is an alteration in the hematin pigments.

Gamma (γ) hemolysis: no change at all.

Gelatin is not hydrolyzed except by two varieties of *Streptococcus faecalis* (vars. *liquefaciens* and *zymogenes*).

Litmus milk is acidified by all species except *S. equi, S. acidominimus,* and *S. equinus.* With other species simple acidification may occur without clotting or reduction of litmus. In still others clotting occurs.

Litmus may also be reduced either before or after clotting, depending on the species. Acid but no gas is produced from carbohydrates. Lactose is fermented by all species except *S. equi* and *S. equinus*. The acid produced is dextrorotatory.

Differentiation of species is based on numerous characteristics, including hemolysis of blood, decarboxylation of tyrosine, salt and dye tolerances, and growth at limiting pH values.

Serological methods have a special application in the differentiation of the beta hemolytic streptococci.

Aerobic to microaerophilic.

Catalase negative.

Devoid of cytochrome pigments.

Optimal temperature, 37° C.

Species that are pathogenic to man and animals occur mainly on those hosts. They are responsible for such infections as sore throats and scarlet fever in man, mastitis in cattle, and strangles in horses. The fecal streptococci are found in the alimentary canal of both man and animals. The "lactic" streptococci, which are responsible for the souring of milk and which are used commercially in cheese manufacture, are widespread in milk and milk products.

The following are recent papers relevant to the systematics of *Streptococcus:*

Barnes, E. M., J. App. Bacteriol., *27*, 1964, 461.

Fuller, R., and Newland, L. G. M., J. Gen. Microbiol., *31*, 1963, 431.

Gordan, D. F., Jr., Morgan, M. E., and Tucker, J. S., App. Microbiol., *11*, 1963, 171.

Hartman, P. A., Reinbold, G. W., and Saraswat, D. S., Int. J. Syst. Bacteriol., *16*, 1966, 197.

Jones, D., Deibel, R. H., and Niven, C. F., J. Bacteriol., *88*, 1964, 602.

Mead, G. C., Nature, *204*, 1964, 1224.

Michel, M. F., and Willers, J. M. N., J. Gen. Microbiol., *37*, 1964, 381.

Raj, H., and Colwell, R. R., Can. J. Microbiol., *12*, 1966, 353.

Sharpe, M. E., and Fewins, B. G., J. Gen. Microbiol., *23*, 1960, 621.

Shattock, P. M. F., Enterococci in Chemical and Biological Hazards in Foods, Iowa State University Press, 1963.

Sims, W., J. App. Bacteriol., *27*, 1964, 432.

Smith, D. G., and Shattock, P. M. F., J. Gen. Microbiol., *29*, 1962, 731.

Whittenbury, R., J. Gen. Microbiol., *38*, 1965, 279.

Pediococcus (Pe.di.o.coc'cus) Balcke, 1884, emend. Mees, 1934. *M p. 529*. (Balcke, Wochnschr. Brau., *1*, 1884, 257; Mees, Ondersoekingen over de Biersarcina. Thesis, Delft, 1934, 92.)

DIFFERENTIATING CHARACTERS: Unicellular, nonsporing, noncapsulated, nonphotosynthetic, spherical organisms, less than 2 μ in diameter; occur singly, in pairs, in tetrads and in clusters, with the tetrads predominating in acid media; Gram positive; *aerobic;* heterotrophic; produce *optically inactive lactic acid* in yeast-extract-glucose-tryptone-phosphate broth; do not liquefy gelatin; do not reduce nitrates to nitrites or nitrogen gas or produce detectable amounts of gas from carbohydrates; do not grow in media with ammonia as the sole source of nitrogen; no growth at pH 9.0; fat not hydrolyzed.

Type species: *Pediococcus cerevisiae* Balcke.

NOTES: The genus *Pediococcus* has been completely revised by Günther and White (J. Gen. Microbiol., *26*, 1961, 185) and Coster and White (J. Gen. Microbiol., *37*, 1964, 15). The *Manual* listed only two species, *P. cerevisiae* and *P. acidilactici*. These authors regard the latter as a variety of *P. cerevisiae* and include in the genus three other species conforming to the above amended definition of the genus.

P. cerevisiae grows profusely in tomato juice broth; initiates growth at pH 8.6 after 5 days of incubation; produces ammonia from arginine; lowers the pH in glucose-yeast extract broth in 18 days (or less) to pH 4.0; catalase positive (*cf. Manual*). The optimum temperature for growth lies between 30° and 37° C.

P. parvulus gives moderate growth in tomato juice broth; does not grow at pH 8.6 but does at pH 4.4; grows in the presence of 4 per cent but poorly with 6.5 per cent sodium chloride; does not produce ammonia from arginine or produce catalase.

P. damnosus has an optimum temperature of 22° C., with no growth at 37° C.; does not grow with 4 per cent sodium chloride; does not produce ammonia from arginine or produce catalase; grows at pH 8.6 in 5 days but not at pH 4.4.

P. halophilus is dependent on the presence of sodium chloride, giving maximum growth after 48 hours with 7 to 10 per cent. Growth could be initiated at pH 8.6 after 5 days but not at pH 4.4. It does not produce ammonia from arginine or produce catalase.

For further details on the genus *Pediococcus*, see the above papers and also the following:

Coster, E., and White, H. R., J. Gen. Microbiol., *37*, 1964, 15.

Deibel, R. H., and Niven, C. F., J. Bacteriol., *79*, 1960, 175.

Delwiche, E. A., J. Bacteriol., *81*, 1961, 416.

Dobrogosz, W. J., and Stone, R. W., J. Bacteriol., *84*, 1962, 716, 724.

Dobrogosz, W. J., and De Moss, R. D., J. Bacteriol., *85*, 1963, 1350, 1356.

Dobrogosz, W. J., and De Moss, R. D., J. Bacteriol., *86*, 1963, 887.

Dobrogosz, W. J., and De Moss, R. D., Intern. Bull. Bacteriol. Nomen. Taxon., *12*, 1962, 185.

Günther, H. L., Coster, E., and White, H. R., Intern. Bull. Bacteriol. Nomen. Taxon., *12*, 1962, 189.

Whittenbury, R., J. Gen. Microbiol., *40*, 1965, 97.

Leuconostoc (Leu.co.nos′toc) van Tieghem, 1878, emend. Hucker and Pederson, 1930. *M p. 531.* (van Tieghem, Ann. sci. nat., *6*, Sér. 7, 1878, 170; Hucker and

Pederson, N. Y. State Agr. Expt. Sta. Bull., *167*, 1930, 66.)

DIFFERENTIATING CHARACTERS: Unicellular, colorless, spherical organisms, less than 2μ in diameter; arranged in chains; produce gas in Eldredge tubes when growing in yeast-extract-glucose-tryptone-phosphate broth. The lactic acid produced is *levorotatory;* frequently produce a copious slime when grown in sucrose broth; Gram positive; *aerobic;* heterotrophic.

Type species: *Leuconostoc mesenteroides* (Cienkowski) van Tieghem.

NOTES: Three species, differentiated on the fermentation of sucrose and pentoses, are described. Nonmotile. When grown in sucrose media the cells of two species (*L. mesenteroides* and *L. dextranicum*) form a capsular material, which is a dextran.

The organisms grow on meat infusion agar but are favored by the addition of sugars and yeast extract or vegetable extract. Colonies are small and grayish white.

Gelatin is not liquefied.

Litmus milk is rendered acid and coagulated.

Indole is not produced.

H_2S is not produced.

Nitrites are not produced from nitrate.

Acid is produced by all species from glucose, lactose, fructose, and galactose. Other sugars may be attacked.

Lactic acid, acetic acid, and ethyl alcohol are produced and CO_2 is liberated. All species produce a *levorotatory* lactic acid. Some dextrorotatory acid may also be produced. The amount of CO_2 produced may not be sufficient to be detected with Durham tubes. Its evolution is usually demonstrated with Eldredge tubes.

Optimal temperature, 20° to 28° C.

Usually found producing slime in sucrose solutions or in milk products.

For further information see:

Whittenbury, R., Archiv. Mikrobiol., *53*, 1966, 317.

Peptostreptococcus (Pep.to.strep.-to.coc′cus) Kluyver and van Niel, 1936. *M*

p. 533. (Zentr. Bakteriol. Parasitenk., Abt. II, *94*, 1936, 391, 395, and 401.)

DIFFERENTIATING CHARACTERS: Unicellular, colorless, spherical organisms, less than 2 μ in diameter; arranged in pairs and chains only; Gram positive; *anaerobic;* heterotrophic; do *not* ferment acetate with the production of methane.

Type species: *Peptostreptococcus anaerobius* (Krönig emend. Natvig) Kluyver and van Niel.

NOTES: Thirteen species are described. They are differentiated on morphological and biochemical characteristics. Arranged in pairs or short to long chains and only rarely in clusters (*P. evolutus*). Nonmotile; Gram positive.

Twelve of the 13 species will grow on meat infusion agar without special enrichment, but media containing blood and carbohydrates are preferred. Veillon's semisolid agar is used extensively. Colonies of the different species vary in size from the very minute to 1 to 2 mm. in diameter.

Hemolysis of blood agar is either absent (γ) or of the green α-type.

Species give a turbid or flocculent growth in peptone water. Three species (*P. anaerobius, P. foetidus,* and *P. productus*) produce gas from the peptone.

Gelatin is liquefied by only one species (*P. evolutus*).

H$_2$S is rarely produced from peptone but is frequently produced in the decomposition of fresh animal fluids, *e.g.*, blood or serum.

Only one species (*P. magnus*) fails to produce acid from carbohydrates. Five species also produce gas. Three of these produce gas from peptone alone.

Among the byproducts of fermentation are acetic, formic, valerianic, butyric, propionic, and lactic acids and CO$_2$, H$_2$, and NH$_3$. The fetid odor of some cultures is due to the organic acids.

Lactose is fermented and litmus milk is acidified and curdled by 7/13 species.

All species are, on primary isolation, strictly *anaerobic.* Three (*P. evolutus, P.*

paleopneumoniae, P. morbillorum) become aerotolerant on subculture.

The optimal temperature is 37° C.

Species in the genus have been isolated mainly from putrefactive lesions in the natural cavities of the human and animal body, particularly from the female genital organs, gangrenous conditions of various organs, and inflammations of the alimentary canal.

Lactobacillus (Lac.to.ba.cil′lus) Beijerinck, 1901. *M p. 542.* (Arch. néerl. sci., Haárlem. Sér. 2, *7*, 1901, 212.)

DIFFERENTIATING CHARACTERS: Unicellular, nonphotosynthetic, nonsporing, rod-shaped organisms, less than 2 μ wide, which occasionally show bifurcations and rudimentary branching; occur singly and in chains; nonmotile; Gram positive; nonacid-fast; *aerobic* or *anaerobic;* heterotrophic; grow poorly on meat infusion agar but well on media containing carbohydrates and yeast extract; colonies are usually 1 mm. or less in diameter and colorless; grow in glucose broth, producing a final pH below 6.0; glucose converted quantitatively by homofermentative species to lactic acid, and by heterofermentative species to lactic acid, acetic acid, alcohol, and carbon dioxide, with visible gas produced only by the latter. Acid produced from lactose by all species except *L. delbrueckii* and *L. brevis;* lactic acid not metabolized; not known to survive heating to 72° C. for 15 minutes.

Type species: *Lactobacillus caucasicus* Beijerinck.

NOTES: Fifteen species are described, and they are separated in the *Manual* on the nature of byproducts of fermentation, fermentation of lactose, temperature of growth, and optical rotation of acid produced.

The morphology of the organisms varies with the species and conditions of cultivation. Some species, principally those producing only lactic acid from glucose (homofermenters) retain the simple rod shape throughout their growth. Many of the other species produce uniform rods in the early stages of development but become extremely pleomorphic while the colonies are still microscopic in size. Bifurcations are common with *L. bifidus*.

Growth on meat infusion agar without added carbohydrate is very poor or absent. Optimal growth occurs on yeast or plant extract media containing glucose. Colonies vary in size from less than 1 mm. with most species to 2 to 3 mm. (*L. bifidus*). Pigmentation is rare. Occasional yellow, orange, or rust-red colonies are produced.

Gelatin is not liquefied.

Litmus milk is acidified and clotted by 7/15 species, principally the homofermentative types having an optimal temperature of 37° C. or above.

Acid is produced from glucose and maltose by all species. Lactose is fermented by all but *L. delbrueckii*, *L. leichmannii*, and some strains of *L. brevis*. Fructose and galactose are fermented by all species except *L. caucasicus*.

Eleven of the 15 species are homofermentative, producing lactic acid alone or with only traces of volatile acids. The optical rotation of the acid produced varies with the species.

Four of the 15 species are heterofermentative, producing, in addition to lactic acid, appreciable quantities of volatile substances (acetic acid, ethyl alcohol) and CO_2. Copious gas production is noted only with *L. brevis*. The optical rotation of lactic acid produced varies with the species.

Lactate is *not* metabolized.

Catalase negative.

The optimal temperature for growth varies with the species. All the heterofermentative species grow at 28° to 32° C. as do 3/11 homofermentative species. The others grow best at 37° to 45° C. The latter species are important in the industrial production of lactic acid.

Frequently found in fermenting plant juices, nearly always in association with yeasts, since both are aciduric. Always found in mature cheese of the cheddar type, in the feces of milk-fed infants, and in the vaginal canal.

Attention is drawn to the description of new species of *Lactobacillus*, *L. heterohiochi* and L. *homohiochi* (Kitahara, Kaneko, and Goto, J. Gen. App. Microbiol., Japan, *3*, 1957, 102), which cause spoilage in Japanese rice wine (sake). *Lactobacillus bifidus* and similar forms producing bifurcations are placed in the genus *Bifidobacterium* by Prévot. Pine and Howell (J. Gen. Microbiol., *15*, 1956, 428) note the close similarity of *L. bifidus* to *Actinomyces israelii* and *A. naeslundii*; *L. bifidus* differs from the latter only in its failure to reduce nitrates and its more active production of acid from sugars and preference for lactose over glucose. *Lactobacillus bifidus* is serologically unrelated to the *Actinomyces* spp.

Some recent publications relevant to the systematics of *Lactobacillus* are as follows:

Clark, R. T. J., J. Gen. Microbiol., *20*, 1959, 549.

Deibel, R. H., and Evans, J. B., J. Bacteriol., *79*, 1960, 356.

Demain, A. L., Rickes, E. L., Hendlin, D., and Barnes, E. C., J. Bacteriol., 81, 1961, 147.

Dennis, D., and Kaplan, N. O., J. Biol. Chem., *235*, 1960, 810.

Domagk, G. F., and Horecker, B. L., J. Biol. Chem., *233*, 1958, 283.

Efthymisu, C., and Hansen, P. A., J. Infect. Diseases, *110*, 1962, 258.

Ford, J. E., and Rogosa, M., J. Gen. Microbiol., *25*, 1961, 249.

Gemmell, M., and Hodgkiss, W., J. Gen. Microbiol., *35*, 1964, 519.

Gibbons, R. J., and Doetsch, R. N., J. Bacteriol., *77*, 1959, 417.

Glastonbury, J., and Knox, K. W., J. Bacteriol., *31*, 1963, 73.

Hammond, B. F., Rosan, B., and Williams, N. B., J. Bacteriol., *88*, 1964, 1807.

Hankin, L., and Squires, S., App. Microbiol., *8*, 1960, 209.

Knox, K. W., J. Gen. Microbiol., *31*, 1963, 59.

Lovtrup, S., and Shugar, D., J. Bacteriol., *82*, 1961, 623.

De Man, J. C., Antonie van Leeuwenhoek, *26*, 1960, 77.

Niven, C. F., Jr., Buettner, L. G., and Evans, J. B., App. Microbiol., *2*, 1954, 26.

Rogosa, M., App. Microbiol., *23*, 1960, 197.

Sharpe, M. E., Ann. Inst. Pasteur (Lille), *12*, 1961, 128.

Eubacterium* (Eu.bac.te'ri.um) Prévot, 1938, *M p. 552*. (Ann. Inst. Pasteur, *60*, 1938, 294.)

DIFFERENTIATING CHARACTERS: Unicellular, colorless, unbranched, nonsporing, rod-shaped organisms, less than 2 μ wide; arranged singly, in pairs, in clusters, and occasionally in chains; nonmotile; Gram positive; nonacid-fast; *anaerobic;* heterotrophic; grow in peptone water, often producing gas in the absence of carbohydrates (13/20); produce acid (and possibly gas) from carbohydrates (17/20). The acid byproducts vary with the species but include propionic, butyric, lactic, acetic, and formic acids.

Type species: *Eubacterium foedans* (Klein) Prévot.

NOTES: The differentiating characters given above are not very satisfactory. The genus differs mainly from some species of *Propionibacterium* and *Butyribacterium* in its apparent ease of growth in peptone media and from *Ramibacterium* in the arrangement of cells. The differentiation of some species from *Catenabacterium* is not clear. In the *Manual* the keys given on p. 542 separate *Eubacterium* on lack of chain formation; yet in keys to *Eubacterium* on p. 552, species are specifically separated on chain formation.

Twenty species are described. They are separated in the *Manual* on production of gas in media, odor, liquefaction of gelatin,

action on milk, blood hemolysis, arrangement of cells, production of ethanol, reduction of nitrates, reduction of neutral red and phenosafranine, and on pathogenicity.

All species grow in peptone water; 13/20 species produce *gas* from peptone, and many of these have an offensive odor, attributable to the liberation of volatile amines and ammonia.

Gelatin is liquefied by only 4/20 species.

Coagulated serum is liquefied by only one. Acid is produced from a variety of carbohydrates by 15/20 species. The coincident gas production by some species may be from peptone. *Propionic, butyric (cf. Propionibacterium* and *Butyribacterium*) lactic, acetic, formic, and valerianic acids are produced. A few also produce aldehydes, ketones, and acetylmethylcarbinol.

Indole is not produced.

All species are *anaerobic* and have been isolated from a variety of gangrenous and suppurative infections in various parts of the body; also from feces of man and animals and decomposing meat.

Several species are pathogenic to laboratory animals.

Bladen, Nylen, and Fitzgerald (J. Bacteriol., *88*, 1964, 763) describe the fine structure of a species of *Eubacterium* isolated from the rat cecum.

Catenabacterium (Ca.te.na.bac.te'ri.um) Prévot, 1938. *M p. 560*. (Ann. Inst. Pasteur, *60*, 1938, 294.)

DIFFERENTIATING CHARACTERS: Unicellular, colorless, nonsporing, straight or curved, rod-shaped organisms, less than 2 μ wide; occur as S-shaped, filamentous, pleomorphic forms or as regular rod-shaped cells in long chains; nonmotile; Gram positive, nonacid-fast; *anaerobic;* heterotrophic; may produce gas from peptone (3/7); ferment glucose with the production of *propionic*, lactic, *butyric*, acetic, and formic acids, volatile amines, alcohol, aldehydes, and acetoin.

Type species: *Catenabacterium helminthoides* (Lewkowicz) Prévot.

---

* The name *Eubacterium* as used by Prévot is a later homonym of *Eubacterium* Janke and hence is illegitimate (Buchanan, private communication).

NOTES: They are separated in the *Manual* on gas production, liquefaction of gelatin, coagulation of milk, growth requirements, and cultural characteristics.

The genus has seven species. With one exception they grow in peptone media without added carbohydrates or serum. The three species producing gas from peptone have a pronounced fetid odor. Byproducts of growth in glucose-peptone water by these species include propionic acid (2/3), lactic acid (3/3), acetic acid (1/3), butyric acid (1/3), volatile amines (3/3), formic acid (3/3), alcohol (3/3), aldehydes (1/3), and acetylmethylcarbinol (3/3).

Lactic and butyric acids are produced by one of the non-gas-forming species. The type of byproduct is not specified for the others.

The distinction between the genus and species of *Propionibacterium* and *Butyribacterium* is not clear. Further information on the species is required before a decision can be reached.

Species have been isolated from cases of appendicitis, gangrene of the lung, uterine infections, pleurisy, dental caries, the normal mouth, and from pond mud.

Ramibacterium (Ra.mi.bac.te′ri.um) Prévot, 1938. *M p. 563.* (Ann. Inst. Pasteur, *60*, 1938, 294.)

DIFFERENTIATING CHARACTERS: Unicellular, colorless, nonsporing, straight or curved rods, less than 2 μ wide and arranged in Y- or V-shaped formations *suggestive* of branching; nonmotile; Gram positive; nonacid-fast; *anaerobic;* heterotrophic; growth in peptone water, in the absence of carbohydrates, with the production of gas. Acids, principally lactic, acetic, butyric, propionic, formic, and valerianic, are produced from carbohydrates.

Type species: *Ramibacterium ramosum* (Veillon and Zuber) Prévot.

NOTES: Six species are described. They are separated in the *Manual* on the production of indole, coagulation of milk, reduction of neutral red, and production of organic acid.

The above differentiating characteristics are not very satisfactory. The principal difference from *Catenabacterium* and *Eubacterium* is the arrangement of the cells. The species are clearly differentiated from *Propionibacterium* and *Butyribacterium* by the production of gas from and growth in peptone.

Gelatin is not liquefied.

Litmus milk is acidified and clotted by 3/6 species.

Ammonia is produced from peptone.

Alcohols, ketones, volatile amines, and acetoin are also produced.

Species have been isolated from cases of dental infection, pleurisy, and appendicitis and from feces. Some are pathogenic to laboratory animals.

Cillobacterium (Cil.lo.bac.te′ri.um) Prévot, 1938. *M p. 566.* (Ann. Inst. Pasteur, *60*, 1938, 294.)

DIFFERENTIATING CHARACTERS: Unicellular, colorless, nonsporing unbranched, straight or curved, rod-shaped organisms; pleomorphic; *motile* with peritrichous flagella; Gram positive; nonacid-fast; *anaerobic;* heterotrophic; grow in peptone water with the production of gas; carbohydrates fermented by 4/5 species with the production of lactic, acetic, butyric, valerianic, and formic acids.

Type species: *Cillobacterium moniliforme* Prévot.

NOTES: Six species are described. They are separated in the *Manual* on gelatin liquefaction, coagulation of milk, fermentation of glucose and cultural characteristics.

Biochemical tests have not been uniformly applied, but the following observations have been made.

Indole is produced by 4/4 species.

Nitrites are produced from nitrates by 3/3.

Neutral red is reduced by 4/5.

Gelatin is liquefied by 5/6 species.

Litmus milk is not rendered acid or alkaline, although gas may be produced.

Optimal temperature, 37° C.

The organisms have been found in lesions of warm-blooded animals and in the intestinal tract. Most species are pathogenic to the guinea pig.

Bryant, Small, Bouma, and Robinson (J. Bacteriol., *76*, 1958, 529) described a new cellulolytic species of *Cillobacterium* (*C. cellulosoluens*) from the rumen contents of cows.

Propionibacterium (Pro.pi.on.i.-bac.ter'i.um) Orla-Jensen, 1909. *M p. 569.* (Zentr. Bakteriol. Parasitenk., Abt. II, *22*, 1909, 337.)

DIFFERENTIATING CHARACTERS: Unicellular, nonphotosynthetic, nonsporing organisms, less than 2 μ wide; pleomorphic, occurring as chains of cocci in acid media under anaerobic conditions or as rods with occasional rudimentary branching under aerobic conditions; nonmotile; Gram positive; nonacid-fast; heterotrophic; poor growth in media without added carbohydrate; produce propionic acid, acetic acid, and carbon dioxide from glucose *and from lactic acid;* catalase positive.

Type species: *Propionibacterium freudenreichii* van Niel.

NOTES: There are 11 recognized species. All of these, when grown aerobically in yeast extract media containing carbohydrates are very pleomorphic, club-shaped, and branched rods. Nonmotile and nonsporing.

Anaerobically the morphology of cells is more uniform, but the shape of cells frequently differs in neutral media from that in acid media; the former are spherical and resemble streptococci, but the latter are usually rod-shaped.

Growth on peptone media without carbohydrates is very poor or absent. All species examined require pantothenic acid and biotin as growth factors. Two require *p*-aminobenzoic acid, and all are *stimulated by* but do not require thiamin.

Growth in stab cultures is usually good. Color varies with the species. *P. rubrum* and *P. thoenii* are brownish red. Other species vary from cream to yellowish orange, the darker color appearing in the more aerobic growth near the top of the stab.

Colonies are usually moist and butyrous. Those of *P. peterssonii* are dry.

In a yeast-peptone medium *all* species ferment *lactic acid*, pyruvic acid, dihydroxyacetone, and glycerol to *propionic* acid, acetic acid, and CO_2. The amount of CO_2 formed may be too small to be detected by the Durham tube method.

With the exception of *P. freudenreichii* and *P. shermanii*, *all* species produce propionic acid from glucose, lactose, maltose, fructose, mannose, galactose, and sucrose, but *not* from inulin or dulcitol.

P. freudenreichii does not ferment lactose, maltose, or sucrose, and *P. shermanii* fails to ferment maltose and sucrose.

Differentiation of species is based on their action on other carbohydrates.

P. arabinosum and *P. pentosaceum* are notable for their action on pentoses.

Litmus milk is slowly acidified and clotted by all but *P. arabinosum*.

Indole is not produced.

Gelatin is not liquefied.

Nitrates are not reduced to nitrites by any species except *P. pentosaceum*, which reduces through nitrite to nitrogen.

Catalase positive (*P. arabinosum* very weak).

Optimal temperature, 30° C.

Found in dairy products, particularly in "shot-hole" cheese of the Gruyère and Edam types.

Moore and Cato (J. Bacteriol., *85*, 1963, 870) have carried out a detailed re-examination of the fermentation patterns of *Corynebacterium acnes* and have demonstrated clearly that the three ATCC strains 11827, 6921, and 6922 are all capable of fermenting lactate under anaerobic conditions to propionate, acetate, and small quantities of succinate and have recommended that the proposal of Douglas and Gunter (J. Bacteriol., *52*, 1956, 15) to place the organism in the genus *Propionibacterium* be adopted. The author concurs with this.

For other information on the genus see the following:

Allen, S. H. G., Kellermeyer, R. W., Stjernholm, R. L., and Wood, H. G., J. Bacteriol., *87*, 1964, 171.

Molinari, R., and Lara, F. J. S., Biochem. J., *75*, 1960, 57.

Butyribacterium (Bu.ty.ri.bac.te'-ri.um) Barker and Haas, 1944. *M p.* 577. (J. Bacteriol., *47*, 1944, 301.)

DIFFERENTIATING CHARACTERS: Unicellular, colorless, unbranched, nonsporing, rod-shaped organisms, less than 2 μ wide; arranged singly and in short chains; nonmotile; Gram positive; nonacid-fast; *anaerobic;* heterotrophic; acid is produced from glucose and maltose but not from lactose or fructose; *butyric acid*, acetic acid, and carbon dioxide produced from glucose, maltose, *and also from lactic acid.*

Type species: *Butyribacterium rettgeri* Barker and Haas.

NOTES: There is only one species listed. Straight or slightly curved, unicellular, rod-shaped organisms, 0.7 by 2.3 μ.

No growth occurs on meat infusion agar. Colonies, 2 mm. in diameter in 4 days at 37° C., are produced on glucose-cysteine agar or tryptone yeast extract lactate agar. Colonies are circular, translucent, grayish white, convex to umbonate, glistening, and smooth. Edges are entire or slightly irregular.

Acetic acid, butyric acid, and CO_2 are produced from glucose and maltose. The gas may not be sufficient to be evolved.

Xylose, arabinose, lactose, sucrose, trehalose, rhamnose, mannitol, sorbitol, dulcitol, and glycerol are not fermented.

Lactate is readily fermented and converted to butyric acid without visible gas production. Wittenberger and Flavin (J. Biol. Chem., *238*, 1963, 2529) have shown that the organism requires lipoic acid for the fermentation of lactate but not for pyruvate or glucose.

Indole negative.

H_2S negative.

Catalase negative.

Optimal temperature, 37° C.

Isolated from the intestine of the white rat.

Zymobacterium (Zy.mo.bac.te' ri.-um) Wachsman and Barker, 1954. *M p.* 577. (J. Bacteriol., *68*, 1954, 400.)

DIFFERENTIATING CHARACTERS: Unicellular, colorless, unbranched, nonsporing, spindle-shaped rods, less than 2 μ wide; occur as long, intertwined chains in liquid media; nonmotile; Gram positive; nonacid-fast; *aerobic* to *anaerobic;* heterotrophic; acid and gas produced from glucose in glucose-peptone water; glucose fermented in a yeast-like manner with the production of ethyl alcohol and small amounts of acetic acid and carbon dioxide.

Type species: *Zymobacterium oroticum* Wachsman and Barker.

NOTES: There is only one listed species. Rod-shaped organisms, 0.3 to 0.6 μ by 1.2 to 2.0 μ with tapering ends, usually occurring in long, intertwined chains.

Growth on meat infusion media is not stated.

Small, round, convex colonies are produced on tryptone yeast extract glucose agar.

No growth in milk.

Indole is not produced.

Acid and gas are produced from glucose, fructose, sucrose, lactose, maltose, arabinose, galactose, and mannitol. Lactic acid, glutamic acid, and glycerol are not utilized.

Glucose fermentation yields predominantly ethyl alcohol (1.3 moles per mole of glucose) and CO_2 and possibly lactic and formic acid. The fermentation is slow.

Orotic acid is fermented with the production of ammonia.

Starch is not hydrolyzed.

Nitrites are not produced from nitrates.

Catalase negative.

Anaerobic to microaerophilic.

Isolated from bay mud.

Corynebacterium (Co.ry.ne.bac.te'-ri.um) Lehmann and Neumann, 1896. *M* *p. 579.* (Bakteriol. Diag., 1 Aufl., *2*, 1896, 390.)

DIFFERENTIATING CHARACTERS: Nonphotosynthetic, nonsporing, rod-shaped organisms, less than 2 μ wide, which appear in smears in palisade or Chinese letter forms; rarely show rudimentary branching; nonmotile (29/33) or motile with polar flagella (4/33); Gram positive; nonacidfast; *aerobic* (29/33) or *anaerobic* (4/33); heterotrophic; acid produced from glucose (27/33) and lactose (15/33); gas also produced by 2/33. Butyric acid is not recorded among the byproducts, and propionic acid, recorded for only one species, is not produced from lactic acid.

Type species: *Corynebacterium diphtheriae* (Flügge) Lehmann and Neumann.

NOTES: The distinction between this genus and the genus *Brevibacterium* is not very clear. The organisms in the genus *Brevibacterium* are considered to be uniform, nonpleomorphic rods arranged singly and at random. Most, but not all, species of the genus *Corynebacterium* are very pleomorphic cells with clubbed ends, curved axes, and irregular staining. The last character has been shown in some species to be due to a multicellular nature of each organism, although this is *not apparent without special stains applied to demonstrate cell walls.* This may be the most useful criterion for separation from *Brevibacterium*.

The cells of many species of the genus *Corynebacterium*, when examined in stained smears from agar plate cultures, appear to be arranged in palisades or Chinese letter forms, a characteristic attributed by most authors to a peculiar mode of division, which results in the temporary adherence of cells after division. The fact that such cells, once dispersed in a fluid so that they occur singly when smears are examined immediately, are found to have regrouped in palisades on standing suggests an entirely different explanation for this phenomenon, based on cell surface characteristics (author's note).

The organisms will grow on meat infusion agar. Colonies vary with the species but usually exceed 1 mm. in diameter, are circular, entire, and butyrous. They are either grayish white or are pigmented cream, yellow, or red. Blue granules are produced in yellow colonies of *C. insidiosum*.

Gelatin is liquefied by 10/33 species.

Litmus milk is rarely acidified even by species that ferment lactose in peptone or serum bases. It is sometimes turned alkaline and is only occasionally peptonized.

Acid but no gas is produced from glucose by 27/33 species. Two anaerobic species (*C. avidum* and *C. diphtheroides*) produce gas.

Several other sugars are fermented by different species.

Indole production is recorded for only 3/33 species.

Aerobic except *C. acnes,*[*] *C. parvum, C. granulosum, C. avidum,* and *C. diphtheroides*.

The optimal temperature varies with the habitat. Animal parasites and commensals have an optimum of 37° C. Those isolated from plant diseases, plants, soil, and so on have an optimum closer to 30° C.

Approximately half the aerobic species cause infections in animals. *C. diphtheriae* is the cause of diphtheria. The others mainly cause caseous lesions in various parts of the body.

The remaining aerobic species are pathogens of plants.

Some recent additions of species to the genus *Corynebacterium* include: *C. barkeri* (Dias, Bilimoria, and Bhat, J. Indian Inst. Sci., *44*, 1962, 59); *C. laevaniformans* (Dias and Bhat, Antonie van Leeuwenhoek, *28*, 1962, 63; *30*, 1964, 176); *C. manihot* (Collard, J. App. Biol., *26*, 1960, 115); and *C. rubrum* (Crowle, Antonie van Leeuwenhoek, *28*, 1962, 183).

Soda and Cleverdon (Antonie van Leeuwenhoek, *26*, 1960, 98) have shown that the plant pathogens *C. flaccumfaciens, C.*

* See *Note* to *Propionibacterium*.

michiganense, C. rathayi, C. poinsettiae, and *C. insidiosum* showed only low titer cross-agglutinations with some strains of *Flavobacterium* and *Xanthomonas* and are themselves nearly serologically specific.

Listeria (Lis.te′ ri.a) Pirie, 1940, *M p.* 597. (Science, *91*, 1940, 383.)

DIFFERENTIATING CHARACTERS: Unicellular, colorless, nonsporing, unbranched, straight, rod-shaped organisms; motile with peritrichous flagella; Gram positive; nonacid-fast; *aerobic;* heterotrophic; produce acid but no gas from glucose, salicin, and esculin; pathogenic to warm-blooded animals, causing monocytosis.

Type species: *Listeria monocytogenes* (Murray *et al.*) Pirie.

NOTES: There is only one species. It is a rod-shaped organism, 0.4 to 0.5 μ by 0.5 to 2.0 μ, arranged singly.

The organism grows well on nutrient agar, producing circular, smooth, butyrous, milky colonies, 1 to 2 mm. in diameter.

Gelatin is not liquefied.

Litmus milk is acidified and reduced.

Indole is not produced.

H_2S is not produced.

Nitrites are not produced from nitrates.

Acid but no gas is produced from glucose, lactose, maltose, sucrose, trehalose, melibiose, starch, rhamnose, glycerol, salicin, and dextrin. Mannose, xylose, arabinose, mannitol, dulcitol, inositol, and inulin are not attacked.

Aerobic. Optimal temperature, 37° C.

The organism is pathogenic to man and animals, producing a disease characterized by a marked increase in the number of mononuclear leukocytes in the blood.

For some recent papers on *Listeria monocytogenes*, see the following:

Edwards, M. R., and Stevens, R. W., J. Bacteriol., *86*, 1963, 414.

Gerard, K. F., Sbarra, A. J., and Bardawil, W. A., J. Bacteriol., *85*, 1963, 349.

King, E. O., and Seeliger, H. P. R., J. Bacteriol., *77*, 1959, 122.

Erysipelothrix (E.ry.si.pe′ lo.thrix) Rosenbach, 1909. *M p. 599.* (Ztschr. f. Hyg., *63*, 1909, 367.)

DIFFERENTIATING CHARACTERS: Unicellular, colorless, nonsporing, unbranched, rod-shaped organisms; occur singly, in chains, and as long filaments; nonmotile; Gram positive; nonacid-fast; *aerobic;* heterotrophic; grow on meat infusion agar, producing pinpoint transparent colonies on agar in 24 hours at 37° C., which extend on further incubation to 1.5 mm.; only acid produced from glucose and lactose and some other carbohydrates but not from esculin; final pH in glucose broth about 6.0; H_2S produced; pathogenic, causing swine erysipelas, human erysipeloid, mouse septicemia, and infections in sheep, birds, and fish.

Type species: *Erysipelothrix insidiosa* (Trevisan) Langford and Hansen.

NOTES: There is only one species. The cells are 0.2 to 0.4 μ by 0.5 to 2.5 μ. Filaments are common in rough colonies.

Colonies on meat infusion agar are barely visible in 24 hours at 37° C. but enlarge to 1.0 to 1.5 mm. in 48 to 72 hours. They are transparent, with a bluish sheen by reflected light, circular, and entire.

On tellurite agar they are an intense black.

A test tube brush-like growth appears in a gelatin stab.

Litmus milk is not changed.

Indole is not produced.

H_2S is produced.

Acid but no gas is produced from glucose, galactose, fructose, and lactose. Other sugars may be fermented.*

Esculin is not hydrolyzed.

The final pH in yeast-extract trypticase glucose broth is about 6.0.

Nitrites are not produced from nitrate.

Catalase negative.

Aerobic.

Temperature range 16° to 41° C; optimum, 37° C.

* For fermentation patterns under different conditions see White and Schuman (J. Bacteriol., *82*, 1961, 595).

Optimal pH, 7.4 to 7.8.

The organism tolerates 7 per cent NaCl, 0.2 per cent phenol, and 0.05 per cent potassium tellurite.

Microbacterium (Mic.ro.bac.te' ri.-um) Orla-Jensen, 1919. *M p. 600*. (The Lactic Acid Bacteria, 1919, 179.)

DIFFERENTIATING CHARACTERS: Unicellular, colorless, unbranched, nonsporing, rod-shaped organisms, less than 2 μ wide, arranged in angular fashion similar to *Corynebacterium;* nonmotile;* Gram positive; nonacid-fast; *aerobic;* heterotrophic; grow well on meat infusion agar, producing grayish or yellowish colonies; produce acid but no gas from carbohydrates; glucose, fructose, and mannose fermented; catalase positive; resist heating to 72° C. for 15 minutes.

Type species: *Microbacterium lacticum* Orla-Jensen.

NOTES: There are only two species, *M. lacticum* and *M. flavum*, listed in the *Manual*. They differ in their action on starch and maltose.

Gelatin is not liquefied.

Litmus milk is slightly acidified or not changed.

Indole is not produced.

Hydrogen sulfide is not produced.

Lactose and maltose are fermented by *M. lacticum* only.

Starch is hydrolyzed by *M. lacticum*.

Nonlipolytic.

Ammonia is not produced from peptone or arginine.

Found in dairy products.

Cellulomonas (Cel.lu.lo.mo' nas) Bergey *et al.*, 1923, 1952. *M p. 601*. (Bergey *et al.*, Bergey's Manual of Determinative Bacteriology, 1st ed., 1923; Clark, Intern. Bull. Bacteriol. Nomen. Taxon., *2*, 1952, 50.)

DIFFERENTIATING CHARACTERS: Unicellular, nonphotosynthetic, non-sporing,

* A third species, which is motile with peritrichous flagella, has been described by Bolcato (Antonie van Leeuwenhoek, *23*, 1957, 355).

straight or curved, rod-shaped organisms, less than 2 μ wide; unbranched or showing only rudimentary branching; arranged singly or in palisades; motile with peritrichous flagella or nonmotile; Gram variable; nonacid-fast; *aerobic;* heterotrophic; produce acid but no gas from glucose and lactose (except *C. acidula*); grow in 0.5 per cent peptone water containing a filter paper strip and completely disintegrate or markedly weaken the paper; produce clearing in a precipitated cellulose agar plate.

They *do not* hydrolyze agar, utilize phenol, oxidize ethyl alcohol quantitatively to acetic acid, produce ethyl alcohol in quantities from glucose, fix gaseous nitrogen, or deposit iron.

Type species: *Cellulomonas biazotea* (Kellerman *et al.*) Bergey *et al.*

NOTES: Pleomorphic, unicellular, rod-shaped organisms, 0.3 to 0.8 μ by 1 to 2 μ, capable of hydrolyzing cellulose when grown in 0.5 per cent peptone.

There are ten listed species, six of which are motile with peritrichous flagella. The Gram stain is reported to be variable.

The organisms grow well on meat infusion agar. The colonies are translucent to opaque and may be milky white to yellow.

Broth cultures are turbid.

Gelatin is hydrolyzed by all species except *C. acidula*.

Starch is hydrolyzed by all species.

Nitrite is produced from nitrate by 7/10 species.

Acid but no gas is produced from glucose, lactose, maltose, sucrose, and starch by all species except *C. acidula*, for which only the glucose reaction is recorded.

Cellulose is hydrolyzed when 0.5 per cent peptone is used as the base.

Optimal temperature, 28° C.

The organisms are found in soil and decomposing plant tissue.

Arthrobacter (Ar.thro.bac' ter) Conn and Dimmick, 1947. *M p. 605*. (J. Bacteriol., *54*, 1947, 300.)

DIFFERENTIATING CHARACTERS: Unicellular, nonphotosynthetic, nonsporing organisms, less than 2 μ wide, which exhibit a definite cycle of development. In aged cultures they are coccoid. In some species the cells are very uniform in size and resemble micrococci. In others the cocci vary in size, with some cells, called *cystites*, several times larger than the majority. When transferred to a fresh medium, the cocci "germinate" to produce rod-shaped cells. Germination may occur at more than one point, which often gives rise to an appearance of branching. The newly formed rods elongate and divide. At the point of division the rods grow out at an angle to the original axis until the total length is approximately twice the original. This form of growth simulates branching, which does *not* occur. Division occurs at the angle and the elongation and division is repeated. In older cultures the rods transform into a mass of cocci, which completes the cycle. Since the cyclic development is the major characteristic of the genus *Arthrobacter*, studies on the phenomenon are of considerable interest. Chan (J. Bacteriol., *87*, 1964, 641) describes a marked aberration in *A. globiformis* due to biotin deficiency. Ensign and Wolfe (J. Bacteriol., *87*, 1964, 924) found that cultures of *A. crystallopoietes* could be cultured in the coccal stage only in a defined medium containing $(NH_4)_2SO_4$, $MgSO_4 \cdot 7H_2O$, glucose, trace metals, and phosphate buffer. Addition of a variety of organic substances restored the cycle. Somewhat similar observations were reported earlier by Stevenson (Can. J. Microbiol., *7*, 1961, 569; *9*, 1963, 467) for *A. globiformis*. Stevenson (1963) has also found that the large cystites could be obtained in pure populations by introducing inoculum from a rich medium into a minimal one. When transferred to an adequate medium they produced rods. Gram variable; *aerobic;* heterotrophic.

Type species: *Arthrobacter globiformis* (Conn) Conn and Dimmick.

NOTES: Nonmotile except *A. simplex, A. citreus,* and *A. atrocyaneus.*

The *Manual* (seventh edition) lists nine species, eight of which grow readily on meat infusion agar. Six will also use ammonia nitrogen and grow well on soil infusion media. Colonies are usually 1 to 2 mm. in diameter in 48 hours and are opaque and cream to yellowish.

A. terregens will not grow on peptone media without the addition of soil extract or an extract of *Arthrobacter pascens*.

When growing on nicotine agar, *Arthrobacter oxydans* produces a soluble blue pigment.

Gelatin is hydrolyzed by all species except *A. terregens*.

Litmus milk is unchanged (2/9) or becomes alkaline and is later peptonized.

Starch is hydrolyzed by 5/9 species.

Acid only is produced from glucose by six species. A few other carbohydrates are fermented.

Voges-Proskauer negative.

Indole negative (9/9).

Nitrites are produced from nitrate by 7/9 species.

Catalase positive (except *A. tumescens*).

Optimal temperature, 20° to 25° C.

Found in soil and on plants.

Some new species that have been added to the genus *Arthrobacter* include *A. atrocyaneus* (Kuhn and Starr, Arch. Mikrobiol., *36*, 1960, 175). *A. polychromogenes* (Schippers-Lammertse, Muijers and Klatser-Oedekerk, Antonie van Leeuwenhoek, *29*, 1963, 1); *A. duodecadis* and *A. flavescens* (Lochhead, Arch. Mikrobiol., *31*, 1958, 163); and *A. crystallopoietes* (Ensign and Rittenberg, Arch. Mikrobiol., *47*, 1963, 137).

For other papers relevant to the systematics of *Arthrobacter* see the following:

Cadmus, M. C., Gasdorf, H., Lagoda, A. A., Anderson, R. F., and Jackson, R. W., App. Microbiol., *11*, 1963, 488.

Gillespie, D. C., Can. J. Microbiol., *9*, 1963, 509.

Gillespie, D. C., Can. J. Microbiol., *9*, 1963, 516.

Katznelson, H., and Mason, A., Can. J. Microbiol., *8*, 1962, 588.

McFarland, G. R., and Doetsch, R. N., Exptl. Cell Research, *23*, 1961, 528.

Mulder, E. G., and Antheunisse, J., Ann. Inst. Pasteur, *105*, 1963, 46.

Shetna, Y. I., and Bhat, J. V., Ann. Inst. Pasteur, *28*, 1962, 289.

Veldkamp, H., van deu Berg, G., and Zevenhuizen, L. P. T. M., Antonie van Leeuwenhoek, *29*, 1963, 35.

Bacillus (Ba. cil' lus) Cohn, 1872. *M p. 613.* (Beitr. Biol. Pflanzen., *1*, Heft 2, 1872, 146 and 175.)

DIFFERENTIATING CHARACTERS: Unicellular, nonphotosynthetic, rod-shaped organisms, less than 2 μ wide, which produce endospores; motile with peritrichous flagella or nonmotile; arranged singly or in chains; *aerobic;* heterotrophic.

Type species: *Bacillus subtilis* Cohn, emend. Prazmowski.

NOTES: Twenty-five species are described. Differentiation is based on morphological characters and a wide range of physiological characters. As with most genera, not all species have been uniformly examined, so proper comparisons cannot be made. The following comments are restricted to those characters which have been uniformly examined.

Unicellular, rod-shaped organisms, which produce elliptical or spherical endospores. In 14 of the 25 listed species the width of the endospore exceeds that of the vegetative rod and results in a swelling of the rod in the central, subterminal, or terminal position, depending on the position of the spore. The resulting cells have fusiform, clavate, or racket-shaped appearances. In the remaining 10 species the width of the endospore does not exceed that of the vegetative cell. It is important to recognize the fact that more than 50 per cent of the species of *Bacillus* have spores that are wider than the rod. Such swollen spores are frequently referred to as *clostridial*, a term that creates confusion with the genus *Clostridium*, a group of *anaerobic* sporing rods in which the swollen spore predominates.

Considered as a genus, the vegetative cells of *Bacillus* fall into two main size groups: (*a*) those with cells greater than 0.9 μ in width (usually 1.0 to 1.5 μ), of which there are four listed species, including the anthrax bacillus (*B. anthracis*); and (*b*) those with cells less than 0.9 μ in width (0.3 to 0.9 μ).

Cells may have rounded or square ends and are arranged singly, in pairs, and not infrequently in chains. Only two species (*B. anthracis* and *B. popilliae*) are listed as nonmotile. The others are peritrichously flagellated. A few species are capsulated.

The genus is traditionally regarded as Gram positive. Two species are listed as Gram negative and 10 others as Gram variable.

All species except *B. larvae* grow well on meat infusion agar. Several species have been listed as using ammonia nitrogen, but the conditions of the test leave this open to question.

The colony type varies with the species and also markedly within a species on different media under different conditions of growth. Rhizoid, fimbriate, crenate, serrate, lobate, undulate, and entire colonies are common. They vary from 1 to several mm. in width. *Bacillus circulans* is most unusual. The entire colony is mobile and migrates over the medium, following a watchspring course. *B. alvei* spreads rapidly over the medium in a manner similar to *Proteus*. Most colonies are opaque and whitish. A few are pigmented.

Only 3/25 species do *not* liquefy gelatin. The majority also actively hydrolyze casein, resulting in peptonization and an alkaline reaction in milk.

The marked liberation of ammonia in protein and peptone media may lead to complete neutralization of acids produced from carbohydrates and so result in a false negative reaction in peptone sugars. For this reason sugar fermentations in the Smith classification of the genus are done concurrently in mineral media with ammonia nitrogen. Since the media are initially neutral, acid production is readily detected.

Starch is hydrolyzed by 14/25 species.

Acid and gas are produced from carbohydrates by B. polymyxa and B. macerans. All other species produce acid only or no reaction.

All species are aerobic.

The optimal temperature varies with the habitat. B. stearothermophilus has an optimum between 50° and 65° C. and does not grow at 37° C.

Found mainly in soil.

A few species are pathogenic. B. anthracis causes anthrax in man and animals. B. pulvifaciens and B. larvae cause diseases of honey bee larvae, and B. popilliae and B. lentimorbus cause diseases of the larvae of the Japanese beetle.

See p. 181 for a digest of Prévot's treatment of the genus Bacillus and the genus Clostridium.

For further information see:

Larkin, J. M., and Stokes, J. L., J. Bact., 91, 1966, 1667.

Marshall, B. J., and Ohye, D. F., J. Gen. Microbiol., 44, 1966, 41.

Clostridium (Clos. tri′ di.um) Prazmowski, 1880. M p. 634. (Untersuchungen über die Entwickelungsgeschichte und Fermentwirkung einiger Bacterien-Arten, Inaug. Diss., Leipzig, 1880, 23.)

DIFFERENTIATING CHARACTERS: Unicellular, nonbranching, nonphotosynthetic, rod-shaped organisms, not more than 2 μ wide; motile with peritrichous flagella or nonmotile; endospores are produced; anaerobic,* heterotrophic.

Type species: Clostridium butyricum Prazmowski.

NOTES: Ninety-three species are described. Included in the genus as an appendix is a description of Methanobacterium

* All species except C. carnis, C. histolyticum, C. lacunarum, C. tertium, and C. pectinovorum are strict anaerobes. These five species are regarded as anaerobic but aerotolerant to a certain degree.

omelianski. This organism oxidizes primary alcohols to acids and secondary alcohols to ketones while reducing CO_2 quantitatively to methane; glucose is not metabolized.

Differentiation in the genus is based on morphological and physiological characteristics. The vegetative rods vary in width from 0.3 to 2.0 μ and in length from 1.5 to 12 μ. Straight or slightly curved; occasionally pleomorphic and twisted or spindle-shaped. Motile (78/93) with peritrichous flagella or nonmotile (13/93). Motility is not recorded for two species. Occur singly, in pairs, and frequently in chains, depending on the species.

The Gram stain is recorded as negative for 15/93 species. The remainder are Gram positive. Several of the latter are reported as Gram variable; usually these are Gram positive in very young cultures.

Thirteen species are recorded as granulose positive. Granulose is a substance found in cells in a granular form; it stains blue with iodine.

All species produce endospores, although in some instances only under critical conditions. Endospores are oval, cylindrical, or spherical and occur in a central, subterminal, or terminal position, depending on the species. In only three species is the width of the spores less than that of the vegetative cell. In the remainder, swelling of the rods ranges from a minor type in which the slight bulge gives the rod a spindle shape to pronounced bulging, which results in club-, racquet-, and spoon-shaped cells, depending on the shape and position of the spore and the relative sizes of the rod and the spore.

There is no record of growth occurring in synthetic media with ammonia nitrogen. The majority of species grow on meat infusion agar. Some require more complex media. Fourteen of the 36 species for which the reaction on blood is recorded are hemolytic. Colonies vary with the species. Some are minute, colorless colonies; others are large and spreading. The conditions of cultivation in sealed containers normally result in a high relative humidity, which aids the spreading types.

Some species produce brightly pigmented red or orange colonies, *viz*, *C. venturellii*, *C. roseum*, *C. saturnirubrum*, *C. chromogenes*, *C. corallinum*, *C. aurantibutyricum*, and *C. felsineum*. Others produce yellowish pigments.

Gelatin is liquefied by 39/87 species. Six are not recorded.

Loeffler's inspissated serum is liquefied by 10/56 species for which the reaction is recorded.

Cooked meat medium is turned slightly pink from its original brown and undergoes no subsequent blackening or digestion with a number of species. Gas is frequently produced but is rarely malodorous. This reaction is characteristic of those species with *strong saccharolytic* activity but with only weak or no proteolytic activity.

Other species initially turn the meat pinkish, but this is rapidly followed by a blackening of the meat (attributable to reaction between H_2S produced and Fe from the blood pigments) and its subsequent digestion. Such cultures are exceedingly malodorous because of the production of skatole, mercaptans, and H_2S. Species that cause this series of changes are weakly saccharolytic and strongly proteolytic.

Other species cause no change in the appearance or color of the meat or may cause a slight blackening without digestion because of production of H_2S from soluble organic material or from sulfates.

Carbohydrates are fermented with the production of acid and gas by 82/93 species. The remainder do not ferment carbohydrates. Several of the above species *produce gas from peptone water alone.*

The byproducts of sugar fermentations include: (*a*) acetic, butyric, formic, propionic [*C. virens* and *C. propionicum* (?)], and lactic acids (*C. pectinovorum*); (*b*) isopropyl alcohol (*C. aurantibutyricum* and *C. pectinovorum*); (*c*) *both* ethyl and butyl alcohols (*C. acetobutylicum, C. kaneboi, C. butylicum, C. beijerinckii, C.*

TABLE 13
Prévot's genera of the sporing rods

	Gram stain	Motility	Swollen spores	Terminal spores	Capsules
Bacillus	+	+	−	−	
Bacteridium	+	−	−	−	
Innominatus	−	+	−	−	
Endosporus	−	+	+	−	
Paraplectrum	−	−	+	−	
Inflabilis	+	−	+	−	−
Welchia	+	−	+	−	+
Clostridium	+	+	+	−	−
Terminosporus	−	+	+	+	
Caduceus	−	−	+	+	
Plectridium	+	+	+	+	
Acuformis	+	−	+	+	

Note: Although aerobiosis or anaerobiosis does not appear as a differential character, the genera *Bacillus, Bacteridium,* and *Innominatus* are aerobes or facultative anaerobes. Those placed in other genera are, with rare exceptions, anaerobes.

iodophilum, C. toanum, C. aurantibutylicum, C. felsineum, and *C. flavum*); (*d*) butyl alcohol (*C. muelleri* and *Cl. saturnirubrum*); and (*e*) ethyl alcohol (*C. carbonei, C. spumarum, C. cellobioparum, C. dissolvens, C. thermocellum,* and *C. thermocellulaseum*).

Care should be exercised in interpreting sugar fermentation with the genus *Clostridium*. Some species may reduce the acid-base indicator to a colorless substance without producing acid. When bromcresol purple is used, such reduced tubes closely resembles tubes in which acid is produced but are usually much lighter in color. Another indicator should be added to check this.

Similarly, gas may be produced without acid production.

Litmus milk undergoes numerous changes, depending on the species. Purely saccharolytic species that ferment lactose will produce acid, coagulate the casein, and reduce the litmus. If gas is produced the curd may be shattered (*e.g., C. perfringens*).

Strongly proteolytic types will normally

cause complete peptonization and leave the milk like a yellow, oily liquid.

Other species may cause no change.

Starch hydrolysis and subsequent fermentation is recorded for 31 species, of which 18 are recorded as negative. Some species react differently on corn and potato starch.

Cellulose hydrolysis and fermentation occur with 10 of the 23 species for which the reaction is recorded. The gas produced frequently has a high content (67 per cent) of methane (*cf. Methanobacterium omelianski*).

Pectins are hydrolyzed by 10/12 species.

Indole is produced by 11/68 species.

Nitrite is produced from nitrate by 14/63 species.

Atmospheric nitrogen fixation is recorded for 11 species. In most cases the quantity is so small that it can be detected only by isotope procedures. *C. butyricum* is the classical nitrogen-fixing anaerobe.

PATHOGENICITY: Twenty-two of the listed species are pathogenic to one or more laboratory animals.

The following species, exclusively soil organisms, have been recorded from cases of gas gangrene in man or animals. They are mainly strongly saccharolytic species: *C. multifermentans, C. gummosum, C. fallax, C. septicum, C. chauvoei, C. novyi, C. aerofoetidum, C. sporogenes* (rarely), *C. bifermentans, C. perfringens, C. sphenoides, C. innominatum, C. paraputrificum, C. capitovale.*

C. botulinum Type A: the cause of botulism, a toxic disease; it is found in soil and produces a powerful exotoxin, which is responsible for food poisoning.

C. botulinum Type C: causes limberneck in chickens.

C. chauvoei: causes blackleg in cattle.

C. haemolyticum: causes icterohemoglobinuria in cattle.

C. novyi Type B: causes black disease of sheep.

C. tetani: a nonsaccharolytic and weakly proteolytic species; the cause of tetanus.

C. felsineum and other pectolytic species are used in the retting of flax.

C. acetobutylicum is used for the commercial production of butyl alcohol and acetone.

Optimal temperature varies with the habitat. Some species are thermophilic (*C. thermocellum* and *C. thermocellulaseum* have an optimal temperature of 55° to 60° C.).

See p. *181* for a digest of Prévot's treatment of the genus *Bacillus* and the genus *Clostridium.*

Mycobacterium (My.co.bac.te' ri.-um) Lehmann and Neumann, 1896. *M p. 695.* (Bakteriol. Diag., 1 Aufl., *2*, 1896, 108.)

DIFFERENTIATING CHARACTERS: Nonphotosynthetic, rod-shaped organisms, less than 2 μ wide, which may be unbranched or show rudimentary branching only; nonmotile; acid-fast; no endospores produced; Gram positive; heterotrophic; not known to deposit iron about the cells.

Type species: *Mycobacterium tuberculosis* (Zopf) Lehmann and Neumann.

NOTES: Fourteen species are listed in the *Manual.* The rods are usually irregular in shape, the long axis being twisted. Occasional branches have been reported among the cells of four species (*M. smegmatis, M. phlei, M. fortuitum,* and *M. tuberculosis*). Because of their hydrophobic nature some species do not stain readily with water-soluble dyes.

According to Bisset (J. Gen. Microbiol., *3*, 1949, 93), these organisms are multicellular. Only a few cultures have been examined.

The organisms are heterotrophic. Soil species can be cultivated on media with simple carbon compounds such as citrate, succinate, and malate with ammonia nitrogen.

Parasites of cold-blooded animals and fish are cultured readily on meat infusion agar.

Pathogens of warm-blooded animals require complex media for good growth and develop slowly even on these. Media commonly employed usually contain glycerol and egg.

M. paratuberculosis appears to require an unspecified component of tubercle or other acid-fast bacteria for primary culture.

M. leprae and *M. lepraemurium* have not been cultivated on artificial media.

Colonies vary with the species. Some are dry, wrinkled, and crumb-like and may be pigmented, usually yellow or orange. Others are smooth, moist, and butyrous. The dry colonies are difficult to emulsify.

Slight gelatin liquefaction is recorded for *M. phlei* only.

Reactions in litmus milk are recorded for only six species. One species produces acid and coagulation (*M. marinum*). The others produce no change (four species) or a slight alkalinity (one).

Acid but no gas is produced from glucose and some other carbohydrates by three of the listed species. Lactose is never fermented. Some carbohydrates are assimilated without acid production.

Indole is not produced.

Nitrites are produced from nitrates by the three soil species.

Optimal temperature lies between 25° and 37° C., depending on the species.

PATHOGENICITY: Diseases caused are listed below:

M. phlei and M. smegmatis: saprophytic.

M. fortuitum: a soil form that has been isolated from infections of the lymph glands in cattle and abscesses in man.

M. marinum: causes tuberculosis of fish and frogs and also infects mice and pigeons.

M. thamnopheos: a parasite of snakes.

M. ulcerans: causes ulcers in man and infects rats and mice.

M. tuberculosis: causes primarily human tuberculosis.

M. bovis: causes primarily bovine tuberculosis.

M. microti: causes primarily tuberculosis of voles.

M. avium: causes primarily tuberculosis of birds.

M. paratuberculosis: causes Johne's disease of cattle.

M. leprae: causes human leprosy.

M. lepraemurium: causes rat leprosy.

Some recent papers relevant to the systematics of *Mycobacterium* are as follows:

Bojalil, L. F., and Cerbón, J., J. Bacteriol., *81*, 1961, 338.

Cater, J. C., and Redmond, W. B., Can. J. Microbiol., *7*, 1961, 697.

Cerbón, J., and Bojalil, L. F., J. Gen. Microbiol., *25*, 1961, 7.

Csillag, A., J. Gen. Microbiol., *30*, 1963, 21.

Davis, J. B., Chase, H. H., and Raymond, R. L., App. Microbiol., *4*, 1956, 310.

Gastambide-Odier, M., J. Bacteriol., *77*, 1959, 748.

Goldman, D. S., and Lornitzo, F. A., J. Biol. Chem., *237*, 1962, 3332.

Gordon, R. E., and Rynearson, T. K., Can. J. Microbiol., *9*, 1963, 737.

Gordon, R. E., and Mihm, J. M., J. Gen. Microbiol., *21*, 1959, 736.

Gordon, R. E., J. Gen. Microbiol., *43*, 1966, 329.

Imeda, T., and Convit, J., J. Bacteriol., *83*, 1962, 43.

Jones, R. J., and Jenkins, D. E., Can. J. Microbiol., *11*, 1965, 127.

Juhasz, S. E., and Böniche, R., Can. J. Microbiol., *11*, 1965, 235.

Knaysi, G., J. Bacteriol., *77*, 1959, 532.

Kwapinski, J. B., and Snyder, M. L., J. Bacteriol., *82*, 1961, 632.

Mathews, M. M., Photochem. Photobiol., *2*, 1963, 1.

Rodda, G. M. J., Aust. J. Exp. Biol. Med. Sci., *17*, 1964, 457.

Tsukamura, M., J. Gen. Microbiol., *42*, 1966, 7.

Mycococcus (My′ co.coc.cus) Krassilnikov, 1938. *M p. 707*. (Mikrobiologiya (U.S.S.R.), *7*, Part I, 1938, 335.)

DIFFERENTIATING CHARACTERS: Unicellular, nonsporing, nonphotosynthetic organisms; highly pleomorphic; occur mainly as coccoid forms, frequently of variable size and occasionally, especially in liquids, as rod-shaped cells, which are frequently branched. Large lemon-shaped cells are not uncommon;* occur singly and in chains; motility not recorded; Gram positive; nonacid-fast; *aerobic;* heterotrophic.

Type species: *Mycococcus albus* Krassilnikov.

NOTES: Six species are described. They are separated in the *Manual* on chromogenesis and action on milk.

Colonies are pigmented white, dark brown, red, orange, or yellow. In one species they are slimy and spreading.

Litmus milk is acidified and coagulated by one species, coagulated and peptonized by three, and unchanged by two.

Acid is produced from glucose and other carbohydrates by four species.

Citrate and acetate are metabolized by 2/4 species.

Starch is hydrolyzed by 2/4.

Sucrose is inverted by 3/4.

Nitrite is produced from nitrate by 2/3.

Paraffin is metabolized by 1/4 species.

Nocardia (No. car' di.a) Trevisan, 1889. *M p. 713.* (I Generi e le Specie delle Batteriacee, 1889, p. 9.)

DIFFERENTIATING CHARACTERS: Nonphotosynthetic organisms, which, during the early stages of growth, produce a well-defined mycelium, less than 2 μ in width, which later fragments completely into branched or unbranched bacillary elements. When aerial mycelium is produced it also fragments into rods and coccal elements but does not produce differentiated conidia (see G.14). The fragmentation may begin within a few hours or be delayed for several days; endospores not formed; *aerobic;* Gram positive; heterotrophic; nonmotile (or if motile, they have flagella) Becker, Lechevalier, and Lechevalier (App. Microbiol., *13*, 1965, 236) have shown that the cell walls of several species of *Nocardia* have, in common with *Pseudonocardia*, *Micropolyspora*, *Thermomono-*

* Resting cells formed in old cultures germinate like spores of *Actinomycetes*.

spora, and *Mycobacterium rhodochrous*, glutamic acid, muramic acid, alanine, glucosamine, and *meso*-diaminopimelic acid, galactose, and usually arabinose as major constituents.

Type species: *Nocardia farcinica* Trevisan.

NOTES: The genus is represented by 40 species. Some species bear a resemblance to the genus *Arthrobacter*, the essential differentiating factor being the formation of a definite branching mycelium in the early stages of growth with species of *Nocardia*. In the subsequent disintegration of the mycelium extensive fragmentation may give rise to coccoid bodies, which are similar in appearance to the aged cultures of *Arthrobacter*. Angulation of cells but no branching is observed in *Arthrobacter*.

According to Bisset and Moore (J. Gen. Microbiol., *3*, 1949, 387), the individual rods of *Nocardia* are multicellular and, when branching occurs, the branch is separated from the rod by a septum at the point of origin. This warrants further examination.

Subsequent growth of individual rods resulting from the fragmentation of the mycelium in *Nocardia* results in the formation of the zigzag pattern commonly found in microcolonies.

Certain species of *Nocardia* in which fragmentation is delayed may produce thickened aerial hyphae, which abstrict cells from the tip, proceeding towards the base and finally involving the whole mycelium. Early stages in this change may be confused with *Streptomyces*, e.g., *N. fordii* and *N. paraffinae*. Gordon (J. Bacteriol., *75*, 1958, 239) has described true conidia formation in *N. asteroides*. If the contention of Bisset and Moore (J. Gen. Microbiol., *3*, 1949, 387) is correct, these species may, in fact, belong to the genus *Streptomyces*.

Pleomorphic forms are not uncommon. Swellings and bud-like processes are often produced.

There have been records of motility in some cultures of *Nocardia*.

Acid fastness occurs in some species, particularly in tissue lesions. It is infrequent in cultures.

The organisms grow well on laboratory media. Colonies are usually opaque, and white, yellow, orange, red, green, or black. They may be smooth and butyrous, or wrinkled and dough-like in consistency. The intensity of pigmentation varies with the medium employed.

Ammonia nitrogen is used by some species.

Gelatin is liquefied by 14/40 species. Litmus milk is coagulated and peptonized by 8/40 and rendered alkaline and peptonized by 2/40; it is turned alkaline only by 6/40 and remains unchanged by the remainder. Pellicle formation and pigmentation of the milk may occur.

Nitrite is produced from nitrate by 9/20 species.

Records of carbohydrate fermentation and assimilation are very fragmentary. Seven of 13 species tested produce acid but no gas from glucose. Of these only one produces acid from lactose.

Sixteen species are reported to metabolize paraffins, naphthalene, or phenols.

Two species, of marine origin, attack chitin, alginates, agar, and gum arabic.

Optimal temperatures lie between 25° and 37° C.

PATHOGENICITY: The following species are pathogenic to man and animals:

N. farcinica: bovine farcy.

N. asteroides: cerebral abscesses.

N. leishmanii: lung disease, pericarditis.

N. caprae: lesions in goats.

N. pretoriana: mycetoma of the chest wall.

N. transvalensis: mycetoma of the foot.

N. madurae: mycetoma of the foot.

N. lutea: actinomycosis of the eye.

N. blackwellii: hock infection in foals.

N. rangoonensis: human pulmonary infection.

N. caviae: lesions in guinea pigs.

N. gibsonii: acholuric jaundice.

N. africana: mycetoma of the foot.

N. fordii: spleen infection.

The only plant disease recorded is that of gall of blueberry (*N. vaccinii*).

The nature and distribution of the human and animal infections suggest that all these species are soil inhabitants.

Still one of the most important papers dealing with the growth of *Nocardia* spp. is that of McClung (Lloydia, *12*, 1949, 137), to which constant reference should be made. Other equally important recent papers of relevance to the systematics of *Nocardia* are as follows:

Adams, J. N., and McClung, N. M., J. Bacteriol., *80*, 1960, 281.

Adams, J. N., and McClung, N. M., J. Bacteriol., *84*, 1962, 206.

Adams, J. N., J. Gen. Microbiol., *33*, 1963, 420.

Davis, G. H. G., and Freer, J. H., J. Gen. Microbiol., *23*, 1960, 163.

Gordon, R. E., and Mihm, J. M., J. Bacteriol., *73*, 1957, 15.

Gordon, R. E., and Mihm, J. M., J. Bacteriol., *75*, 1958, 239.

Gordon, R. E., and Mihm, J. M., J. Gen. Microbiol., *27*, 1962, 1.

Gordon, R. E., and Mihm, J. M., Ann. N. Y. Acad. Sci., *98*, 1962, 628.

Juhasz, S. E., and Böniche, R., Beiträge Zur Klinik der Tuberkulose, *130*, 1965, 155.

Kwapinski, J. B., and Seeliger, H. P. R., Mycopathologia and Mycologia Applicata, *25*, 1965, 173.

McClung, N. M., Lloydia, *12*, 1949, 137.

Nolof, G., and Hirsch, P., Arch. Mikrobiol., *44*, 1962, 266.

Zamora, A., Bojalil, L. F., and Bastarrachea, F., J. Bacteriol., *85*, 1963, 549.

Pseudonocardia (Pseu.do.no.car'di.a) Henssen, 1957. (Archiv. Mikrobiol., *26*, 1957, 373.)

DIFFERENTIATING CHARACTERS: Filamentous branching rods less than 2 μ wide, producing a septate substrate mycelium and unbranched aerial mycelium. The substrate mycelium may resemble that of *Nocardia* but does not disintegrate. The aerial mycelium transforms into long chains of cylindrical spores of variable length. Spores may also form on the substrate mycelium; Gram positive; nonacid-fast; facultative aerobes.

Type species: *Pseudonocardia thermophila* Henssen.

NOTES: Henssen describes a single species isolated on cellulose media inoculated with soil. Becker, Lechevalier, and Lechevalier (App. Microbiol., *13*, 1965, 236) have shown that the cell walls are of their Type IV or "Nocardia-type" (see under *Nocardia*).

Actinomyces (Ac.ti.no.my'ces) Harz, 1877. *M p. 742.* (In Bollinger, Zentr. med. Wiss., *15*, 1877, 485.)

DIFFERENTIATING CHARACTERS: Nonphotosynthetic, filamentous, rod-shaped organisms, which, in young cultures, produce a well-defined mycelium, which later fragments into simple branched and unbranched rods; nonmotile; Gram positive; heterotrophic; anaerobic to microaerophilic.

Type species: *Actinomyces bovis* Harz.

NOTES: The *Manual* lists three species: *A. bovis*, *A. israelii*, and *A. baudetii*. Pine *et al.* (J. Gen. Microbiol., *23*, 1960, 403) do not mention *A. baudetii* but cite a new species, *A. naeslundii*, which will grow aerobically in the presence of CO_2 but not in its absence. Buchanan and Pine (J. Gen. Microbiol., *28*, 1962, 305) have also described a new facultative anaerobic species, *A. propionicus.*

All species produce a branching mycelium in the initial stages of growth; this branching is evident in microcolonies of all but *A. bovis* after 24 hours of incubation. *A. bovis* branches initially but fragments very quickly, so that day-old colonies are smooth with entire margins.

Colonies, including those of *A. bovis*, can be strongly adherent.

All species grow anaerobically. *A. propionicus* also grows aerobically, and *A. naeslundii* will do so with added CO_2.

They are all catalase negative.

Gelatin is not liquefied.

Nitrate is reduced by *A. naeslundii* and

A. propionicus.

Indole is produced.

They produce acid but no gas from glucose, fructose, galactose, lactose, and usually maltose and sucrose.

No acid is produced from glycerol, and lactate is not metabolized.

Starch is hydrolyzed by *A. bovis.*

Species vary in their fermentation of xylose, mannitol, raffinose, and starch.

Optimum temperature, 37° C.

The true habitat is not known. From the sites of infections and history of cases, all species probably occur in soil or are normal inhabitants of body cavities.

A. bovis causes actinomycosis in cattle.

A. israelii causes actinomycosis in man and cattle.

A. naeslundii and *A. propionicus* have been isolated from eye infections.

A. baudetii has been reported from cats and dogs.

Serological studies by King and Meyer (J. Bacteriol., *85*, 1963, 186) have shown that there is no cross reaction between *A. bovis* and *A. israelii*. Cross reactions between *A. israelii* and *A. naeslundii* occur through a single common antigen. There was no cross reaction with any anaerobic diptheroid, including *Corynebacterium acnes.*

Compared with *Propionibacterium*, *A. propionicus* cannot produce propionic acid from lactate and is catalase negative.

For additional reading see the following:

Buchanan, B. B., and Pine, L., Sabouraudia, *3*, 1963, 26.

Kwapinski, J. B., J. Bacteriol., *86*, 1963, 179.

Kwapinski, J. B., and Seeliger, H. P. R., Zentral. Bakt., *195*, 1963, 805.

Overman, J. R., and Pine, L., J. Bacteriol., *86*, 1963, 656.

Pine, L., and Hardin, H., J. Bacteriol., *78*, 1959, 164.

Slack, J. M., Winger, A., and Moore, D. W., Jr., J. Bacteriol., *82*, 1961, 54.

Jensenia (Jen.se'ni.a) Bisset and Moore, 1950. (J. Gen. Microbiol., *4*, 1950, 280; also *3*, 1949, 387.)

Type species: *Jensenia canicruria.*

NOTE: Since the first edition of the *Guide* was published, the type culture of this organism has been studied by Adams and McClung (J. Bacteriol., *80*, 1960, 281) and by Gordon and Mihm (Can. J. Microbiol., *7*, 1961, 108). Adams and McClung noted the close similarity of the organism to *Nocardia rubra*. Strains of the latter organism have been assigned to *Mycobacterium rhodochrous* by Gordon and Mihm. The latter authors have found that the type culture of *Jensenia canicruria* possesses the morphology and the physiological properties of *Mycobacterium rhodochrous*. On glycerol agar the cells were pleomorphic rods and cocci: nonacid-fast. After 4 days on Bennett's agar, the colonies were dense with smooth edges or a few outcropping filaments, which fragmented into short forms.

The biochemical reactions were almost identical with the species reactions of *M. rhodochrous*. It is recommended that the genus *Jensenia* be rejected.

Streptomyces (Strep. to . my′ces) Waksman and Henrici, 1943. *M p. 744.* (J. Bacteriol., *46*, 1943, 339.)

DIFFERENTIATING CHARACTERS: Filamentous, nonphotosynthetic, rod-shaped organisms, less than 2 μ in width, which in young cultures produce a branching mycelium that does not disintegrate entirely as the culture ages. Chains of conidia are produced from aerial hyphae; sporangia are not produced; nonmotile; endospores not produced; *aerobic;* Gram positive; heterotrophic.

Type species: *Streptomyces albus* (Rossi-Doria, emend. Krainsky) Waksman and Henrici.

NOTES: a. Cultures of *Actinoplanes* or *Streptosporangium* on some laboratory media are morphologically similar to *Streptomyces*.

b. Certain species of *Nocardia* in which fragmentation is delayed may produce thickened aerial hyphae, which abstrict cells from the tip, proceeding towards the base and finally involving the whole mycelium. Early stages in this change may be confused with *Streptomyces*, e.g., *N. fordii* and *N. paraffinae.*

The *Manual* lists 150 species. Apart from morphological and cultural characters, information on the species is exceedingly fragmentary. Germination of conidia may be unipolar or multipolar. In the early stages of development a radiating mycelium is produced, which stains uniformly Gram positive. Side branches in some species are of the same width as the main filament. In others a bud-like outgrowth attached to the main mycelium by a very thin stalk grows out to form the side branch. According to Bisset and Moore (J. Gen. Microbiol., *3*, 1949, 387), the mycelium consists of a number of unicellular components, which branch without producing a septum at the point where the branch leaves the mother cell.

For further details see Hopwood (J. Gen. Microbiol., *22*, 1960. 295).

In addition to glucosamine, glutamic acid, and alanine, the *Streptomyces* contain major amounts of glycine and LL-diaminopimelic acid (Becker *et al., vide infra*).

The conidia-producing branches have characteristic shapes and arrangements, which are used for purposes of separation. They may occur at random or in clusters. They may be unbranched or monopodially or dichotomously branched, or branching may occur in the form of whorls on the main aerial hypha. The terminal portion from which the conidia are produced may be straight or spiral. Spiral forms are open or compact and may be of the sinistrorse (left-hand spiral) or dextrorse (right-hand spiral) type.

The production of conidia results from the reorganization of the cytoplasm *within* the aerial hypha, and the chain of conidia is produced within and finally separates from the original wall of the aerial hypha.*

* T. R. Vernon, Actinomycetes in New Zealand Soils. Paper read at the Congress of the Australian and New Zealand Association for Advancement of Science, Dunedin, 1957.

Similar sheaths were illustrated by Flaig et al. (Zentral. Bakt. Parasitenk., Abt. II, *108*, 376, 1955). Glauert and Hopwood (J. Biochem. Biophys. Cytol., *10*, 1961, 505) studied the process of spore formation in thin sections of *Streptomyces violaceoruber*. The inner layers of the aerial hypha grew inwards to form septa separating the spores. The outer layer consisted of a basketwork of interlacing fibers and remained intact for a time, forming a sheath around the developing spores. In the maturing spore the outer layer of the cytoplasmic membrane is thicker than that of the aerial mycelium. Multilayering in the spore walls has not been satisfactorily explained. Similar, but less precise, observations were made earlier by Moore and Chapman (J. Bacteriol., *78*, 1959, 878) with an unidentified smooth-walled streptomycete. They considered the form of spore formation to be comparable to that of "oidia in some Eumycota wherein the transverse cell walls also become double prior to disjunction." Nuclear material was much more condensed in the spores than in the vegetative cells but lacked any membrane. This probably accounts for the frequent reference to "nuclei" by Drechsler (Botan. Ges., *67*, 1919, 147). Rancourt and Lechevalier (Can. J. Microbiol., *10*, 1964, 311) describe the same process for *S. virido-chromogenes* and *S. violaceus*. They believe that the gap between the sheath and the ingrowing septa is filled with a material with about the same electron density as cytoplasm. This developed into an intersporal pad.

Conidia may be spherical, oval, or cylindrical and smooth or sculptured. Their formation usually results in the surface of colonies becoming powdery and dry. The conidial layer frequently has a different pigmentation from the main mycelium. Conidia stain intensely Gram positive, in sharp contrast to the almost Gram negative appearance of the aged mycelium from which the conidiophores arise. Conidia are nonmotile. Chlamydospores are frequently produced in the mycelium proper.

No clear statement appears in the *Manual* regarding the nutritional requirements of the *Streptomyces*. Many species are capable of growth on synthetic media with ammonia nitrogen, and they are not infrequently found as contaminants in organic carbon-free media. The appearance of the colonies varies with the type of medium employed. In all media upon which growth occurs the mycelium penetrates into the agar, and the initial colonies are usually circular and partly submerged and have a dull, waxy appearance. The agar is frequently depressed around the margin of the colony. If no aerial mycelium is formed, the colony may continue to develop in this form. Where aerial mycelium is produced the surface of the colony becomes floccose and, with the production of the conidia, eventually powdery.

Stress within the developing colonies frequently causes apparent splitting of the colonies. In some species droplets of guttation water appear on the surface of the colony and upon drying out leave craters in the surface.

Most species have a pronounced earthy odor*. Many produce pigments, either insoluble and confined to the mycelium or soluble and diffusing into the medium. Green, yellow, orange, red and purple, and dark-brown pigments are common.

Production of conidia may fail entirely on some media and be prolific on others. Species that maintain the permanent branching character of the mycelium (*cf. Nocardia*) but that fail to produce conidia under conditions of cultivation are placed in a group of "sterile species."

Gelatin is liquefied by 138/150. Ten species are negative, and two are not recorded.

Starch is hydrolyzed by 119 species; it is not hydrolyzed by 7 others. Twenty-four species are not recorded.

* Gerber and Lechevalier (*vide infra*) have described the separation of a neutral oil having a strong earthy smell from *Streptomyces griseus*.

Sucrose is inverted by 13/25 species.

Cellulose is hydrolyzed by 24/51.

Loeffler's inspissated serum is liquefied by 10/19.

Blood is hemolyzed by 5/13 species.

Litmus milk is coagulated and peptonized or peptonized without coagulation by 119 of 138 species tested. Because sugar fermentations are rarely recorded, it is not possible to state the true nature of the coagulum. It is possibly a soft rennet type of clot.

Nitrite is produced from nitrate by 85 of the 107 species tested.

Tyrosinase is produced by only 5/23 species. (This test is of some importance in the identification of species causing potato scab disease.)

The conventional sugar reactions (*acid* or *acid and gas*) are recorded for only two species. In one of these discrimination is made between *acid production from* and *assimilation* of carbohydrates. Because *Streptomyces* usually grow in the form of a surface pellicle with no turbidity in liquids, their main development is highly oxidative and acid byproducts do not appear in amounts sufficient to cause a change in the indicator.

Carbon assimilation tests have been reported for only nine species.

Aerobic.

Optimal temperature is dependent on habitat. Many have an optimum at 25° C. and others at 37°. Only four species, *S. thermophilus, S. thermofuscus, S. thermodiastaticus,* and *S. casei* are thermophilic; they grow at 50° to 65° C.

Streptomyces species are almost exclusively soil organisms. Eight species have been isolated from diseases in man. They are *S. listeri, S. galtieri* (septicemia in dogs), *S. upcottii* and *S. kimberi* (acholuric jaundice), *S. hortonensis* (parotid abscess), *S. beddardii* (splenic anemia), *S. somaliensis* (yellow grained mycetoma), *S. panjae* (abdominal ulcer), and *S. willmorei* (streptothricosis of liver).

The following species have been isolated from potato scabs: *S. clavifer, S. fimbriatus, S. carnosus, S. craterifer, S. gracilis, S. praecox, S. setonii, S. praefecundus, S. viridogenes, S. loidensis, S. scabies* (principal species), *S. tenuis, S. marginatus,* and *S. sampsonii.*

S. ipomoeae and *S. poolensis* have been isolated from sweet potatoes and *S. tumuli* from mangels.

A large number of species produce antibiotics. It is largely due to this that so many ill-defined species are recorded.

The recent literature on the genus *Streptomyces* is extensive. Much attention has been paid to genetics, phage sensitivities, cytological studies, and general systematics. Only papers relevant to the last named are listed here. Those of Baldacci *et al.*, Pridham *et al.*, and Tresner and Backus are particularly relevant to the international cooperative effort by the Subcommittee on *Streptomyces* to revise the classification of the genus.

Becker *et al.* (*vide infra*) record that the cell walls of *Streptomyces* species examined were of their "type I" or "Streptomyces-type," containing glucosamine, glutamic acid, alanine, muramic acid, glycine, and LL-diaminopimelic acid as major constituents.

See also the following:

Baldacci, E., Farina, G., and Vegetti, G., Giorn. Microbiol., *10*, 1962, 165.

Becker, B., Lechevalier, M. P., and Lechevalier, H. A., App. Microbiol., *13*, 1965, 236.

Frontali, C., Hill, L. R., and Silvestri, L. G., J. Gen. Microbiol., *38*, 1965, 243.

Gerber, N. N., and Lechevalier, H. A., Appl. Microbiol., *13*, 1965, 935.

Gilardi, E., Hill, L. R., Turri, M., and Silvestri, L. G., Giorn. Microbiol., *8*, 1960, 204.

Green, A., and Spalla, C., Giorn. Microbiol., *10*, 1962, 175.

Krassilnikov, N. A., J. Bacteriol., *79*, 1960, 75.

Kuster, E., Microbiol. Españ., *16*, 1963, 193.

Lechevalier, H., and Lechevalier, M. P., Ann. inst. Pasteur, *108*, 1965, 662.

Pridham, T. G., Hesseltine, C. W., and Benedict, R. G., App. Microbiol., *6*, 1958, 52.

Szabo, G., Barabas, G., and Vályi-Nagy, T., J. Bacteriol., *84*, 1962, 1342.

Tresner, H. D., and Backus, E. J., App. Microbiol., *11*, 1963, 335.

Waksmania (Waks.ma'ni.a) Lechevalier and Lechevalier, 1957. (J. Gen. Microbiol., *17*, 1957, 104.)

Lechevalier (Intern. Bull. Bacteriol. Nomen. Taxon., *15*, 1965, 139) has credited Nonomura and Ohara with precedence of the name **Microbispora** over *Waksmania* on the grounds that the two are identical and that *Microbispora* has the earlier publication date.

DIFFERENTIATING CHARACTERS: Filamentous, nonphotosynthetic, rod-shaped organisms, less than 2 μ wide, which in young cultures produce a branching mycelium that does not disintegrate as the culture ages. Conidia are produced in pairs, either sessile or on short (1 to 6 μ) conidiophores on the aerial mycelium or at the apex of an aerial hypha, with only one conidium of the pair attached to the mycelium. Sporangia are not produced; nonmotile; endospores not produced; *aerobic;* Gram positive; heterotrophic.

The cell walls of *Microbispora* have been shown by Becker, Lechevalier, and Lechevalier (App. Microbiol., *13*, 1965, 236) to be of their "type-III" or "Maduraetype," containing glucosamine, glutamic acid, alanine, muramic acid, and *meso*-diaminopimelic acid.

Type species: *Waksmania rosea* Lechevalier and Lechevalier, 1957.

NOTES: This genus is not described in the *Manual*. Only one species is described. The vegetative mycelium is 0.3 to 1.2 μ in width. The paired conidia appear to arise by septation of the conidiophore, followed by swelling of the two isolated cells. When mature, the conidia are easily separated. They are 1.5 to 2.0 μ in diameter, spherical to subglobose.

Growth occurs on a range of media both synthetic and complex. Excellent conidia formation occurs on rice, oatmeal, and mixed meal extract agars. The growth is a bright orange-pink.

Litmus milk is peptonized slowly without acid formation or coagulation.

Gelatin is slowly hydrolyzed.

Cellulose is slightly hydrolyzed.

Starch hydrolysis is variable according to the medium used.

No other information is given.

Aerobic.

Optimal temperature range, 25° to 35° C.

No antibiotics produced.

Found in soil.

Micropolyspora (Mic.ro.po.ly'spo.ra) Lechevalier, Solotorovsky, and McDurmont, 1961. (J. Gen. Microbiol., *26*, 1961, 11.)

DIFFERENTIATING CHARACTERS: Fine mycelium (about 1 μ in diameter), which is differentiated into: (*a*) a substrate (primary) mycelium, which grows into and forms a compact layer on top of agar media; (*b*) an aerial (secondary) mycelium, which arises from the substrate mycelium and grows in the air away from the agar surface. Both the substrate hyphae and the aerial hyphae bear chains of conidia that are produced either directly on the mycelium or on sporophores that branch from the mycelium. *Aerobic;* Gram positive; heterotrophic.

Type species: *Micropolyspora brevicatena* Lechevalier, Solotorosvky and McDurmont.

NOTES: The cell walls contain "type IV" or "*Nocardia*-type" cell wall constituents. Glucosamine, muramic acid, alanine, glutamic acid, *meso*-diaminopimelic acid, arabinose, and galactose are major constituents.

The mycelium shows no evidence of fragmentation *in situ* on the agar but disintegrates readily when smears are made. Spores are produced by abstriction from the tip of a short sporophore or by successive buddings directly from the mycelium. Isolated from soil.

Thermomonospora (Ther.mo.mo.no'-spo.ra) Henssen, 1957. (Arch. Mikrobiol., *26*, 1957, 373.)

DIFFERENTIATING CHARACTERS: Filamentous, nonphotosynthetic, rod-shaped organisms less than 2 μ wide, which produce a branching mycelium that does not disintegrate as the culture ages. Conidia are produced singly on the tips of short conidiophores *on the aerial mycelium only;* Gram positive; *aerobic:* heterotrophic.

Type species; *Thermomonospora fusca* (Waksman, Umbreit, and Gordon) Henssen.

NOTES: Henssen described three species, *T. fusca*, *T. lineata*, and *T. curvata*. The organisms can grow at the relatively high temperatures of 50° to 65° C., but this is not considered a good differential character. Becker, Lechevalier, and Lechevalier (App. Microbiol., *13*, 1965, 236) record that cell walls of *Thermomonospora viridis* are of their "type IV" or "*Nocardia*-type," with glucosamine, muramic acid, alanine, glutamic acid, *meso*-diaminopimelic acid, arabinose, and galactose as major constituents.

See also notes to *Thermoactinomyces*.

Micromonospora (Mic.ro.mo.nos'-po.ra) Ørskov, 1923. *M p. 822.* (Investigations into the Morphology of the Ray Fungi, Copenhagen, 1923, 147).

DIFFERENTIATING CHARACTERS: Filamentous, nonphotosynthetic, rod-shaped organisms, less than 2 μ wide; produce, in young cultures, a branching substrate mycelium only, which does not disintegrate completely as the culture ages. Conidia are produced singly on short side branches, not in sporangia; endospores not produced; Gram positive; heterotrophic; nonmotile; no growth at 50° C.

Becker, Lechevalier, and Lechevalier (App. Microbiol., *13*, 1965, 236) have shown that the cell walls of *Micromonospora* are of their "type II" or "*Micromono-*

spora-type" shared with *Actinoplanes* and *Amorphosporangium*. They contain glucosamine, muramic acid, alanine, glutamic acid, glycine, and *meso*-diaminopimelic acid.

Type species: *Micromonospora chalcea* (Foulerton) Ørskov.

NOTES: The genus is represented in the *Manual* by five species. All species have similar morphological characters. The short conidia-bearing hyphae appear in clusters towards the center of the developing colonies. Branching of the conidiophores occurs, but each branch bears only one conidium. Conidia stain very intensely when first formed but may develop a hollow appearance as they age. They are ellipsoidal or spherical.

According to Bisset and Moore (J. Gen. Microbiol., *3*, 1949, 387), individual cells in the mycelium are unicellular and branch without producing a septum at the point where the branch leaves the mother cell.

Information on nutritional requirements in the *Manual* is lacking. Growth occurs on glucose-asparagine agar and other synthetic media. Colonies are opaque, smooth, or rugose, and are usually pigmented a deep yellow, orange, or green. The pigment is not soluble. Obvious aerial mycelium is usually lacking. It is limited to short conidiophores. The spore layer may be dark brown to black. Colonies are difficult to emulsify.

Iron is precipitated from ferric ammonium citrate by some species (author's note).

Gelatin is liquefied by all species.

Litmus milk is peptonized by 4/4 species.

Starch is hydrolyzed by all species.

Cellulose is hydrolyzed by 2/5.

Sucrose is inverted by 3/5.

No information has been given on the reactions on other carbohydrates.

Nitrites are produced by 3/5 species.

Aerobic or *anaerobic.**

Optimal temperature is 35° to 37° C.

* Hungate (J. Bacteriol., *51*, 1946, 51) describes an anaerobic cellulose-digesting organism belonging to this genus.

All species have been isolated from the soil.

Thermoactinomyces (Ther.mo.ac.ti.-no.my'ces) Tsiklinsky, 1899. *M p. 824.* (Ann. inst. Pasteur, *13*, 1899, 501; and *17*, 1903, 206.)

DIFFERENTIATING CHARACTERS: Filamentous, nonphotosynthetic, rod-shaped organisms, less than 2 μ wide; produce, in young cultures, a branching mycelium, which does not disintegrate as the culture ages; conidia are produced singly on short conidiophores on both the aerial and substrate mycelium, which may be simple or branched; sporangia not produced; no endospores produced; Gram positive; heterotrophic; will grow at 50° C.

Becker, Lechevalier, and Lechevalier (App. Microbiol., *13*, 1965, 236) have shown that the cell walls of *Thermoactinomyces* are of their "type III" or "Maduraetype," containing glucosamine, muramic acid, alanine, glutamic acid, and *meso*-diaminopimelic acid as major constituents.

Type species: *Thermoactinomyces vulgaris* Tsiklinsky.

NOTES: There are only three listed species (see below). The morphology is similar in all three. Growth occurs readily on synthetic and nutrient agar. Colonies prior to sporulation are colorless or yellowish. They become powdery on sporulation, the conidial layer being white or grayish green. A soluble wine-colored pigment is produced on glucose-yeast agar by one species.

Gelatin is liquefied by all species.

Litmus milk is coagulated and peptonized by 2/3.

Starch is hydrolyzed by 2/3 species.

No information is given on the reactions on carbohydrates.

Aerobic.

Optimal temperature: all species will grow at 50° C.; two of the three will grow at 37° C.

Isolated from high temperature composts.

The *Manual* lists three species of *Thermoactinomyces*, *T. vulgaris*, *T thalpophilus*, and *T. monosporus*. Küster and Locci

(Intern. Bull. Bacteriol. Nomen. Taxon., *14*, 1964, 109) consider the first two synonymous and the third as a *nomen dubium* or synonymous with *Thermoactinomyces viridis* Schuurmans *et al.*, which they transfer to the genus *Thermomonospora*. *Thermoactinomyces glaucus* Henssen is also considered a *nomen dubium*, thus leaving the genus *Thermoactinomyces* monospecific and defined and characterized *by the presence of an aerial mycelium and the formation of single spores on both the aerial and the vegetative mycelium*. Strains are mainly thermophilic, but the authors quote Thirumalachar as having found mesophilic forms. It thus differs from *Micromonospora* in the formation of a spore-bearing aerial mycelium.

Küster and Locci (Arch. Mikrobiol., *45*, 1963, 188) note that spores in pairs and short chains are very occasionally produced on the aerial mycelium only, with single spores on the substrate mycelium. Henssen (Arch. Mikrobiol., *26*, 1957, 373) states that the aerial mycelium arises from lateral and terminal branches of the substrate mycelium and also from arches produced aerially from the substrate mycelium; she uses the latter character to distinguish the genus *Thermoactinomyces* from *Thermomonospora* Henssen. Similar arches are mentioned by Küster and Locci and by Corbaz, Gregory, and Lacey (J. Gen. Microbiol., *32*, 1963, 449) in their description of the organism, which they name *Micromonospora vulgaris*, objecting to the use of growth temperature as a generic character (which Küster and Locci have not used).

Dermatophilus (Der.ma.to'phi.lus) van Saceghem 1915. (Bull. Soc. Pat. exot., *8*, 1915, 354.)

DIFFERENTIATING CHARACTERS: Branching mycelium produced from coccoid bodies undergoes a primary subdivision by transverse septa laid down progressively 5 to 30 μ behind the tip of the hypha as growth proceeds. This is followed by progressive division of each cell by further transverse septa until individual cells are only 0.3 to 0.5 μ

long. Then logitudinal and radial division of each cell occurs with progressive widening of the hypha, sometimes 8- to 10-fold, producing sarcina or mulberry-like packets of coccoid cells. At this stage the hyphal cell mass is enclosed in mucus. Individual cocci may germinate to produce hypha, but most ultimately swell and produce motile cocci, which free themselves from the gelatinous matrix; *aerobic;* Gram positive; heterotrophic.

Type species: *Dermatophilus congolensis* van Saceghem.

NOTES: The single species causes mycotic dermatitis in cattle and sheep and possibly other animals. The fine structure of the organism has been studied and supports the general observations made by light microscopy. (For references see Key at Section G, 11b.) Becker, Lechevalier, and Lechevalier (App. Microbiol., *13*, 1965, 236) note that the cell walls are of their "type III" or "Madurae-type," with glucosamine, muramic acid, alanine, glutamic acid, and *meso*-diaminopimelic acid as major constituents. Walls of a similar type occur in *Nocardia madurae, Microbispora rosea,* and *Thermoactinomyces vulgaris.*

Microellobosporia (Mic.ro.el.lo.bo.-spo′ri.a) Cross, Lechevalier, and Lechevalier, 1963. (J. Gen. Microbiol., *31*, 1963, 421.)

DIFFERENTIATING CHARACTERS: Fine mycelium (about 1.0 μ in diameter), which is differentiated into: (*a*) a substrate (primary) mycelium, which grows into and forms a compact layer on top of the agar; and (*b*) an aerial (secondary) mycelium, which arises from the substrate mycelium and grows in the air away from the agar surface. The aerial hyphae bear sporangia on short sporangiophores. The sporangia contain a single row of nonmotile sporangiospores, usually numbering 2 to 5. The substrate mycelium produces similar structures, which were likewise interpreted as being sporangia containing a single row of nonmotile spores. *Aerobic;* Gram positive; heterotrophic.

Type species: *Microellobosporia cinerea* Cross, Lechevalier, and Lechevalier.

NOTES: Sporangia vary in length from 2 to 9 μ and in diameter from 1.5 to 3.6 μ, depending on the number and size of the spores, which are usually 2 to 5 per sporangium.

The fine structure of the sporangia has been described by Rancourt and Lechevalier (J. Gen. Microbiol., *31*, 1963, 495). The mycelium contains as major elements the glucosamine, muramic acid, alanine, and glutamic acid common to most streptomycetes and in addition glycine and LL-α-ε-diaminopimelic acid (Becker, Lechevalier, and Lechevalier, App. Microbiol., *13*, 1965, 236).

Actinoplanes (Ac.ti.no.pla′nes) Couch, 1950. *M p. 826.* (J. Elisha Mitchell Sci. Soc., *66*, 1950, 87.)

DIFFERENTIATING CHARACTERS: Filamentous, nonphotosynthetic organisms, less than 2 μ in width, which produce, in young cultures, a branching mycelium, which does not disintegrate as the culture ages; conidia, 1 to 1.5 μ in diameter, are produced in coiled chains or irregularly within sporangia. The sporangia are 8.4 to 20 μ in diameter, borne on unbranched, aerial hyphae; conidia are *motile* and germinate to produce the branched mycelium, which penetrates into submerged plant tissue; no endospores produced; *aerobic;* Gram positive; heterotrophic.

Becker and Lechevalier (App. Microbiol., *13*, 1965, 236) have shown that the cell walls of *Actinoplanes* are of their "type II" or "*Micromonospora*-type." See under *Micromonospora.*

Type species: *Actinoplanes philippinensis* Couch, 1950.

NOTES: Only one species is listed.

Streptosporangium (Strep.to.spo.-ran′gi.um) Couch, 1955. *M p. 828.* (J. Elisha Mitchell Sci. Soc., *71*, 1955, 148.)

DIFFERENTIATING CHARACTERS: Filamentous, nonphotosynthetic organisms, which produce, in young cultures, a branching mycelium that does not disintegrate as the culture ages. Spherical, nonmotile conidia, 1.8 to 2.0 μ in diameter, are produced in coils within sporangia. The sporangia are 7 to 19 μ in diameter and are produced apically on simple or branched aerial hyphae. Conidia are forcibly ejected from a protuberance that forms on the sporangia when the latter are immersed in water. Growth over the surface of submerged plant tissue; no endospores produced; *aerobic;* Gram positive; heterotrophic.

Becker, Lechevalier, and Lechevalier (App. Microbiol., *13*, 1965, 236) have shown that the cell walls of *Streptosporangium* are of their "type II" or "*Micromonospora*-type." See under *Micromonospora*.

Type species: *Streptosporangium roseum* Couch.

NOTES: Only one species is listed.

Ampullariella (Am.pul.la.ri.el'la) Couch, 1963. (J. Elisha Mitchell Sci. Soc., *79*, 1963, 52.)

DIFFERENTIATING CHARACTERS: Filamentous, branching, sparingly septate organisms less than 2 μ wide. Produce bottle-shaped, flask-shaped, digitate, or otherwise irregular sporangia. Spores are rod-shaped and are arranged in chains within the sporangium; motile with one polar flagellum; grow saprophytically on a variety of plant and animal materials.

Type species: *Ampullariella regularis* Couch.

NOTES: The genus was originally published under the name *Ampullaria*, which proved to be invalid. It was later corrected. (Couch, Intern. Bull. Bacteriol. Nomen. Taxon, *14*, 1964, 137.)

Three species were described but differentiated on the shape and size of sporangia. Spherical sporangia range from 10 to 35 μ in diameter and urceolate ones from 8 to 20 μ by 12 to 30 μ.

Spirillospora (Spi.ril.lo'spo.ra) Couch, 1963. (J. Elisha Mitchell Sci. Soc., *79*, 1963, 52.)

DIFFERENTIATING CHARACTERS: White to pale yellowish branching mycelium less than 2 μ wide. Produce sporangia that are spherical to vermiform. Spores are short to long rods, spiral in shape; weakly motile, with one or more polar flagella.

The genus is at present monotypic.

Type species: *Spirillospora albida* Couch.

NOTE: The sporangia, when spherical, range from 5 to 24 μ in diameter with an average of 10 μ. Spores 0.5 to 0.7 μ by 2 to 6 μ. Becker, Lechevalier, and Lechevalier (App. Microbiol., 13, 1965, 236) have shown that *Spirillospora* has cell walls of their "type II" or "*Micromonospora* type." See under *Micromonospora*.

Amorphosporangium (A.mor.pho.-spo.ran'gi.um) Couch, 1963. (J. Elisha Mitchell Sci. Soc., *79*, 1963, 52.)

DIFFERENTIATING CHARACTERS: Filamentous branching septate microorganisms less than 2 μ in width; produce sporangia that are very irregular in shape. Spores are short rods and are nonmotile; *aerobic;* heterotrophic.

There is a single species.

Type species: *Amorphosporangium auranticolor* Couch.

NOTES: Sporangia are exceedingly irregular, much lobed, and usually wider than tall; 6 to 25 μ wide and 8 to 15 μ tall. Spores are 0.5 to 0.7 μ by 1 to 1.5 μ.

Cell walls contain glucosamine, muramic acid, alanine, glutamic acid, glycine, and *meso*-diaminopimelic acid (Becker, Lechevalier, and Lechevalier, App. Microbiol., *13*, 1965, 236). They belong to the authors' "type II" or "*Micromonospora*-type."

Caryophanon (Ca.ry.o'pha.non) Peshkoff, 1940. *M p. 831.* (J. Gen. Biol. (U.S.-S.R.), *1*, 1940, 611.)

DIFFERENTIATING CHARACTERS: Colorless, uniseriately multicellular, rod-shaped microorganisms, which may exceed 2 μ in diameter; do not produce endospores; motile with peritrichous flagella; *aerobic;* Gram negative. Provost and Doetsch (J. Gen. Microbiol., *28*, 1962, 547) state that *Caryophanon* is Gram positive.

Type species: *Caryophanon latum* Peshkoff.

NOTES: Only two species, *C. latum* and *C. tenue*, are listed. The former reaches 3 μ in width and the latter, 1.5 μ. Individual rods are composed of a series of cells much wider than long and are terminated at both ends with hemispherical cells. Rods may be joined to form long chains. Individual cells within the rod may separate as flat, cylindrical units. These may predominate at pH 7.0. Uneven development of cells within the rods may result in some grotesque shapes.

Nuclear material can be demonstrated by special staining methods.

Both species grow well on peptone-yeast extract-acetate agar and on dung infusion agar at pH 7 to 8. Rough colonies predominate in old cultures.

No information is given on biochemical and other properties.

Found in fresh cow dung.

Lineola (Li.ne.o'la) Pringsheim, 1950. *M p. 832.* (J. Gen. Microbiol., *4*, 1950, 198.)

DIFFERENTIATING CHARACTERS: Unicellular, colorless, nonsporing, rod-shaped organisms, less than 2 μ wide and 10 to 15 μ long; motile with peritrichous flagella; arranged in chains usually over 100 μ long. Individual rods are characterized by constrictions, which later develop into cross walls, followed by division. Cells may branch, the branching appearing at or near the site of constriction but not visibly connected to the main axis. Form small, bluish-white iridescent colonies on peptone-yeast extract agar, particularly with added acetate. Larger, spreading, fimbriate colonies are also produced in a patch-like fashion.

Type species: *Lineola longa* Pringsheim.

NOTES: Two species are described. No other information is available.

Bennett, and Canale-Parola (Archiv. Mikrobiol., *52*, 1965, 197) claim that *Lineola longa* is a species of *Bacillus*.

Oscillospira (Os.cil.lo.spi'ra) Chatton and Pérard, 1913. *M p. 834.* (Compt. rend., *65*, 1913, 1159.)

DIFFERENTIATING CHARACTERS: Multicellular, colorless organisms, more than 2 μ in width; motile with peritrichous flagella; produce a large endospore, apparently by fusion with several cells within the trichome; occur in large numbers in the cecum of the guinea pig.

Type species: *Oscillospira guilliermondii* Chatton and Pérard.

NOTES: There is only a single species. It is a colorless, multicellular, rod-shaped organism, straight or slightly curved; approximately 5 μ wide and up to 100 μ long. Individual cells are 1 to 2 μ long. Cells within the rod are usually square-ended, whereas terminal cells are hemispherical. Separation of long rods into shorter forms is preceded by the formation of a biconcave disc similar in appearance to that formed by *Oscillatoria* in the formation of hormogonia. Occasionally, large oval spores are produced at some point in the rod.

The organism is peritrichously flagellated but is rarely seen to be motile in microscopic preparations.

It has never been isolated; therefore information on its nutritional and biochemical properties is lacking.

Found in the cecum of the guinea pig.

Arthromitus (Ar.thro.mi'tus) Leidy, 1849. *M p. 835.* (Proc. Acad. Nat. Sci., Phila., *4*, 1849, 227.)

DIFFERENTIATING CHARACTERS: Colorless, uniseriately multicellular, rod-shaped microorganisms, which develop from a holdfast attached to the wall of the alimentary canal of millipedes, toads, and insects. Nonmotile; endospores are produced in individual cells and are obliquely situated.

Type species: *Arthromitus cristatus* Leidy.

NOTES: There are four listed species. The individual cells in the trichomes are longer than wide and vary in width from 0.6 to 5.0 μ, depending on the species. Trichomes may be over 2000 μ long.

Morphological data only are given.

Coleomitus (Co.le.o.mi'tus) Duboscq and Grasse, 1930. *M p. 836.* (Arch. zool. exp. et gén., *70*, 1930, Notes et Rev., 28.)

DIFFERENTIATING CHARACTERS: Colorless, uniseriately multicellular organism with a hyaline sheath; 0.3 μ wide and up to 320 μ

long. Individual bacillary elements are 3 to 4 μ long. Endospores, 0.8 to 0.9 μ by 1.7 to 2.0 μ, each containing an eccentrically placed volutin granule, are produced.

Type species: *Coleomitus pruvotii* Duboscq and Grasse.

NOTES: Only one species is described. Described from the intestines of termites.

Simonsiella (Si.mon.si.el'la) Schmid, 1922. *M p. 833.* (Zentr. Bakteriol. Parasitenk., Abt. I, Orig., *88*, 1922, 504.)

DIFFERENTIATING CHARACTERS: Multicellular organisms strongly compressed in ribbon-like filaments. Filaments divide into hormogonia-like units in which the individual cells are closely apposed and the terminal cells are rounded; motile with gliding motility.

Type species: *Simonsiella muelleri* Schmid, 1922, emend. Steed, 1962.

NOTES: The *Manual* lists three species, *S. muelleri*, *S. crassa*, and *S. filiformis*. The organisms have been isolated and studied by Steed (J. Gen. Microbiol., *29*, 1962, 615), who has reassigned *S. filiformis* to the genus *Alysiella* Langeron (*vide infra*). Those retained in the genus *Simonsiella* had the dimensions of *S. crassa*. The amended description of this species is as follows: *S. crassa* Schmid, 1922, emend. Steed, 1962. Multicellular, unbranched, nonsporing, ribbon-like filaments, 3 to 4 μ wide and 1 to 1.5 μ thick, consisting of closely apposed cells 0.6 μ long, with the free faces of the terminal cells rounded. The filaments appear to divide by constriction into hormogonia-like units about 4.5 μ long, which may remain attached for some time. Filaments may attain a length of 50 μ or more. Phase-dense areas may occur centrally in the intercalary cells and as apical thickenings in the terminal cells. The filaments exhibit gliding motility when the broad face is presented to the solid medium but are immotile and show a pronounced tendency to curl when on their edges. Gram negative, basophilic. Agar colonies: after 3 to 4 days, low convex, 1 to 3 mm. in diameter, smooth, undulate, translucent. Pigment and odor absent. Broth: granular and turbid, giving a moderate whitish sediment. Aesculin: no hydrolysis. Gelatin: liquefied. Casein: hydrolyzed. Litmus milk: peptonized. Starch: no hydrolysis. Sodium hippurate: no hydrolysis. Inspissated serum: liquefied. Blood agar: β-hemolysis. Methylene blue not reduced. Nitrate may be reduced to nitrite. Catalase positive. Urease negative. Indole not produced. Methyl red test negative. Voges-Proskauer test negative. Hydrogen sulfide produced. No growth on Simmons' citrate medium. Carbohydrates are fermented (not oxidized); acid but no gas produced from glucose, fructose, ribose, sucrose, maltose, trehalose, inulin; and there is variable acid production from arabinose and mannitol, on agar or in shallow liquid media. Acid not produced from rhamnose, sorbose, xylose, galactose, mannose, lactose, melibiose, cellobiose, raffinose, melezitose, glycerol, erythritol, sorbitol, dulcitol, inositol, or salicin. Aerobic. Optimum temperature, 37° C. Source: isolated from sheep saliva.

Alysiella (A.ly.si.el'la) Langeron, 1923. (Ann. Parasit. hum. comp., *1*, 1923, 113.)

DIFFERENTIATING CHARACTERS: Multicellular organisms, strongly compressed in ribbon-like filaments. Organisms appear to occur in pairs in filaments that tend to break up into groups of four or more cells in which the terminal cells are not rounded; motile with gliding motility.

Type species: *Alysiella filiformis* (Schmid, 1922) Langeron, 1923, emend. Steed, 1962.

NOTES: This genus is not listed in the *Manual*. The description of the type species is as follows: Multicellular, unbranched, nonsporing, ribbon-like filaments, whose cells appear to occur in pairs with a relatively weak linkage between each pair or group of four cells. The filaments are of uniform width throughout, and the terminal cells are similar to every other cell of the filament in being flat or slightly biconcave. Each cell is 2 to 3 μ wide, about 0.6 μ long, and 0.5 to 1 μ thick. Phase-dense areas may be present in the cells and often occur along one side of the filament. Length of filaments is extremely variable. Gliding motility is exhibited on solid media. Gram negative, basophilic. Agar colonies: after 3 to 4 days, low convex, 1 to 1.5 mm. in diameter, smooth, undulate, translucent, and often with a narrow fringe of gliding filaments and slime trails. Pigment and odor absent. Broth: granular and turbid, giving a moderate whitish sediment. Aesculin: no hydrolysis. Gelatin: liquefaction slight or absent. Casein: no hydrolysis. Litmus milk: unchanged. Starch: no hydrolysis. Sodium hippurate: no hydrolysis. Inspissated serum: no liquefaction. Blood agar: β-hemolysis. Methylene blue not reduced. Nitrate not reduced to nitrite. Catalase positive. Urease negative. Indole not produced. Methyl red test negative. Voges-Proskauer test negative. Hydrogen sulfide may be produced. No growth on Simmons' citrate medium. Carbohydrates are fermented (not oxidized); acid but no gas produced from glucose, fructose, sucrose, maltose, and trehalose; variable acid production from ribose and inulin, on agar or in shallow liquid media. Acid not produced from arabinose, rhamnose, sorbose, xylose, galactose, mannose, lactose, melibiose, cellobiose, raffinose, melezitose, glycerol, erythritol, mannitol, sorbitol, dulcitol, inositol, or salicin. Aerobic. Optimum temperature, 37° C. Source: isolated from sheep saliva.

Thiospirillopsis (Thi.o.spi.ril.lop'sis) Uphof, 1927. *M p. 840*. (Arch. Hydrobiol., *18*, 1927, 81.)

DIFFERENTIATING CHARACTERS: Colorless, uniseriately multicellular organisms with a spiral axis. Motile without flagella. When they are growing in the presence of H₂S, sulfur is deposited internally.

Type species: *Thiospirillopsis floridana* Uphof.

NOTES: A single species has been described. The organism is 2 to 3 μ wide and individual cells are 3 to 5 μ long.

Found in sulfur spring waters of Florida.

Saprospira (Sap.ro.spi'ra) Gross, 1911.

M p. 894. (Mitt. Zool. Stat. Neapel, *20*, 1911, 190.)

DIFFERENTIATING CHARACTERS: Colorless, flexible microorganisms with a spiral axis, 0.5 to 1.2 μ wide and exceeding 30 μ in length. The spiral is apparently constantly sinistral. There are no visible filaments wound around the main axis. Multicellular. Motile with a gliding rotating mobility on solid surfaces. Aerobic.

Type species: *Saprospira grandis* Gross.

NOTES: *Saprospira grandis* has been isolated and studied by Lewin (Can. J. Microbiol., *8*, 1962, 555). It is the same organism as that described by Dyar (J. Bacteriol., *54*, 1947, 483) under the name of *Spirochaeta plicatilis*. It is clearly not a spirochaete. It is multicellular, but the cross walls, revealed clearly at intervals of 0.7 to 1.0 μ in thin sections by the electron microscope, are very difficult to see even by phase contrast microscopy. They become apparent, however, in dying cells, which disintegrate into units 1 to 2.5 μ in length.

Fox and Lewin (Can. J. Microbiol., *9*, 1963, 753) report on the pigmentation of three species described by Lewin (Can. J. Microbiol., *11*, 1965, 135). These species, *S. thermalis*, *S. flammula*, and *S. albida*, differ in pigmentation and nutritional requirements.

Beggiatoa (Beg.gi.a.to'a) Trevisan, 1842. *M p. 838*. (Prospetto della Flora Euganea, 1842, 56.)

DIFFERENTIATING CHARACTERS: Colorless, uniseriately multicellular, flexible organisms; motile without flagella; when growing in the presence of hydrogen sulfide, they deposit sulfur inside the cells.

Type species: *Beggiatoa alba* (Vaucher) Trevisan.

NOTES: Six species are listed. They are differentiated solely on the width of the cells, which ranges from less than 1 μ to more than 70 μ. The validity of the differentiation is questionable.

Once thought to be strictly autotrophic and dependent on H₂S for their metabolism, they have been shown to be heterotrophic and not dependent on H_2S. Their isolation is difficult.

Isolation of *Beggiatoa* species has been made by Fauste and Wolfe (J. Bacteriol., *81*, 1961, 99), Scotten and Stokes (Arch. Mikrobiol., *42*, 1962, 353), Morita and Staue (J. Bacteriol., *85*, 1962, 940), and Pringsheim (Am. J. Botany, *51*, 1964, 898), all using the method prescribed by Cataldi (Rev. Inst. Bacteriol., Buenos Aires, *9*, 1940, 393).

More recently, Burton and Morita (J. Bacteriol., *88*, 1964, 1755) have demonstrated that the addition of undenatured catalase markedly improves growth.

Despite the above claims, only one strain of the cultures isolated by Pringsheim has been claimed to deposit sulfur. No clear indication is given by any of the authors of grounds for differentiation of the others from *Vitreoscilla*. The exposure of cultures to H_2S by Burton and Morita does not constitute proof of sulfur deposition as it occurs naturally, inasmuch as the treatment is lethal (author's experience and also that of Fauste and Wolfe). Fauste and Wolfe in their *"Discussion"* do, however, claim that cells "deposited refractile granules" when growing with low concentrations of H_2S, but they give no evidence of identity of the granules.

If the various claims for isolation can be substantiated, it seems clear that *Beggiatoa* species are heterotrophs, able to grow, as a rule, on acetate supplemented in some instances by vitamin B_{12} or other growth factors. They produce peroxide, which proves lethal as the cultures age. Lysis of the cells can be minimized by the addition of calcium to the medium. Granules other than sulfur have been shown to be polyhydroxybutyrate.

For further comments, see Starr and Skerman (Ann. Revs. Microbiol., *19*, 1965, 407).

Found in stagnant waters, both fresh and salt.

For further information see:

Burton, S. D., Morita, R. Y., and Miller, W., J. Bacteriol., *91*, 1966, 1192.

Thioploca (Thi.o.plo′ca) Lauterborn, 1907. *M p. 841.* (Ber. deut. botan. Ges., *25*, 1907, 238.)

DIFFERENTIATING CHARACTERS: Colorless, uniseriately multicellular, flexible organisms occurring in bundles in a common gelatinous sheath; motile without flagella; when growing in the presence of hydrogen sulfide, they deposit sulfur inside the cells.

Type species: *Thioploca schmidlei* Lauterborn.

NOTES: Four species are listed. It is possible that they may be algae. Closely related blue-green algae such as *Hydrocoleus* and *Microcoleus* may appear very pale and deposit sulfur internally and thus resemble *Thioploca*.

Species differentiation is based upon size. Width varies from 1 to 9 μ.

Found in fresh waters and marine muds containing H_2S.

Maier and Murray (Can. J. Microbiol., *11*, 1965, 645) have examined the fine structure of *Thioploca ingrica*.

Thiothrix (Thi′o.thrix) Winogradsky, 1888. *M p. 842.* (Beitr. Morph. Physiol. Bakteriol., I, Schwefelbacterien, Leipzig, 1888, p. 39.)

DIFFERENTIATING CHARACTERS: Cells occur in nonmotile, segmented trichomes, which are differentiated into base and tip and surrounded by a delicate sheath. Trichomes grow attached at the base to solid objects by means of gelatinous holdfasts. Reproduction is by transverse fission of the segments and by rod-shaped, so-called conidia, which probably are the apical segments that become free. Temporarily, the conidia show creeping motility, become attached to solid objects, and develop into new trichomes. When growing in the presence of H_2S, the organisms deposit sulfur internally.

Type species: *Thiothrix nivea* (Rabenhorst) Winogradsky.

NOTES: There are seven listed species, differentiated on the size of the trichome, which varies in diameter from less than 1 μ to 30 μ. Some are halophilic. Found in fresh and salt water containing H_2S.

Compare this genus with *Sphaerotilus*.

Vitreoscilla (Vit.re.os.cil′la) Pringsheim, 1949. *M p. 845.* (Bacteriol. Revs., *13*, 1949, 70; see also J. Gen. Microbiol., *5*, 1951, 127 and 147.)

DIFFERENTIATING CHARACTERS: Colorless, Gram negative, uniseriately multicellular* organisms, 2.0 μ wide or less, which are motile by a gliding action; not flagellated; *aerobic;* do not deposit sulfur internally when exposed to hydrogen sulfide.

Type species: *Vitreoscilla beggiatoides* Pringsheim.

NOTES: There are nine species listed, of which one is claimed to be nonmotile. There are two principal morphological forms: (*a*) those in which the cells are cylindrical and square-ended and closely abutted to form a continuous thread with parallel sides and (*b*) those in which the individual cells are barrel-shaped, giving the thread a beaded appearance. The latter type shows a marked tendency to break up into hormogonia-like fragments, whereas the former produces continuous threads. End cells are usually rounded but may be pointed (*V. conica*). None of the described species exceeds 2.0 μ in width. The tips of the threads may oscillate during movement.

Growth occurs readily on several types of organic media, provided the concentration of ingredients is not too high. A concentration of 0.1 to 0.3 per cent peptone is

* Multicellularity similar to that found in some blue-green algae (*Oscillatoria, Anabaena*, and others) is assumed to exist in the genus *Vitreoscilla* as evidenced by the key given in the *Manual* to differentiate the genus *Vitreoscilla* from *Bactoscilla*. *Vitreoscilla* is described as "trichomes divided into cells which are not separated by empty interspaces," as opposed to *Bactoscilla*, which is described as "trichomes divided into cells separated by empty interspaces." This difference needs to be carefully checked. In the Comprehensive Key *Bactoscilla* has been inserted in both the *multicellular* and *unicellular* sections.

adequate. The pH should not be below 6.5 and the agar should not be too hard. Colonies are colorless and characteristic of gliding organisms. They are usually flat and lace-like as a result of the migration and curling of the gliding organisms. At the margin of colonies short or long threads are almost invariably found migrating out ahead of the main growth, a characteristic rarely if ever seen with even actively motile flagellated bacteria.

Differentiation of species is at present based solely upon the width of trichomes and size and shape of the individual cells.

Found in dung and rotting vegetable matter, particularly in damp situations.

Costerton, Murray, and Robinow (Can. J. Microbiol., *7*, 1961, 329) describe the fine structure of a species of *Vitreoscilla*.

Bactoscilla (Bac.tos.cil′la) Pringsheim, 1949. *M p. 848.* (Bacteriol. Revs., *13*, 1949, 72; J. Gen. Microbiol., *5*, 1951, 144.)

DIFFERENTIATING CHARACTERS: Colorless, rod-shaped organisms, less than 2 μ wide, arranged in long chains, which are motile by a gliding motion on solid surfaces; not flagellated; Gram negative.

Type species: *Bactoscilla flexibilis* Pringsheim.

NOTES: A single species is described. Individual cells are 0.4 to 0.5 μ wide and are comparatively rigid. Bending of the chains occurs at the junction between the rods.

Microscilla (Mic.ros.cil′la) Pringsheim, 1951. *M p. 849.* (Bacteriol. Revs., *13*, 1949, 72; J. Gen. Microbiol., *5*, 1951, 127 and 140.)

DIFFERENTIATING CHARACTERS: Colorless, unicellular, filamentous, flexible microorganisms less than 2 μ wide and more than 10 μ long; arranged singly; motile by gliding action on a solid surface; not flagellated; Gram negative; *aerobic;* heterotrophic. Do not form microcysts. Not known to deposit iron.

Type species: *Microscilla marina* Pringsheim.

NOTES: Differentiation of these cells from those of *Cytophaga* apparently rests only on size and their extremely rapid movement. Cells range from 10 to 100 μ in length, depending on the species.

Three species are described, one of marine and two of fresh water origin. Growth occurs on 0.1 per cent peptone or yeast extract agar with sea water for the marine species. Colonies are colorless or orange, and microscopic examination of the margins reveals advancing tongues of actively gliding organisms.

Leucothrix (Leu'co.thrix) Oersted, 1844, emend. Harold and Stanier, 1955. *M p. 850*. (Oersted, De regionibus marinis, elementa topographiae historiconaturalis freti Oeresund, Copenhagen, 1844, 44; Harold and Stanier, Bacteriol. Revs., *19*, 1955, 54; *Pontothrix* Nadson and Krassilnikov, Compt. rend. acad. sci. U.S.S.R., A. No. 1, 1932, 243).

DIFFERENTIATING CHARACTERS: Colorless, uniseriately multicellular organisms, which taper from the base to the apex and are attached at the basal end to a solid object. Single, nonflagellated cells separate from the apex and are reputed to glide, form rosettes, produce holdfasts, and develop into new threads. *Aerobic*. Sulfur is not deposited internally with growth in the presence of hydrogen sulfide.

Type species: *Leucothrix mucor* Oersted.

NOTES: Harold and Stanier record no sheath. They claim, however, that their organism is identical with *Pontothrix*, which was originally recorded as encased in a sheath several microns wide. Pringsheim (Bacteriol. Revs., *21*, 1957, 69) states that *Leucothrix* has a sheath.

The single species studied is halophilic and develops best in 16 per cent salt on rotting marine algae. Optimal temperature, 25° C.

For further information see:

Brock, T. D., Science, *144*, 1964, 870.

Brock, T. D., and Mandel, M., J. Bacteriol., *91*, 1966, 1659.

Achromatium (A.chro.ma'ti.um) Schewiakoff, 1893, *M p. 852*. (Über einen neuen bacterienähnlichen Organismus des Süsswassers, Habilitationsschrift, Heidelberg, 1893.)

DIFFERENTIATING CHARACTERS: Large, unicellular organisms, more than 2 μ wide, which are spherical to short cylindrical with hemispherical ends. They exhibit a slow, jerky, rolling motion. No flagella have been demonstrated. They divide by constriction. In their natural habitat they contain sulfur and large spherules of calcium carbonate, but both are environmental characters.

Type species: *Achromatium oxaliferum* Schewiakoff.

NOTES: Two species have been described, one from fresh and brackish mud and one from marine mud. Cells vary in size from spheres 5 to 7 μ in diameter to large forms 35 to 100 μ. They have never been isolated.

THE SLIME BACTERIA

GENERAL CHARACTERS: The vegetative cells of slime bacteria are flexible, Gram negative rods of low refractive index, which are, without exception, motile by a slow gliding movement on solid surfaces. Because of this the colonies produced are initially flat, and at the margins single cells or groups of cells can be observed migrating away from the main body of cells—frequently leaving a visible trail of slime behind. Cells that have advanced some considerable distance may return along the same trail to join the main mass of cells. See Plate 27, Fig. 1a.

Vegetative cells are of two types. One is rod-shaped with blunt, rounded ends and resembles that of ordinary bacteria. The other is fusiform and is usually more flexible than the rod form.

No cell wall similar to that found with the flagellated bacteria is demonstrable by staining methods. There are no flagella. At present any suggestions about the mode of locomotion are purely speculative.

Resting cells are produced by all genera other than *Cytophaga*. They occur in fruiting bodies of various types in all other genera except *Sporocytophaga*, in which they occur among the rod forms within the colonies.

Each resting cell is formed from a single cell. In some the cells merely become shorter and thicker. In others the rods transform into spherical or elliptical resting cells. These are surrounded by a refractile, deeply staining wall and are referred to as microcysts. Electron microscope studies on *Myxococcus* have shown that, in the formation of the microcyst, a capsule is formed that is partially dissolved and shed during germination.

The type of fruiting body varies with different genera. Resting cells may occur within cysts in the fruiting body or remain separated but embedded, as a rule, in a mass of slime. Fruiting bodies may be sessile or stalked.

The slime bacteria are commonly found in the decomposing dung of herbivorous animals and decaying plant materials in general. Some are of marine origin and digest chitin and agar. Many terrestrial forms are active cellulose digesters. Others may be pathogens of man or animals. Some genera, like *Cytophaga*, *Sporocytophaga*, and *Myxococcus*, are readily cultured on cellulose or bacterial cell agars. Many others,

although producing fruiting bodies on sterile dung pellets layered on moist soil, have proved refractory to further culture.

Methods for the isolation of many fruiting myxobacters, including *Chondrococcus*, *Myxococcus*, *Podangium*, and *Chondromyces*, have been described recently by McCurdy (Can. J. Microbiol., *9*, 1963, 282), who has also succeeded in persuading *Chondromyces* to produce fruiting bodies in the absence of other microorganisms (Can. J. Microbiol., *10*, 1964, 935). Failure to fruit appears, in some cases at least, to be due to toxicity of components of the medium.

Cytophaga (Cy.to′pha.ga). Winogradsky, 1929. *M p. 858.* (Ann. Inst. Pasteur *43*, 1929, 578.)

DIFFERENTIATING CHARACTERS: Unicellular, nonphotosynthetic, flexible, rod-shaped organisms less than 2 μ wide and 10 μ or less in length; arranged singly; motile by a gliding motion on solid surfaces; not flagellated; Gram negative; *aerobic;* heterotrophic; no microcysts or resting cells are formed. Not known to deposit iron.

Type species: *Cytophaga hutchinsonii* Winogradsky.

NOTES: Eleven species are listed, three of which are obligate halophiles. They are fusiform or round-ended rods varying from 0.3 to 1.0 μ wide and, on the average, 2 to 10 μ long. Two species extend to 20 μ (see *Microscilla*). In old cultures degenerate coccoid forms, not microcysts, are formed.

Nine of 11 species have been cultured on various media, including filter paper silica gels, glucose-mineral salts media, starch agar, peptone agar, and sea water-peptone agar.

In the more restrictive media, growth is in the form of a barely visible film, like etching on the surface. On richer media, raised, moist colonies may be produced. Colonies are usually pigmented yellow, orange, pink, olive green, or gray.

Agar is hydrolyzed by marine species particularly.

Four species examined utilize, but do not

produce, acid from a wide range of carbohydrates. Heated carbohydrates are often toxic.

Of six species tested, four use NH_3 and NO_3 for nitrogen. All six use peptone and yeast extract.

Cellulose is hydrolyzed by 7/8 species. Ability to hydrolyze precipitated cellulose in agar plates is dependent upon agar sufficiently soft to permit migration of the cells through the medium.

Gelatin is liquefied by 4/5 species.

Information on other biochemical tests is too fragmentary to record.

Aerobic; optimal temperature, 22° to 30° C.

Found in rotting vegetable matter in soil and water, both fresh and marine.

For further information see:

Follett, E. A. C., and Webley, D. M., Antonie van Leeuwenhoek, *31*, 1965, 361.

Mandel, M., and Leadbetter, E. R., J. Bacteriol., *90*, 1965, 1795.

Archangium (Ar.chan'gi.um) Jahn, 1924, *M p. 863.* (Beitr. botan. Protistologie. I, Die Polyangiden. Geb. Borntraeger, Leipzig, 1924, 167.)

DIFFERENTIATING CHARACTERS: Unicellular, nonphotosynthetic, flexible, rod-shaped microorganisms, 0.5 to 0.6 μ by 4 to 10 μ; motile by a gliding motion on solid surfaces. Fruiting bodies are formed, in which cylindrical resting cells are produced in a mass of convoluted tubules embedded in slime; not in definite cysts; *aerobic;* heterotrophic; Gram negative; not known to deposit iron.

Type species: *Archangium gephyra* Jahn.

NOTES: Five species are listed, none of which appears to have been isolated in pure culture. Descriptions are based mainly on the type of fruiting bodies observed on dung pellets or rotting vegetable matter. The tubules, the mass of which forms the fruiting body, vary in width from 40 to 90 μ and may be incompletely septate. The convoluted mass of tubules gives the fruiting bodies an irregular surface. The fruiting bodies are sessile and yellow, orange or red in color and approximately 0.5 to 1 mm. in width; distinguished from *Stelangium* by the depressed nature of the fruiting bodies. The rod-shaped resting cells, which are shorter and wider than the corresponding vegetative cells, are packed within the tubules.

Found in soil. Fruiting bodies have been found mainly on rotting animal excreta.

For further information see:

Kühlwein, H., and Reichenbach, H , Archiv. Mikrobiol., *48*, 1964, 179.

Stelangium (Ste.lan'gi.um) Jahn, 1911. *M p. 866.* (Kryptogamenflora der Mark Brandenburg, V, Pilze I, Lief 2, 1915, p. 205.)

DIFFERENTIATING CHARACTERS:* Unicellular, nonphotosynthetic, flexible, rod-shaped microorganisms less than 2 μ wide; arranged singly; motile by a gliding motion on solid surfaces; no flagella; cylindrical resting cells are produced within an upright, finger-like, sessile fruiting body that is not encysted; *aerobic;* heterotrophic; Gram negative; not known to deposit iron.

Type species: *Stelangium muscorum* (Thaxter) Jahn.

NOTES: There is only one species listed. The fruiting body is a bright orange-yellow, 90 to 300 μ long and 10 to 50 μ wide, and occasionally forked. Resting cells are 1 to 1.3 μ by 4 to 6 μ. Found on liverworts.

Sorangium (So.ran'gi.um) Jahn, 1924. *M p. 866.* (Beitr. botan. Protistologie. I, Die Polyangiden. Geb. Borntraeger, Leipzig, 1924, 73).

DIFFERENTIATING CHARACTERS: Unicellular, nonphotosynthetic, flexible, rod-shaped microorganisms *with blunt, rounded ends;* less than 2 μ wide; arranged singly; motile by a gliding motion on solid surfaces. Fruiting bodies are produced, in which rod-shaped resting cells are formed in well-de-

---

* Resting cells but not vegetative cells have been described. The statement regarding the vegetative cell is hypothetical but is based on the measurements given for the resting cells and the general characteristics of myxobacteria.

fined cysts, which are *predominantly angulated* but may be spherical or cylindrical. Cysts are grouped in slime envelopes to form the fruiting bodies, which are sessile; *aerobic;* heterotrophic; Gram negative; not known to deposit iron.

Type species: *Sorangium schroeteri* Jahn.

NOTES: Eight species are listed. The vegetative cells vary from 0.4 to 1.3 μ wide and 2.0 to 6.0 μ long, according to species.

Fruiting bodies may be limited to small groups of cysts distributed throughout decomposing cellulose fibers (*S. nigrum*), or they may be in organized structures containing large numbers of cysts and measuring from 0.05 to 1 mm. wide. Cysts are described as angular for only four of the eight species. The others are cylindrical to spherical. They vary in size with species from forms 1.6 to 3.2 μ wide containing only 10 resting cells (*S. cellulosum*) to forms 18 to 22 μ by 12 to 22 μ. Colors are bright orange, brown, yellow, or black. They are embedded in slime. Cysts are sometimes grouped as primary and secondary cysts within a sorus.

The resting cells are shorter and thicker than the vegetative forms. They average 0.3 to 0.8 μ by 3 to 5 μ for listed species.

Found in rotting dung, soil, and decaying vegetation.

For further information see:

Gillespie, D. C., and Cook, F. D., Can. J. Microbiol., *11*, 1965, 109.

Peterson, E. A., Gillespie, D. C., and Cook, F. D., Can. J. Microbiol., *12*, 1966, 221.

Polyangium (Po.ly.an'gi.um) Link, 1809. *M p. 870.* (Mag. Ges. Naturforsch. Feunde Berlin, *3*, 1809, 42.

DIFFERENTIATING CHARACTERS: Unicellular, nonphotosynthetic, flexible, rod-shaped microorganisms less than 2 μ wide; arranged singly; motile by a gliding motion on solid surfaces; no flagella. Resting cells produced in cysts, which are spherical or elongate and coiled. Cysts are embedded in slime to form a sorus, which is sessile. *Aerobic;* heterotrophic; Gram negative; not known to deposit iron.

Type species: *Polyangium vitellinum* Link.

NOTES: Although the *Manual* key to families suggests a predominance of long, tapering rods, seven species for which this character is mentioned are described as cylindrical rods with *rounded ends*. They vary in size from 0.4 to 1.2 μ wide (average 0.8 μ) by 3 to 12 μ long.

Cysts are predominantly spherical or cylindrical. *P. cellulosum* is described as having polygonal cysts caused by pressure on cylindrical cysts. Cysts vary in size from 8 to 200 μ in width, according to species. They may be yellow, orange, rose, brown, or smoky gray in color.

Fruiting bodies formed from cyst aggregates vary from approximately 0.1 to 3 mm. in width and are sessile. Resting cells are rod-shaped and shorter than the vegetative cells.

Fifteen species have been recorded.

Found in damp, rotting timber, soil, and dung.

Synangium (Syn.an'gi.um) Jahn, 1924. *M p. 877.* (Beitr. botan. Protistologie. I, Die Polyangiden. Geb. Borntraeger, Leipzig, 1924, p. 79.)

DIFFERENTIATING CHARACTERS: There is a single species listed. The vegetative rods are 0.9 to 1.0 μ by 3 to 8 μ, with rounded ends. They are motile by a gliding action on solid surfaces; no flagella. Resting cells, 2.5 to 6.0 μ by 0.6 to 1.0 μ, are produced in cysts, which have apical hair-like processes 7 to 30 μ long and which are attached at the base to form a discoid or spherical cluster supported on a stalk up to 1 mm. high. *Aerobic;* heterotrophic; Gram negative; not known to deposit iron.

Type species: *Synangium sessile* (Thaxter) Jahn.

NOTES: Initially white, the fruiting body finally turns an orange color.

Found in decaying wood. Crude cultures have been maintained on hay.

Podangium (Po.dan'gi.um) Jahn, 1924. *M p. 877.* (Beitr. botan. Protistologie. I,

Die Polyangiden. Geb. Borntraeger, Leipzig, 1924, 80.)

DIFFERENTIATING CHARACTERS: Unicellular, nonphotosynthetic, flexible, rod-shaped microorganisms, less than 2 μ wide, arranged singly; 2 to 7 μ long; motile by a gliding action on solid surfaces; no flagella. Resting cells are rod-shaped and are produced in spherical, cylindrical, or disc-shaped cysts, which are borne singly on stalks; *aerobic;* heterotrophic; Gram negative; not known to deposit iron.

Type species: *Podangium erectum* (Schroeter) Jahn.

NOTES: Four species are described. Cysts are, on the average, 25 to 50 μ wide. The disc-shaped cyst of *P. boletus* is 100 μ by 40 to 50 μ. Stalks range from 7 to 80 μ and may be square or round and sometimes have a distinct foot. Resting cells are rod-shaped.

Fruiting bodies are white, yellow, orange, or brown.

McCurdy (Can. J. Microbiol., *9*, 1963, 282) reports the successful cultivation of *Podangium.*

Chondromyces (Chon.dro′my.ces or Chon.dro.my′ces) Berkeley and Curtis, 1874. *M p. 879.* (Berkeley, Notes on North American Fungi, Grevillea, *3*, 1874, 97.)

DIFFERENTIATING CHARACTERS: Unicellular, nonphotosynthetic, flexible, rod-shaped microorganisms, less than 2 μ wide; arranged singly; motile by a gliding motion on solid surfaces. Rod-shaped resting cells are produced in cysts, several of which are borne on a common stalk. *Aerobic;* heterotrophic; Gram negative; not known to deposit iron.

Type species: *Chondromyces crocatus*, Berkeley and Curtis.

NOTES: Eight species are described. The vegetative rods measure from 0.5 to 1.3 μ wide by 2 to 11 μ long. Ends are rounded or pointed.

The cysts vary considerably in shape, according to species. They may be spindle-shaped, bell-shaped, conical, cylindrical, or spherical. They vary from 9 to 80 μ wide and 16 to 100 μ long. The majority are a

bright orange in color. The cysts are attached by pedicles to the main stalk. The latter may be more than 0.5 mm. high. In *Chondromyces catenulatus,* cysts are joined in chains and several chains are attached by one end to the common stalk.

Found on rotting vegetable matter.

McCurdy (Can. J. Microbiol., *9*, 1963, 282; *10*, 1964, 935) reports the isolation and production of fruiting bodies by *Chondromyces crocatus* in media in the absence of other microorganisms.

Myxococcus (Myx.o.coc′cus) Thaxter, 1892. *M p. 883.* (Botan. Gaz., *17*, 1892, 403.)

DIFFERENTIATING CHARACTERS: Unicellular, nonphotosynthetic, flexible, rod-shaped microorganisms less than 2 μ wide; arranged singly; motile by a gliding motion on solid surfaces; no flagella. Spherical or elliptical resting cells (microcysts) are produced by transformation of the rods but are *not contained in cysts.* Fruiting bodies are formed by the segregation of the rod-shaped cells with the formation of a raised spherical, conical, or pear-shaped structure, sessile or on a broad short stalk, in which the microcysts are embedded in slime. *Fruiting bodies* are deliquescent. *Aerobic;* heterotrophic; Gram negative; not known to deposit iron.

Type species: *Myxococcus fulvus* (Cohn, emend. Schroeter) Jahn.

NOTES: Nine species are listed, of which six have been recognized. The vegetative rods are pointed or rounded and measure approximately 0.4 to 1.3 μ by 2 to 10 μ. The *microcysts* are spherical or elliptical, 0.8 to 1.2 μ by 1.0 to 1.8 μ. Some have highly refractile walls. All stain intensely. The fruiting bodies may be more than 0.5 mm. in size and are white, orange, red, or yellow-green in color.

Good growth of some species has been achieved on bacterial cell agar, cellulose agar, and nutrient agar.

Found in decaying vegetable matter.

Dworkin and Voelz (J. Gen. Microbiol., *28*, 1962, 81) have shown that microcyst formation in *Myxococcus xanthus* involves a shortening and thickening of the entire vegetative cell, with a subsequent increase in refractility. Germination is preceded by the casting off of a sheath, followed by the elongation and loss of refractility of the cell. Voelz and Dworkin (J. Bacteriol., *84*, 1962, 943) studied the changes in thin sections under the electron microscope.

Formation of the microcyst involved the formation of a capsule but no drastic reorganization of the limiting cell membranes. On germination there is a separation of the inner cell and outer sheath, followed by the dissolution of a segment of the outer sheath and the emergence of the cell.

Adye and Powelson (J. Bacteriol., *81*, 1961, 780) have compared the chemical compositions of the cell walls of vegetative cells and the microcysts. Amino acids in hydrolysates were the same. Walls of microcysts yielded arabinose, glucose, rhamnose, galactosamine, and glucosamine, whereas vegetative cells yielded galactose, glucose, rhamnose, and hexosamine. There was also evidence of fucose, mannose, and muramic acid.

Dworkin (J. Bacteriol., *86*, 1963, 69) and Leadbetter (Nature, *200*, 1963, 1127) discuss aspects of the nutrition of *Myxococcus*.

For further information see:
Burchard, R. P., and Dworkin, M., J. Bacteriol., *91*, 1966, 535.
Burchard, R. P., Gordon, S. A., and Dworkin, M., J. Bacteriol., *91*, 1966, 896.
Dworkin, M., and Gibson, S. M., Science, *146*, 1964, 243.
Dworkin, M., and Sadler, W., J. Bacteriol., *91*, 1966, 1516.
Ensign, J. C., and Wolfe, R. S., J. Bacteriol., *90*, 1965, 395.
Sadler, W., and Dworkin, M., J. Bacteriol., *91*, 1966, 1520.
Voelz, H., Archiv. Mikrobiol., *51*, 1965, 60.
Voelz, H., Voelz, U., and Ortigoza, R. O., Archiv. Mikrobiol., *53*, 1966, 371.

Chondrococcus (Chon.dro.coc'cus) Jahn, 1924. *M p. 886.* (Beitr. botan. Protistologie. I, Die Polyangiden. Geb. Borntraeger, Leipzig, 1924, 85.)

DIFFERENTIATING CHARACTERS: Unicellular, nonphotosynthetic, flexible, rod-shaped microorganisms, less than 2 μ wide; arranged singly; motile by a gliding motion on solid surfaces; no flagella; spherical or elliptical resting cells (microcysts) are produced by transformation of the rods, but they are *not contained in cysts*. Fruiting bodies, formed by the segregation and transformation of the rods to microcysts, are *firm and not deliquescent. Aerobic;* heterotrophic; Gram negative; not known to deposit iron.

Type species: *Chondrococcus coralloides* (Thaxter) Jahn.

NOTES: Seven species are described. The vegetative rods are 0.4 to 0.8 μ wide and 2 to 12 μ long. Microcysts are 1 to 2 μ in diameter or approximately 0.7 by 1.2 μ. Some have thick, refractile walls. The fruiting body varies with the species. In some it is a depressed disc-like structure, lobed or convoluted, and 80 by 160 μ in size. In others it may have a swollen base and a narrow tip like a partly inflated balloon. Occur singly or in groups. Colors are pink, red, yellow, or violet. Some fruiting bodies are more than 0.5 mm. across.

Found on dung of animals and birds and on lichens.

McCurdy (Can. J. Microbiol., *9*, 1963, 282) reports the successful isolation of *Chondrococcus.*

Angiococcus (An.gi.o.coc'cus) Jahn, 1924. *M p. 889.* (Beitr. botan. Protistologie. I, Die Polyangiden. Geb. Borntraeger, Leipzig, 1924, 89.)

DIFFERENTIATING CHARACTERS: Unicellular, nonphotosynthetic, flexible, rod-shaped microorganisms, less than 2 μ wide; arranged singly; motile by a gliding motion on solid surfaces; no flagella. Spherical *microcysts* are *produced in disc-shaped cysts,* which are aggregated to form a fruiting body; *aerobic;* heterotrophic; Gram negative; not known to deposit iron.

Type species: *Angiococcus disciformis* (Thaxter) Jahn.

NOTES: There are two species. The vegetative cells are 0.4 to 0.6 μ by 1.5 to 3.0 μ. The disc-like cysts are 10 to 20 μ thick and 35 to 150 μ in diameter and are yellow, orange, or pink in color.

Found on decaying organic matter.

Sporocytophaga   (Spo.ro.cy.to'-pha.ga) Stanier, 1940. *M p. 890.* (J. Bacteriol., *40*, 1940, 629.)

DIFFERENTIATING CHARACTERS: Unicellular, nonphotosynthetic, Gram negative, flexible, rod-shaped microorganisms, motile by a gliding motion on solid surfaces; no flagella; microcysts are produced by direct transformation of rods to spherical or elliptical resting cells *without aggregation*

into a fruiting body; *aerobic;* heterotrophic; Gram negative; not known to deposit iron.

Type species: *Sporocytophaga myxococcoides* (Krzemieniewska) Stanier.

NOTES: Three species are listed. The rods are 0.3 to 0.7 μ by 2.5 to 8.0 μ and very flexible. No cell wall is revealed by special stains.

The colonies on agar vary with the nutritional quality of the medium from a fine etch-like growth to a raised, moist, spreading growth. The colonies are yellow or orange.

Microcysts are spherical or oval and occur among the rods in the colonies.

All species use ammonia, nitrate, and peptone for a nitrogen source. Cellulose is hydrolyzed. Glucose is metabolized if unheated.

The optimal temperature is 25° to 30° C.

Found in soil and composts.

EXTREMELY FLEXIBLE SPIRAL ORGANISMS ACTIVELY MOTILE IN FREE SOLUTION BUT WITHOUT FLAGELLA; AXIAL FILAMENTS REVEALED BY ELECTRON PHOTOMICROGRAPHS IN ALL TYPES SO FAR EXAMINED

Recent studies of the spirochaetes have been reviewed by Starr and Skerman (Ann. Revs. Microbiol., *19*, 1965, 407). It seems clear that all the recognized spirochaetes have a spirally wound body encased in a loosely fitting membrane, attached, at least in some forms, by radially arranged fibers to the cell body. Both the cell wall and the envelopes appear to be triple-layered membranes. Curiosity regarding the fate of the longitudinal "axial filaments" during transverse division has revealed that the organisms produce subpolarly inserted flagella, which pass backwards from the ends towards the center, where they overlap. Some evidence of periodicity has been

found occasionally in the "flagella" and occasionally in the enveloping envelope. These findings have not been generally established but have been shown to be valid for *Leptospira pomona* (Ritchie and Ellinghavsen, J. Bacteriol., *89*, 1965, 223) and for *Treponema microdentium* (Listgarten and Socransky, J. Bacteriol., *88*, 1964, 1087).

A study on the metabolism of *Treponema zuelzeri* by Veldkamp (Antonie van Leeuwenhoek, *26*, 1960, 104) has shown that it metabolizes glucose in the same manner as *Escherichia coli*, except that no ethanol is produced.

The genus *Saprospira* has been removed

from the *Spirochaetales*. It lacks axial fibers and is clearly a member of the gliding organisms.

Spirochaeta (Spi.ro.chae'ta) Ehrenberg, 1833. *M p. 893*. (Abhandl. Berlin Akad., 1833, 313.)

DIFFERENTIATING CHARACTERS: Colorless, unicellular, flexible microorganisms with a spiral axis, 0.25 to 0.75 μ wide and *exceeding 30 μ in length*. Wound around the main spiral of the cell is a small group of fine fibrils, having the appearance of a single *axial filament* under the ordinary microscope. Very actively motile and exhibiting remarkable flexibility; no flagella; no cross striations; do not deposit sulfur internally; Gram negative.

Type species: *Spirochaeta plicatilis* Ehrenberg.

NOTES: Five species are described, differentiated solely on the basis of size and the shape of the ends, which may be rounded or pointed. Some species exceed 300 μ in length. The cells stain violet with Giemsa. The apparent axial filament observed with the standard microscope is composed of a number of filaments.

Found in waters, particularly among decomposing plant residues.

Cristispira (Cris.ti.spi'ra) Gross, 1910. *M p. 895*. (Mitt. Zool. Stat. Neapel, *20*, 1910, 41.)

DIFFERENTIATING CHARACTERS: Colorless, Gram negative, flexible microorganisms with a spiral axis; 0.5 to 3.0 μ wide, and *exceeding 30 μ in length*. Wound around the main spiral is a group of approximately 40 fibrils forming a colorless veil, called a crista, which stands out from the cell. Fibrils are not visible under the light microscope but are visible under phase contrast (author's note). The crista, composed of these fibrils, is visible with the light microscope. Cross striations are present; do not deposit sulfur internally.

Type species: *Cristispira balbianii* (Certes) Gross.

NOTES: Three species are described. Differentiation is on size, shape of the ends, and the spiral width and amplitude.

Found in the crystalline style of oysters and other bivalves.

Ryter and Pillot (Ann. Inst. Pasteur, *109*, 1965, 552) examined the fine structure of *Cristispira*. The organisms are unicellular but contain numerous large vesicles. Their structure is similar to other spirochaetes. They have several hundred fibrils in the crista.

Borrelia (Bor.rel'i.a) Swellengrebel, 1907. *M p. 897*. (Ann. inst. Pasteur, *21*, 1907, 582.)

DIFFERENTIATING CHARACTERS: Colorless, unicellular, flexible microorganisms with a shallow spiral axis; 0.25 to 0.5 μ wide and 8 to 16 μ long; motile without flagella; no fibrils are visible around the cells with a light microscope, but they are revealed by electron microscopy. *Stain readily;* Gram negative.

Type species: *Borrelia anserina* (Sakharoff) Bergey *et al.*

NOTES: Of 28 species recorded, only 8 seem to have been cultured. Differentiation is based solely on source, mode of transmission, and the nature of the infection. Most species are hematophytic or occur on mucous membranes.

Many species cause relapsing fever in man.

For further information see Starr and Skerman (Ann. Revs. Microbiol., *19*, 1965, 407).

Leptospira (Lep.to.spi'ra) Noguchi, 1917. *M p. 907*. (J. Exptl. Med., *25*, 1917, 753.)

DIFFERENTIATING CHARACTERS: Unicellular, colorless, flexible organisms, 0.1 to 0.2 μ thick, wound in a very fine coil and hooked at one or both ends. A single axial filament, visible only with the electron microscope, is wound around the main coils of the organism; *aerobic;* can be cultivated *in vitro* in semisolid rabbit plasma media; not readily stained; stain with Giemsa's stain or by silver impregnation methods; visible under dark ground illumination. Actively motile in free solution.

Type species: *Leptospira icterohaemorrhagiae* (Inada and Ido) Noguchi.

NOTES: The *Manual* lists only two species: *L. icterohaemorrhagiae*, representative of the parasitic species, and *L. biflexa*, representative of the saprophytic species.

Numerous serotypes of the pathogenic leptospirae have been identified by agglutination-lysis and cross absorption tests.

Apart from size, there is no clear means of differentiation between *Leptospira* and *Spirochaeta*. Is it possible that a better mode of differentiation could be found in the number of axial filaments revealed by electron microscopy?

For further information see Starr and Skerman (Ann. Revs. Microbiol., *19*, 1965, 407).

See also:

Baseman, J. B., Henneberry, R. C., and Cox, C. D., J. Bacteriol., *91*, 1966, 1374.

Treponema (Tre.po.ne′ma) Schaudinn, 1905. *M p. 904*. (Deut. med. Wochschr., *31*, 1905, 1728.)

DIFFERENTIATING CHARACTERS: Color-less, unicellular, flexible microorganisms with a spiral axis in which spirals are acute and regular or irregular; 0.25 to 0.3 μ wide and 3 to 18 μ long. Visible under dark ground illumination; no fibrils are visible under these conditions, but they have been demonstrated by electron microscopy (four in *T. pallidum*); do not stain by Gram; motile without flagella; *anaerobic*.

Parasites of man and animals.

Type species: *Treponema pallidum* (Schaudinn and Hoffmann) Schaudinn.

NOTES: Eight species are recorded, some of which have been cultured in sterile tissue cultures under strictly anaerobic conditions. Differentiation is based on morphology, source, and the nature of the infection, if any.

Certain species cause syphilis (*T. pallidum*), pinta, (*T. cuniculi*), and yaws (*T. pertenue*).

For further information see Starr and Skerman (Ann. Revs. Microbiol., *19*, 1965, 407).

PLEUROPNEUMONIA AND PLEUROPNEUMONIA-LIKE ORGANISMS

Mycoplasma (My.co.plas′ma) Nowak, 1929. *M p. 914*. (Ann. inst. Pasteur, *43*, 1929, 1349.)

DIFFERENTIATING CHARACTERS: Small, spherical bodies, 150 to 300 mμ in diameter, which germinate to produce filaments, approximately 0.2 μ wide and from 2 to 50 μ long, which are sparsely or richly branching. At a later stage of growth, small endomycelial corpuscles develop in the filaments by a process of successive condensation and constriction. As a result, the homogeneous filaments are retransformed into chains of close-set spherical bodies, which are released by fragmentation; highly resistant to penicillin and sulfathiazole; colonies on agar have a dense, granulated central area, which penetrates into the agar and which is surrounded by a translucent, flat, peripheral zone, or the colonies consist of a pearly film containing numerous spots due to calcium or magnesium soaps; do not ferment lactose, sucrose, mannitol, or dulcitol.

Type species: *Mycoplasma mycoides* (Borrel *et al.*) Freundt.

NOTES: Fifteen species are described in the *Manual*, separated on pathogenicity, hosts, and cultural and biochemical properties. L-phase colonies of some bacteria bear a strong resemblance to the colonies of *Mycoplasma*. The latter are generally more opaque, more heavily marked on the surface, tend to revert to the normal bacillary form in penicillin-free semisolid media, are more difficult to subculture, do not require cholesterol for growth, and ferment the same carbohydrates as the parent organism.

OBLIGATE PARASITES OF THE ANIMAL KINGDOM

NOTE: The following genera have been placed in the order *Rickettsiales* in the *Manual*.

Rickettsia (Ri.ckett′si.a) da Rocha-Lima, 1916. *M p. 935*. (Berlin. klin. Wochschr., *53*, 1916, 567.)

DIFFERENTIATING CHARACTERS: Small, often pleomorphic, rod-shaped to coccoid organisms, which usually occur intracytoplasmically in lice, fleas, ticks, and mites. Occasionally occur extracellularly in gut lumen. Nonfilterable. Gram negative. Have not been cultivated in cell-free media. Pathogenic species parasitic on man and other animals. Cause mild to severe typhus-like infections in appropriate vertebrate hosts of arthropod vectors; intracytoplasmic, occasionally intranuclear, in tissues. Etiological agents of epidemic typhus, murine or endemic typhus, Rocky Mountain spotted fever, tsutsugamushi disease, rickettsial pox, and other diseases. Many related organisms, described as symbiotes in arthropods not pathogenic for vertebrates, have been assigned here, but information is much less complete than for the pathogenic forms, and their congeneracy with the type species is uncertain. Phylogenetic relationships remain to be established.

Type species: *Rickettsia prowazekii* da Rocha-Lima.

Coxiella (Co.xi.el′la) Philip, (1943) 1948. *M p. 947*. (Subgenus *Coxiella* Philip, Am. J. Hyg., *37*, 1943, 306; *Coxiella* Philip, Public Health Repts., U. S., *63*, 1948, 58.)

DIFFERENTIATING CHARACTERS: Small, pleomorphic, rod-shaped, or coccoid organisms occurring intracellularly in the cytoplasm of infected cells and possibly extracellularly in infected ticks. Filterable. Stain lightly with aniline dyes. Gram negative. Have not been cultivated in cell-free media. Parasites of man and other animals. Includes the etiological agent of Q fever. Produces no typhus-like rash or Weil-Felix titer in man. Not dependent on arthropod transmission in the infectious cycle.

Type species: *Coxiella burnetii* (Derrick) Philip.

Ehrlichia (Ehr.li′chi.a) Moshkovskiy, (1937) 1945. *M p. 949*. (Subgenus *Ehrlichia* Moshkovskiy, Compt. rend. soc. biol., *126*, 1937, 382; *Ehrlichia* Moshkovskiy, Uspekhi Sovremennoĭ Biol., *19*, 1945, 10.)

DIFFERENTIATING CHARACTERS: Small, often pleomorphic, usually coccoid organisms occurring intracytoplasmically in the circulating monocytes of suitable mammalian hosts. Parasitic. The etiological agents of tick-borne diseases of dogs, cattle, and sheep.

Type species: *Ehrlichia canis* (Donatien and Lestoquard) Moshkovskiy.

Cowdria (Cow′dri.a) Moshkovskiy,

(1945) 1947. *M p. 950*. (Subgenus *Cowdria* Moshkovskiy, Uspekhi Sovremennoï Biol., *19*, 1945, 18; *Cowdria* Moshkovskiy, Science, *106*, 1947, 62.)

DIFFERENTIATING CHARACTERS: Small, pleomorphic, spherical or ellipsoidal, occasionally rod-shaped organisms occurring intracellularly in ticks and characteristically localized in clusters inside vacuoles in the cytoplasm of vascular endothelial cells of host vertebrates. Gram negative. Have not been cultivated in cell-free media. Not transovarially transmitted in tick vectors. The etiological agent of heartwater of cattle, sheep, and goats.

Type species: *Cowdria ruminantium* (Cowdry) Moshkovskiy.

Neorickettsia (Ne.o.ri.ckett'si.a) Philip *et al.*, 1953. *M p. 951*. (Philip, Hadlow, and Hughes, Riassunti delle Comunicazioni, 6th Congr. intern. microbiol., Rome, *2*, 1953, 256.)

DIFFERENTIATING CHARACTERS: Small, coccoid, sometimes pleomorphic (in the form of short rods, crescents, and even rings), intracytoplasmic organisms, which occur in the reticuloendothelial cells of certain mammals and in tissues of at least mature fluke vectors. No intranuclear forms have been observed. Nonfilterable. Nonmotile. Not cultivable on cell-free media. The etiological agent of a helminth-borne disease of canines.

Type species: *Neorickettsia helminthoeca* Philip *et al.*

Wolbachia (Wol.ba'chi.a) Hertig, 1936. *M p. 953*. (Parasitology, *28*, 1936, 472.)

DIFFERENTIATING CHARACTERS: Microorganisms possessing the general characteristics of the rickettsiae and exhibiting not only minute, bacterium-like forms, appearing with dark field illumination as luminous rods and points, but also enlarged forms, within the body of which are contained one to several smaller individuals. Pleomorphism is characteristic, and it is usually found in organisms in an intracellu-lar location; the few extracellular species, e.g., *Wolbachia melophagi*, may eventually be regarded as not belonging to this genus.

Type species: *Wolbachia pipientis* Hertig.

Symbiotes (Sym.bi.o'tes) Philip, 1956. *M p. 956*. (Can. J. Microbiol., *2*, 1956, 267.)

DIFFERENTIATING CHARACTERS: Rickettsia-like, pleomorphic organisms living chiefly intracellularly in arthropod tissues and approaching most nearly the true symbiotic or commensalistic relationship to their hosts; this is evidenced by the development in the host of special organs, or mycetomes, although no species of the *Rickettsiales* is yet known to be confined to such a location.

Type species: *Symbiotes lectularius* (Arkwright *et al.*) Philip.

Rickettsiella (Ri.ckett.si.el'la) Philip, 1956. *M p. 957*. (Can. J. Microbiol., *2*, 1956, 267.)

DIFFERENTIATING CHARACTERS: Minute, intracellular, rickettsia-like organisms, which are pathogenic for certain insect larvae but which are not known to be pathogenic for any vertebrates. Filterable. Associated with microscopic, intracellular, crystalline inclusions and reported to infect cell nuclei (although this needs to be confirmed).

Type species: *Rickettsiella popilliae* (Dutky and Gooden) Philip.

Chlamydia (Chla.my'di.a) Rake, 1956. *M p. 958*. (*Prowazekia* Coles, Ann. N. Y. Acad. Sci., *56*, 1953, 461; *Chlamydia* Rake, Bergey's Manual of Determinative Bacteriology, 7th ed., 1957.)

DIFFERENTIATING CHARACTERS: Coccoid and spherical cells with a developmental cycle. Gram negative. Occur intracytoplasmically. Noncultivable in chicken embryonic tissues. Have not yet been cultivated in tissue culture. Susceptible to the action of sulfonamides and of antibiotics. Cause ophthalmic and urogenital diseases in man; transferable to other primates.

Type species: *Chlamydia trachomatis* (Busacca) Rake.

Colesiota (Co.le.si.o'ta) Rake, 1948. *M p. 959.* (Bergey's Manual of Determinative Bacteriology, 6th ed., 1948, 1119.)

DIFFERENTIATING CHARACTERS: Usually coccoid cells, but pleomorphism is marked. Gram negative. Occur intracytoplasmically as colonies. Cause ophthalmic diseases in sheep.

Type species: *Colesiota conjunctivae* (Coles) Rake.

Ricolesia (Ri.co.le'si.a) Rake, *M p. 959.*

DIFFERENTIATING CHARACTERS: Usually coccoid cells, but pleomorphism is marked. Gram negative. Occur intracytoplasmically as scattered growth. Cause ophthalmic diseases of warm-blooded animals.

Type species: *Ricolesia pullorum* (Zhdanov and Korenblit) Rake.

Colettsia (Co.lett'si.a) Rake, *M p. 961.*

DIFFERENTIATING CHARACTERS: Large, pleomorphic cells occurring intracytoplasmically. Apparently nonpathogenic but may be saprophytic. Found only in the conjunctival cells of goats, sheep, and cattle.

Type species: *Colettsia pecoris* Rake.

Miyagawanella (Mi.ya.ga.wa.nel'la) Brumpt, 1938. *M p. 961.* (Ann. parasitol. humaine et comparée, *16*, 1938, 153.)

DIFFERENTIATING CHARACTERS: Coccoid cells with a developmental cycle. Occur intracytoplasmically. Gram negative. Cultivable in chicken embryonic tissues in tissue culture. Susceptible to sulfonamides and antibiotics. Pathogenic, causing various diseases in warm-blooded animals.

Type species: *Miyagawanella lymphogranulomatosis* Brumpt.

Bartonella (Bar.to.nel'la) Strong, Tyzzer, and Sellards, 1915. *M p. 969.* (J. Am. Med. Assoc., *64*, 1915, 808.)

DIFFERENTIATING CHARACTERS: Microorganisms that multiply in fixed tissue cells and on erythrocytes. On the red blood cells in stained films, the organisms appear as rounded or ellipsoidal forms or as slender, straight, curved, or bent rods occurring either singly or in groups. Characteristically occur in chains of several segmenting organisms, sometimes swollen at one or both ends and frequently beaded (Strong *et al.*, J. Am. Med. Assoc., *61*, 1913, 1715), without a distinct differentiation of nucleus and cytoplasm. In the tissues they are situated within the cytoplasm of endothelial cells as isolated elements and are grouped in rounded masses. Possess independent motility. Reproduce by binary fission. May be cultivated by unlimited serial transfers on cell-free media. Occur spontaneously in man and in arthropod vectors. One species has been recognized, and it is known to be established only on the South American continent and perhaps in Central America. Human bartonellosis may be manifested clinically by one of the two syndromes constituting Carrión's disease (Oroya fever or verruga peruana) or by an asymptomatic infection.

Type species: *Bartonella bacilliformis* Strong *et al.*

Grahamella (Gra.ha.mel'la) Brumpt, 1911. *M p. 971.* (Bull. soc. pathol. exotique, *4*, 1911, 514.)

DIFFERENTIATING CHARACTERS: Microorganisms occurring within the erythrocytes of lower mammals. Morphologically these organisms bear a resemblance to, but are less polymorphic than, the species in *Bartonella* and stain more deeply with Giemsa's stain than do the bartonellae. Neither motility nor flagella have been demonstrated. Not acid-fast. Gram negative. Several species have been cultivated on nonliving media. Growth is favored by the addition of hemoglobin. In cultures, the slight propensity to grow in unbranched filaments is variable; rods and coccoids with indistinct contours are commonly cemented together in dense masses. Aerobic. Parasitic. Splenectomy has little effect on the course of infection. Nonpathogenic. Not affected by arsenicals. The etiological agent of grahamellosis of rodents and of some other vertebrates.

Type species: *Grahamella talpae* Brumpt.

Haemobartonella (Hae.mo.bar.to.-nel′la) Tyzzer and Weinman, 1939. *M p. 972.* (Am. J. Hyg., *30*, 1939, 141.)

DIFFERENTIATING CHARACTERS: Parasites of the red blood cells. There is no demonstrable multiplication in tissues, and cutaneous eruptions are not produced. Typically rod-shaped or coccoid organisms, which show no differentiation into nucleus and cytoplasm. The morphological range may vary with the type of host employed. Stain well with Romanowsky-type stains and poorly with many other aniline dyes. Not acid-alcohol-fast. Gram negative. Not cultivated indefinitely in cell-free media. Distributed over the surface of the erythrocytes and possibly sometimes within them. Rarely produce disease in animals without splenectomy. The experimental host range is restricted; an organism infective for one species of rodent may commonly infect other rodents but not primates. Markedly influenced by arsenotherapy but, so far as is known, do not respond to penicillin. Occur naturally as parasites of vertebrates. Transmitted by arthropods. Geographical distribution of the best-studied species is similar to that of the vertebrate host and may be world-wide.

Type species: *Haemobartonella muris* (Mayer) Tyzzer and Weinman.

Eperythrozoon (Ep.e.ryth.ro.zo′on) Schilling, 1928. *M p. 977.* (Klin. Wochschr., *72*, 1928, 1854.)

DIFFERENTIATING CHARACTERS: Microorganisms found in blood plasma and on erythrocytes. Stain well with Romanowsky-type dyes and then appear as rings, coccoids, or short rods, 1 to 2 μ in greatest dimension, and stain bluish or pinkish violet; show no differentiation of nucleus and cytoplasm with this technique. Not acid-alcohol-fast. Gram negative. Not cultivated in cell-free media. Splenectomy ac-

tivates latent infection. Arthropod transmission has been established for one species.

The organisms in this genus have been considered as belonging to the *Protozoa* by Neitz, Alexander, and du Toit (Onderstepoort J. Vet. Research, *3*, 1934, 268) and to the bacteria by Mesnil (Bull. soc. pathol. exotique, *22*, 1929, 531) and by Tyzzer (in Weinman, Trans. Am. Phil. Soc., *33*, 1944, 244). The evidence at hand favors the inclusion of this group among those organisms which are not clearly protozoan in nature but which appear to be closely related to the bacteria.

Type species: *Eperythrozoon coccoides* Schilling.

Anaplasma (A.na.plas′ma) Theiler, 1910. *M p. 981.* (Rept. Gov. Vet. Bacteriol. for 1908–1909, Dept. Agr., Transvaal, 1910, 7.)

DIFFERENTIATING CHARACTERS: Organisms that parasitize red blood cells. There is no demonstrable multiplication in other tissues. In blood smears fixed with May-Grünwald and stained with Giemsa's stain, these organisms appear in the erythrocytes as spherical chromatic granules, which stain a deep reddish violet. No differentiation into nucleus and cytoplasm is shown. Occur naturally as parasites of ruminants. Transmitted by arthropods. Situated at or near the margin and/or at or near the center of the red blood cells. The position within the erythrocyte or host differences or both factors serve as bases for differentiating species. Attempts at cultivation in a variety of media have failed. Produce disease in nonsplenectomized and in splenectomized ruminants. The natural and experimental host range is fairly wide; these organisms occur in members of the families *Bovidae* and *Camelidae*. Influenced by Aureomycin and Terramycin. Widely distributed throughout the world.

Type species: *Anaplasma marginale* Theiler.

METHODS

The Pope and Skerman Mineral Salts Media for the Cultivation of Autotrophs and Nonexacting Heterotrophs

The authors have failed to find any plausible reason for the very large number of different formulas given for the preparation of inorganic media. In most, certain constituents have a specific function, but the majority of the constituents are obviously intended to provide trace elements and do so in quantities far in excess of the requirements of the organisms. Phosphates are usually included to provide a buffer and, to a minor extent, to provide phosphate for metabolic purposes. The former function is of very doubtful significance in other than the fixing of the initial pH of the medium inasmuch as in most cases the main criterion is growth, and a perceptible turbidity is apparent as a rule before any marked metabolic changes occur. Only when the metabolic byproducts are important may there be any reason for strong buffering of the medium, and even in such cases the desirability of it is questionable.

Excessive phosphate inevitably results in the precipitation of large quantities of insoluble phosphates, with the resultant clouding of the medium, which makes it useless when development of turbidity is the main index of growth.

In the formulation of the following basal medium, one of the most complex yet published, that of Meiklejohn for *Nitrosomonas* (J. Gen. Microbiol., *4*, 1950, 185), which involved use of the Hoagland and Snyder "A-Z" trace element mixture, was critically examined with the view of retaining all the elements represented but eliminating the precipitate that forms. The investigation was aided by the chance observation that yeasts grow well in Wickerham's defined medium for yeasts (Northern Regional Research Laboratories Tech. Bull. No. 1029) with the phosphate reduced from 1 gm. to 1 mg. per L.

For the preparation of the various mineral salts media the solutions described in Tables 14 and 15 are required. They should all be prepared with glass-distilled water and acid-cleaned glassware.

PREPARATION OF THE BASAL MINERAL SALTS MEDIUM

Step 1: Pipette into a 1-L. standard flask the following amounts of solutions from Group B: 10.0 ml. of Solutions 1 and 2 and 0.1 ml. of each of Solutions 3 through 10.

Step 2: Add approximately 600 ml. of 0.0074 M H_3PO_4 (Solution 3, Group A) and 210 ml. of water.

Step 3: Adjust the pH to 7.0 with N NaOH (1, Group A).

Step 4: Add 0.1 ml. of Solutions 11 and 12 from Group B.

Step 5: Take 0.1 ml. of the $MnCl_2$ solution (13, Group B), add 9.9 ml. of 0.074 M H_3PO_4 (2, Group A), and adjust the pH to 7.0. Autoclave and filter. Add the filtrate to the medium.

Step 6: Add 10 ml. of Solution 14, Group B, and 0.1 ml. of 15 and 16, Group B.

Step 7: Using the neutralized 0.0074 M

213

TABLE 14
Group A

Solution	Amount	Procedure
1. N NaOH	1 L.	Sterilize at 121° C. for 20 min.
2. 0.074 M H_3PO_4	1 L.	Sterilize as for Solution 1 (above)
3. Solution from 2, above	200 ml.	Dilute to 2000 ml. (0.0074 M); sterilize as for Solution 1
4. Solution from 3, above	1 L.	Neutralize with use of N NaOH; sterilize as for Solution 1
5. $NaHCO_3$ in 100 ml. of water	8.333 gm.	Sterilize as for Solution 1
6. $CaCl_2$ in 100 ml. of water	5.0 gm.	Sterilize as for Solution 1
7. $NaNO_2$ in 100 ml. of water	50.0 gm.	Sterilize as for Solution 1
8. Glucose in 100 ml. of water	10.0 gm.	Sterilize at 110° C. for 25 min.
9. Mannitol in 100 ml. of water	10.0 gm.	Sterilize as for Solution 8
10. Sucrose in 100 ml. of water	10.0 gm.	Sterilize as for Solution 8
11. Sodium citrate in 100 ml. of water	2 gm., anhydrous (or 2.77 gm., hydrated)	Sterilize at 121° C. for 20 min.
12. Phenol in 100 ml. of water	10.0 gm.	Sterilize as for Solution 11
13. $Na_2S_2O_3$ in 100 ml. of water	10.0 gm.	Sterilize as for Solution 11
14. 0.5 N HCl	100 ml.	Sterilize as for Solution 11
15. 0.0167 M H_3PO_4	1 L.	Neutralize 500 ml. with N NaOH; sterilize as for Solution 11
16. Monoethylamine hydrochloride in 100 ml. of water	5 ml.	Sterilize by filtration

TABLE 15
Group B

Solution	Amount	Solvent required	Final concentration
	per 100 ml. solvent		*μg./L. medium*
1. NaCl	3.0 gm.	0.0074 M H_3PO_4	300,000
2. $(NH_4)_2SO_4$	6.6 gm.	0.074 M H_3PO_4	660,000
3. $LiCl_2$	21.0 mg.	0.0074 M H_3PO_4	21
4. $CuSO_4 \cdot 5 H_2O$	80.0 mg.	0.0074 M H_3PO_4	80
5. $ZnSO_4 \cdot 7 H_2O$	106.0 mg.	0.0074 M H_3PO_4	106
6. H_3BO_4	600.0 mg.	0.0074 M H_3PO_4	600
7. $Al_2(SO_4)_3 \cdot 18 H_2O$	123.0 mg.	0.0074 M H_3PO_4	123
8. $NiCl_2 \cdot 6 H_2O$	110.0 mg.	0.0074 M H_3PO_4	110
9. $CoSO_4 \cdot 7 H_2O$	109.0 mg.	0.0074 M H_3PO_4	109
10. $TiCl_4$	60.0 mg.	0.074 M H_3PO_4	60
11. KBr	30.0 mg.	Water	30
12. KI	30.0 mg.	Water	30
13. $MnCl_2 \cdot 4 H_2O$	629.0 mg.	0.074 M H_3PO_4	629
14. $MgSO_4 \cdot 7 H_2O$	1.4 gm.	Water	140,000
15. $SnCl_2 \cdot 2 H_2O$	36.0 mg.	Water	36
16. $FeSO_4 \cdot 7 H_2O$	300.0 mg.	Water	300

H_3PO_4 (Solution 4, Group A), make the final volume to 1 L.

Step 8: Sterilize at 121° C. for 20 minutes.

This solution is crystal clear and will remain so for long periods if kept in acid-washed glassware. It provides a complex mineral salts base with ammonium-N, which has been found suitable, after addition of specific components, for a wide range of autotrophic and exacting heterotrophic bacteria. With the omission of the ammonium sulfate it is a suitable base for nitrogen-fixing bacteria. It may not be the *best* base, but in all cases tested (see below) it has been found satisfactory for taxonomic purposes.

MEDIUM FOR NITROSOMONAS

1. Liquid Medium: Adjust the pH of the basal mineral salts medium to 8.2 before sterilizing. Add aseptically 20 ml. of the sterile $NaHCO_3$ solution (Solution 5, Group A) per L.

2. Silica Gel Plates: In the preparation of the silica gel plates the medium is diluted 1:2. To allow for this, prepare a double strength basal mineral salts medium (D.S.B.M.S.M.) as follows:

Follow the instructions for the single strength medium to Step 2. Add 105 ml. of distilled water and make the volume up to approximately 400 ml. with the use of the 0.0167 M H_3PO_4 (Solution 15, Group A). Neutralize with N NaOH (Step 3). Then follow Steps 4, 5, and 6 as indicated. Make the final volume to 500 ml. with the use of the neutralized 0.0167 M H_3PO_4 (Solution 15, A) and sterilize at 121° C. for 15 minutes.

Prepare the silicic acid by the method of Pramer (see Preparation of Silica Gel).

Before gels can be prepared it is necessary to determine the quantity of N NaOH (Solution 1, Group A) required to adjust the pH to the desired level after the addition of $NaHCO_3$ and the $CaCl_2$ solutions (5 and 6, Group A, respectively).

As a trial, mix 10 ml. of silicic acid and 10 ml. of D.S.B.M.S.M.

Neutralize with N NaOH and note the amount added (x). Add 0.4 ml. of the $NaHCO_3$ solution (5, Group A), and then adjust the pH to 8.2 with N NaOH (1, Group A). Divide the sample (approximately 20 ml.) into four aliquots and add varying amounts of the $CaCl_2$ solution to each. Allow 2 to 3 hours to gel, and then determine the most suitable amount of $CaCl_2$ solution (y) required for the whole 20-ml. sample (approximately 0.6 to 0.8 ml. is required).

Before proceeding to pour the plates, prepare another test plate as follows: Mix:

Silicic acid.................... 10 ml.
D.S.B.M.S.M.................. 10 ml.
N NaOH (1, Group A)........... x ml.
$CaCl_2$ solution (6, Group A)...... y ml.
Inoculum..................... 1 ml.
$NaHCO_3$ solution (5, Group A)... 0.4 ml.

Immediately determine the pH and add N NaOH (Solution 1, A) until the pH rises to 8.2. Note this amount (x_1).

To prepare the plates substitute the value of ($x + x_1$) for x in the previous mix.

Allow 2 hours to gel and then incubate in a humid chamber at 28° C.

MEDIUM FOR NITROBACTER

1. Liquid Medium: Prepare the basal mineral salts medium with *omission* of the ammonium sulfate (Solution 2 of Group B) and sterilize.

Add aseptically 8 ml. of the $NaNO_2$ solution (7, Group A) and 20 ml. of the sterile $NaHCO_3$ solution (5, Group A) per L. of medium. Adjust the pH aseptically to 8.8 with sterile N NaOH (1, Group A).

2. Silica Gels: Proceed as for *Nitrosomonas* with *omission* of the ammonium sulfate (2, Group B) in the preparation of the double strength basal mineral salts medium (D.S.B.M.S.M.). Then mix:

Silicic acid.................... 10 ml.
D.S.B.M.S.M.................. 10 ml.
$NaNO_2$ solution (7, Group A).... 0.16 ml.

Neutralize with N NaOH (1, Group A), noting the amount used (x). Add 0.4 ml. of the $NaHCO_3$ solution (5, Group A), and then adjust the pH to 8.8. Divide the sample into four aliquots; add varying amounts of CaCl₂ solution (7, Group A) to each and allow to stand for 2 to 3 hours to gel. Determine the amount of CaCl₂ solution (y) that will give the optimal gel in the total (approximately 20 ml.) sample.

Prepare another mix as follows:

Silicic acid...................	10 ml.
D.S.B.M.S.M.................	10 ml.
NaNO₂ solution (7, Group A)...	0.16 ml.
Inoculum....................	1 ml.
N NaOH (1, Group A).........	x ml.
CaCl₂ solution (6, Group A).....	y ml.
NaHCO₃ solution (5, Group A)...	0.4 ml.

Determine the pH immediately; adjust to pH 8.8 with N NaOH (1, Group A) and note the amount (x_1).

To prepare plates substitute the value of ($x + x_1$) for x in the previous mix.

Allow 2 hours to set and then incubate at 28° C. in a humid chamber.

NITROGEN-FREE LIQUID MEDIUM FOR DETECTION OF NITROGEN-FIXING ORGANISMS

Prepare the basal mineral salts medium with *omission* of the ammonium sulfate (2, Group B) and substitution of 110 ml. for 210 ml. of water in Step 2. Adjust the pH to 7.0* and sterilize at 121° C. for 15 minutes. Cool and add aseptically 100 ml. of Group A Solution 8 (glucose), 9 (mannitol), or 10 (sucrose).

Note: If the latter solutions show any trace of yellow color, prepare separately 10 per cent solutions of glucose, sucrose, and mannitol and sterilize by filtration. Add aseptically 1 ml. of sugar to 10 ml. of solution.

The medium should be dispensed in layers not more than 1 cm. deep in Erlenmeyer flasks. Flasks must be incubated in a sealed container over N H₂SO₄ to remove ammonia from the air or in a chamber through which ammonia-free air is continuously passed.

* *Beijerinckia* does not grow in this medium at a pH of 4.5 but grows readily at pH 6.4.

LOW PH MEDIUM FOR ACIDURIC SPECIES OF *Thiobacillus*

Prepare the basal mineral salts medium. Add 10 gm. of Na₂S₂O₃ or 10 gm. of sulfur per L. Adjust the pH to 4.5 and sterilize at 121° C. for 20 minutes.

The medium should be dispensed in layers not more than 1 cm. deep in Erlenmeyer flasks.

NEUTRAL MEDIUM FOR NONACIDURIC SPECIES OF *Thiobacillus*

Follow the preparation of the basal medium, except at Step 2 add 110 ml. of water instead of 210, and at Step 7 make the final volume to 900 ml. instead of 1000. Sterilize at 121° C. for 20 minutes. Cool. Then add aseptically 100 ml. of sterile Na₂S₂O₃ solution (13, Group A) and 20 ml. of sterile NaHCO₃ solution (5, Group A).

The medium should be dispensed in a depth of not more than 1 cm. in Erlenmeyer flasks.

PHENOL MINERAL SALTS MEDIUM FOR *Mycoplana*

Prepare the basal mineral salts medium, but substitute 110 ml. of water for the 210 ml. at Step 2, and make the final volume to 900 ml. at Step 7.

Sterilize at 121° C. for 15 minutes.

Add aseptically 100 ml. of the sterile phenol solution (12, Group A). Adjust the pH, if necessary, with sterile N NaOH (1, Group A).

Dispense the medium in layers not more than 1 cm. deep in Erlenmeyer flasks. At least three transfers should be achieved before growth of an organism is considered positive.

CITRATE MINERAL SALTS MEDIUM

Prepare the basal mineral salts medium but substitute 110 ml. of water for the 210 ml. at Step 2 and make the final volume to 900 ml. at Step 7.

Sterilize at 121° C. for 20 minutes.

Add aseptically 100 ml. of the sodium

citrate solution (11, Group A) and adjust the pH aseptically to between 6.7 and 6.9 with sterile 0.5 N HCl (14, Group A).

ALKYLAMINE MEDIUM FOR *Protaminobacter*

Prepare the basal mineral salts medium but omit the ammonium sulfate (2, Group B); substitute 160 ml. of water for the 210 ml. at Step 2; and make the final volume to 900 ml. at Step 7.

Sterilize at 121° C. for 20 minutes. Add aseptically 100 ml. of the sterile alkylamine solution (16, Group A).

Dispense the medium aseptically in layers not more than 1 cm. deep in Erlenmeyer flasks.

Note: If monoethylamine hydrochloride is used it will require neutralizing before it is added to the medium.

AUTOTROPHIC MEDIUM FOR *Hydrogenomonas*

Prepare the same medium as that employed for *Nitrosomonas*, but adjust the pH to 7.0. Incubate under an atmosphere of 10 per cent CO_2, 30 per cent air, and 60 per cent hydrogen.

AUTOTROPHIC MEDIUM FOR *Methanomonas*

Use the same medium as for *Hydrogenomonas* but incubate under an atmosphere of 50 per cent methane and 50 per cent air. (See Preparation of Gases.)

AUTOTROPHIC MEDIUM FOR *Carboxydomonas*

Use the same medium as for *Hydrogenomonas* but incubate under an atmosphere of 20 per cent oxygen and 80 per cent carbon monoxide. (See Preparation of Gases.)

CELLULOSE MINERAL SALTS MEDIUM (AGAR)

Prepare the *double strength* basal mineral salts medium as for *Nitrosomonas*. Sterilize at 121° C. for 20 minutes.

Prepare a 3 per cent clarified agar (p. 275); adjust the pH to 7.0 and sterilize at 121° C. for 20 minutes.

To prepare the plates, melt the agar and hold the agar, the double strength basal medium, and the precipitated cellulose (p. 228) at 60° C.

Mix the agar and basal medium in equal quantities and pour 10-ml. amounts into sterile Petri dishes. Allow to gel.

Add one volume of the cellulose suspension aseptically to the double strength basal medium and thoroughly agitate to disperse the cellulose. Mix the suspension in equal amounts with clarified agar and pour in 5-ml. amounts evenly over the surface of the prepared gels. Allow to gel.

Note: The concentration of the agar used will vary with the brand. The final gel must be just firm, otherwise the cellulose-digesting organisms are unable to reach the cellulose fibers.

Incubate the plates in a humid chamber for several weeks after inoculation.

FILTER PAPER AGAR

Prepare as for cellulose mineral salts medium (agar) above, with substitution of a filter paper for the layer of cellulose agar. Double the quantity of the medium placed in the dish to allow for evaporation, and incubate in a humid chamber.

Preparation of Silicic Acid Sols

To prepare an ion-exchange column take approximately a 70-cm. length of 25-mm. glass tubing and fit it at one end with a glass tap and mount it vertically in a stand. Place some glass beads in the base and cover with a layer of glass wool.

Pack 120 gm. (wet weight) of IR-120 Amberlite resin in the tube and add sufficient 2 N HCl to cover the resin. Remove any air bubbles from the glass column with a glass rod. Open the tap and pass 1000 ml. of 2 N HCl through the column. Drain and then flush with distilled water until the effluent no longer gives a test for chloride with silver nitrate. Leave the column full of water.

Immediately after using the column for the preparation of the silicic acid, wash it again with water and regenerate with 2 N HCl.

Prepare 500 ml. of a solution of sodium silicate containing 1.5 per cent of SiO_2 and allow it to flow through the column at 5 ml. per minute. Check the pH of the effluent and collect for use when the pH falls below 3.4. Adjust the pH of the sol to 2.0 with HCl. The sol should be stable at this pH. Sterilize at 110° C. for 25 minutes.

Reproduced by permission from D. Pramer, App. Microbiol., *5*, 1957, 392.

Autotrophic Media for *Nitrosomonas* and *Nitrobacter*

NaCl......................... 0.3 gm.
$MgSO_4 \cdot 7 H_2O$............... 0.14 gm.
$FeSO_4 \cdot 7 H_2O$................ 0.03 gm.
H_2O......................... 90 ml.
0.1 M KH_2PO_4*.............. 10 ml.
+$(NH_4)_2SO_4$ (for *Nitrosomonas*). 0.66 gm.
+$NaNO_2$ (for *Nitrobacter*)...... 0.5 gm.

Dilute to 1000 ml. and add 10 gm. of powdered $CaCO_3$ and 0.4 ml. of a trace element solution supplying Mn, 22 μg.; B, 21 μg.; Cu, 17 μg.; Zn, 16 μg.; and Co, 14 μg.

Dispense in layers not more than 1 cm. deep in Erlenmeyer flasks. Sterilize at 121° C. for 15 minutes.

Reproduced by permission from J. Meiklejohn (personal communication).

Quantitative Determination of Ammonium-N

Distill a sample of 2 ml. containing 20 to 500 μg. of ammonium-N with 1 ml. of 5 N NaOH in a Markham microdistillation apparatus. Use 2 ml. of 0.5 per cent boric acid containing 40 ml. per L. of Conway and O'Malley's indicator (bromocresol green, 0.033 per cent, and methyl red, 0.066 per cent in alcohol; it keeps indefinitely).

After about 10 ml. of distillate have been collected, titrate the contents of the receiver in a stream of CO_2-free air with N/70 sulfuric acid from a 1.0-ml. burette. The end point is sharp, and estimations are re-

* Previously boiled for 30 minutes, cooled, and made up to volume.

peatable to within 0.010 ml. ($\equiv$ 1.0 μg. per ml. of ammonium-N in the sample).

Reproduced by permission from H. Lees and J. H. Quastel, Biochem. J., *40*, 1946, 803.

Quantitative Determination of Nitrate in Culture Media

Volumetric: If the sample to be examined contains no more than a few micrograms of nitrite, this can be ignored. If the nitrite is present in large amounts, remove it from the sample by adding a crystal of potassium iodide in the presence of sulfuric acid and bubbling nitrogen through the sample. Apply a spot test for nitrite before proceeding.

To 3 ml. of the sample containing 20 to 500 μg. of inorganic nitrogen in a hard glass tube, add 0.15 gm. of iron and 3 ml. of 8 per cent sulfuric acid. Place the tube in a beaker of water at 70° C. When the main effervescence has subsided, close the tube tightly with a rubber bung and set it aside overnight. This procedure reduces all inorganic nitrogen compounds to ammonia. Proceed as for the determination of ammonia with the use of the whole sample or a measured aliquot in the Markham still.

The titration of the distillate is equivalent to the (nitrate + nitrite + ammonium)-N in the 3-ml. sample, and from this the nitrate-N can be determined by subtraction of the (nitrite + ammonium)-N.

Reproduced by permission from H. Lees and J. H. Quastel, Biochem. J., *40*, 1946, 803.

Note: If polarographic equipment is available, nitrate can be determined by the method described by Skerman and MacRae, Can. J. Microbiol., *3*, 1957, 215.

Quantitative Determination of Nitrite

Dilute a sample containing approximately 0.5 to 5.0 μg. of nitrite-N to 11 ml. with distilled water. Add 2 ml. of Griess-Llosvay reagent. After 30 minutes read the color density in a photoelectric colorimeter with the use of a suitable filter and determine the nitrite-N concentration from a curve prepared from a series of standard nitrite solutions.

GRIESS-LLOSVAY REAGENTS

1. Sulfanilic Acid Solution: Dissolve 0.5 gm. in 30 ml. of glacial acetic acid. Add 100 ml. of distilled water and filter. The reagent is stable for 1 month.

2. α-Naphthylamine Solution: This should not be more than 1 week old.

Dissolve 0.1 gm. of α-naphthylamine in 100 ml. of boiling distilled water. Cool and add 30 ml. of glacial acetic acid. Filter. For use mix Solutions 1 and 2 in equal quantities.

STANDARD NITRITE SOLUTION

Dissolve 0.493 gm. of pure sodium nitrite in water. Make up to 1 L. Dilute 10 ml. of this solution to 1 L. This final solution contains 0.001 mg. of N as nitrite. The standard curve should be prepared over a range of 0.0005 to 0.001 mg. of nitrite nitrogen.

Reproduced by permission from H. Lees and J. H. Quastel, Biochem. J., *40*, 1946, 803.

The Reduction of Nitrate to Nitrite

Note: This reaction is dependent on a number of factors.

1. It obviously will not occur if the medium in which the nitrate is incorporated does not support the normal growth of the organism concerned. The test need not be restricted to the use of the peptone basal medium normally employed, but for comparative purposes the behavior of the organism in the nitrate-peptone water should be recorded.

2. It will not occur if the organism receives a supply of oxygen adequate for all respirational needs during growth as may occur in (a) still cultures of slow-growing cells in which the medium is distributed in shallow layers that admit oxygen by diffusion as rapidly as it is utilized by the cells, or (b) in aerated cultures. This is due to one of two factors. The nitrate-reducing enzyme is not formed in the presence of an adequate oxygen supply, and the enzyme, once formed, does not function under such conditions.

There are reports of strictly aerobic autotrophic organisms, which will use nitrate as the sole source of nitrogen; this suggests that reduction is occurring in the presence of oxygen. In view of the generally slow growth of such organisms and the presence of adequate amounts of ammonia in the average laboratory air, such reports must be considered with caution. It is possible that some intracellular mechanism is involved in the reduction of nitrate for synthetic purposes.

Under anaerobic conditions, such as exist in deep still cultures incubated aerobically after the dissolved oxygen is utilized by the growing cells *and* under strictly anaerobic conditions, nitrate may be reduced to nitrite, ammonia, nitrous oxide, or gaseous nitrogen.

With organisms in which the reduction is limited to nitrite the latter is readily detected. With the others the detection of nitrite will depend on the degree to which it accumulates at any time during growth and the actual time at which the test is performed. For this reason simple testing of the medium for nitrite at a fixed time interval after inoculation is valid only if the test is positive. A negative reaction is inconclusive.

The use of suspensions of cells grown anaerobically in the presence of nitrate to adapt them to nitrate reduction in tests employing a substrate and nitrate is also subject to error, inasmuch as in the presence of certain substrates some organisms will reduce nitrate to nitrogen without any detectable production of nitrite.

PROCEDURE

Select the medium most suited to the growth of the organism. Incorporate in the medium 0.2 per cent KNO_3, dispense in 5-ml. amounts in 150- by 13-mm. tubes, and sterilize. Allow the tubes to cool in air for 24 hours to permit the oxygen in the medium to equilibrate with air (except where required for anaerobic cultures). Inoculate the medium and cover it with a sterile paraffin seal. Incubate in a water bath at the optimal temperature. Observe the development of turbidity in the medium, and begin spot tests for nitrite as soon as the medium becomes obviously turbid to the naked eye. At this stage there is rarely any dissolved oxygen left in the medium. Remove the test samples with a warmed sterile dropping pipette, and reseal the paraffin after the removal of the sample. Continue the tests until maximal turbidity has been reached and for 12 hours beyond this time.

If the nitrite test is at any stage positive, record as "nitrite produced from nitrate" and specify the medium. If the latter is not nitrate-peptone water, the comparative reaction in nitrate-peptone water should be included and recorded even if no growth occurs.

If nitrite tests are continually negative and there is no evidence of gas production, it is unlikely that nitrate is reduced.

Gas production may be due to evolution of nitrogen or nitrous oxide. The nature of the gas has not, as yet, any taxonomic significance. It should be remembered, however, that some organisms produce gas from peptone water alone under anaerobic conditions; therefore nitrate-free controls should be used.

1. THE STARCH-IODIDE SPOT TEST FOR NITRITE

Reagents: Starch Iodide Solution

Starch.......................... 0.4 gm.
$ZnCl_2$........................... 2.0 gm.
H_2O............................. 100 ml.
Dissolve the $ZnCl_2$ in 10 ml. of water. Boil and add the starch. Dilute to 100 ml., allow to stand for 1 week, and filter. Add an equal volume of a 0.2 per cent solution of KI.

Hydrochloric Acid

Concentrated HCl............... 16 ml.
Water.......................... 84 ml.

Test

Using clean glass dropping pipettes, place 1 drop of each reagent in the depression of a white spot test plate. Add 1 drop of the culture. A blue color indicates the presence of nitrite.

The test depends on the formation of nitrous acid and its subsequent reaction with potassium iodide with the liberation of iodine, which turns the starch blue. The test is not entirely specific. Control tests should be made with uninoculated media. Avoid the use of metal implements in taking samples.

2. THE SULFANILIC ACID-α-NAPHTHYLAMINE METHOD

Reagents

See under Quantitative Determination of Nitrite.

Spot Test

To 1 drop of the mixture of Solutions 1 and 2, add 1 drop of the culture. The development of a pink color indicates the presence of nitrite.

Reference: The general procedures are the author's recommendation.

Autotrophic Medium for *Hydrogenomonas*

KH_2PO_4..................... 0.1 gm.
NH_4NO_3..................... 0.1 gm.
$MgSO_4 \cdot 7 H_2O$............... 0.02 gm.
$FeSO_4 \cdot 7 H_2O$............... 0.001 gm.
$CaCl_2 \cdot 2 H_2O$................ 0.001 gm.
Distilled water to 100 ml.

Adjust the pH to between 6.8 and 7.2. Where desired, incorporate 1.5 per cent washed agar. For autotrophic growth, supplement the base with 0.05 per cent $NaHCO_3$. Autoclave stock solutions of the $NaHCO_3$ separately, flush with CO_2, and add to the sterile medium before inoculation.

Incubate under an atmosphere of 10 per cent CO_2, 30 per cent air, and 60 per cent hydrogen.

Reproduced by permission from A. Schatz and C. Bovell, J. Bacteriol., *63*, 1952, 87.

Medium for the Cultivation of *Carboxydomonas*

KNO_3	2.0 gm.
K_2HPO_4	1.0 gm.
$MgSO_4 \cdot 7 H_2O$	0.1 gm.
Peptone	0.2 gm.
H_2O	1000 ml.

Dissolve the ingredients and adjust the pH to 7.2. Sterilize at 121° C. for 20 minutes.

For an agar medium use only sufficient agar to make a moderately firm gel. An agar that is too hard inhibits growth.

Incubate under an atmosphere of 80 per cent CO and 20 per cent O_2.

Reference: A. Kistner, Proc. Koninkl. Ned. Akad. Wetenschap., Ser. C., *56*, 1953, 443.

Autotrophic Medium for *Methanomonas*

$NaNO_3$	2.0 gm.
$MgSO_4 \cdot 7 H_2O$	0.2 gm.
$FeSO_4 \cdot 7 H_2O$	0.001 gm.
Na_2HPO_4	0.21 gm.
NaH_2PO_4	0.09 gm.
$CuSO_4 \cdot 5 H_2O$	200.0 μg.
H_3BO_3	60.0 μg.
$MnSO_4 \cdot H_2O$	30.0 μg.
$ZnSO_4 \cdot 7 H_2O$	300.0 μg.
MoO_3	15.0 μg.
KCl	0.04 gm.
$CaCl_2$	0.015 gm.
H_2O	1000 ml.

Dissolve the salts and sterilize. Incubate under an atmosphere of 50 per cent methane and 50 per cent air.

Reproduced by permission from J. W. Foster (personal communication).

A Simple Apparatus for Observing the Oxidation of Carbon Monoxide, Hydrogen, or Methane by Growing Cultures

The apparatus is illustrated in Figure 4. *A* consists of a 10-ml. graduated pipette sealed at the tip and joined above the 0.0-ml. mark to a 12-ml. tube fitted with a 12-mm. side arm and pear-shaped bulb with a 16-mm. outlet. The tube is plugged at the outlet with cotton wool and sterilized.

B is a glass tube of 6-mm. outside diameter, bent so that the external arm lies parallel to the main axis of the tube when the tube is inserted as illustrated. The external end is unconstricted and is plugged with cotton wool. The internal end is only slightly constricted and extends into the tube until it almost touches the wall when the rubber stopper *D* fits snugly into the base of the side arm. A small 1-mm. aperture, *E*, is made in the tube exterior to the rubber stopper.

A cotton wool plug is rolled around the stem of *B* between the rubber stopper and the bend. The lower end (bearing the stopper) is inserted into a 150- by 16-mm. tube; and the assembly is sterilized.

A third tube, *C*, bent in the same manner as *B* but without the small hole *E* and with the external end extended to a length that brings its tip level with the top of the graduated tube, completes the apparatus. This tube is fitted with a rubber stopper similar to *D*.

Method for Use: Pipette 40 ml. of the sterile synthetic medium into the tube *A* and inoculate the medium. Replace the plug in *A* with tube *B*, leaving the stopper *D* only loosely seated in its base.

Connect *B* to the gas-mixing burette and, holding the tube on its side, loosen the stopper *D* and allow a quantity of gas to escape into the pear-shaped bulb to exclude the air in tube *B*. Then turn the tube upright and collect approximately 9 ml. of gas. If too much is collected it can be released by inclining the tube. Disconnect

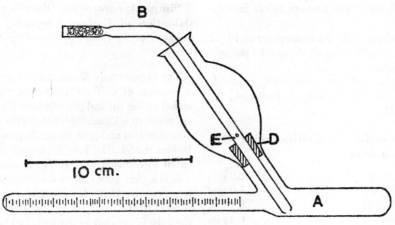

FIG. 4

the gas supply and seat D firmly into the side arm. Supporting the tubes by the outlet tube, immerse them for 20 minutes in a water bath at a temperature as near that of the room as possible. *Holding the tubes by the outlet tubes*, slightly tilt the tube until the menisci in the closed arm and pear-shaped bulb are level; read the gas volume (V_1) and note at the same time the temperature of the water bath. *All subsequent gas volume readings must be taken at the same temperature.* Incubate the tubes on their sides attached to a rocking arm in a water bath. This provides a maximal gas-liquid contact area during incubation. The small aperture E allows movement of liquid between the two bulbs, but the position of the internal end of B does not allow escape of gas.

After incubation adjust to room temperature to eliminate errors due to gas expansion. Replace tube B with tube C. Seat the stopper well into the side arm and introduce water through C, while holding the tube in the vertical position by the outlet tube, until the levels in the closed arm and in C are equal. Read the gas volume (V_2).

Release the stopper in the side arm and insert 4 pellets of solid sodium hydroxide (approximately 0.4 gm.) into the closed tube. Seal the tube and slowly rock it on its side in a water bath at room temperature for 20 minutes to absorb CO_2 and re-equilibrate the temperature. Place in a vertical position, readjust the levels through C, and again read the volume (V_3). The difference ($V_2 - V_3$) is CO_2.

Release C and introduce 0.5 gm. of solid pyrogallic acid by allowing it to drop through into the closed arm. Reseal; rock the tubes to absorb the oxygen; equilibrate the temperature; adjust the levels; and read the volume (V_4). The difference ($V_3 - V_4$) is oxygen. The residual gas will be hydrogen, carbon monoxide, or methane, depending upon the mixture used for culture.

If the final gas analysis is compared with the initial one, the ratio of gas oxidized to oxygen utilized can be determined.

Reference: Author's recommendation.

Preparation of Gases

CARBON MONOXIDE FOR GROWTH OF *Carboxydomonas*

Close a round-bottomed 500-ml. flask with a rubber stopper fitted with a gas outlet tube just penetrating the stopper and a dropping funnel with the lower end reaching almost to the bottom of the flask. Add concentrated sulfuric acid to the flask so that the tip of the dropping funnel is immersed. Place concentrated formic acid in approximately half this volume in the dropping funnel. Place the flask over a steam bath and connect the gas outlet tube via a concentrated NaOH wash bottle or soda-lime tube to the gas-collecting apparatus.

Heat to 100° C. and then admit the concentrated formic acid drop by drop until the required amount of gas has been collected. Allow for the exclusion of air before collecting the gas.

$$HCOOH + H_2SO_4 \rightarrow H_2SO_4H_2O + CO$$

Reproduced by permission from G. D. Parkes and J. W. Mellor, Mellor's Modern Inorganic Chemistry, Longmans, Green and Company, New York, 1947, p. 359.

HYDROGEN

Use apparatus similar to that employed for the preparation of carbon monoxide but eliminate the wash bottle.

Place granulated zinc in the flask and cover with water until the lower end of the dropping funnel is immersed. Add concentrated sulfuric acid by drops from the dropping funnel. Allow a volume of gas equal to at least twice the volume of the flask to escape before collecting over water in a gas burette.

CARBON DIOXIDE

Prepare the CO_2 in the same way as hydrogen, but substitute cracked marble for the granulated zinc and concentrated hydrochloric acid for the sulfuric acid. Collect over dilute sulfuric acid.

OXYGEN

Medically pure oxygen is so widely available that the preparation of oxygen is usually unnecessary. It may be prepared as follows:

Mix equal quantities of potassium chlorate and *carbon-free* manganese dioxide in a wide-mouth Florence flask and connect via a *wide* delivery tube, through a soda-lime tube, to the gas-collecting burette. Heat the mixture carefully over a flame until the gas is evolved. CO_2 and chlorine are removed in the soda-lime tube.

METHANE

Pure methane may be prepared by reducing methyl iodide in alcohol with a copper zinc couple.

Add 100 gm. of zinc dust to 250 ml of a 4 per cent aqueous solution of copper sulfate. Shake thoroughly and then allow the powder to settle. Wash several times with water by decantation and then dry.

Place the powder in a 100-ml Erlenmeyer flask fitted with a stoppered dropping funnel and a gas outlet tube. Allow a mixture of equal volumes of methyl iodide and absolute ethyl alcohol to drop slowly onto the zinc copper couple. Collect the methane over water after allowing the air from the flask to escape.

Reproduced by permission from C. Weygand, Organic Preparations, Interscience Publishers, New York, 1945, p. 41.

Apparatus for the Collection and Mixing of Gases

In culturing autotrophic gas-utilizing organisms, it is necessary to prepare gas mixtures of various types. This can be done simply with the apparatus shown in Figure 5. This consists of a series of 500-ml. gas-collecting burettes, A, B, C, and D, connected at the base via a manifold to a 3-L. reservoir, E, containing dilute sulfuric acid, and via taps at the top to a second manifold closed at both ends by taps F and G. The tube from tap G is connected to the gas generator and both G and F are opened. Gas is allowed to stream through G and F to expel air or any previous gas. Then with F still open, the tap to A is opened and then F is closed. The gas is diverted into A and dilute acid is expelled to E. If desired, E may be lowered to reduce the back pressure on the gas generator. With A nearly filled, open F and then close A immediately. Disconnect the gas generator and then close G and F. Repeat with other gas to B and C. Any number of gas burettes may be employed, but allowance must be made for mixing.

To prepare a mixture of 200 ml. of A,

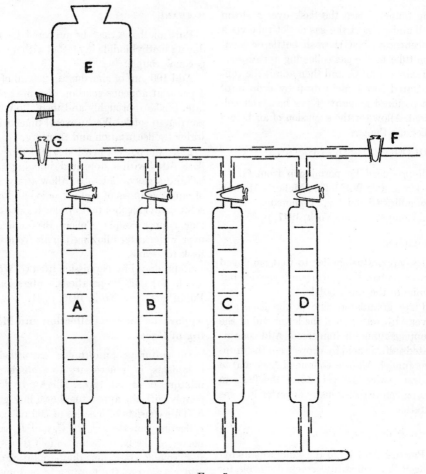

FIG. 5

100 ml. of B, and 200 ml. of C and D, open F and then A to flush out the manifold. Close F. Lower E so that its meniscus is level with the 200-ml. mark in D. Open D and let the gas flow in, adjusting E so that its meniscus is finally level with the water in D at the 200-ml. mark. Close D and A. Raise E and open B and F to flush the manifold. Close F. Lower E to the 300-ml. level of D and open D. Allow gas from B to flow into D to the required level. Close D and B. Raise E and open C and F to flush the manifold. Close F. Lower E to the 500-ml. mark in D and open D. Allow gas from C to flow in to the required level. Close D and C and replace F.

To discharge D into the required containers, open G and D and flush the manifold. Close G. Connect F to the apparatus and open F. Allow some of the gas mixture to flow through the connection to the apparatus to expel any air before admitting the gas.

References: Author's recommendation.

Autotrophic Medium for Aciduric Species of Thiobacillus

NH_4Cl	0.1 gm.
KH_2PO_4	3.0 gm.
$MgCl_2 \cdot 6\,H_2O$	0.1 gm.
$CaCl_2$	0.1 gm.
$Na_2S_2O_3 \cdot 5\,H_2O$	5.0 gm.

Or sulfur.................... 10.0 gm.
Distilled water............... 1000 ml.

Adjust the pH to 4.2. If thiosulfate is used, steam for 1 hour on 3 successive days. If sulfur is used, sterilize the rest of the medium at 121° C. for 20 minutes, and steam the sulfur in a separate tube and add aseptically.

Reproduced by permission from C. D. Parker and J. Frisk, J. Gen. Microbiol., *8*, 1953, 344.

Autotrophic Medium for Nonaciduric Species of Thiobacillus

$(NH_4)_2SO_4$.................. 0.1 gm.
K_2HPO_4..................... 4.0 gm.
KH_2PO_4..................... 4.0 gm.
$MgSO_4 \cdot 7\ H_2O$.............. 0.1 gm.
$CaCl_2$....................... 0.1 gm.
$FeCl_3 \cdot 6\ H_2O$.............. 0.02 gm.
$MnSO_4 \cdot 4\ H_2O$.............. 0.02 gm.
$Na_2S_2O_3 \cdot 5\ H_2O$.............. 10 gm.
Distilled water............... 1000 ml.

Adjust the pH to 6.6, and steam for 1 hour on 3 successive days.

Reproduced by permission from C. D. Parker and J. Frisk, J. Gen. Micribiol., *8*, 1953, 344.

Autotrophic Medium for *Thiobacillus ferrooxidans*

$FeSO_4 \cdot 7\ H_2O$.............. 130.0 gm.
$MgSO_4 \cdot 7\ H_2O$.............. 1.0 gm.
$(NH_4)_2SO_4$.................. 0.5 gm.
Distilled water.............. 1000 ml.

Dissolve the ingredients and adjust the pH to between 2.0 and 2.5 with sulfuric acid. Autoclave at 121° C. for 15 minutes and allow to stand. A voluminous precipitate of ferric hydroxide settles out. Remove the supernatant aseptically and distribute as required, preferably in layers not more than 1 cm. deep in Erlenmeyer flasks.

To prepare an agar medium dissolve the ferrous sulfate in 300 ml. of the water and sterilize separately. Dissolve the other ingredients plus 20 gm. of agar in the re-

maining water and sterilize. Mix the two solutions just before plate pouring.

Reproduced by permission from K. L. Temple and A. R. Colmer, J. Bacteriol., *62*, 1951, 605.

Autotrophic Medium for *Ferrobacillus*

LIQUID MEDIUM

$(NH_4)_2SO_4$.................... 0.15 gm.
KCl........................ 0.05 gm.
$MgSO_4 \cdot 7\ H_2O$.............. 0.50 gm.
K_2HPO_4..................... 0.05 gm.
$Ca(NO_3)_2$................... 0.01 gm.

Dissolve the salts in 1000 ml. of distilled water. Sterilize at 121° C. for 15 minutes. Prepare a stock solution consisting of 10 per cent $FeSO_4 \cdot 7\ H_2O$ in distilled water and sterilize by filtration; add 1 ml. aseptically to each 100 ml. of the above medium. The resultant medium is opalescent. Refrigerate the medium so that oxidation does not occur.

SOLID MEDIUM

This may be prepared with silicic acid. The inorganic solution for such a solid medium is prepared as follows:

$(NH_4)_2SO_4$.................... 6.0 gm.
KCl........................ 0.05 gm.
$MgSO_4 \cdot 7\ H_2O$.............. 0.50 gm.
$Ca(NO_3)_2$................... 0.01 gm.

Dissolve the salts in 250 ml. of distilled water. Dispense in 25-ml. aliquots in 125-ml. Erlenmeyer flasks and sterilize for 15 minutes at 121° C. Sterilize a buffer solution consisting of 13.5 gm. of K_2HPO_4 in 100 ml. of distilled water separately. Prepare the ferrous sulfate solution as for the liquid medium.

Prepare the silicic acid sol (p. *217*).

Add 1 ml. of ferrous sulfate solution to 75 ml. of the silicic acid sol and 1 ml. of the sterile phosphate buffer to 25 ml. of the sterile salts solution. Mix the solutions and allow to set for 24 hours.

Reproduced by permission from W. Leathen, N. A. Kinsel, and S. A. Braley, Sr., J. Bacteriol., *72*, 1956, 700.

Phenol Mineral Salts Medium for *Mycoplana*

The original medium described by Gray and Thornton is prepared as follows:

K_2HPO_4...................... 1 gm.
$MgSO_4 \cdot 7\ H_2O$............... 0.2 gm.
NaCl......................... 0.1 gm.
$CaCl_2 \cdot 2\ H_2O$............... 0.1 gm.
$FeCl_3$....................... 0.02 gm.
$(NH_4)_2SO_4$............... 0.5 to 1.0 gm.
Or KNO_3................ 0.5 to 1.0 gm.
Phenol...................... 10 gm.

Dissolve the ingredients, adjust the pH to 7.0, and sterilize at 121° C. for 20 minutes.

Serial transfers of the organisms must be achieved before growth in this medium is recorded as positive.

NOTE: The above medium yields a precipitate that is not desirable when turbidity is used as an index of growth. An equally satisfactory medium, which is free of precipitate, is described under Pope-Skerman Mineral Salts Media for the Cultivation of Autotrophs and Nonexacting Heterotrophs.

Reproduced by permission from P. H. Gray and H. G. Thornton, Zentr. Bakteriol. Parasitenk., Abt. II, *73*, 1928, 74.

Alkylamine Media for the Identification of *Protaminobacter*

The original medium employed by den Dooren de Jong is prepared as follows:

$MgCl_2$........................ 2.0 gm.
K_2HPO_4...................... 10.0 gm.
Tap water.................... 1000 ml.
Washed agar.................... 14 gm.

Dissolve the ingredients, filter, and adjust the pH to 7.0. Distribute in 20-ml. quantities and sterilize at 121° C. for 20 minutes.

Prepare a 5 per cent solution of the alkylamine. Neutralize with HCl. (Either monoethylamine or dimethylamine satisfies the requirements of the described species.*) Sterilize by filtration and store in

* If the hydrochlorides of the alkylamines are used, they do not need neutralization.

sterile screw-capped bottles or glass ampoules.

To prepare the medium, melt the agar base and cool to 50° C. Add 1 ml. of the alkylamine solution to 20 ml. of the agar base and pour.

NOTE: Since the majority of agars available commercially contain quantities of metabolizable materials, growth of organisms on the above medium is not an indication of use of the alkylamine. A liquid medium prepared with glass-distilled water should be employed as a final check on the ability of the organism to grow with the use of the alkylamine as sole carbon and nitrogen source.

A liquid medium prepared by the above formula is turbid. An equally satisfactory growth medium, which is free of precipitate, is described under Pope-Skerman Mineral Salts Media for the Cultivation of Autotrophs and Nonexacting Heterotrophs.

Reproduced by permission from den Dooren de Jong, Zentr. Bakteriol. Parasitenk., Abt. II, *71*, 1927, 218.

Koser's Citrate Medium

Organisms capable of utilizing citrate as the sole source of carbon will grow in the following medium:

NaCl.......................... 5 gm.
$MgSO_4 \cdot 7\ H_2O$............... 0.2 gm.
$NH_4H_2PO_4$..................... 1 gm.
Sodium citrate................. 2 gm.
K_2HPO_4...................... 1 gm.
Distilled water............... 1000 ml.

Dissolve the salts in the water, adjust the pH to between 6.7 and 6.9. Filter, dispense, and sterilize at 121° C. for 15 minutes.

Inoculate from an agar culture and make at least three serial transfers before registering a definite positive result.

Reference: S. A. Koser, J. Bacteriol., *9*, 1924, 59.

Christensen's Citrate Agar (1949)

Test for citrate utilization in the presence of organic nitrogen.

Sodium citrate................ 3 gm.
Glucose...................... 0.2 gm.
Yeast extract................. 0.5 gm.
Cysteine monohydrochloride..... 0.1 gm.
Ferric ammonium citrate........ 0.4 gm.
Monopotassium phosphate........ 1 gm.
Sodium chloride................ 5 gm.
Sodium thiosulfate............. 0.08 gm.
Phenol red.................... 0.012 gm.
Agar.......................... 15 gm.
Distilled water................ 1000 ml.

Tube and sterilize at 121° C. for 15 minutes and slant (1-inch butt, 1.5-inch slant).

The ferric ammonium citrate and sodium thiosulfate may be omitted from the formula, if desired, inasmuch as they do not affect the value of the medium as an indicator for citrate utilization.

Inoculation: Inoculate the medium over the entire surface of the slant.

Incubation: 37° C. for 7 days. Positive reactions are indicated by alkalinization of the medium and development of a red color, particularly on the slant of the agar. This medium is of particular value in the differentiation of shigellae and anaerogenic, nonmotile *Escherichia coli* biotypes (Edwards, Fife, and Ewing, 1956).

Reference: W. H. Ewing, Enterobacteriaceae, Biochemical Methods for Group Differentiation, U. S. Department of Health, Education and Welfare, Public Health Service Publication No. 734, 1962.

Ammonium Salts Citrate Medium

Test for the utilization of sodium citrate and ammonium salts.

Sodium chloride................ 5 gm.
Magnesium sulfate............. 0.2 gm.
Ammonium dihydrogen phosphate.. 1 gm.
Dipotassium phosphate........... 1 gm.
Sodium citrate................... 2 gm.
Agar (washed vigorously for 3 days) 20 gm.
Water........................ 1000 ml.

Add 40 ml. of 1:500 bromthymol blue indicator solution. Sterilize at 121° C. 15 minutes and slant so as to obtain a 1-inch butt and a 1.5-inch slant.

Inoculation: Prepare a saline suspension from a young agar slant culture and inoculate the slant of the medium with a straight wire from the saline suspension. If desired, the butt of the medium may be stabbed.

Incubation: 37° C. for 4 days. If equivocal results are obtained, as sometimes happens with members of the Providence group, for example, the test should be repeated and incubated at room temperature for 7 days. The above-mentioned medium is available from several commercial sources under the name of Simmons' citrate agar. These preparations are quite satisfactory.

Author's note: Citrate-utilizing organisms release the sodium ion, rendering the medium alkaline. It turns a deep blue.

Caution: Take care that plates are not incubated in a sealed atmosphere where other organisms are releasing ammonia from other media.

Reference: W. H. Ewing, Enterobacteriaceae, Biochemical Methods for Group Differentiation, U. S. Department of Health, Education and Welfare, Public Health Service Publication No. 734, 1962.

Sodium Malonate Broth (Leifson, 1933, Modified)

Test for utilization of malonate.

Yeast extract.................... 1 gm.
Ammonium sulfate............... 2 gm.
Dipotassium phosphate.......... 0.6 gm.
Monopotassium phosphate....... 0.4 gm.
Sodium chloride................. 2 gm.
Sodium malonate............... 3 gm.
Glucose...................... 0.25 gm.
Bromthymol blue............. 0.025 gm.
Distilled water................ 1000 ml.

Sterilize at 121° C. for 15 minutes.

Inoculation: Inoculate from a young agar slant or broth culture. (A 3-mm. loopful of broth culture is preferred.)

Incubation: 37° C. for 48 hours. Positive results are indicated by a change in the color of the indicator from green to Prussian blue. Leifson's malonate broth, modified by the addition of a small amount of yeast extract and glucose, is of considerable value in the differentiation of salmonellae and members of the Arizona group.

Reference: W. H. Ewing, Enterobacteriaceae, Biochemical Methods for Group Differentiation, U. S. Department of Health, Education and Welfare, Public Health Service Publication No. 734, 1962.

Cellulose Strip-Peptone Medium

Peptone	5.0 gm.
NaCl	5.0 gm.
Tap water	1000 ml.

Steam until dissolved. Adjust the pH to 7.4 and filter if necessary. Dispense in 5-ml. amounts in 150- by 13-mm. tubes.

In each tube place a 70- by 10-mm. strip of Whatman No. 1 filter paper. Sterilize at 121° C. for 15 minutes.

Preparation of Precipitated Cellulose

Carefully add 100 ml. of concentrated sulfuric acid to 60 ml. of water in a flask cooled by running water, with care to direct the neck of the flask away from the body. Cool to 70° C. and to a 5-ml. sample add 0.3 gm. of Whatman No. 1 filter paper. If the paper dissolves rapidly and subsequently chars, proceed as follows (if the paper does not dissolve prepare a slightly more concentrated acid):

Place a series of ten 150- by 18-mm. tubes in a rack in a water bath at 70° C. Into these tubes pipette 0.2, 0.4, 0.6, 0.8, 1.0, 1.2, 1.4, 1.6, 1.8, and 2.0 ml. of water, respectively. To each add 10 ml. of the diluted sulfuric acid and mix. To each tube add 0.3 gm. of filter paper (torn into small pieces). In the higher acid concentrations the paper usually dissolves and chars. In the lower concentrations it will disintegrate but may not char. When dispersed in water this disintegrated paper yields a mass of fine fibers, which scintillate in reflected light and settle out rapidly on standing. These fibers are too coarse for a good cellulose medium. At an intermediate acid concentration the paper is reduced to a gelatinous mass, which slowly turns brown if allowed to stand. If this is rapidly diluted

a mass of finely divided particles is produced, which remains suspended for some period and does not scintillate in reflected light. This material is suitable for the preparation of precipitated cellulose agar.

Note the degree of dilution of the acid and dilute the bulk accordingly. Hold at 70° C. and add 3 gm. of Whatman No. 1 filter paper (torn in small pieces) to each 100 ml. of acid. Rotate the flask until slight yellowing (charring) is evident and then empty the contents rapidly into a 5-L. flask containing 2000 ml. of tap water. The resulting opalescent suspension should remain dispersed for some time and show no evidence of scintillation in reflected light. Allow this to stand until the cellulose settles and siphon off the supernatant. Centrifuge the deposit and resuspend in water to wash it free of acid. Repeat the process several times until 10 ml. of the suspension will no longer produce an acid reaction after the addition of 1 ml. of 0.1 N NaOH.

Titrate a sample with 0.1 N NaOH and then neutralize the bulk.

Centrifuge the cellulose and then resuspend in 20 ml. of water. Progressively dilute a 1-ml. sample until 5 ml. of the diluted sample dispensed in a 10-cm. Petri dish still give a perceptible opalescence. Note the degree of dilution and dilute the bulk of the cellulose by *half* this amount. (It is further diluted in the preparation of the medium.)

Sterilize at 121° C. for 20 minutes.

Reference: Author's recommendation.

Alternative Method for the Preparation of Cellulose for Cellulose Agar

Reflux 2 gm. of high-grade filter paper with 300 ml. of 2.5 N HCl at 105° C. for 15 minutes. This treatment unhinges chemically all available primary linkages in the fibrous cellulose. Immediately wash the cellulose free of acid on a Buchner filter, first with water, then with 5 per cent (v/v) ammonium hydroxide, and finally with distilled water. Resuspend to 5 per cent solids and place in a Waring Blendor and blend till the pulp is reduced to a thick creamy consistency (approximately 10 hours). Then dilute 1:5 with water and continue the blending for a further 8 to 10 hours. This product will normally be suitable for use without further dilution or concentration.

The finely divided crystalline cellulose flocks on standing but can be readily redispersed. When the cellulose suspension has been mixed with the agar, cool the mixture to 50° C. in a water bath and redisperse the cellulose immediately before pouring the plates. Prior cooling helps to prevent settling of the cellulose while the agar is solidifying.

Reference: Adapted from O. A. Battista, American Scientist, *53*, 1965, 151.

Oxidation of Cellulose to Oxycellulose

This test was used by Winogradsky for differentiation of the genera *Cellfalcicula* and *Cellvibrio*. He claimed that these organisms grow on cellulose without the production of reducing substances and rarely with the production of any visible change in the paper other than the production of a pigmented and sometimes mucoid growth. No clearing of the medium occurs when the organisms are cultured on precipitated cellulose (hydrocellulose) agar.

Winogradsky (Ann. inst. Pasteur, *43*, 1929, 549) based his claim for the "oxidation of cellulose to oxycellulose" on the following: (a) increased solubility of the cellulose when heated in 2 per cent NaOH at 120° C. for 30 minutes; (b) production of a yellow to brown color when the paper was heated to 100° C. in 1 per cent NaOH; and (c) increased intensity of staining with basic dyes, such as methylene blue. These properties are similar to those given by chemically produced oxycellulose of the acidic type.

Although the utilization of cellulose by these organisms is not questioned, Fåhraeus (1947) has discussed the validity of the above reactions as evidence of the production of "oxycellulose" and claims that the materials giving the above reactions are polysaccharides synthesized by the developing organisms. He quotes the following observations of Norman and Bartholomew (Proc. Soil Sci. Soc. Am., *5*, 1940, 242):

"(a) The mucilage is closely associated with the bacterial cells.

"(b) Any oxidative process would give rise not only to short-chain soluble fragments but also to long-chain insoluble material which should be easily detectable. On analysis it was, however, found that the residual cellulose was not more oxidized than initially.

"(c) The presence of pentose units in an oxycellulose from cotton is impossible, but the furfural yield in the determinations exceeded that which would be expected on the basis of uronic units present, and implies that some pentose groups must be involved.

"(d) Oxycellulose could only be formed by an extra-cellular oxidative process, which would be unique, if the cell was intact, and no energy would be derived by the cell until chain-splitting had taken place to such an extent that the fragments were water-soluble and therefore could pass into the cell."

Fåhraeus further states: "It is true that some of the above reasons are open to criticism,* but on the whole they seem to be sufficient for rejecting Winogradksy's theory of oxidative decomposition."

For utilization of cellulose the following method of Fåhraeus is suggested:

Filter the liquid culture medium through a Jena 1G3 sintered glass crucible under suction, retaining the cellulose. Fill the crucible with 12 per cent HCl and stir. Suck off the liquid.

Treat the cellulose in the same manner with the following in the sequence indicated: (a) water, (b) 5 per cent ammonia, (c) water, (d) alcohol (twice), and (e) ether.

---

* "The authors [Norman and Bartholomew] do not accept an oxidative decomposition because intermediates are not to be found; but no hydrolysis products had been established either."

After treatment with ether, suck the cellulose dry.

Dry at 50° C. for 1 hour and at 103° C. for 1 hour. Allow to cool in a desiccator over granulated $CaCl_2$ or silica gel and weigh.

Reference: G. Fåhraeus, Symbolae Botan. Upsalienses, *9*, 1947, 1.

Bacteriochlorophyll

Examine a dense suspension of the organisms with a calibrated hand spectroscope. Photosynthetic organisms containing bacteriochlorophyll show an absorption band at 590 mμ. This band is absent from both the cells and the extract after extraction with 85 per cent ethyl alcohol, but a second band appears in the extract at 774 mμ, as indicated by a spectrophotometer.

See also p. *96*.

Chlorobium Chlorophyll

The green cells of *Chlorobium* lack the absorption bands of plant chlorophyll at 635 to 650 mμ and of bacteriochlorophyll at 590 mμ. Examination with a spectrophotometer reveals an absorption peak at approximately 750 mμ.

Carotenoid Pigments

These pigments are yellow, orange, red, or brown. They are insoluble in water and alcohol but dissolve in chloroform, ether, or other fat solvents. They give a deep-blue color with concentrated sulfuric acid or antimony trichloride.

Extract a heavy suspension of the cells with the following solution to remove chlorophyll pigments (if any):

Saturated KOH................. 20 ml.
Ethanol, 40%.................. 40 ml.
Tap water..................... 60 ml.

Wash the extracted cells thoroughly with water, centrifuge, and transfer some of the packed cells to a slide. Blot dry and add 1 drop of sulfuric acid. If carotenoids are present the cells will turn blue.

Reproduced with the permission of Franckh'schen Verlagshandlung, Stuttgart, from the journal Mikrokosmos, *34*, 1941, 121.

NOTE: In most instances a blue color reaction can be obtained by application of the sulfuric acid directly to the dense mass of unextracted cells. Red organisms that contain prodigiosin but no carotenoids do not turn blue.

Extraction and Identification of Prodigiosin in the Genus *Serratia*

Direct examination of a heavy suspension of *Serratia* with a hand spectroscope will reveal two absorption bands at 490 to 510 mμ and 540 to 560 mμ.

Wash the growth from three heavily inoculated plates with approximately 75 ml. of sterile saline. Add 7.5 gm. of NaOH pellets slowly with continuous shaking. The color changes from pink to orange. After 2 hours add 96 per cent alcohol and light petroleum (b.p. 40° to 60° C.) in amounts approximately equal to the volume of the solution (75 ml. of each). Shake the mixture thoroughly and draw off the lower alcohol-saline layer and re-extract it with further small quantities of petroleum ether until no more color is removed.

Mix the petroleum fractions, and extract the pigment with repeated additions of 85 per cent v/v ethyl alcohol containing 1 per cent glacial acetic acid. Upon transfer to the alcohol, the pink color returns.

Dilute the alcoholic extract with an equal amount of distilled water and add aqueous 2 N NaOH until the color changes to orange.

Extract repeatedly, by gentle shaking, with chloroform and then evaporate the latter to dryness *in vacuo* with slight warming. Dissolve the residue in 5 ml. of 85 per cent ethyl alcohol and determine the absorption in a spectrophotometer. In this acid solution an absorption peak is produced at approximately 540 mμ.

No similar peak is obtained after identical extraction methods are applied to photosynthetic bacteria or bacteria containing carotenoid pigments (author's note). Prodigiosin does not give a blue color with sulfuric acid.

Reproduced by permission from R. Hubbard and C. Rimington, Biochem. J., *46*, 1950, 220.

Isolation and Growth of *Chromatium*

MEDIUM FOR ISOLATION

The complete medium used for this purpose cannot be subjected to autoclave temperatures because of the incompatibility of some of the constituents at high temperatures. A basal medium is prepared to which sterile solutions of other substances are added after the medium has cooled.

The solution of sodium sulfide acts both as a source of the HS^- and as a deoxygenating agent. Unless it is kept in a tightly sealed container in the absence of oxygen it should always be prepared before use.

Basal Medium

NH_4Cl	0.1 gm.
KH_2PO_4	0.1 gm.
$MgCl_2$	0.05 gm.
NaCl (for marine species)	30.0 gm.
Agar	20.0 gm.
Tap water	925.0 ml.

Dissolve the mineral salts in the tap water; add the agar and then heat to 121° C. for 15 minutes to dissolve the agar. Distribute in the required quantities in test tubes or screw-capped bottles. Sterilize at 121° C. for 15 minutes. For a *liquid medium* omit the agar.

Sterile Sodium Bicarbonate

$NaHCO_3$	5 gm.
H_2O	100 ml.

Sterilize at 121° C. for 15 minutes.

Sterile Sodium Sulfide

$Na_2S \cdot 9 H_2O$	5 gm.
H_2O	100 ml.

Sterilize at 121° C. for 15 minutes.

For use of the *complete medium* melt the required number of tubes of basal medium and cool to 45° C. To each 10-ml. amount of basal medium add aseptically 0.4 ml. of $NaHCO_3$ solution and 0.2 ml. of $Na_2S \cdot 9$ H_2O solution.

ISOLATION

To obtain crude cultures of *Chromatium* species, place a layer of marine mud mixed with decaying algae in the base of a wide-mouthed glass jar, cover with sea water, and expose to light. The reddish growth that appears on the wall of the container nearest the light source usually contains *Chromatium*. Its growth is dependent on the reduction of sulfate in the mud and the consequent liberation of H_2S.

Pure Cultures

Two procedures may be adopted:

1. Deep Tube Isolation: This method has been used successfully by van Niel and others.

Emulsify a small amount of the reddish growth (checked microscopically for the morphological type) in a quantity of complete sterile liquid medium.

Prepare a series of melted deeps of the complete medium and hold at 45° C. Make serial dilutions of the *Chromatium* suspension in these tubes and then allow the tubes to set.

Cover each tube to a depth of 2 cm. with a 50:50 mixture of paraffin wax and liquid paraffin sterilized by heating to 160° C. for 1 hour.

Incubate at 25° to 28° C. with exposure to light. Well-isolated reddish colonies appear in the higher dilutions after a period of 3 to 7 days. Select a suitable tube, sterilize the outer surface, cut the glass, remove the tube, and then aseptically dissect out the colony in a sterile Petri dish. Emulsify the colony in sterile complete medium and repeat the process of serial dilutions to ensure purity.

Pure cultures can be maintained through subculture in these agar deeps at 2-month intervals.

2. Agar Streak Isolation: This technique is that normally employed for surface inoculation in Petri dish cultures. It has been employed quite successfully in this laboratory. Incubate the inoculated Petri dish anaerobically. Expose the plate to light and to 25° to 28° C. for 4 to 7 days. Pick off typical colonies, check for purity by replating, and maintain in deeps as in *1*.

Reference: These directions were taken from the formulary of the Hopkins Marine Station, Pacific Grove, California, where they were attributed to Helge Larsen.

Isolation and Growth of *Rhodospirillum*

ENRICHMENT MEDIUM

NH$_4$Cl	1.0 gm.
K$_2$HPO$_4$	0.5 gm.
MgCl$_2$	0.2 gm.
NaCl	2.0 gm.
Yeast extract	0.1 gm.
H$_2$O	900 ml.

Dissolve and sterilize at 121° C. for 20 minutes.

Prepare separately and sterilize by filtration: (*a*) 5.0 gm. of NaHCO$_3$ and 50.0 ml. of H$_2$O, (*b*) ethyl or amyl alcohol or 4 per cent alanine, and (*c*) 0.1 N H$_3$PO$_4$.

Add the sterile sodium bicarbonate solution and 1.5 to 2.0 gm. of either sterile ethyl or amyl alcohol *or* 50 ml. of 4 per cent alanine. Adjust the pH to 7 with sterile 0.1 N H$_3$PO$_4$.

Enrichment: The most suitable inoculum is mud in which there is a large amount of organic matter undergoing decomposition in a position exposed to light.

Place a layer of the inoculum in a 50-ml. ground-glass-stoppered bottle, fill the bottle to capacity with the medium, and insert the stopper to exclude air. Incubate in an illuminated cabinet at 30° C. with the vessels located approximately 4 inches from a 25-watt tungsten filament lamp.

A reddish growth usually appears in 3 days in the solution and the mud on the side of the vessel exposed to light. Of the three substrates suggested, ethyl alcohol and alanine are the most suitable.

Harvest 1 ml. of this enriched material, particularly from the reddish area, into a second bottle of the medium. Development of the red *Rhodospirillum* will usually occur in 2 days.

ISOLATION MEDIUM

In the enrichment medium, anaerobic conditions are rapidly established by contaminating organisms. For pure cultures, deoxygenation is effected by the addition of Na$_2$S·9 H$_2$O. To improve growth, the concentration of yeast extract is increased from 0.01 to 0.2 per cent. To solidify the medium, 1.5 to 2.0 per cent agar is added.

Prepare the medium as for the enrichment but substitute 2.0 gm. of yeast extract for the 0.1 gm. in the original medium and reduce the amount of sodium bicarbonate from 5.0 gm. to 2.0.

Prepare separately a solution containing 1.0 gm. of Na$_2$S·9 H$_2$O in 10 ml. of water and sterilize at 121° C. for 15 minutes. Add this solution to the medium before finally adjusting the pH. Dispense as desired.

Isolation: The organisms may be isolated by the shake tube method or by pour plating. In the former, anaerobic conditions will be rapidly established in the agar deeps as a result of removal of oxygen by the sodium sulfide.

If pour plates are used, the anaerobic method involving pyrogallic acid and sodium carbonate is recommended.

Reproduced by permission from C. B. van Niel, Bacteriol. Revs., *8*, 1944, 1.

Isolation and Growth of *Rhodomicrobium*

To suppress contaminants, the medium used for the isolation of *Rhodomicrobium* is more restrictive than that used for its subsequent maintenance.

MAINTENANCE MEDIUM

Yeast Extract-Mineral Salts Base

Yeast extract	2.0 gm.
NaCl	2.0 gm.

(NH₄)₂SO₄.................... 1.0 gm.

K₂HPO₄...................... 0.5 gm.

MgSO₄·7 H₂O................ 0.1 gm.

Water....................... 700 ml.

Agar (if required).............. 15 gm.

Dissolve the ingredients by steaming, filter if necessary, and sterilize at 121° C. for 15 minutes.

Sterile Sodium Bicarbonate

Dissolve 5 gm. of NaHCO₃ in 100 ml. of H₂O and sterilize at 121° C. for 15 minutes.

Sterile Sodium Sulfide

Dissolve 0.1 gm. of Na₂S·9 H₂O in 100 ml. of water and sterilize at 121° C. for 15 minutes. This must be prepared immediately before use.

Sterile Ethyl Alcohol

Add 2.0 ml. of ethyl alcohol to 100 ml. of water and sterilize by Seitz filtration.

Sterile 5 Per Cent H₃PO₄

Prepare the solution and sterilize at 121° C. for 15 minutes.

Melt the yeast extract agar base and cool to 50° C. Warm the other solutions to 50° C. and add to the agar. Adjust the pH to between 6.8 and 7.2 with sterile 5 per cent H₃PO₄, with all aseptic precautions observed. Dispense aseptically.

ISOLATION MEDIUM

Prepare a medium similar to the maintenance medium, but omit the yeast extract and agar. Dispense in glass-stoppered bottles and inoculate with mud. Completely fill the bottles to exclude air. Incubate under continuous illumination from 25-watt tungsten filament lamps at 25° to 30° C.

When the reddish pigmented growth is apparent, examine microscopically for *Rhodomicrobium*. The medium is not specific and permits the development of other photosynthetic organisms. *Rhodomicrobium*, if present, tends to predominate after 7 days of incubation.

To isolate pure cultures, use the maintenance medium dispensed as deeps in soda glass tubes and follow the shake tube procedure outlined for *Chromatium*.

Selection of colonies of *Rhodomicrobium* is facilitated by the deep-red color and characteristic convoluted surface of the colonies.

Reproduced by permission from E. Duchow and H. C. Douglas, J. Bacteriol., *58*, 1949, 409, and from R. G. E. Murray and H. C. Douglas, J. Bacteriol., *59*, 1950, 157.

Isolation and Growth of *Rhodopseudomonas*

Medium for Enrichment: Use media and techniques identical to those recommended for *Rhodospirillum*. Ethyl alcohol is the recommended substrate.

Medium for Isolation: Because most species of *Rhodopseudomonas* can be cultured aerobically in the dark or anaerobically with exposure to light, two alternatives are available for final isolation.

Isolate anaerobically in the same manner as species of *Rhodospirillum* or culture aerobically on the following medium.

Difco peptone................. 10 gm.

Difco yeast extract............. 5 gm.

NaCl......................... 5 gm.

H₂O......................... 1000 ml.

Agar......................... 15 gm.

Dissolve at 121° C. for 15 minutes, clarify, and adjust the pH to 7.0.

Sterilize at 121° C. for 15 minutes.

Check red colonies harvested from this medium for their ability to grow anaerobically with exposure to light.

Reproduced by permission from C. B. van Niel, Bacteriol. Revs., *8*, 1944, 1.

Isolation and Growth of *Chlorobium*

This organism is a photosynthetic, strictly anaerobic green bacterium containing *Chlorobium* chlorophyll, which has its absorption band at approximately 750 mμ (in the invisible infrared region). It oxidizes sulfide with deposition of sulfur outside the cell. It occurs in fresh water and marine muds.

PREPARATION OF ENRICHMENT CULTURES

Liquid Medium for Enrichment

Since the conditions of enrichment are highly selective, prepare the following liquid medium and use without sterilization.

NH_4Cl............................	1.0 gm.
KH_2PO_4.........................	1.0 gm.
$MgCl_2$............................	0.5 gm.
$NaHCO$............................	2.0 gm.
$Na_2S \cdot 9 H_2O$.................	1.0 gm.
$NaCl$..10 to 30 gm. depending on habitat	
$FeCl_3 \cdot 6 H_2O$................	0.0005 gm.
Tap water.....................	1000 ml.

Adjust the pH to 7.3 with phosphoric acid.

NOTE: Prepare this medium just before use. Do not attempt to store it, inasmuch as it is very unstable.

Select mud from a locality where there is free exposure to light and active decomposition of organic matter with liberation of H_2S. Place a layer 0.5 to 1.0 cm. deep in the bottom of 50-ml. wide-mouthed ground-glass-stoppered bottles, and fill the bottles to capacity with the liquid enrichment medium. Insert the stoppers to exclude air and incubate at 25° to 30° C. with the bottles placed approximately 4 inches from 25-watt tungsten filament lamps.

Green bacteria will usually appear in 3 to 7 days. If there is an overgrowth of red or purple bacteria, different sources of raw material should be tested.

Even in cultures in which green bacteria appear, the red and purple organisms will subsequently develop. Do not delay isolation unnecessarily.

PURE CULTURE ISOLATION

Chlorobium Agar

NH_4Cl............................	1.0 gm.
KH_2PO_4.........................	1.0 gm.

$MgCl_2$.........................	0.5 gm.
$NaCl$..0 to 30 gm. depending on source of inoculum	
Agar....................	10 to 15 gm.
Tap water....................	700 ml.

Autoclave to dissolve. If the agar is not to be used immediately, sterilize at 121° C. for 15 minutes.

Prepare the following solutions immediately before use and sterilize at 121° C. for 15 minutes: (*a*) $NaHCO_3$, 2gm.:H_2O, 100 ml.; (*b*) $Na_2S \cdot 9 H_2O$, 1 gm.:H_2O, 100 ml.; (*c*) $FeCl_3 \cdot 6 H_2O$, 5 mg.:H_2O, 100 ml.; and (*d*) N H_3PO_4 .

For use, melt the agar and cool to 45° C. in a water bath.

Warm solutions *a*, *b*, and *c* to 45° C., add aseptically to the agar, and mix well.

Adjust the pH to 7.3 with sterile phosphoric acid.

Distribute the medium aseptically in 10-ml. amounts in sterile 150- by 16-mm. soda glass tubes held in the water bath at 45° C.

Make the isolation by the shake tube method (see methods of isolation for *Chromatium*).

Reproduced by permission from H. Larsen, Kgl. Norske Videnskab. Selskabs, Skrifter, 1953; and from H. Larsen, C. S. Yocum, and C. B. van Niel, J. Gen. Physiol., *36*, 1952, 161.

The Determination of Thiosulfate, Sulfate, Sulfite, Sulfide, Sulfur, Polythionate, and Dithionate

Reference: J. L. Mangan, N. Z. J. Sci. Tech., Sect. B, *30*, 1949, 323.

The following pattern of analysis is based mainly on procedures developed by Mangan and, with his and the publisher's permission, is reproduced almost *in toto*. The methods for elemental sulfur are derived from the sources indicated.

The initial determination of pH is important inasmuch as it gives an indication of the nature of the organism and the end products produced.

The insoluble elemental sulfur in the medium and the bulk of the cystine are removed by centrifugation or filtration and determined separately.

All inorganic sulfur compounds other than S^0 are determined by Mangan's procedures, about which he comments as follows:

"The method described below uses only one sample of the solution, and upon this can be carried out estimations of dithionate, polythionate (includes tri-, tetra- and pentathionates), thiosulfate, sulfate, sulfite and sulfide. The method depends on the solubilities of the lead salts, and the above compounds can be separated into four groups.

"Group I consists of dithionate and the higher polythionates since their lead salts are freely soluble in water and aqueous alcohol.

"Group II consists of lead sulfate and thiosulfate which, although slightly soluble in water, are quite insoluble in 65 per cent v/v alcohol-water.

"Group III consists of lead sulfite, which is insoluble in water and aqueous alcohol but soluble in sodium hydroxide solution.

"Group IV consists of lead sulfide which is insoluble in sodium hydroxide solution.

"Group II is separated from Groups III and IV by its preferential solubility in ammonium acetate solution, lead sulfate and thiosulfate being very soluble, while lead sulfite is only slightly soluble and lead sulfide insoluble.

"The groups thus separated are analysed for their components. In group I polythionate is determined in the presence of dithionate by its oxidation to sulfate under alkaline conditions. After determination of the sulfate formed, dithionate, which is quite stable to oxidation is hydrolyzed by the reaction

$$H_2S_2O_6 + H_2O \xrightarrow{\text{acid}} H_2SO_4 + H_2SO_3$$

and the sulfur dioxide determined by the Monier-Williams method* for sulfite. In

* "Official Methods of Analysis, Association of Official Agricultural Chemists, 7th ed., 1950, p. 471."

group II thiosulfate is determined by titration with iodine, and sulfate then determined by the barium chloride method. Sulfite in group III is estimated by iodine titration. Sulfide in group IV is oxidized to sulfur by excess standard iodine in acid solution, and the excess iodine remaining is determined by thiosulfate titration.

Procedure: (a) Determine the pH of the culture. (b) Set aside a representative sample for total sulfur determination. (c) Centrifuge the remainder at 5000 r.p.m. to remove visible solids. Decant, resuspend the residue in distilled water, and recentrifuge. Repeat the washing and then mix the original supernatant and washings and dilute to a defined volume.

The liquid and solid fractions are treated separately.

Use of the Liquid Fraction: Use one 10-ml. aliquot of the liquid to determine the inorganic sulfur compounds by Mangan's procedures. If the concentration of sulfite and sulfide prove to be negligible, a second aliquot may be used for a separate determination of the sulfate. A third aliquot may be used for the determination of dissolved cystine.

Use of the Solid Fraction: The insoluble cystine is extracted from the insoluble residue with dilute HCl and diluted to a defined volume for analysis.

The residue after acid extraction is dried *in vacuo;* sulfur is extracted with carbon tetrachloride and subsequently oxidized to sulfate, precipitated with barium, and weighed.

ANALYSIS OF THE INORGANIC SULFUR COMPOUNDS BY MANGAN'S METHODS

Reagents

Lead Acetate: Dissolve 20 gm. of pure lead acetate in 65 ml. of water with warming and make to a volume of 200 ml. with alcohol.

Ammonium Acetate: Dilute 286 ml. of glacial acetic acid with an equal volume of water and add 0.88 ammonia until the pH is approximately 6.0. Bromthymol blue can be used as an indicator, and ammonia is added until a green color is obtained. If excess ammonia is added, the excess may be boiled off. Make the solution to 1 L. It is approximately 5 M.

Benzidine Reagent: Use 1.6 gm. of benzidine to 20 ml. of N HCl and add 45 ml. of water. Warm the solution to dissolve the benzidine and make the volume to 200 ml. with alcohol.

Method

Pipette 10 ml. of the approximately neutral solution into a 50-ml. centrifuge tube and add 20 ml. of 95 per cent ethanol. Add 0.5 ml. of 10 per cent NaCl as a carrier and mix. Add excess lead acetate reagent; usually 8 ml. is enough. Centrifuge at 2000 r.p.m. for 15 minutes; check complete precipitation with a drop of lead acetate, and decant the supernatant into a 250-ml. beaker. Resuspend the precipitate uniformly in 65 per cent ethanol and recentrifuge. Combined supernatant and washings constitute Group I, containing di-, tri-, tetra-, and penta-thionates.

Suspend the insoluble lead salts in 8 ml. of ammonium acetate reagent. Dilute the mixture to 40 ml. with distilled water containing 5 per cent sucrose or glycerol to prevent oxidation of sulfite. Add 2 to 3 drops of isobutanol to prevent surface effects and spin down the solid material in a centrifuge. Commercial wetting agents should not be used, as they often interfere with the starch iodide end point and some also contain sulfate. Decant the supernatant into a 250-ml beaker and wash the solids with glycerol water. The ammonium acetate extract and washings make Group II, containing sulfate and thiosulfate.

Suspend the remaining solid material in 1.0 ml. of 10 per cent NaOH and dilute to 40 ml. with glycerol water. In the absence of sulfide, this is Group III, containing sulfite. When sulfide is present, centrifuge the tubes, decant the supernatant, and wash the residue with glycerol water and add to the supernatant to give Group III. The insoluble residue is Group IV.

Method for Group I

To remove excess lead, add bromthymol blue indicator, followed by a suspension of $NaHCO_3$ until the indicator changes to blue-green. Filter the lead carbonate precipitate with suction and wash it with 65 per cent ethanol, collecting filtrate and washings in a 250-ml. beaker. Add 0.5 gm. of pure sodium peroxide, and oxidize the higher polythionates to sulfate by heating at 80° C. on a water bath for 15 minutes. *Dithionate* is not affected by this treatment. To decompose the remaining peroxide, add 5 drops of 1 per cent cobaltous acetate and heat until all signs of peroxide decomposition cease. Place in an ice bath and cool to 5° C.; add concentrated HCl dropwise until just acid to bromphenol blue. The pH should be near 2.8, which gives the minimal solubility of benzidine sulfate. Slowly introduce benzidine reagent in 1-ml. aliquots at 2-minute intervals with stirring. Ten milliliters is usually enough for quantities of polythionate sulfur in the range of 0.25 to 1.75 mg. in about 70 ml. Leave in ice water for 15 minutes and filter through a prepared Gooch crucible. After washing with aqueous alcohol, suspend the benzidine sulfate and asbestos in 100 ml. of distilled water, and titrate near the boiling point with 0.02 N NaOH and the use of phenol red indicator. Near the end point boil for a few minutes before completing the titration.

ml. of 0.02 N NaOH $\times$ 0.32

$$= mg. \text{ of polythionate-S}$$

Dithionate decomposes under strong acid conditions as follows:

$$H_2S_2O_6 + H_2O \xrightarrow{HCl} H_2SO_4 + H_2SO_3$$

Make the filtrate and washings from the previous test alkaline with NaOH and distill off the alcohol. Wash the aqueous solution into a 500-ml. 3-necked flask equipped with a dropping funnel, an inlet for CO_2, and a reflux condenser fitted at the top with a down tube dipping into 3 per cent hydrogen peroxide. Bring the total volume to 200 ml. with water. Pass a stream of CO_2 to remove all air and bring the liquid to the boil. Introduce 35 ml. of HCl (specific gravity 1.17) through the dropping funnel without admitting air. Reflux for 1 hour. Then cut off water from the condenser. Just before steam enters the peroxide, disconnect the apparatus from the heat source. SO_2 arising from dithionate decomposition is driven over into the peroxide, where it is oxidized to sulfuric acid. A blank determination is required. Determine the sulfuric acid by titration with 0.02 N NaOH with the use of bromphenol blue as an indicator *or* precipitate as barium sulfate and weigh.

ml. 0.02 N NaOH $\times$ .321 $\times$ 2

$$= \text{mg. dithionate-S}$$

137.35 $\times$ 2 $\times$ gm. of $BaSO_4$

$$= \text{mg. of dithionate-S}$$

Method for Group II

Thiosulfate: The ammonium acetate extract has a pH of 6.0. Lead salts do not affect the titration of thiosulfate, but the pH is of importance.

Adjust the pH below 5.0 by adding 10 ml. of 20 per cent v/v HCl. Add starch indicator and titrate with 0.02 N iodine.

1.282 $\times$ ml. of 0.02 N I_2

$$= \text{mg. of thiosulfate-S}$$

Sulfate: This can be determined with sufficient accuracy in the presence of ammonium and lead salts. To the solution after titration of the thiosulfate, add 5 ml. of concentrated HCl, followed by an excess of 2.5 per cent $BaCl_2$ added by drops in the cold. Set aside for 1 hour. Then filter onto a weighed Gooch crucible, wash thoroughly with hot water, ignite at 600° C., and weigh.

If lead chloride should precipitate when the concentrated hydrochloric acid is added, dilute and warm to dissolve it. The precipitation of the barium sulfate must be carried out at room temperature.

Sulfate may also be determined directly on aliquots of medium free of sulfide and sulfite. Dilute 20 ml. to 100 ml. with water. Acidify with 0.5 ml. of concentrated HCl and treat with $BaCl_2$ in the cold to precipitate sulfate. Allow the sample to stand for 24 hours and filter through 9-cm. No. 40 Whatman paper. Wash with hot water, dry, and incinerate. When the ash is white, add 1 drop of concentrated H_2SO_4 and incinerate, driving off excess acid.

Method for Group III

Sulfite is determined on the alkaline extract. Dilute to 75 ml. with water containing sucrose or glycerol and add dilute HCl with stirring until acid to bromphenol blue. Add starch indicator and titrate with 0.02 N iodine.

$$0.321 \times \text{ml. of } I_2 = \text{mg. of sulfite-S}$$

Method for Group IV

Suspend the black precipitate of lead sulfide in a small amount of water and wash into a 250-ml. Erlenmeyer flask with a stopper. Add 10 to 15 ml. of 0.02 N iodine, followed by 10 ml. of 20 per cent v/v HCl. Close the flask and allow to stand for several minutes. Dilute to 100 ml. and back titrate with 0.02 N thiosulfate. A blank determination should be made.

$$0.321 \times \text{ml. of } I_2 = \text{mg. of sulfide-S}$$

Elemental Sulfur: Vacuum dry the residue remaining after acid extraction of the insoluble material in the culture to remove cystine. Place the dried residue in a thimble in the Soxhlet apparatus and extract at least 12 times with carbon tetrachloride. Separate the extract and evaporate to dryness. Heat it in an oven at 60° to 70° C. for 20 minutes, then cool to room temperature.

Working in a fume cupboard add 10 ml. of a saturated solution of bromine in carbon tetrachloride, cover, and allow to stand for 30 minutes with intermittent agitation.

Add 15 ml. of concentrated nitric acid and allow to stand for an additional 30 minutes with intermittent agitation. Evaporate on a hot plate to approximately 5 ml. Add 20 ml. of concentrated HCl and evaporate to approximately 5 ml. Add 50 ml. of distilled water, filter, and wash with 2 per cent HCl. Add 2 drops of bromthymol blue indicator (0.1 gm. of indicator dissolved in 16.0 ml. of 0.01 N NaOH and diluted to 250 ml.) and then ammonia until the solution turns blue. Add HCl 1 drop at a time until the solution is distinctly acid and then add 5 drops in excess. Dilute to 150 ml. and heat to boiling; add 10 per cent $BaCl_2 \cdot 2\ H_2O$ solution by drops until no more precipitate forms, and then add 50 per cent excess. Cover the beaker and digest on a steam bath for at least 1 hour. Cool and filter through an asbestos filter in a Gooch crucible that has been ignited at 500° C. and weighed. Wash thoroughly with hot water. Ignite in a muffle furnace at 500° C. for at least 20 minutes. Cool in a desiccator and weigh. The difference in weight is S as $BaSO_4$.

Reference: Methods of Analysis, A.O.A.C., 7th ed., 1950. Reproduced with a modification by permission from the Association of Official Agricultural Chemists. Note: The substitution of CCl_4 for CS_2 is made by the author and is *not* sanctioned by the Association of Official Agricultural Chemists.

Total Sulfur: Place the sample in a 200-ml. Kjeldahl flask fitted with a W-gooseneck condenser and glass beads. Into the goose neck, place 0.5 ml. of 10 per cent iodic anhydride and add enough water to fill the two bottom elbows. Into the flask place 0.5 ml. of 10 per cent iodic anhydride, followed by 2 to 3 ml. of a mixture of 2 parts of 66 per cent perchloric acid and 1 part of fuming nitric acid. Join the flask and condenser, and bring the flask to a gentle boil. Heat until the digestion liquid becomes colorless or only slightly yellow. Cool a little and then empty the condenser contents into the flask and flush with a little water. Heat again slowly until only a few milliliters remain. Add 25 ml. of water,

followed by 10 per cent hydrazine hydrate added by drops to reduce the iodic acid to iodide. Enough is added to dispel the yellow color that first appears. Neutralize to phenolphthalein, acidify slightly with HCl, heat, and treat with a slight excess of 5 per cent barium chloride to precipitate sulfate.

$$137.35 \times \text{gm. of } BaSO_4 = \text{mg. of sulfur}$$

Cystine: In a 25-ml. volumetric flask place a 5.0-ml. sample containing 0.2 to 1.0 mg. of *l*-cystine in dilute HCl. Add 3.0 ml. of 5 per cent NaOH from a burette and allow to stand for 15 minutes at room temperature with occasional swirling. Then add 2 ml. of sodium β-naphthoquinone-4-sulfonate (containing 3 mg. per ml. of the naphthoquinone reagent purified by recrystallization from 50 per cent alcohol) followed within 10 seconds by 8.0 ml. of 10 per cent Na_2SO_3 in 0.5 N NaOH. Allow color to develop for 45 minutes. Add 3.0 ml. of 5 N NaOH followed by 2.0 ml. of 2.0 per cent sodium hydrosulfite in 0.5 N NaOH, and adjust the volume to 25 ml. with water. Mix and read within 2 minutes in a Klett-Summerson colorimeter with a Wratten 58 filter. Compare with standard controls.

Reproduced by permission from M. X. Sullivan, Public Health Repts. U. S., *44*, 1929, 1421; and from F. A. Csonka, H. Lichtenstein, and C. A. Denton, J. Biol. Chem., *156*, 1944, 571.

Extraction and Crystallization of Elemental Sulfur from Organisms that Deposit Sulfur Internally

Immerse a clean slide in clarified agar; drain and remove the agar from one side. Place a small drop of a dense suspension of the culture on the agar and cover with a coverslip. Place a drop of water against one side of the coverslip and a drop of pyridine against the other. Set the slide up under the low or high power of the microscope.

Place a piece of filter paper on the slide against the water drop, so that the water is drawn away from the coverslip. The pyridine is thus drawn across the slide under the coverslip.

Sulfur granules will dissolve in the pyridine but should recrystallize extracellularly as rhombic or monoclinic crystals. The rapid recrystallization is thought to be due to the absorption of the water from the pyridine-water mixture by the agar so that the pyridine is left supersaturated with sulfur.

Reproduced by permission from V. B. D. Skerman, G. Dementjeva, and B. J. Carey, J. Bacteriol., *73*, 1957, 504.

The Production of Sulfide (H_2S)

Microbial production of sulfide results from the reduction of sulfate or the decomposition of organic sulfur compounds such as cystine, methionine, and glutathione. Since the nutritional requirements of organisms that are potentially capable of producing hydrogen sulfide are very broad, any one medium will not suit all types. The recommendations are for this reason directed towards the test for the sulfide rather than media used for the growth of the organism. Nevertheless, for taxonomic purposes, comparative reactions on specific media are desired, and suggestions have been made for consideration.

H_2S *per se* does not exist in a medium at pH 7.0. The sulfur is present predominantly as the ^-SH ion. The solubility of this will determine the extent to which H_2S will be liberated from the medium. This is important in the application of the lead acetate strip technique.

H_2S production does not occur when an adequate supply of oxygen is available for cell metabolism. Therefore conditions of incubation that permit a high degree of aeration should not be used.

Growth "aerobically" on the surface of an agar plate does not necessarily constitute aerobic conditions within the colony. On the contrary, the availability of oxygen to cells within a colony more than one cell deep is very poor. This permits the production of H_2S and the formation of black colonies on iron-containing media, *e.g.*, glucose-blood-cystine agar for *Pasteurella tularensis*.

MEDIA

1. Mineral Salts Media: The essential feature of any mineral salts medium is that it contains at least one of the salts in the form of a soluble sulfate in a concentration not less than 500 mg. per L. If an iron salt is present, the production of sulfide will result in the production of black iron sulfide.

If the concentration of iron is too small, it may be necessary to use the lead acetate paper method or to test the culture for sulfide by the methylene blue procedure.

2. Organic Media: Any organic liquid medium containing sufficient cystine may be used, but for comparative purposes the following media are recommended: (*a*) peptone water plus 0.01 per cent cystine and 0.05 per cent sodium sulfate; (*b*) ferric ammonium citrate agar; and (*c*) ferrous chloride gelatin.

In the two iron-containing media, production of sulfide is indicated by the production of black iron sulfide. Production of sulfide in the peptone medium may be detected by the lead acetate paper strip method or the methylene blue method.

THE LEAD-ACETATE PAPER METHOD

Cut filter paper into 50- by 10-mm. strips and immerse them in a 5 per cent solution of lead acetate. Dry in air. Sterilize in a suitable container at 121° C. for 15 minutes.

Following inoculation of the liquid medium, insert a strip of the sterilized paper between the plug and the glass with the lower end above the liquid level. Incubate.

If H_2S is liberated during the growth of the organism, the lower portion of the paper will turn black. If, after incubation, there has been no color change, remove the plug and add 0.5 ml. of 2 N HCl; replace the paper and plug without delay. The addition of the acid will liberate any dissolved sulfide, which will react with the lead to yield the black lead sulfide.

If heat is applied to assist the reaction, use a control tube of uninoculated medium to eliminate any possibility that the reaction is caused by decomposition of the medium.

THE METHYLENE BLUE METHOD

The test is based on the reaction in acid solution between p-amino-dimethyl aniline and sulfide in the presence of ferric chloride to form methylene blue. The test is extremely sensitive and 0.01 p.p.m. of sulfide may be detected. The color developed is proportional to the sulfide concentration.

Test

To the 5 ml. of the culture add 0.5 ml. of amine-sulfuric acid solution and 0.1 ml. of ferric chloride solution. Spin the tube to mix.

Results

A blue color is positive for H_2S, pink is negative for H_2S.

Reagents

Stock Amine-HCl Solution: The commercial p-amino-dimethyl aniline may be received as a mixture of crystal and liquid. Drain the crystals and press dry between filter papers. If the original material is entirely liquid, cool until it has partially solidified. If the dry crystals are dark, melt them in a closed vessel and again partially solidify by slow cooling. Seeding may be necessary to prevent excessive supercooling. Again dry the crystals. Add a known amount of the amine gradually to concentrated HCl in a beaker surrounded with ice. The final solution should contain 20 gm. of amine in 100 ml. of solution.

Amine-Sulfuric Acid Solution: Add 500 ml. of concentrated H_2SO_4 to 480 ml. of water and cool; add 20 ml. of amine-HCl solution.

Ferric Chloride Solution: Dissolve 45 gm. of $FeCl_3$ (*or* $FeCl_3 \cdot 6\ H_2O$, 75 gm.) in enough water to make 100 ml. of solution.

Reference: R. Pomeroy, Sewage Works

J., *8*, 1936, 572. Reproduced by permission of the Federation of Sewage and Industrial Wastes Association.

Peptone-Cystine-Sulfate Medium for Sulfide Production

Peptone...................... 10 gm.
Cystine...................... 0.1 gm.
Na_2SO_4...................... 0.5 gm.
Distilled water............... 1000 ml.

Dissolve the ingredients. Adjust the pH to 7.0 and filter if necessary. Dispense in 5-ml. amounts in 150- by 13-mm. tubes and sterilize at 121° C. for 15 minutes.

Reference: Author's recommendation.

Ferrous Chloride Gelatin for Sulfide Production and Gelatin Liquefaction

Liebig's meat extract........... 7.5 gm.
Peptone (Parke-Davis)......... 25.0 gm.
NaCl...................... 5.0 gm.
Tap water................... 1000 ml.
Gelatin...................... 120 gm.
10% $FeCl_2 \cdot 4\ H_2O$............... 5 ml.

Dissolve all ingredients except the ferrous chloride. Adjust the pH to 7.6 and filter if necessary. Sterilize at 110° C. for 25 minutes.

Immediately before use melt the medium and add the required amount of sterile ferrous chloride solution. Dispense aseptically in 150- by 13-mm. tubes and cool promptly. Seal the tubes with sterile stoppers.

Inoculate by stabbing and incubate for 60 days at about 20° C.

Reproduced by permission from F. Kauffmann, The Enterobacteriaceae, 2nd ed., Munksgaard, Copenhagen, 1954.

Ferric Ammonium Citrate Agar (for Sulfide Production)

Black colonies on ferric ammonium citrate agar indicate the production of hydrogen sulfide by the organism.

Peptone...................... 10.0 gm.
Yeast extract.................. 2.0 gm.
Sodium chloride............... 5.0 gm.

Ferric ammonium citrate........ 0.3 gm.
Agar........................ 14.0 gm.
Tap water.................. 1000 ml.
Dissolve by heating to 121° C. for 15 minutes. Adjust the pH to 7.0 and filter if necessary. Dispense in 5-ml. quantities in 150- by 13-mm. tubes. Sterilize at 120° C. for 15 minutes.

Inoculate the tubes by stabbing the medium with a wire. H_2S production is indicated by the production of black iron sulfide.

Reference: The origin of this medium is not known.

Hydrogen Sulfide Test

Triple sugar iron agar (a modification of Kligler's iron or of Krumweide's triple sugar agar).
Beef extract.................... 3 gm.
Yeast extract................... 3 gm.
Bacto-peptone................. 15 gm.
Proteose peptone (Difco).......... 5 gm.
Lactose....................... 10 gm.
Sucrose....................... 10 gm.
Glucose....................... 1 gm.
Ferrous sulfate................ 0.2 gm.
Sodium chloride................ 5 gm.
Sodium thiosulfate............. 0.3 gm.
Agar......................... 12 gm.
Phenol red................... 0.024 gm.
Distilled water............... 1000 ml.
Polypeptone (BBL) may be substituted for the Bacto-peptone and proteose peptone in the formula given above.

After sterilization at 121° C. for 15 minutes, slant the medium with a deep butt (1-inch butt, 1.5-inch slant).

Inoculation: Stab the butt of the medium and streak the slant.

Incubation: 37° C. Observe daily for 7 days for blackening caused by hydrogen sulfide production.

Reference: W. H. Ewing, Enterobacteriaceae, Biochemical Methods for Group Differentiation, U. S. Department of Health, Education and Welfare, Public Health Service Publication No. 734, 1962.

Peptone Water

Peptone....................... 10 gm.
NaCl.......................... 5 gm.
Tap water.................... 1000 ml.
Dissolve the ingredients and adjust the pH to 7.2. Filter if necessary. Dispense in 150- by 13-mm. tubes and sterilize at 121° C. for 15 minutes.

0.1 Per Cent Peptone Agar

Peptone....................... 1.0 gm.
Agar......................... 14 gm.
Tap water.................... 1000 ml.
Dissolve by heating to 121° C. for 15 minutes. Adjust the pH to 7.0 and filter. Sterilize at 121° C. for 15 minutes.

Peptone Yeast Extract Acetate Agar

Bacto-yeast extract............. 5.0 gm.
Bacto-peptone................. 5.0 gm.
Sodium acetate................. 0.1 gm.
Agar.................... 15 to 20 gm.
Distilled water............... 1000 ml.
Dissolve by heating to 121° C. for 15 minutes. Adjust the pH to between 7.4 and 7.6 and filter if necessary. Sterilize at 121° C. for 15 minutes.

Reproduced by permission from E. G. Pringsheim and C. F. Robinow, J. Gen. Microbiol., *1*, 1947, 267.

Papain Digest Broth and Agar

The Concentrate: Mix 500 gm. of defatted and minced ox heart with 1000 ml. of distilled water and 1 gm. of papain. Digest in a water bath at 60° C. for 15 to 24 hours. Add 5 gm. of NaCl and steam for 90 minutes. Filter while very hot through paper pulp or clarifying pad (Ekwip DO).

Add 35 ml. of N NaOH and autoclave at 121° C. for 20 minutes. Filter while hot. Cool and adjust the pH to between 7.4 and 7.6 with N HCl. Distribute in 1-L. screwcap bottles for storage. Sterilize at 121° C. for 15 minutes.

Dilution of the digest for use is based on the amino-N content. A dilution containing

1 mg. of NH_2-nitrogen per 10 ml. is suitable for most purposes in place of broth and peptone waters. It is excellent for indole tests.

Estimation of Amino-Nitrogen: Place a 10-ml. sample in a 150-ml. conical flask. Add 30 to 40 ml. of distilled water and 0.5 ml. of phenolphthalein indicator. Titrate with 0.1 N NaOH from a burette until a pink end point is reached. Take the reading (R_1) and then add 10 ml. of neutral formalin to the mixture; titrate again to the same end point (R_2). If the NaOH is 0.1 N,

$$1.4 \ (R_2 - R_1) = \text{mg. of amino-N in 10 ml.}$$

For use: Dilute the concentrate to contain 4 mg. of amino-N per 10 ml. Adjust the pH to 7.0. Filter if necessary and distribute. This is papain digest broth.

To prepare papain digest agar, add 2.0 per cent agar to the broth before adjusting the pH. Autoclave at 115° C. for 20 minutes to dissolve the agar. Adjust the pH to 7.0, filter if necessary, and sterilize at 115°C for 20 minutes.

Meat Infusion Agar

Free a bullock's heart of fat and mince it. To every 500 gm. of mince add 1000 ml. of water, 10 gm. of peptone, and 5 gm. of NaCl. Steam for 60 to 90 minutes, stirring occasionally to break up the clump of meat that forms. Filter through cotton wool. Add N NaOH till the solution is just pink to phenolphthalein (usually 25 ml. for heart meat). Heat to 121° C. for 15 minutes and filter while very hot through a pleated filter paper. Readjust the pH to between 7.4 and 7.6. Add 14 to 20 gm. of agar per L., heat to dissolve, filter if necessary, and sterilize at 121° C. for 20 minutes.

Reproduced by permission from H. D. Wright, J. Pathol. Bacteriol., *37*, 1933, 257.

Media for the Detection of Lipolytic Organisms

BASAL MEDIUM

Peptone	15 gm.
Yeast extract	5 gm.
Sodium chloride	5 gm.

Agar	15 gm.
Water	1000 ml.

Dissolve the ingredients at 121° C. for 20 minutes. Adjust the pH to 7.5 and filter. Add the required amount of fat, mix well, and sterilize at 121° C. for 20 minutes.

PREPARATION OF NILE BLUE SULFATE

Prepare a saturated aqueous solution of Nile blue sulfate. Precipitate the oxazine base from it by the addition of N NaOH by drops until precipitation is complete. Filter and wash the precipitate with distilled water with the pH adjusted to 7.5. Dry and store for use.

Fats vary in the intensity with which they stain. Tripropionin, tributyrin, tricaproin, tricaprylin, triolein, beef tallow, butter fat, coconut oil, corn oil, cottonseed oil, lard, linseed oil, and olive oil all stain bright red.

Tricaprin, trilaurin, trimyristin, tripalmitin, and tristearin decrease in the intenity of staining with the increase in molecular weight.

PREPARATION OF THE DYED FAT

Prepare a saturated solution of the Nile blue sulfate oxazine base and mix 1 ml. with 10 ml. of the fat. If necessary, work in a heated water bath to liquefy the fat and maintain it in the liquid state throughout the washing process.

With tributyrin and similar triglycerides, which are liquid at room temperature, add double the quantity of ether to the fat-dye mixture in a separatory funnel; separate the red ether-soluble fat layer from the water layer and wash several times with water. Finally, separate the ether-fat layer and evaporate off the ether. (Keep away from flames!) Separate the fat from the residual water and sterilize at 121° C. Store in a refrigerator. For use add 1 ml. of the dyed fat to 10 ml. of the melted basal medium, mix well, and pour.

With fats that solidify at room temperature, wash the dyed fat with several changes of heated water and then disperse the fat in a melted 0.5 per cent neutral agar solution in the proportion of 10 ml. of fat to 90 ml. of agar.

Sterilize the mixture at 121° C. for 20 minutes, cool until solidified, and then shake vigorously until the fat is emulsified.

For use melt the fat emulsion and the culture medium, and add 1 ml. of the fat emulsion to 20 ml. of the basal medium. Mix well and allow to set.

NOTE: With Nile blue sulfate, the fat stains red and fatty acids stain blue. Hydrolysis of the fat will result in a blue halo around the colonies. In some cases the change in cloudiness of the medium may be more dramatic than the color change.

Similar methods can be employed with the basis of neutral red, methylene blue, and malachite green prepared as for Nile blue sulfate. In the respective cases, the neutral fats are orange-yellow, red, and olive green, and the fatty acids are red, blue, and blue-green. One of these may prove suitable if Nile blue is reduced.

Reproduced by permission from M. A. Collins and B. W. Hammer, J. Bacteriol., 27, 1934, 473; and from G. Knaysi, J. Bacteriol., 42, 1941, 587.

Alternative Methods for Fat Hydrolysis

Bulder's Method

This method is for use with liquid fats.

Inoculate the organism onto a suitable clear basal medium. Dry the surface of the plates slightly after inoculation and then spray the sterile oil over the surface with an atomizer that will give droplets in the vicinity of 30 μ in diameter. Incubate the plates and examine through the base with a microscope.

Fat droplets around fat hydrolyzing colonies become irregular in shape, granular, and opaque.

Reference: C. J. E. A. Bulder, Antonie van Leeuwenhoek, 21, 1955, 433.

Sierra's Method with Tween Detergents

Prepare a basal medium containing the following:
Difco Bacto-peptone.......... 10.0 gm.

NaCl........................ 5.0 gm.
CaCl$_2$·H$_2$O................... 0.1 gm.
Distilled water............... 1000 ml.

Adjust the final pH to 7.4. Sterilize the medium in 500-ml. amounts in flasks and cool to 40° to 50° C. Sterilize the Tweens (Tween 40, Tween 60, and Tween 80) separately by autoclaving at 120° C. for 20 minutes. Add 5 ml. of the selected Tween to a flask of agar and shake until well distributed. Pour the plates and inoculate and incubate in the usual way.

With organisms having lipolytic activity, an opaque halo develops around the colony. The halos are composed of calcium soaps with crystal forms characteristic of the Tweens used.

Reference: G. Sierra, Antonie van Leeuwenhoek, 23, 1957, 15.

Burdon's Method of Fat Staining

Technique: (a) Prepare the film, let it dry thoroughly in the air, and fix it by heat in the usual way. (Chemical fixation has no special advantages and may result in some loss of demonstrable lipid.) (b) Flood the entire slide with Sudan black solution (0.3 gm. of the powdered stain in 100 ml. of 70 per cent ethyl alcohol), and allow the slide to remain undisturbed at room temperature for 5 to 15 minutes. A staining period of less than 5 minutes will often suffice, but the intracellular lipid is colored somewhat more intensely when the staining is continued for 5 minutes or longer. No further staining apparently occurs after the solution precipitates and turns a greenish or brownish color, but no harm is done if the stain is allowed to dry completely over the film. (c) Drain off excess stain and blot the slide thoroughly dry. (d) Clear the slide with c.p. xylol by dipping it in and out of the solvent in a Coplin jar or by adding xylol from a dropping bottle. Blot the cleared slide dry. (e) Counterstain with safranine (0.5 per cent aqueous solution) for 5 to 10 seconds (for ordinary bacteria or fungi), or with dilute carbol fuchsin (Ziehl's carbol fuchsin diluted 1:10 with distilled water) for 1 to 3 minutes (for acid-fast organisms). Overstaining with the counterstain must be avoided. (*f*) Wash in water, blot, and dry the slide.

Examine the stained film with an oil immersion lens and critical illumination. Fat droplets appear blue-black or blue-grey. The rest of the cell is pink.

Reference: K. L. Burdon, J. Bacteriol., *52*, 1946, 665.

Production of Acid or Acid and Gas from Carbohydrates, Sugar, Alcohols, and Glucosides

NOTE: Production of acid may be the result of an oxidative process (*e.g.*, glucose to gluconic acid) or a fermentative one. The great majority of descriptions of biochemical properties in which acid production is mentioned refer to the latter type of reaction. The fermentative reactions occur simply because the medium is dispensed in such a manner that solution of O_2 from air by diffusion rarely meets the demand of the growing cell population. Although tubes are incubated aerobically, processes occurring in the tubes are essentially anaerobic.

The necessity to discriminate between the oxidative and the fermentative production of acid is becoming more apparent. The method suggested by Hugh and Leifson (p. *246*) has considerable practical merit.

In any method used for the detection of acid production, the observation is usually restricted to a visible change in the color of an acid-base indicator. If the test is performed in an inorganic basal medium, the degree of color change will be dependent on the buffer capacity of the medium. For this reason the concentration of buffering salts such as phosphates should be reduced to a minimum consistent with metabolic requirements.

In media that contain amino-nitrogen the liberation of ammonia may, in some cases, be sufficient to neutralize all the acid produced and yield a false negative reaction. If a negative reaction is thought to be due to this, retesting in a mineral salts medium (if growth occurs) or in a medium with a smaller amount of organic nitrogen,

as suggested by Hugh and Leifson, may yield a positive result.

In all the media recommended for acid production in these notes the substrates are sterilized in concentrated (usually 10 per cent) solutions and added aseptically after the sterilization of the medium. Sterilization by filtration is recommended, but, provided the solutions are prepared in distilled water and do not turn yellow, heat sterilization at 110° C. for 25 minutes is satisfactory for other than di- and polysaccharides, which may undergo a degree of hydrolysis. Heat sterilization of the substrate in the peptone base is widely practiced and, where positive results are obtained, is usually satisfactory. However, with some organisms, negative reactions in such media are meaningless, because the solution is rendered toxic by the heat treatment.

METHODS

Mineral Salts Base

The basal mineral salts medium described by Pope and Skerman (p. *213*) is recommended for this purpose. Add 2.0 ml. of a 1.6 per cent alcoholic solution of bromcresol purple per L. before final adjustment of the pH. Distribute in 5-ml. amounts in 150- by 13-mm. tubes, insert a Durham tube, and sterilize by heating to 121° C. for 20 minutes. Add the filtered substrates aseptically to a final concentration of 1.0 per cent.

Acid production is indicated by a change in the color of the indicator from purple to yellow. Gas, if produced, accumulates in the Durham tube.

Peptone Base

Prepare as above with the 1 per cent peptone water used in place of the mineral salts base.

Hiss's Serum Water Base

This base is employed for organisms that will not grow or that grow poorly in peptone water.

Peptone...................... 5.0 gm.

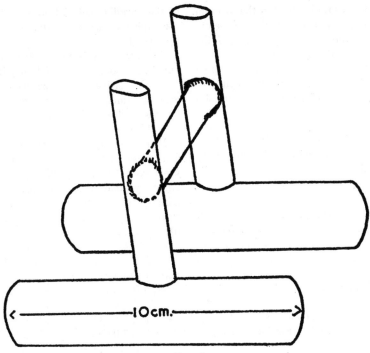

FIG. 6

K₂HPO₄...................... 1.0 gm.
Water...................... 1000 ml.

Dissolve by steaming for 15 minutes. Adjust the pH to 7.4. Add 8 ml. of Andrade's indicator (*vide infra*). Sterilize at 115° C. for 10 minutes. Cool to 50° C. and add 100 ml. of sterile ox serum. Add the substrates aseptically to a final concentration of 1 per cent and dispense aseptically in 5-ml. amounts in sterile 150- by 13-mm. tubes.

Andrade's Indicator

Acid fuchsin................. 0.5 gm.
Distilled water.............. 100.0 ml.
N NaOH (4 gm./100 ml.)..... 1000.0 ml.

The Durham tube is omitted from this basal medium, because acid production that changes the color from colorless to pink may be accompanied by a coagulation of the serum, which renders the gas tube inoperative.

Other Bases

Organisms that will not grow in any of the above bases must be tested in a base in which they will grow. In reporting such results a simultaneous report should be made of other bases tested and found unsuitable.

The Eldredge Tube for Detection of Carbon Dioxide Evolution

The Eldredge tube is illustrated in Figure 6.

Place 20 ml. of the medium in one of the horizontal arms, plug both vertical arms with cotton wool, and sterilize. Inoculate the medium and then pipette 20 ml. of freshly prepared 0.1 N barium hydroxide into the second horizontal arm. Cut off the tops of the cotton wool plugs, push them down slightly into the tubes and seal the vertical arms with rubber stoppers. Incubate for 14 days.

Copious evolution of CO_2 from the culture will result in a precipitation barium carbonate in the horizontal arm. Titrate the residual barium hydroxide with 0.1 N hydrochloric acid, with the use of phenolphthalein as an indicator. This result will give only, by difference, the evolved carbon dioxide. The CO_2 dissolved in the medium should be liberated by acidification before titration of the barium hydroxide, if the total CO_2 output is required.

Reproduced by permission from Manual of Methods for the Pure Culture Study of Bacteria, Society of American Bacteriologists, Biotech Publications, 1953.

Differentiation of Oxidative and Fermentative Production of Acid from Carbohydrates

MEDIUM

Peptone....................... 2.0 gm.
NaCl........................ 5.0 gm.
K_2HPO_4....................... 0.3 gm.
Agar........................ 3.0 gm.
Bromthymol blue (1% aque-
    ous solution)................ 3.0 ml.
Distilled water................ 1000 ml.

Dissolve the ingredients and adjust the pH, if necessary, to 7.1. Sterilize at 121° C. for 20 minutes.

Prepare 10 per cent aqueous solutions of the carbohydrates and sterilize by Seitz filtration. Add 10 ml. of the sterile carbohydrates aseptically to every 100 ml. of the sterile, melted medium and dispense in 5-ml. amounts in sterile 150- by 13-mm. tubes.

Inoculate two tubes of each carbohydrate with each organism by stabbing with inoculum from a fresh slope culture. Cover the surface of one tube with sterile paraffin (petrolatum).

READING THE TESTS

Fermentative organisms produce acid throughout both tubes. Oxidative organisms produce acid in the open tube only. In the latter, acid appears first at the surface and then progressively towards the base.

Slow oxidative reactions are sometimes preceded by a slight alkaline reaction.

Author's Note: Dr. P. H. A. Sneath (personal communication) has suggested the use of long, narrow tubes and the elimination of the paraffin (petrolatum) seal to avoid the unpleasantness associated with washing the sealed tubes.

Reproduced by permission from R. Hugh and E. Leifson, J. Bacteriol., *66*, 1953, 24.

An alternative method based on the same general principles has been recommended by the Subcommittee on *Staphylococcus* and *Micrococcus*.

Preparation of Inoculum: Grow the organism for 24 hours at 37° C. on tryptone yeast extract agar containing the following:
Difco-tryptone.................. 10 gm.
Difco-yeast extract.............. 1 gm.
Agar........................... 15 gm.
pH............................ 7.2

Preparation of Medium: Dissolve the following ingredients in distilled water: Difco-tryptone, 10 gm.; Difco-yeast extract, 1.0 gm.; glucose, mannitol, or other carbohydrate, 10 gm.; bromcresol purple, 0.04 gm.; and Difco-agar, 2.0 gm. Adjust the pH to 7.0 and dispense into 16- by 120-mm. test tubes; these are two-thirds filled. Autoclave for 20 minutes at 115° C.

Use of Medium: Before use, steam the medium for 10 to 15 minutes to remove dissolved oxygen; then solidify by placing tubes in iced water. Then immediately and heavily inoculate a tube with a wire loop, making certain that the inoculum reaches the bottom of the tube. Cover the surface of the tube with a 25-mm., or more, layer of a sterile paraffin oil. Incubate for 5 days at 37° C.

Interpretation of Result: Acid is produced anaerobically if the indicator changes to yellow throughout the tube; if glucose is the substrate, the organism is a *Staphylococcus.* If no acid is produced when glucose is the substrate or if acid is found only at the surface, indicating oxidative breakdown of the sugar, the organism is a *Micrococcus.*

Reference: Intern. Bull. Bacteriol. Nomen. Taxon., *15*, 1965, 109.

Litmus Milk

For the preparation of this medium use (*a*) fresh machine-separated milk *or* (*b*) fresh milk, steamed for 20 minutes and allowed to stand for 18 hours for the fat to rise, after which the fat-free milk is siphoned off aseptically *or* (c) good quality *spray-dried* powdered skim milk reconstituted by dissolving 100 gm. per L. of distilled water.

Add to the milk an alcoholic solution of litmus (*vide infra*) sufficient to give a distinct color (usually 40 ml. per L.). Adjust the pH to 7.0 by the addition of 1 N NaOH. Do not rely on visual adjustment. A glass electrode should be used. Steam for 15 minutes on 3 successive days with incubation at 37° C. between steamings.

Alcoholic Litmus Solution: Grind 50 gm. of litmus in a mortar with 150 ml. of 40 per cent alcohol. Transfer to a flask, and boil gently on a steam bath for 1 minute. Decant the fluid and add another 150 ml. of 40 per cent alcohol to the residue; boil again for 1 minute. Decant and mix the extracts. Allow to settle overnight and make up to 300 ml. with 40 per cent alcohol.

Add N HCl drop by drop to adjust the pH to 7.0.

The Identification of Butyric, Propionic, and Acetic Acids in Cultures

Acidify the culture with phosphoric acid to about pH 2. Distill, with the addition of silicone antifoam if necessary.

Estimate the amount of volatile acids in the distillate by titrating an aliquot with standard alkali and phenolphthalein indicator. Extract the bulk of the distillate with ether; evaporate the ether and convert the acids to their ammonium salts by the addition of the calculated amount of N NH_4OH. Prepare solutions of ammonium butyrate, propionate, and acetate by neutralizing these acids with N NH_4OH.

The unknown acids are separated and identified by paper chromatography of their ammonium salts and comparison with the ammonium salts of known acids.

Place small spots (5 to 10 μl.) of the liquids about 2 cm. from the ends of strips of Whatman No. 3 filter paper (17 by 1.5

cm.), dry briefly in air, fix the other ends in slits in cork stoppers, and suspend the papers in test tubes of suitable size, with the end dipping into the developing solvent.

Prepare the solvent by shaking together the following reagents, and use the upper of the two layers that separate.

Water	4 parts by vol.
NH_4OH (concentrated)	1 part by vol.
Ethanol (95%)	1 part by vol.
Redistilled *n*-butanol	4 parts by vol.

Allow the solvent to ascend the paper strips for about 4 hours. Remove the strips from the tubes, allow to drain for 30 to 60 minutes on filter paper, and spray them with an indicator solution (200 mg. of methyl red and 200 mg. of bromthymol blue in 500 ml. of a 1:5 solution of formalin in alcohol; final pH, 5.2). Finally, dip the strips into the vapor from 3 per cent NH_4OH. Mark the orange-red spots immediately.

It is important to remember that the ammonium salts of the volatile acids are themselves volatile. Hence, do not use heat when applying spots to paper; do not leave the strips for more than 1 or 2 hours between the time of applying the spots and developing the chromatogram; and do not dry the chromatogram completely before spraying with the indicator.

Reproduced by permission from R. E. B. Duncan and J. W. Porteous, Analyst, *78*, 1953, 641; and from A. J. G. Barnett and R. E. B. Duncan, J. Sci. Food Agr., *5*, 1954, 120.

Extraction and Determination of Optical Rotation of Lactic Acid

The culture should contain at least 2 gm. of lactic acid. Clarify by adding one-twentieth of its volume of 25 per cent zinc sulfate. Neutralize to a pH between 7.6 and 7.8 with 20 per cent sodium hydroxide, and centrifuge off the resulting zinc hydroxide precipitate.

Acidify the clarified solution to pH 2 with sulfuric acid and extract three times with ether (total volume of ether about 1 L.). If appreciable amounts of volatile acids or succinic acid are present, they should be removed beforehand, but this is not necessary with homofermentative bacteria.

Add water (10 ml.) to the ether extract, and distill off the ether. Make the remaining solution up to 50 ml., and titrate 1 ml. to determine the total quantity of extracted acid. Then boil the solution for 10 minutes with a calculated excess of zinc carbonate; filter off the excess carbonate and wash. Evaporate the filtrate on a water bath until crystallization begins. Add alcohol to a concentration of 50 per cent and allow the mixture to stand overnight to crystallize. Filter off the product; wash with 95 per cent alcohol and then with ether, air-dry, and place in a desiccator over calcium chloride.

To test the optical form of the zinc lactate, the water of crystallization and the specific rotation are determined.

1. Weigh a 2-gm. sample of the salt accurately, dry to constant weight at 110° C., and calculate the amount of water of crystallization. Optically active salt contains 2 molecules (12.89 per cent) of water; the inactive salt contains 3 molecules (18.17 per cent).

2. Weigh 1 gm. of the anhydrous salt accurately, dissolve in distilled water, and dilute to 25 ml. at 20° C. Determine the rotation of polarized light in a polarimeter, and calculate the specific rotation from the observed rotation by the formula

$$\alpha = \frac{100 \cdot a}{b \cdot c}$$

where α is the specific rotation, a is the observed rotation, b is the length of the polarimeter tube in decimeters, and c is the concentration in gm. per 100 ml. of solution.

The rotation of the active zinc salt is *opposite* to that of the free acid and varies slightly with concentration; a 4 per cent solution (w/v) has a specific rotation of ±8.1 to 8.6.

Reproduced by permission from C. S.

Pederson, W. H. Peterson, and E. B. Fred, J. Biol. Chem., *68*, 1926, 151.

See also Biochem. J., *26*, 1932, 846; and Ind. Eng. Chem., *27*, 1935, 1492.

The Demonstration of Alcohols in Cultures

Place 20 ml. of the culture in a distilling flask and collect 10 ml. of distillate. Pipette 1 ml. of this into a 250-ml. flask, and add 10 ml. of oxidizing mixture (0.2 gm. of potassium dichromate in 100 ml. of 19 N sulfuric acid). Stopper the flask and mix the contents thoroughly. Allow to stand for 30 minutes; add 100 ml. of water and 0.5 gm. of KI. After the latter is dissolved, titrate the liberated iodine with N sodium thiosulfate, adding 0.5 ml. of starch indicator *just before* the end point. If no iodine is liberated, repeat with the use of less of the distillate.

Do a blank determination by substituting 1 ml. of water for the distillate. The difference in titration between the test and the blank is a measure of the amount of dichromate reduced by the alcohol in the distillate: (1 mmole of ethanol = 4 m.eq. of dichromate).

The method is not specific for ethanol, inasmuch as all volatile alcohols react.

Analysis of Gases for Pure Culture Studies

Gases that are commonly encountered either as byproducts of fermentations or as substrates for oxidation are CO, CO_2, CH_4, H_2, H_2S, N_2, N_2O, and O_2.

The most accurate method of analysis is possibly by means of the mass spectrograph, but this is outside the scope of most laboratories.

The technique of gas chromatography is relatively inexpensive and proves to be the ideal tool in microbiological work, particularly for the qualitative identification of gases before quantitative analysis. The technique is at present in use in this laboratory, and its investigation by others is recommended.

Nitrous oxide is found only in the specific case of nitrate reduction with some bacteria. The gas is very soluble in water but can be removed under reduced pressure. It is only sparingly soluble in potassium hydroxide, alkaline pyrogallol, and ammoniacal cuprous chloride. Ignited phosphorus burns vividly in the gas, decomposing it and liberating nitrogen. It does not form brown fumes with nitric oxide. Burned with an electrically heated iron or nickel wire, it yields its own volume of nitrogen.

Carbon monoxide, although metabolized by some bacteria, is not a byproduct. In experiments involving this gas, the end product of the oxidation is carbon dioxide. The gases can be separated from one another and from oxygen by successive absorption in Hempel pipettes in 36 per cent potassium hydroxide for CO_2; alkaline pyrogallol (30 per cent pyrogallic acid and 60 per cent KOH mixed in the ratio of 2:7) for oxygen; and freshly prepared ammoniacal cuprous chloride (prepared by dissolving 11.5 gm. of cuprous chloride in 43 ml. of concentrated ammonia and 50 ml. of water for carbon monoxide.

Mixtures of carbon dioxide, methane, hydrogen, and hydrogen sulfide can be analyzed in the following manner, adapted from a method described by Lugg.

PREPARATION OF THE SAMPLE AND APPARATUS

The apparatus is shown in Figure 7. Collect the gas sample in a large reservoir. Connect this reservoir and one other containing an equal amount of pure medical oxygen via individual taps to a gas manifold connected to the gas inlet. Arrange the reservoir so that when the taps are opened the gases will flow out at an equal rate.

Place dried silica gel in tube 1 to remove H_2O; anhydrous $CaCl_2$ in tube 2 to remove H_2O; Ascarite in U-tube 3 to remove CO_2; $CdCl_2$ in U-tube 4 to remove H_2S; concentrated NaOH in flask 5 to remove HCl; a mixture of silica gel and anhydrous $CaCl_2$ in U-tube 6 to remove H_2O; alternate layers of P_2O_5 and glass wool in U-tube 10 to remove moisture; Ascarite in tube 11 to absorb CO_2; and alkaline pyrogallol in flask 12 to remove oxygen.

The inert gas that finally leaves flask 12 is probably nitrogen.

Dry gas from tube 6 passes through connection 7 to a copper combustion tube, 8, consisting of a spiral of fine bore copper tubing 6 feet in length heated in an electric muffle furnace at 700° C.

METHOD OF OPERATION

Open taps on U-tubes 3, 4, 10, and 11, and flush through with O_2. Use 1 L. of O_2.

Make sure the temperature of the electric muffle is 700° C. Shut off the O_2, and close the taps on U-tubes 3, 4, 10, and 11.

Remove the four U-tubes 3, 4, 10, and 11 by rolling back the rubber connections and pulling the U-tubes upwards. Dry with a cloth, allow to equilibrate in a balance for 15 minutes, and weigh.

Replace the U-tubes and then flush with an additional 500 ml. of O_2.

Close the tap from the gas manifold, refill the reservoir with O_2 to the same level as that of the gas mixture, then open the taps of both reservoirs to the gas manifold. Open the taps on U-tubes 3, 4, 10, and 11, and check the time and also the temperature of the muffle furnace. Start the analysis by opening the tap from the manifold. Adjust this tap so that the gas flow from each reservoir is about 5 to 10 ml. per minute.

Measure the gas volume of the mixture before and after each run. The gas volume can be as low as 100 ml. or as high as 500 ml. When the required amount of gas has been passed through the apparatus, shut off the sample reservoir, but allow the O_2 to keep flowing. Refill the reservoir with O_2, and allow another 500 ml. to flow through the apparatus. Then shut off the manifold and close the taps of U-tubes 3, 4, 10, and 11. Remove the U-tubes, weigh, and note the differences in weights before and after the run.

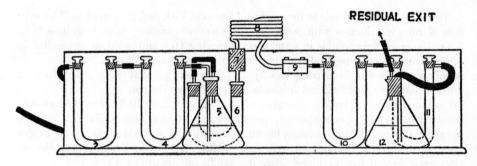

FRONT ELEVATION

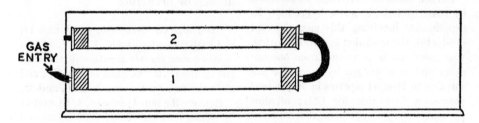

BACK ELEVATION

FIG. 7

CALCULATION

For CO_2

Amount of weight gained = amount of CO_2 passed in grams.

$\therefore$ 1 gm. molecular weight of CO_2

$$= 22.4 \text{ L. at N.T.P.}$$

$$44 \text{ gm. } CO_2 = 22.4 \text{ L.}$$

$$x \text{ gm. } CO_2 = ? \text{ L. at N.T.P.}$$

For H_2S

$$H_2S + CdCl_2 \rightarrow CdS + 2 HCl$$

In this case there is a loss of weight because of the conversion of $CdCl_2$ to the lighter CdS. Then

G.M.W. $CdCl_2$ − G.M.W. CdS

$$\equiv 22.4 \text{ L. } H_2S,$$

i.e., decrease in weight

$$= x \text{ L. } H_2S \text{ at N.T.P.}$$

From this, calculate the amount of H_2S.

For CH_4 and H_2

$$CH_4 + 2 O_2 \rightarrow CO_2 + 2 H_2O$$

$$2 H_2 + O_2 \rightarrow 2 H_2O$$

The amount of water gained = water due to CH_4 + water due to H_2. The volume of CO_2 produced is equal to the volume of CH_4 oxidized. From the equation

$$44 \text{ gm. } CO_2 \equiv 22.4 \text{ L. } CH_4$$

calculate the volume of CH_4 oxidized and from this the amount of water this CH_4 would yield. The residual water must be due to the oxidation of H_2. Calculate the latter from the equation

$$18 \text{ gm. } H_2O \equiv 22.4 \text{ L. } H_2 \text{ at N.T.P.}$$

The residual gas is inert and is probably N_2.

Reproduced by permission from J. W. H. Lugg, J. Agr. Sci., *28*, 1938, 688.

For smaller quantities of gases, the reader is referred to A. C. Cumming and S. A. Kay, Quantitative Chemical Analysis, Gurney and Jackson, 1934.

Glucose Phosphate Peptone Water

Peptone (Parke-Davis)........ 5 gm.
K$_2$HPO$_4$.................... 5 gm.
Distilled water............... 1000 ml.

Steam until dissolved; filter while hot through filter paper, cool, and adjust the pH to between 7.4 and 7.6. Add 5 gm. of glucose, dispense in 4-ml. quantities in 150-by 16-mm. tubes. Sterilize at 110° C. for 25 minutes.

Reproduced by permission from F. Kauffmann, The Enterobacteriaceae, 2nd ed., Munksgaard, Copenhagen, 1954.

Glucose Yeast Extract Tryptone Phosphate Broth

SOLUTION A

K$_2$HPO$_4$......................... 50 gm.
KH$_2$PO$_4$........................ 50 gm.
Make to 500 ml. with distilled water.

SOLUTION B

MgSO$_4$·7 H$_2$O.................. 20 gm.
NaCl......................... 1 gm.
FeSO$_4$·7 H$_2$O................. 1 gm.
MnSO$_4$·4 H$_2$O................. 1 gm.
Make to 500 ml. with distilled water.

THE MEDIUM

Glucose........................ 10 gm.
Difco-tryptone................. 5 gm.
Yeast extract.................. 3 gm.
Solution A..................... 5 ml.
Solution B..................... 5 ml.
Distilled water............... 1000 ml.

Dissolve the ingredients and sterilize at 110° C. for 25 minutes.

For *isolation* of *Leuconostoc*, but not for subsequent culturing, add 50 ml. of tomato juice or orange juice per L.

Reproduced by permission from C. S. Pederson, personal communication. This medium is a modification of that published by G. J. Hucker and C. S. Pederson, N. Y. State Agr. Expt. Sta. Tech. Bull. No. 167, 1930.

Glucose Tryptic Broth

Glucose....................... 10 gm.
Difco Bacto-tryptone........... 10 gm.
Distilled water............... 1000 ml.

Dissolve the tryptone in the water and then add the glucose. Dispense the broth and sterilize at 110° C. for 25 minutes.

Methyl Red Test

This test depends on the ability of the organism to produce acid from glucose in amounts sufficient to reduce the pH to 4.2 or less and to maintain this low pH for at least 4 days. Some methyl red negative organisms produce sufficient acid to lower the pH to 4.2 but subsequently metabolize the acid produced and give rise to neutral byproducts within the 4-day period. The time interval at which the test is performed is therefore important. Four days is adequate for those enteric organisms which grow at 37° C. and for which this test has been extensively used. No comparable data are available for the more psychrophilic bacteria, but for comparative purposes a similar time interval is recommended at the lower optimal temperature.

In assessing the results of the test in relation to the Voges-Proskauer reaction, organisms that, at the 4-day interval, are both methyl red positive and Voges-Proskauer positive should be incubated for a longer period to determine whether complete conversion of the acid takes place.

METHYL RED SOLUTION

Methyl red.................... 0.1 gm.
Ethanol (95%)................. 300 ml.
Distilled water............... 200 ml.

TEST

Add a few drops of the methyl red solution to the 4-day culture in glucose-phosphate-peptone water. A red color is positive and yellow is negative.

NOTE: It has been suggested that the phosphate should be omitted from the medium for sporing bacilli, because the buffering action of the phosphate prevents the development of the low pH. Nothing is gained by doing this. Mere acid production by species of the genus *Bacillus* is detectable in the usual sugar fermentation tests. To eliminate the phosphate is, in fact, to alter the conditions of the test as normally applied, and the two methods are no longer comparable.

Reproduced by permission from W. M. Clarke and H. A. Lubs, J. Infectious Diseases, *17*, 1915, 160.

Voges-Proskauer Reaction

The test depends on the ability of the organism to produce acid from glucose and subsequently to convert it to acetylmethylcarbinol or 2:3-butylene glycol, both neutral substances. Upon the addition of alkali, followed by vigorous shaking, both substances are oxidized to diacetyl, which reacts with the guanidine nucleus of arginine in peptone to produce a pink color. Creatine is added in the O'Meara modification of the test to provide an added source of the guanidine nucleus and thus accelerate the test.

A positive test is dependent primarily on the ability of the organism to bring about the conversion of the acid to acetoin and secondarily on the time of incubation. All Voges-Proskauer-positive organisms produce the acid first and hence give a positive methyl red test in the early stages of incubation. If the incubation period is too short, the Voges-Proskauer test may be negative or both it and the methyl red tests may be positive. On longer incubation the methyl red test becomes negative and the Voges-Proskauer, strongly positive.

Notes on the time of incubation given under the methyl red test apply equally well here.

Method: Grow the organism in glucose-phosphate-peptone water for 4 days.

Original Test: Add 1 ml. of a 10 per cent solution of KOH to the culture and shake vigorously with air. The color develops slowly, and the test should be read after 18 to 24 hours. A pink fluorescence is positive; no coloration, negative.

O'Meara Modification: Add a knife point of creatine to the culture, followed by 5 ml. of 40 per cent NaOH. Shake the tube thoroughly. A pink color usually appears in about 2 minutes if positive; the development of the color may be delayed, however.

Another method in common use is *Barritt's test:* To the 3-ml. culture add 1 ml. of a fresh 10 per cent alcoholic solution of α-naphthol, and 1.0 ml. of a 20 per cent aqueous solution of potassium hydroxide. Shake well. A bright cherry-red color appears after 5 to 15 minutes, sometimes longer, and will fade after a few hours if acetoin is present in the culture.

The O'Meara test is recommended for general use. If the Barritt method is employed, the O'Meara method should be used for comparison and both tests reported.

Reproduced by permission from R. A. Q. O'Meara, J. Pathol. Bacteriol., *34*, 1931, 401; and from M. M. Barritt, J. Pathol. Bacteriol., *42*, 1936, 441.

Loeffler's Inspissated Serum for Liquefaction Tests

Glucose...................... 2.0 gm.
Peptone...................... 2.0 gm.
NaCl........................ 1.0 gm.
Tap water.................... 200 ml.

Dissolve the ingredients and filter if necessary. Add 400 ml. of blood serum and mix. Dispense in 5-ml. amounts in 150- by 13-mm. tubes and place them in a vertical position in an inspissator. Heat to 80° C. very slowly and hold at this temperature for 6 hours to coagulate the serum. Sterilize by heating to 85° C. for 20 minutes on 3 successive days.

If the glucose-peptone water is sterilized separately, and the serum is collected and added aseptically, only the initial heating is necessary to coagulate the serum.

To detect liquefaction, inoculate by stabbing and incubate for 1 to 2 weeks.

The Hydrolysis of Gelatin

This may be detected by two methods.

1. GELATIN BROTH

Add 25 per cent gelatin to meat infusion or papain digest broth. Steam until all the gelatin is dissolved. Add 80 ml. of N NaOH per L. and then adjust the pH to 7.4. Cool to 50° C. Clarify through paper pulp. Dispense in 5-ml. quantities in 160- by 13-mm. tubes and sterilize at 110° C. for 25 minutes. Do not heat above this temperature or the gelling power will be lost.

Inoculation

Inoculate by stabbing the inoculum down the center of the tube. Incubate at 22° C. for 1 month and record the time at which liquefaction becomes evident if it occurs. For organisms that will grow at this temperature in this basal medium, this procedure is satisfactory.

Liquefaction of the gelatin occurs initially somewhere along the line of inoculation. The subsequent development varies with the organism.

For organisms that will not grow at 22° C., incubation must be carried out at the required optimum. At 37° C. the gelatin melts and liquefaction can be observed only after placing the tube in an ice bath upon removal from the incubator. If only partial liquefaction has occurred, it may not be detected.

2. GELATIN AGAR

This medium is more satisfactory for mesophilic organisms. It is recommended for use with all organisms. The test is limited, of course, to those which will grow on the medium. Other basal media may be employed provided they do not contain precipitable proteins.

Dispense 10 ml. of sterile meat infusion agar or papain digest agar into a sterile Petri dish.

Melt a second 10-ml. quantity of the medium and a gelatin broth (as in method 1, above). Add 1 ml. of the gelatin broth to the agar. Mix well and pour onto the surface of the solidified agar.

Inoculate the medium and incubate at the desired temperature.

To detect hydrolysis flood the plates with a 15 per cent solution of $HgCl_2$ in HCl. The unhydrolyzed gelatin forms a white precipitate with the mercury salt. Always compare with a control plate. Some organisms hydrolyze the gelatin very rapidly and may completely clear the plate in 24 hours.

Acid $HgCl_2$ Solution

$HgCl_2$ .... 15 gm.
H_2O .... 100 ml.
HCl (concentrated) .... 20 ml.
  Mix in the order stated and shake well.

NOTE: This is a modification of the method of W. C. Frazier, J. Infectious Diseases, *39*, 1926, 302.

Urease Production

This test depends on the ability of the organisms to hydrolyze urea with the liberation of ammonia. The rise in pH is indicated by a change in color of the indicator (phenol red) from yellow to pink.

UREA AGAR

Sterile Urea Solution

Dissolve 20 gm. of urea in 100 ml. of distilled water and sterilize by filtration.

Basal Medium

Bacto-peptone .... 1.0 gm.
NaCl .... 5.0 gm.
KH_2PO_4 .... 2.0 gm.
Distilled water .... 1000 ml.

Dissolve the ingredients and steam for 20 minutes. Add 1 gm. of glucose and dissolve by agitation. Add 0.012 gm. of phenol red and mix well. The medium should have a pH of 6.8 to 6.9 and be yellow in color.

Add 20 gm. of agar and dissolve at 121° C. for 20 minutes.

Cool to between 55° and 60° C. in a water bath.

Warm the sterile urea solution to the same temperature and then add aseptically 100 ml. per L. of basal medium.

Distribute aseptically in sterile, screw cap bottles or test tubes and allow to set in a sloping position.

Inoculate and examine daily for 7 days.

Reproduced by permission from W. B. Christensen, J. Bacteriol., *52*, 1946, 561; and from F. Kauffmann, The Enterobacteriaceae, 2nd ed., Munksgaard, Copenhagen, 1954.

Hydrolysis of Agar

Care should be exercised in assessing this characteristic. In agar media that contain solid particles, such as bacterial cells or cellulose or chitin, bacterial attack on these particles may result in their digestion followed by the collapse of the agar. This usually results in a depression in the agar, which remains quite firm.

Inoculate the organism when possible on or into a clarified agar medium that supports luxuriant growth. Incubate for at least 14 days. If surface inoculations are made, the agar is hydrolyzed around the individual colonies, which slowly sink into the softened medium. If agar deeps are inoculated by the stabbing method, liquefaction will progress outwards from the line of the stab.

When special media are used for cultivation, a statement regarding growth on meat infusion agar should be included for comparative purposes.

Chitin Media

PREPARATION OF CHITIN

Scrub and clean crab or lobster shells and soak them for 1 week in 1 per cent HCl; change the acid three times during this period. The acid decalcifies the shells, which should become limp and leathery. Wash the shells well with water and then cut them into strips 0.5 to 1 inch wide.

Soak the strips in 2 per cent KOH for 10 days. During this period heat five times to a temperature just below the boiling point and then cool. This treatment extracts some pigment and removes protein and other organic matter except chitin.

Wash the strips free of alkali and extract with several changes of ethyl alcohol until all color is removed. Dry.

The strips are suitable for use in a liquid mineral salts medium for the growth of crude cultures and maintenance of chitinoclastic organisms.

For use in agar media the chitin must be finely dispersed. Take some of the strips and place them in a 3.0-L. flask. Hold 1500 ml. of cold water in readiness in a second flask. Add 100 ml. of 50 per cent H_2SO_4 to the chitin strips.

As soon as the chitin disappears, dilute the acid rapidly with the 1500 ml. of water. Allow the reprecipitated chitin to settle overnight, decant the supernatant, and wash the chitin by repeated centrifugation until neutral to litmus. Alternatively, dialyze the chitin free of acid by suspending it in a sheet of non-water-proofed cellophane in a stream of running water.

Resuspend the chitin in water to a density such that, after diluting 1:10, 5 ml. dispensed in a 10-cm. Petri dish will give a slight but distinct opalescence.

Distribute in 10-ml. quantities and sterilize at 121° C. for 15 minutes.

PREPARATION OF MEDIA

1. Chitin Strip-Mineral Salts Liquid Medium

K_2HPO_4	1.0 gm.
$MgSO_4 \cdot 7\ H_2O$	0.5 gm.
NaCl.... fresh, 0.5 gm.; marine,	30 gm.
$CaCl_2 \cdot 2\ H_2O$	0.1 gm.
$FePO_4 \cdot 2H_2O$	0.001 gm.
NH_4Cl	1.0 gm.
H_2O	1000 ml.

Dissolve the mineral salts, adjust the pH to 7.0, and distribute in bottles or test tubes. Add a strip of chitin to each container and sterilize at 121° C. for 15 minutes.

2. Chitin Agar

(a) Prepare a mineral salts agar base by the addition of 1.5 to 2.0 per cent agar to the mineral salts medium in 1, above. Dissolve the agar by autoclaving, adjust the pH to 7.0, and distribute in 5- and 10-ml. amounts in suitable containers. Sterilize at 121° C. for 15 minutes.

(b) To prepare chitin agar plates, melt one 10-ml. and one 5-ml. mineral salts agar deep and cool to 45° C. in a water bath. Pour the 10-ml. quantity into a sterile Petri dish and allow to set.

To the 5-ml. quantity add 0.5 ml. of the warmed chitin suspension, mix well, and then pour as a layer on the surface of the mineral salts agar base.

This practice minimizes the time taken for chitinoclastic organisms to bring about a visible change in the suspended chitin in the medium.

ISOLATION OF CHITINOCLASTIC BACTERIA

To obtain enrichment cultures, inoculate soils or marine muds into the mineral medium containing the chitin strips. Incubate at the desired temperature until obvious decomposition has occurred. Subculture to another tube of the same medium and reincubate. When decomposition becomes rapid, inoculate the surface of a chitin agar plate, and pick off the colonies of chitin-hydrolyzing organisms. Purify in the usual manner and maintain in the liquid medium; subculture when the strips of chitin have nearly disappeared.

Reproduced by permission from L. L. Campbell, Jr., and O. B. Williams, J. Gen. Microbiol., 5, 1951, 894; and from A. G. Benton, J. Bacteriol., 29, 1935, 449.

Starch Agar

The hydrolysis of starch is dependent on the growth of the organism on the basal medium in which the starch is incorporated.

Prepare the basal medium in both single and double strength.

Pour a layer (15 ml.) of the sterile single strength medium in a Petri dish and allow it to set.

Prepare a 10 per cent suspension of starch and bring to a boil over an open flame with continuous stirring. Autoclave at 121° C. for 25 minutes.

Dissolve the double strength agar base; mix with an equal quantity of the sterile starch suspension, and pour as a thin layer (5 ml.) over the surface of the single strength agar base.

Refrigerate the plates for 2 days before use. This increases the opacity.

Inoculate the medium and incubate at the desired temperature. Hydrolysis may be indicated by a clearing of the medium around or under the colony. This may be checked by flooding the plate with dilute iodine or 95 per cent ethanol. If iodine is used, unhydrolyzed starch turns blue. If ethanol is used, unhydrolyzed starch forms a white precipitate.

Reference: Author's recommendation.

Alginate Agar

The composition of the following medium is, with minor modification, that described by Waksman and his associates. The method of distribution is one found most satisfactory in the author's laboratory.

Dissolve 10 gm. of sodium alginate in 1 L. of distilled water. Adjust the pH to 7.0 with HCl and then add

$NaNO_3$	2 gm.
KCl	0.5 gm.
$MgSO_4 \cdot 7 H_2O$	0.5 gm.
$FeSO_4 \cdot 6 H_2O$	0.01 gm.
KH_2PO_4	1.0 gm.
NaCl	30 to 35 gm. (required only for marine species)
Agar	20 gm.

Dissolve the salts and the agar, and readjust the pH to 7.0 if necessary. Sterilize at 121° C. for 15 minutes.

For the preparation of agar plates, prepare a mineral salts agar of the above composition with the omission of the sodium alginate. Distribute in 10-ml. amounts in sterile Petri dishes and allow to set. Pour 10 ml. of the alginate agar onto the surface of the mineral base and allow to set.

Inoculate the plates and incubate for 14 days; examine at intervals for clarification of the agar around the colonies. Where this occurs the digestion of the alginate results in a pitting of the agar, which should not be confused with agar hydrolysis.

NOTE: The composition of the medium as described restricts the growth of organisms that do not utilize nitrate. The substitution of ammonium sulfate for the nitrate is recommended, although for comparative studies use of the original medium must be made.

Reproduced by permission from S. A. Waksman, C. L. Carey, and M. C. Allen, J. Bacteriol., *28*, 1934, 213.

Bacterial Cell Suspension Agar for Myxobacteria

Prepare a suspension of the organism (usually *Escherichia coli*) of such a density that 15 ml. dispensed in a 10-cm. Petri dish show a distinct opalescence. Add a quantity of agar that will solidify but not excessively harden the medium. Autoclave at 115° C. for 20 minutes. If necessary, adjust the pH and re-autoclave.

For other methods see McCurdy, Can. J. Microbiol., *9*, 1963, 282; and *10*, 1964, 935.

Capsular Polysaccharide Media Used for Saccharobacterium

BASAL MEDIUM 1

$(NH_4)_2SO_4$	1 gm.
K_2HPO_4	2 gm.
Tap water	1000 ml.

This medium has a pH of 7.4 and does not require adjustment.

BASAL MEDIUM 2

$MgSO_4 \cdot 7 H_2O$	0.2 gm.
$NH_4 \cdot H_2PO_4$	1.5 gm.
$CaCl_2$	0.1 gm.
KCl	0.1 gm.
$FeCl_3$	0.0001 gm.
Distilled water	1000 ml.

This medium has a pH of 7.4 and does not require adjustment.

Addition of more than 0.5 per cent NaCl, 0.3 per cent beef extract, or 0.5 per cent peptone to either medium completely inhibits growth.

The above media, with a suitable carbohydrate, support the growth of the two species originally described (Sickles and Shaw, J. Bacteriol., *28*, 1934, 422).

PREPARATION OF TYPE I PNEUMOCOCCAL POLYSACCHARIDE

The organism selected for preparation of capsular polysaccharide should be freshly isolated or should have undergone several passages through the mouse.

Grow the culture in a suitable medium without neutralization during growth. The semidefined medium of Adams and Roe (J. Bacteriol., *49*, 1945, 401) is recommended. Chill the cultures in an ice-salt bath. Add an equal volume of 95 per cent alcohol chilled to 0° C. Set aside in the cold to settle. Siphon off the supernatant and centrifuge the sediment.

All the following operations must be carried out in the cold (0° to 5° C.) and should not extend over a period of more than 2 or 3 weeks.

Suspend the deposit in 80 ml. of acetate buffer (dissolve 157.5 gm. of $NaC_2H_3O_2 \cdot 3 H_2O$ in distilled water, make up to 3 L., adjust the pH to 6.05 with glacial acetic acid, add toluene as a preservative, and store in the cold). Grind in a slowly rotating 1-L. round-bottomed Pyrex flask for 6 hours with stainless steel balls 2 mm. in diameter, and with the flask partially immersed in ice water.

Transfer the suspension to 50-ml. plastic tubes with a little buffer and centrifuge at 8000 r.p.m. for 30 minutes. (The authors used a Servall SS-2 vacuum centrifuge.) Pour off the slightly yellow viscid supernatant and precipitate the polysaccharide by the addition of 0.5 volumes of cold isopropyl alcohol (Fraction A). Take up the residue from the first grinding with 80 ml. of acetate buffer, and grind for 6 hours as before. Centrifuge and precipitate the polysaccharide from the supernatant with isopropyl alcohol (Fraction B). Discard the cell residue and treat the separate fractions as follows:

Separate the polysaccharide in a refrigerated centrifuge. Dissolve the precipitate in 100 ml. of cold distilled water (0° to 5° C.). To deproteinize the resulting greenish solution, add 50 ml. of chloroform per 150 ml. of solution and agitate intermittently in a Waring Blendor in a cold room at 3° C. To prevent excessive warming, alternately agitate and allow to stand for 5-minute periods each.

Centrifuge the emulsion and separate the clear aqueous chloroform layers. Wash the emulsion layer with 2- by 50-ml. lots of water. Keep these washings to wash additional emulsion layers.

To the aqueous layer add an additional 50 ml. of chloroform and 10 ml. of n-butanol; shake and recentrifuge. A smaller emulsion layer forms. Separate the layers and rewash the emulsion layer with the previous washings.

Repeat the treatment of the aqueous layer with chloroform (and n-butanol?) until no emulsion layer forms.

Combine the washings from the emulsion layers and treat with fresh additions of chloroform (only?) until no emulsion layer forms. Then combine with the main aqueous layer.

Adjust the aqueous layer to a concentration of 3 per cent sodium acetate with saturated sodium acetate solution brought to pH 6.0 with acetic acid.

Add 0.5 volume of cold isopropyl alcohol to precipitate the polysaccharide and leave overnight. Repeat the procedure twice until no middle layer of desaturated protein forms. Centrifuge off the polysaccharide, dissolve in 100 ml. of water and dialyze under negative pressure in Visking (or equivalent) sausage tubing with daily changes of distilled water until negative tests for sodium phosphate and acetate are obtained.

Centrifuge in the cold at 10,000 r.p.m. for 30 minutes to remove any small quantity of sedimentable material. Lyophilize the resulting clear, colorless, highly viscous supernatant.

The above method is suitable for pneumococcal Type I polysaccharide and may also be suitable, with slight modifications (see M. Heidelberger, F. E. Kendall, and H. W. Scherp, J. Exptl. Med., *64*, 1936, 559), for other pneumococcal types.

Reproduced by permission from M. Heidelberger, C. M. MacLeod, H. Markowitz, and A. S. Roe, J. Exptl. Med., *91*, 1950, 341; and from R. Dubos and O. T. Avery, J. Exptl. Med., *54*, 1931, 51.

Carrot or Potato Plug Medium for Detection of Soft Rot Organisms

Select young, clean carrots (or new potatoes), preferably more than 1.5 inches at the widest part. Scrub the surface with a soft brush and then immerse in 0.2 per cent $HgCl_2$ for 2 minutes. Handling the carrot with aseptic precautions, rinse in several changes of sterile tap water in a sterile container. Cut across the center with a sterilized knife. With the use of a sterilized 6-mm. cork borer fitted with a plunger, extract several cores of carrot by plunging the borer through the cut surface as far as possible without breaking through the outside surface. Discharge the plugs into a sterile Petri dish. With a sterile knife, remove a few millimeters of the end of the core that formed the face of the original cut. Cut the plugs into 4- to 5-cm. lengths and transfer them aseptically to tubes of sterile peptone water. Incubate for 3 days to check sterility and store.

When testing an organism for its ability to decompose the carrot, incubate a control tube with the test, and at intervals check the consistency of the carrot plug in the inoculated tube with a stiff mounted needle and compare with the control.

A similar medium may be made with potato.

Reference: Author's recommendation.

Wieringa's Pectate Gel (Dowson's Modification) for Detection of Soft Rot Organisms

PREPARATION OF THE MEDIUM

1. Calcium Agar

Soil extract	500 ml.
NaCl	0.5 gm.
CaCl₂	2.5 gm.
Yeast extract	0.5 gm.
Agar	10.0 gm.

Dissolve the ingredients and adjust the pH to 9.0. Autoclave at 121° C. for 15 minutes. Pour enough to cover the bottom of each Petri dish and place in a desiccator to dry thoroughly (for about 2 days).

2. The "Pectin" Solution

Prepare a 2 per cent sodium polypectate solution by adding the powder slowly, with continuous stirring, to hot distilled water. Add 4 per cent bromthymol blue, and adjust the pH to 8.0 by adding N sodium hydroxide drop by drop. Autoclave at 115° C. for 2 minutes. When cold, pour just enough to cover the surface of the agar plates and leave to set and dry in a desiccator (for about 8 days). The plates are ready for streaking, if no liquid exudes from between the layers of pectate gel and agar when the plates are slightly tipped up. They keep well under a bell jar at laboratory temperature.

NOTE: Dowson (personal communication, September, 1958) recommends the use of citrus sodium pectate (Product No. 24 K12), obtainable from Sunkist Inc., of Ontario, California, U. S. A., or via London from S. and S. Services Ltd., 72 Victoria Street, London, S.W.1.

This product will differentiate between the pectolytic pseudomonads of Paton (Nature, *181*, 1958, No. 4601) and the pec-

tolytic species of *Erwinia*. British pectate made from apples does not.

Reproduced by permission from W. J. Dowson, Nature, *179*, 1957, No. 4561.

Pectate Gel Medium—Unpublished Modification by G. Elis Jones*

BASAL LAYER

MacConkey agar granules (Oxoid CM 7)	5.2 gm.
Calcium chloride (CaCl₂)	0.4 gm.

Dissolve by boiling in 75 ml. of distilled water. Autoclave at 115° C. for 10 minutes.

PECTATE SOLUTION

Sodium polypectate (Exchange brand)	20.0 gm.
Ethanol (absolute)	60 ml.
Disodium ethylenediaminetetraacetate (EDTA)	1.0 gm.
Distilled water	1000 ml.

Exchange brand sodium polypectate is prepared by Sunkist Growers, 720 East Sunkist Street, Ontario, California, U. S. A.

Suspend the sodium polypectate in the ethanol and dissolve the EDTA in water. Add the latter to the former with stirring and adjust the pH to 7.4 with 10 N NaOH, adding the alkali slowly and stirring well. Heat with continuous stirring until the sodium polypectate is dissolved. Dispense as 5-ml. quantities into "bijou" bottles. Autoclave immediately at 115° C. for 10 minutes. Pour plates of the base medium and, when they have set, overlayer with 5 ml. of the pectate solution at 55° C. Allow the pectate to set, then dry overnight at 37° C. with sterile 1.6-mm. thick seed-test filter paper discs in the lid to absorb condensation water. The medium described above is that described by D. J. Stewart, Nature, London, *195*, 1962, 1023. It is especially suitable for the isolation of *Erwinia* from plant material or from soil.

* Mr. Elis Jones, Ministry of Agriculture, Fisheries, and Food, National Agricultural Advisory Service, Block C, Government Building, Brooklands Ave., Cambridge, England.

An alternative method to that given above is to use as base medium nutrient agar containing 5.0 gm. per L. of calcium chloride. Stewart's pectate solution is then poured over this medium as described above. This modification is effective for the isolation of *Pseudomonas*, *Erwinia*, or *Bacillus*. The extent of pitting of the pectate gel, the shape of the pit, and the quantity of liquid depend very much on the drying of the medium. If the medium is to be used for streaking out, the surface should be well dried beforehand. Counts of pectolytic bacteria can be obtained by inoculating dilutions onto the set base before adding the polypectate solution.

Medium for *Zymobacterium* (*oroticum*)

Tryptone	20.0 gm.
Glucose	5.0 gm.
Yeast extract	0.5 gm.
Sodium thioglycollate	0.5 gm.
$MgSO_4 \cdot 7 H_2O$	0.2 gm.
$FeSO_4 \cdot 2 H_2O$	0.005 gm.
$MnSO_4 \cdot 2 H_2O$	0.005 gm.
$NaMoO_4 \cdot 2 H_2O$	0.005 gm.
Phosphate buffer, 0.05 M, pH 7.4	1000 ml.

Dissolve the ingredients and sterilize in sealed containers to prevent oxidation of the thioglycollate. Incubate in the presence of alkaline pyrogallol.

Reproduced by permission from J. F. Wachsman and H. A. Barker, J. Bacteriol., *68*, 1954, 400.

NOTE: The author has found it preferable to omit the thioglycollate from the medium and add it when required. Prepare a solution containing 1000 p.p.m. of thioglycollic acid in 0.001 N HCl. The acid solution is stable. When required, add 1 ml. of the solution to 10 ml. of medium. Usually this causes no percepible change in pH in the average medium.

Media for *Zymomonas*

Isolation Medium: Treat apple juice overnight with 1 gm. of Pectozyme (Norman, Evans, and Rais, Ltd., Manchester, England) per 100 ml. Filter and add 1 per cent Difco-yeast extract. Adjust the pH to 4.5 and filter the medium again. Add agar to 3 per cent (w/v) to make a solid medium. Autoclave the medium at 115° C. for 15 minutes.

Stock Culture Medium: Maintain cultures as stabs in screw-cap bottles containing apple juice diluted 1:4 with water and 1 per cent (w/v) Difco-yeast extract, solidified with 10 per cent (w/v) gelatin at pH 5.5.

Reproduced by permission from N. Millis, J. Gen. Microbiol., *15*, 1956, 521; and from J. L. Shimwell, J. Inst. Brewing, *43*, 1937, 507.

Alcohol Yeast Water for *Acetobacter*

Dissolve 10 gm. of Bacto-tryptose in 1 L. of distilled water, and add 1 gm. of yeast extract and dissolve. Distribute in known quantities in small Erlenmeyer flasks to give a layer not more than 1 cm. deep. Sterilize by autoclaving at 121° C. for 20 minutes.

When cool add 10 per cent by volume of sterile absolute alcohol.

Inoculate the medium and incubate for 1 week or until obvious growth has occurred. To observe acid formation add a few drops of 1.6 per cent alcoholic solution of bromcresol purple.

NOTE: Numerous organisms may grow in this medium without oxidation of the alcohol; thus the test for acid is necessary.

Ethanol Carbonate Agar for Production of Acetic Acid from Alcohol

Dissolve 10 gm. of Difco-yeast extract and 15 gm. of agar in 1000 ml. of water. Add 20 gm. of powdered calcium carbonate, distribute well, and dispense in 15-ml. amounts in screw-capped bottles.

Sterilize ethanol by Seitz filtration. For use melt an agar deep, cool to 50° C., add 0.3 ml. of sterile ethanol, mix well, and pour the plate.

Inoculate heavily in isolated spots on the surface and incubate for 14 days at

26° C. A positive test is shown by clearing of the medium around the colony, resulting from solution of the calcium carbonate.

Reference: J. L. Shimwell, J. G. Carr, and M. E. Rhodes, J. Gen. Microbiol., *23*, 1960, 283.

Production of Dihydroxyacetone from Glycerol

This test is used primarily in the separation of *Acetomonas* from *Pseudomonas*.

MEDIUM

Difco-yeast extract.............. 10 gm.
Glycerol...................... 20 ml.
Agar......................... 15 gm.
Distilled water.............. 1000 ml.

Dissolve the yeast extract and agar by autoclaving; filter if necessary. Add the glycerol and sterilize at 120° C. for 15 minutes. Dispense as plates.

INOCULATION

Inoculate the plates heavily in spots (*c.* 1 cm²) and incubate for 1 to 14 days at 26° C. Flood, in the cold, with Fehling's solution. Production of an aureole of yellow to red copper oxide(s) within 10 minutes round the implanted masses indicates the presence of dihydroxyacetone.

FEHLING'S SOLUTION

1. Dissolve 34.6 gm. of hydrated copper sulfate and make up to 500 ml. with distilled water.
2. Dissolve 173 gm. of Rochelle salt (sodium potassium tartrate) and 60 gm. of sodium hydroxide in distilled water and make up to 500 ml. When required, mix equal quantities of solutions 1 and 2. The mixture has a deep-blue color.

Reference: J. L. Shimwell, J. G. Carr, and M. E. Rhodes, J. Gen. Microbiol., *23*, 1960, 283.

Oxidation of Calcium Lactate through Acetate to Carbonate for *Acetobacter*

Prepare a medium containing 1 per cent (w/v) Difco-yeast extract + 1 per cent (w/v) calcium lactate in 1.5 per cent (w/v) agar.

Inoculate on the surface in isolated spots (*c.* 1 cm²) with a heavy inoculum.

The production of carbonate is shown by the appearance of nodular crystals of calcium carbonate under and/or around the implanted bacterial masses, as seen through the bottom of the inverted plates at a magnification of × 40.

Reference: J. L. Shimwell, J. G. Carr, and M. E. Rhodes, J. Gen. Microbiol., *23*, 1960, 283.

Peptone Yeast Extract Acetate Agar

Difco peptone.................... 3 gm.
Difco yeast extract.............. 2 gm.
Sodium acetate................... 2 gm.
Bromthymol blue............. 0.02 gm.
Agar......................... 15 gm.
Distilled water.............. 1000 ml.

Dissolve the ingredients. Filter if necessary and adjust the pH to 6.5. Sterilize at 120° C. for 15 minutes. Inoculate and incubate for 14 days at 26° to 30° C. Metabolism of the acetate results in an increase in alkalinity due to the free sodium ion.

Reference: Einar Leifson, Antonie van Leeuwenhoek, *20*, 1954, 102.

Wort Agar

Use unhopped sweet beer wort, and adjust the specific gravity to 1.04. Add 2.5 per cent agar. Autoclave to dissolve, filter through paper pulp, and sterilize at 115° C. for 20 minutes.

Since the medium is at an acid pH (5.0 to 5.5), excessive heating should be avoided or the medium will tend to lose its gelling power.

Media for Luminescent Bacteria

TAP WATER LEMCO AGAR

Lemco......................... 10 gm.
Peptone (Oxoid)............... 10 gm.
NaCl.......................... 5 gm.
Agar......................... 14 gm.
Tap water.................. 1000 ml.

Dissolve the ingredients by autoclaving at 121° C. for 15 minutes. Filter if necessary. Adjust the pH to 7.6. Sterilize at 121° C. for 15 minutes.

SEA WATER LEMCO AGAR

Prepare as above but substitute 750 ml. of aged sea water for an equal amount of the tap water.

Reproduced by permission from R. Spencer, J. Gen. Microbiol., *13*, 1955, 111.

3 PER CENT NaCl FISH AGAR

To 500 gm. of fresh, minced, salt water fish add 1 L. of tap water and 10 gm. of peptone. Steam for 1 to 1.5 hours. Filter while hot through cotton wool. Add 30 to 40 ml. of N NaOH. Autoclave and filter off the precipitate while hot. Add 30 gm. of NaCl and readjust the pH to between 7.9 and 8.4. Add 2 per cent agar and autoclave at 121° C. for 20 minutes.

Media for Halophilic Bacteria

MEDIUM A

Difco-yeast extract	10.0 gm.
Proteose peptone	5.0 gm.
Casamino acids	5.0 gm.
KCl	2.0 gm.
Trisodium citrate	3.0 gm.
$MgSO_4 \cdot 7 H_2O$	20.0 gm.
NaCl	200 gm.
Water	1000 ml.

Dissolve the ingredients and adjust the pH to between 7.0 and 7.2.

For a solid medium, add 20.0 gm. of agar, dissolve by heating to 121° C. for 15 minutes, filter, and adjust the medium to a pH between 7.0 and 7.2. Sterilize at 121° C. for 15 minutes.

MEDIUM B

$MgSO_4 \cdot 7 H_2O$	5.0 gm.
$MgNO_3 \cdot 6 H_2O$	1.0 gm.
$FeCl_3 \cdot 7 H_2O$	0.025 gm.
Difco proteose peptone No. 3	5.0 gm.
Glycerol	10.0 gm.
Distilled water	500 ml.

Dissolve and sterilize at 121° C. for 15 minutes. If agar is needed, add 30.0 gm. of it before sterilizing the medium. Filter if necessary.

Sterilize 200 gm. of NaCl in a 3- to 4-L. flask.

Add 50 gm. of skim milk powder to 500 ml. of water and sterilize at 110° C. for 25 minutes.

Add the hot agar to the NaCl, and dissolve as much salt as possible. Allow it to cool to 60° C. Warm the sterile milk to between 50° and 60° C., and then add the milk to the salt mixture and tube or pour aseptically. Care must be exercised in the mixing or the milk will curdle.

Reproduced by permission from N. E. Gibbons, private communication. Medium A is a modification of that described by N. E. Gibbons, Can. J. Microbiol., *3*, 1957, 249; and Medium B is a modification of that published by H. P. Dussault and R. A. Lachance, J. Fisheries Research Board Can., *9*(3), 1952, 157.

Rabbit Dung Agar for Myxobacteria

Rabbit dung pellets	100 gm.
Tap water	250 ml.
Agar	15 gm.

Boil the pellets in the water for 10 minutes and stand overnight. Filter through gauze, expressing as much liquid as possible. Make the volume up to 1000 ml., add the agar, and autoclave at 115° C. for 20 minutes.

Reproduced by permission from S. F. Snieszko, J. McAllister, and E. R. Hitchner, J. Bacteriol., *41*, 1941, 26; and from J. M. Beebe, Iowa State Coll. J. Sci., *15*, 1941, 307.

For other methods see McCurdy, Can. J. Microbiol., *9*, 1963, 282; and *10*, 1964, 935.

Czapek-Dox Medium for Fungi

Sodium nitrate	2.0 gm.
Potassium chloride	0.5 gm.
Magnesium sulfate	0.5 gm.
Ferrous sulfate	0.01 gm.

Potassium dihydrogen phosphate. 1.0 gm.
Glucose...................... 50 gm.
Tap water..................... 1 L.
Sterilize at 111° C. for 25 minutes.

Reproduced by permission from H. Raistrick and W. Rintoul, Phil. Trans. Roy. Soc. London, Ser. B, *220*, 1931, 7.

Ferric Ammonium Citrate Agar for the Deposition of Iron

Peptone...................... 1.0 gm.
Yeast extract................. 0.2 gm.
Ferric ammonium citrate........ 0.5 gm.
Agar........................ 14 gm.
Tap water.................. 1000 ml.

Dissolve, adjust the pH to 7.0, filter if necessary, and sterilize at 121° C. for 20 minutes.

Inoculate and incubate aerobically for 7 days. Organisms that metabolize citrate free the ferric ion that precipitates around the colony. This is iron *deposition*, not *oxidation*. It may have no relationship to the *deposition* of iron referred to with many iron bacteria.

Reference: Author's recommendation.

Blood Agar

For diagnostic work, a blood agar plate must be uniformly thin, free of air bubbles, and with blood cells evenly distributed. Petri dishes are rarely flat in the base. It is therefore common practice to pour a layer of saline agar into the dish to even out the imperfections in the glass and to reduce the thickness of the layer of blood agar required.

Saline Agar: Add 20 gm. of agar and 8.5 gm. of NaCl to 1000 ml. of distilled water. Steam or autoclave to melt, filter, and sterilize by autoclaving at 121° C. for 20 minutes.

Preparation of Blood Agar Plates: Melt the saline agar in a steamer, cool to 60° C., and pour it out in 10-ml. quantities into sterile Petri dishes. Allow the agar to set.

Melt a bottle of sterile papain digest or meat infusion agar, and place it and the container of sterile blood in a water bath at 50° C. Allow 10 minutes for the tem-

peratures to equilibrate. Then add aseptically 10 per cent by volume of the sterile citrated blood (horse, ox, sheep, or human, as desired), and mix uniformly by slowly inverting the bottle several times. *Do not shake*, because frothing must be avoided.

While the blood agar is still warm, pour it in a thin layer over the saline agar.

Allow the plates to set, and incubate for 24 hours at 37° C. to check for sterility. Then refrigerate at 4° C.

Bordet-Gengou Potato Glycerol Blood Agar

1. Preparation of Potato Extract: Clean and peel potatoes. Weigh 250 gm. and cut into thin slices. Add 9 gm. of NaCl and 500 ml. of water. Boil until the potato disintegrates. Filter and adjust the pH to 7.0.

2. Preparation of the Medium: Dissolve 60 gm. of agar in 1500 ml. of water by autoclaving. While still hot, add 500 ml. of heated potato extract, 20 ml. of glycerol, and 20 gm. of Difco-proteose peptone. Distribute as required. To sterilize, steam for 1 hour and then autoclave at 110° C. for 5 minutes.

To prepare plates melt the agar and cool to 55° C. Add 15 per cent by volume of sterile defibrinated horse (or sheep) blood previously warmed to 45° C. Mix well and pour.

Reproduced by permission from T. J. Mackie and J. E. McCartney, Handbook of Practical Bacteriology, E. and S. Livingstone, Edinburgh, 1942.

Liver Extract Agar

Minced beef liver............. 500 gm.
Distilled water............... 1000 ml.

Steam for 1 hour. Adjust the pH to 7.0, and steam for an additional 10 minutes. Pressure filter and then add:

Bacto-tryptone................ 10 gm.
K_2HPO_4...................... 1 gm.
Agar........................ 15 gm.

Steam to dissolve. Adjust the pH to 7.0. Dispense and sterilize at 121° C. for 20 minutes.

Reproduced by permission from E. J. Cameron, J. Assoc. Offic. Agr. Chemists, *19*, 1936, 433.

Embryonic Egg Yolk Agar for *Calymmatobacterium*

Withdraw the yolk aseptically from 4- or 5-day-old chick embryos, and add it to an equal quantity of melted meat infusion agar held at 60° C. in 150- by 16-mm. tubes. Allow to set in a slanting position.

Inoculate the condensation water.

Reproduced by permission from K. Anderson, W. A. DeMonbreun, and E. W. Goodpasture, J. Exptl. Med., *81*, 1945, 25.

Levinthal Media for the Differentiation of the Genus *Haemophilus*

"Levinthal Stock": Prepare Difco-Brain-Heart Infusion Broth according to directions.

While it is boiling vigorously, add 10 per cent by volume of defibrinated horse blood. Filter through Whatman No. 12 filter paper, and sterilize the filtrate by filtration.

"Levinthal Agar": Dissolve 45 gm. of Difco-proteose agar No. 3 and 15 gm. of Bacto-agar in 1000 ml. of water. Add 1000 ml. of sterile "Levinthal Stock."

"Levinthal Agar Plus X-factor": "Levinthal agar" autoclaved at 121° C. for 15 minutes is the "X-factor" medium. The X-factor (hemin of the blood) is stable. Any V-factor is destroyed.

"V-factor" Medium: Emulsify 100 gm. of powdered brewers' yeast in 400 ml. of distilled water. Adjust the pH to 4.6. Boil for 10 minutes. Filter through filter paper. Adjust the pH to 7.0, and sterilize by filtration.

To prepare *"V-factor"* medium add 1 part of yeast extract to 9 parts of melted Difco proteose agar No. 3.

"X- plus V-factor medium": Add 1 part of sterile yeast extract (see V-factor medium) to 9 parts of "Levinthal agar plus X-factor."

Reference: H. E. Alexander in R. J. Dubos, Bacterial and Mycotic Infections of Man, 1st ed., J. B. Lippincott, Philadelphia, 1948, p. 484. Reproduced by permission of the National Foundation, New York.

Blood Cystine Glucose Agar for *Pasteurella tularensis*

Beef infusion	1000 ml.
Peptone	10 gm.
Agar	15 gm.
Sodium chloride	5 gm.
Cystine	1 gm.
Glucose	10 gm.
Defibrinated blood	5 to 8%

Remove all fat from lean beef and grind the meat finely. To each 500 gm. of lean meat add 1000 ml. of distilled water and infuse in the refrigerator for 12 to 18 hours. After refrigeration, skim off all fat and boil vigorously for 30 minutes. Filter through paper and restore the volume with distilled water. Add the peptone, agar, and sodium chloride. Dissolve and adjust the pH to 7.3. Sterilize by autoclaving at 121° C. for 15 minutes. When required for use, add the cystine and glucose, and steam for 1 hour on 3 successive days to melt the agar and to sterilize. Cool to 60° C. and add the blood.

Heat the flask of blood-glucose-cystine agar in a water bath for 2 hours at 60° C.; use care to avoid a higher temperature, which will cause sedimentation. Use this to pour the plates.

Reproduced by permission from D. T. Smith and D. S. Martin, Zinsser's Textbook of Bacteriology, 9th ed., Appleton-Century-Crofts, New York, 1948.

Diphosphothiamine Medium for *Haemophilus piscium*

Difco proteose peptone No. 3	20 gm.
Glucose	10 gm.
NaCl	5 gm.
Tween 40	0.05 gm.
Distilled water	1000 ml.

Dissolve the ingredients, and adjust the pH to 7.3 with NaOH. Sterilize by autoclaving at 121° C. for 15 minutes.

Add diphosphothiamine aseptically to

the basal medium at the rate of 1.0 μg. of diphosphothiamine per ml. of basal medium, *or* add adenosine triphosphate at the rate of 30 μg. per ml. of basal medium.

Reproduced by permission from P. J. Griffin, Arch. Biochem., *30*, 1951, 100, Academic Press, Inc.

The Isolation of *Rhizobium* Spp. from Legume Nodules

ISOLATION FROM THE NODULE

Carefully soak the ground around the plant for 24 hours before removal. Remove the plant with the soil, and place it in a container filled with water to allow the soil to fall away. Wash the roots carefully in several changes of sterile tap water, and then cut off the nodules—preferably healthy ones—from the crown roots, with a small piece of root adhering to each. Immerse successively for 2-minute periods in 70 per cent ethanol and 0.2 per cent mercuric chloride; then transfer aseptically to sterile water and rinse with at least three changes of water.

Crush the nodules between two sterilized slides, and inoculate some of the milky fluid onto legume extract agar or yeast extract mannitol agar. Incubate at 28° C. for several days. Subculture the colonies to slants of the same medium and incubate.

INOCULATION OF SEED

For small seeds the method of Fåhraeus (*vide infra*) is excellent and yields quick results. For large seeds the following method may be used:

Prepare carbon- and nitrogen-free agar and dispense in vessels compatible with the species of the plant being tested.

Sterilize the seeds in the same manner as the nodules. Place the seeds in a sterile Petri dish or other container over a layer of yeast mannitol or legume extract agar. Incubate at 28° C. until germination occurs. Select sterile germinated seeds, immerse them in a suspension of the organism, and then transfer them to the surface of the carbon- and nitrogen-free agar. Expose the containers to daylight, but protect the seeds from direct sunlight. If the culture is a species of *Rhizobium*, nodules will begin to form shortly after the emergence of the first true leaves.

THE FÅHRAEUS PROCEDURE FOR SMALL LEGUMES

Dispense Fahraeus carbon- and nitrogen-free liquid medium in 25-ml. amounts in 150- by 39-mm. tubes, and cover with loose glass caps or plug with cotton wool.

Sterilize some clean microscope slides and 24- by 40-mm. coverglasses at 160° C. in a Petri dish; place only one slide and one coverglass in each dish.

Sterilize the seeds as above and allow them to germinate at room temperature in a shallow layer of water.

When the roots are 10 to 15 mm. long, pipette approximately 0.2 ml. of the carbon- and nitrogen-free medium (containing 0.3 to 0.4 per cent Bacto-agar), melted and cooled to 30° C., to one-half of a slide and immediately transfer a seedling to the slide with a sterile platinum wire so that the root tip is in the agar. Place the coverglass carefully over the agar and the root tip with forceps. Remove the seed coat if it still adheres to the cotyledons.

Transfer the slide to the tube containing the mineral medium.

Inoculate the roots either by adding the inoculum to the agar before preparing the slide or by pipetting a few drops of a heavy suspension to the mineral medium. Incubate at 25° C. in a controlled temperature cabinet under a fluorescent lamp.

To examine, remove the slides and drain off the excess solution with a filter paper. Examine under high power with the use of glycerol as an immersion fluid. Slides may then be returned to the tubes. A phase contrast microscope should be used if available.

Infection of the root hairs coincides, in clover, with the opening of the first true leaves. It is preceded by intense protoplasmic activity and a movement of the cell nucleus to the point of infection. Bulbous swelling and curling of the root hairs are common features. Infection threads are visible within the root hair. Unaffected hairs usually remain straight and normal in form.

Reference should be made to the original paper for a more detailed description and for the excellent illustrations.

FÅHRAEUS CARBON- AND NITROGEN-FREE LIQUID MEDIUM

CaCl₂	0.1 gm.
MgSO₄·7 H₂O	0.12 gm.
KH₂PO₄	0.1 gm.
Na₂HPO₄·2 H₂O	0.15 gm.
Fe citrate	0.005 gm.
Mn·Cu·Zn·B·Mo	Traces
Distilled water	1000 ml.

After autoclaving the pH is 6.5.

For the agar medium add 0.3 to 0.4 per cent agar before sterilization.

Sterilize at 121° C. for 20 minutes.

Reproduced by permission from G. Fåhraeus, J. Gen. Microbiol., 16, 1957, 374.

Legume Extract Agar for *Rhizobium*

Cut up 35 gm. of well-washed alfalfa roots and mix with 10 gm. of soybean meal. Add 3 times the volume of water, steam gently for 1 hour, and then allow to stand overnight. Dilute to 1000 ml. and filter through paper pulp. Add the following:

K₂HPO₄	1.0 gm.
MgSO₄·7 H₂O	0.2 gm.
NaCl	0.1 gm.
CaCl₂	0.1 gm.
FeCl₃	0.001 gm.
Agar	20.0 gm.

Heat to 121° C. for 20 minutes, filter and add:

CaCO₃	5 gm.
Sucrose	10 gm.
Glucose	5 gm.

When the sugars have dissolved, dispense

as required and sterilize at 115° C. for 20 minutes.

Reproduced by permission from H. A. Pittman, J. Dept. Agr., W. Australia, 12, 2nd Ser., 1935, 105.

Yeast Extract Mannitol Agar (Medium "79")

Mannitol	10.0 gm.
K₂HPO₄	0.5 gm.
MgSO₄·7 H₂O	0.2 gm.
NaCl	0.1 gm.
CaCO₃	3.0 gm.
Yeast extract (10%)*	100.0 ml.
Agar	15.0 gm.
Distilled water	900.0 ml.

Each 100 ml. of the yeast extract contains 50 to 60 mg. of amino acid nitrogen.

Reproduced by permission from O. N. Allen, Experiments in Soil Bacteriology, Burgess Publishing Company, Minneapolis, 1949.

Solid Medium for *Leptospira*

Tryptose-phosphate broth (Difco) 0.2 gm.

Agar (Difco) .... 1.0 gm.

Dissolve in 90 ml. of distilled water, adjust the pH to 7.5, and sterilize the medium in the autoclave. Cool to 50° C., and add aseptically 10 ml. of sterile rabbit serum and 1 ml. of hemoglobin preparation. Heat at 56° C. for 30 minutes and then pour plates.

Prepare the hemoglobin preparation by lysing washed and packed sheep erythrocytes in 20 volumes of cold distilled water. Remove the stroma by centrifugation. Sterilize by Seitz filtration.

Reproduced by permission from C. D.

* *To prepare the yeast extract:* Steam 100 gm. of starch-free pressed yeast for 3 to 4 hours in 1000 ml. of water. Allow to stand for 1 week. During this time the yeast cells will settle to the bottom. The clear, straw-colored supernatant liquid should be siphoned, bottled in 100-ml. quantities, and sterilized at 15 pounds of pressure for 45 minutes.

Cox and A. D. Larson, J. Bacteriol., *73*, 1957, 587.

Formate Medium for *Methanococcus*

Sodium formate	15.0 gm.
Ammonium sulfate	1.0 gm.
$CaCl_2 \cdot 2\ H_2O$	0.01 gm.
$MgCl_2 \cdot 2\ H_2O$	0.01 gm.
$FeCl_3 \cdot 6\ H_2O$	0.02 gm.
$MnSO_4 \cdot 4\ H_2O$	0.01 gm.
$Na_2MoO_4 \cdot 2\ H_2O$	0.001 gm.
K_2HPO_4	2.0 gm.
Phenol red indicator	0.003 gm.
Methylene blue	0.002 gm.
Sodium thioglycollate	0.5 gm.
Glass-distilled water	1000 ml.

For a solid medium add 15 gm. of agar.

If a pyrogallol-K_2CO_3 seal is used, the pH of the medium after addition of the inoculum should be 8.3 to 8.5. When an "oxsorbent" seal is employed, the medium after inoculation is adjusted to a pH between 7.5 and 8.0. Cultures are incubated at 30° to 40° C., anaerobically.

Sterilize at 121° C. for 15 minutes.

Reproduced by permission from T. C. Stadtman and H. A. Barker, J. Bacteriol., *62*, 1951, 269.

Glycine Medium for *Peptococcus glycinophilus*

Glycine	3.0 gm.
Bacto-yeast extract	5.0 gm.
Bacto-peptone	5.0 gm.
M Phosphate buffer, pH 7.1	5 ml.
Saturated $CaSO_4$	2.5 ml.
Cysteine HCl	0.2 gm.
$MgSO_4 \cdot 7\ H_2O$	0.05 gm.
$FeSO_4 \cdot 7\ H_2O$	0.01 gm.
Distilled water	1000 ml.

Dissolve the ingredients, adjust the pH to 7.2, and dispense in screw-capped bottles. Sterilize at 121° C. for 15 minutes.

Since cysteine is rapidly oxidized, the medium has a limited life. Do not expose it unnecessarily to air.

Reproduced by permission from B. P. Cardon and H. A. Barker, J. Bacteriol., *52*, 1946, 629.

Isolation and Growth of *Methanobacterium*

AN ENRICHMENT MEDIUM FOR *Methanobacterium*

Barker and Taha Enrichment Medium

Ethanol	10.0 ml.
K_2HPO_4	5.0 gm.
$MgSO_4 \cdot 7\ H_2O$	0.1 gm.
$(NH_4)_2SO_4$	0.3 gm.
$FeSO_4 \cdot 7\ H_2O$	0.02 gm.
Yeast autolysate	5.0 ml.
$CaCO_3$	100 gm.
Water	1000 ml.

Sterilize the above medium by autoclaving

Prepare separately (*a*) 0.5 gm. of Na_2CO_3 and 10.0 ml. of H_2O, and (*b*) 0.1 gm. of $Na_2S \cdot 9\ H_2O$ and 10.0 ml. of H_2O. Sterilize both by autoclaving, and then add aseptically to the above medium. Adjust the pH to between 7.0 and 7.4.

A similar medium containing 15 to 20 gm. of agar per L. may be used for isolation. NOTE: The ethanol is included in the above basal medium before autoclaving. As an alternative it may be sterilized by filtration and added aseptically with the Na_2CO_3 and $Na_2S \cdot 9\ H_2O$.

ISOLATION

Dispense the enrichment medium in glass-stoppered bottles in which a heavy (5 per cent) inoculum of black swamp mud has been placed. Fill to capacity to exclude air and insert stopper. Incubate at 35° C. in the dark. *Methanobacterium* usually develops in a few days as the predominant population. Transfer through the enrichment medium two or three times, and then isolate by the streak plate or shake tube method.

Reproduced by permission from H. A. Barker and S. M. Taha, J. Bacteriol., *43*, 1942, 347.

Isolation and Growth of *Dialister* Sp.

Source of the Organisms: The organisms, obtained from nasopharyngeal washings from patients with epidemic influenza, were originally described by Olitzky and Gates under the name of *Bacterium pneumosintes*. Because of their small size, the organisms pass through the Berkefeld N- and V-filters, and filtered material may be used. The organisms also survive prolonged contact with 50 per cent glycerol, which kills many other bacteria. No growth occurs below pH 7.0 or above pH 8.0.

Smith-Noguchi Medium and Technique for Isolation: Place relatively large pieces (0.6 to 0.8 gm.) of sterile normal rabbit kidney in sterile test tubes measuring 20 by 1.5 cm., one piece to each tube.

Cover the tissue with 8 to 10 ml. of sterile human ascitic fluid at pH 7.8 to 8.0. Seal each tube with 2 ml. of sterile melted paraffin and replace the cotton wool plug.

Incubate for 2 days at 37° C. to check sterility and permit anaerobic conditions to develop.

Inoculation: Nasopharyngeal fluid may be inoculated directly or after filtration through a Berkefeld V- or N- or equivalent filter. Suspected tissue should be macerated in saline.

Inoculate the medium with a capillary pipette pushed through the paraffin. Deposit the inoculum on the surface of the meat. Reseal by applying a heated rod to the surface of the paraffin.

Incubate at 37° C. for 8 to 12 days. With positive cultures a faint haze appears in 5 days and reaches a depth of 3 cm. by the 8th day.

Subculture to blood agar, Loeffler's inspissated serum, or Bordet-Gengou medium and incubate anaerobically. Growth occurs within 7 days at 37° C.

Reproduced by permission from P. K. Olitsky and F. L. Gates, J. Exptl. Med., *33*, 1921, 713.

Isolation and Cultivation of *Desulovibrio*

Desulfovibrio desulfuricans is a strict anaerobe noted for its ability to reduce sulfates. It occurs in soil and marine muds and is of common occurrence in sewage sludge. The following methods are those of Butlin and his associates and of Miller, with modifications suggested by Grossman and Postgate.

MEDIA FOR ISOLATION OF *Desulfovibrio*

The following modifications of media described by Baars (1930) and Starkey (1938) are recommended by Butlin, Adams, and Thomas.

1. Baars' Medium

K_2HPO_4	0.5 gm.
NH_4Cl	1.0 gm.
$CaSO_4$	1.0 gm.
$MgSO_4 \cdot 7 H_2O$	2.0 gm.
Na lactate, 70% solution	5.0 gm.
Tap water	1000 ml.

Dissolve the salts; adjust the pH to within the range of 7.0 to 7.5 and sterilize at 121° C. for 20 minutes.

Prepare separately a 1 per cent solution of $FeSO_4 \cdot (NH_4)_2SO_4 \cdot 6 H_2O$ and sterilize by steaming for 1 hour on 3 successive days. Add 5 ml. of the supernatant per 100 ml. of the above medium immediately before use.

NOTE: This medium has a heavy precipitate but is quite suited for crude cultures.

2. Starkey's Medium

K_2HPO_4	0.5 gm.
NH_4Cl	1.0 gm.
Na_2SO_4	1.0 gm.
$CaCl_2 \cdot 2 H_2O$	0.1 gm.
$MgSO_4 \cdot 7 H_2O$	2.0 gm.
Na lactate, 70% solution	5.0 gm.
Distilled water	1000 ml.

Dissolve the ingredients and adjust the pH to between 7.0 and 7.5. Sterilize at 121° C. for 20 minutes.

NOTE: This medium has a slight precipitate, which may be removed by filtration after sterilization, following which the medium may be resterilized.

Prepare a 1 per cent solution of $FeSO_4 \cdot (NH_4)_2SO_4 \cdot 6 H_2O$ as for medium 1 above, and add 5 ml. per 100 ml. of medium just before use.

For *halophilic strains*, add 1 to 3 per cent NaCl to each of the above media before sterilization, or, alternatively, replace the tap or distilled water with sea water.

DEVELOPMENT OF CRUDE CULTURES

Butlin and his associates recommend the use of the above media with *and without* the addition of sodium sulfite for preparation of enrichment cultures. The sodium sulfite, in concentrations up to 5 per cent, has little effect on the majority of sulfate reducers but materially reduces the development of the nonsulfate reducers.

Prepare a fresh 20 to 30 per cent solution of $Na_2SO_3 \cdot 7 H_2O$ shortly before use and sterilize by filtration. When required, add 10 ml. of the solution to each 100 ml. of medium, and readjust the pH to 7.2 by the addition of sterile N HCl (approximately 2 ml. per 100 ml. of Baars' medium).

Place the inoculum in two 30- to 50-ml. stoppered bottles. One to 2 gm. of soil or sewage sludge is usually adequate. Fill the bottles completely with the media (one with and one without sulfite) and insert the stopper. Incubate at 30° to 50° C.

Growth is usually indicated by the precipitation of black iron sulfide following the reduction of the sulfate by the growing cells. This may take a few days to several weeks. Examine the cultures for vibrios. If they predominate, proceed to the isolation of pure cultures. If not, make subcultures from the black sludge into a fresh medium with the use of a 10 per cent inoculum.

ISOLATION OF PURE CULTURES

Prepare Starkey's medium with the addition of 2 per cent agar and filter clear. Sterilize the medium, add the ferrous salt, and then distribute aseptically in 9-ml. amounts into tubes held in a water bath at 45° to 50° C.

To one series add 1 ml. of 30 per cent sterile $Na_2SO_3 \cdot 7 H_2O$, and 0.2 ml. of sterile N HCl.

Prepare decimal dilutions of the crude cultures. Although not specifically recommended by Butlin and his associates, it is advisable to prepare the dilutions in the liquid medium in the absence of oxygen. The addition of 1 ml. of a sterile solution containing 1000 p.p.m. of thioglycollic acid to each 9 ml. of sterile liquid medium is recommended.

Add 1 ml. of each of the higher dilutions to corresponding tubes of the agar medium. Mix well and allow to set.

Incubate until well-isolated black colonies appear in the higher dilutions.

Alternative: Inoculate the crude culture onto the surface of the agar medium in a Petri dish, with the use of both sulfite-containing and sulfite-free media. Make the transfer preferably in an oxygen-free atmosphere, and seal the dishes in a suitable anaerobic jar without delay.

SUBCULTURE OF ISOLATED COLONIES

The foregoing media are not the most suitable for the culture of species of *Desulfovibrio*. Addition of yeast extract greatly stimulates growth but is omitted from the previous media because it also greatly stimulates contaminants. The following medium, described by Butlin and his associates and modified by Postgate, should be used. The medium is similar in most respects to that published independently by Miller (1950).

K_2HPO_4	0.5 gm.
NH_4Cl	1.0 gm.
Na_2SO_4	1.0 gm.
$CaCl_2 \cdot 6 H_2O$	0.1 gm.
$MgSO_4 \cdot 7 H_2O$	2.0 gm.
Na lactate, 70% solution	3.5 gm.
Difco yeast extract	1.0 gm.
$FeSO_4 \cdot 7 H_2O$	0.002 gm.
Distilled water	1000 ml.

Dissolve the ingredients, adjust the pH to 7.5, and autoclave at 121° C. for 20 minutes. Filter off the sediment, dispense as required, and resterilize.

Prepare separately a 0.6 per cent solution of cysteine hydrochloride in distilled water, and sterilize by autoclaving at 121° C. for 20 minutes. This acid solution has a pH of 1.8 and is relatively stable to oxidation, provided it is not neutralized. Add 1 ml. to each 9 ml. of medium immediately before use. The final concentration of cysteine is 5 μmoles per ml.

Pick black colonies showing the correct morphological types on microscopic examination into the liquid medium. Incubate aerobically.

If it is desired, the cultures may be plated on the same medium containing 2 per cent agar and incubated anaerobically in an atmosphere of hydrogen and 5 per cent CO_2 in a McIntosh and Fildes jar, with a dried pad of absorbent cotton wool, impregnated with lead acetate, between the cultures and the catalyst.

NOTE: Reference should also be made to Grossman and Postgate, Proc. Soc. App. Bacteriol., *16*, 1953, 1; and to Drummond and Postgate, J. App. Bacteriol., *18*, 1955, 307.

Reproduced by permission from K. R. Butlin, M. E. Adams, and M. Thomas, J. Gen. Microbiol., *3*, 1949, 46; J. P. Grossman and J. R. Postgate, Nature, *17*, 1953, 600; and from L. P. Miller, Contrib. Boyce Thompson Inst., *6* (3), 1950, 85.

Bile Solubility Test

This test has been employed to differentiate the pneumococcus, *Diplococcus pneumoniae*, from the other α-hemolytic streptococci. Living cultures of this organism are soluble in bile salts at neutral pH.

Centrifuge the growth from a 5-ml. culture of the organism in glucose-tryptic broth, and resuspend the growth in 0.5 M phosphate buffer, pH 7 to 7.6, containing 2 per cent sodium chloride and 0.05 per cent sodium desoxycholate. Incubate at 37° C. for 60 minutes and examine. Cultures of pneumococci lyse under these conditions.

Reproduced by permission from A. B.

Anderson and P. D'A. Hart, Lancet, *2*, 1934, 359.

Bile Tolerance

Tolerance to bile or bile salts has been used in the description of species in *Lactobacillus*, *Streptococcus*, *Aerococcus*, *Pseudomonas*, *Vibrio*, and *Mycobacterium* and possibly others. The test is usually performed by incorporating in a suitable basal medium concentrations of ox bile, ranging from 5 to 40 per cent. Forty per cent bile blood agar has been used in the differentiation of the genus *Aerococcus* from other micrococci.

Detection of Cholesterol in Cultures of *Streptobacillus*

Macrotechnique: Grow the organisms in 20 per cent serum broth. Centrifuge and wash the deposit three times with saline.

Extract the aqueous residue containing the organisms with acetone twice and pentane three times. Mix the acetone and pentane washings, and then separate the aqueous layer and discard it. Dry the solution over anhydrous sodium sulfate, and then evaporate to dryness with completion of the final stage under reduced pressure.

Dissolve the waxy residue in N alcoholic potash and reflux for 1 hour. Cool and dilute with water. Extract thoroughly with pentane.

Wash the pentane solution with dilute sodium hydroxide and then with distilled water. Dry the pentane solution and then evaporate to dryness.

A crystallized white residue is left. Dissolve in 90 per cent aqueous acetone and recrystallize. Flat plates of cholesterol with a melting point of 147° to 147.5° C. are produced.

Reproduced by permission from S. M. Partridge and E. Kleineberger, J. Pathol. Bacteriol., *52*, 1941, 219.

Digitonin Test for Cholesterol

A 0.5 per cent solution of digitonin in 50 per cent alcohol will precipitate cholesterol from solution.

Catalase Production

Catalase is an enzyme containing a hematin as the prosthetic group and is capable of decomposing hydrogen peroxide to gaseous oxygen and water. It is widely distributed in nature and is present in most aerobic cells. The function of catalase is to remove the toxic product H_2O_2 resulting from coupled oxidation-reduction processes involving oxygen.

$$2 H_2O_2 \rightarrow 2 H_2O + O_2$$

Pour 1 ml. of H_2O_2 (10 volumes per cent) over the surface of a 24-hour agar slope culture. If catalase is present, bubbles of oxygen will be released from the surface of the growth.

Reproduced by permission from W. W. C. Topley and G. S. Wilson, Principles of Bacteriology and Immunity, 1st ed., Edward Arnold and Company, London, 1929, p. 239.

The Oxidase Test

KOVACS' OXIDASE TEST

Lay a piece of Whatman No. 1 filter paper about 6 cm. square in a Petri dish. Drop two or three drops of 1 per cent tetramethylparaphenylene diamine hydrochloride on the center of the paper. Remove the suspect colony with a platinum rod and smear it thoroughly on the reagent-impregnated paper in a line 3 to 6 cm. long. If the test is positive the transferred colony turns dark purple in 5 to 10 seconds. Prepare the reagent every 2 weeks and keep in a dark glass-stoppered bottle in a refrigerator.

Reference: N. Kovacs, Nature, London, *178*, 1956, 703.

CYTOCHROME OXIDASE TEST

This method is a modification of a test employed by Gaby and Hadley (1954) for the identification of *Pseudomonas* cultures. As shown by Ewing and Johnson (1960), the modified method is of great value in the differentiation of *Aeromonas* and *Vibrio*, as well as *Pseudomonas* and *Alcaligenes*, cultures from members of the family *Enterobacteriaceae*. Members of the aforementioned groups gave positive tests whereas all *Enterobacteriaceae* tested were negative.

Nutrient agar slant cultures incubated at 37° C., or at a lower temperature if required, are recommended. After incubation two or three drops of each reagent are introduced and the tube is tilted so that the reagents are mixed and flow over the growth on the slant. Positive reactions are indicated by the development of a blue color in the growth within 2 minutes. The majority of positive cultures produce strong reactions within 30 seconds. Any very weak or doubtful reaction that occurs after two minutes should be ignored. Plate cultures may be tested by allowing an equal parts mixture of the reagents to flow over isolated colonies.

Test Reagents

A. Ethyl alcohol, 95–96 per cent.. 100 ml.
   Alpha naphthol............ 1 gm.
B. Distilled water............ 100 ml.
   Para-aminodimethylanilino
    HCl.................... 1 gm.
(Reagent B should be prepared frequently and should be stored in a refrigerator when not in use.)

See W. L. Gaby and C. Hadley, J. Bacteriol., *74*, 1957, 356, and W. H. Ewing and J. G. Johnson, Internat. Bull. Bacteriol. Nomen. Taxon., *10*, 1960, 223.

Reference: W. H. Ewing, Enterobacteriaceae, Biochemical Methods for Group Differentiation, U. S. Department of Health, Education and Welfare, Public Health Service Publication No. 734, 1962.

Peroxidase Test

Place a few milligrams of crystalline benzidine hydrochloride in a test tube with 3 ml. of glacial acetic acid. After the crystals have dissolved, add an equal volume of hydrogen peroxide. A peroxidase-containing substance in contact with this solution turns blue. Place a drop on a colony and observe the color change. Alternatively perform the test in a manner similar to that used for oxidase in Kovacs' test.

Reference: L. R. Anderson, J. Bacteriol., *20*, 1930, 371.

Benzidine Test for Iron Porphyrins

Partially dissolve 1 gm. of benzidine dihydrochloride in 20 ml. of glacial acetic acid. Add 30 ml. of distilled water, heat gently, cool, and then add 50 ml. of ethyl alcohol (95 per cent). The development of a yellow color on storage does not alter the sensitivity of the reagent. It is stable in the refrigerator for at least 1 month.

To test for peroxidase, flood the young, well-developed agar plate cultures with the benzidine reagent and then add an approximately equal volume of freshly prepared 5 per cent hydrogen peroxide. If the culture possesses iron porphyrin compounds, a blue-green to deep-blue coloration promptly develops.

The test is usually negative in broth cultures, but a positive reaction can be obtained by resuspending the sediment of centrifuged broth cultures in 0.5 ml. of the reagent and then adding 0.5 ml. of 5 per cent hydrogen peroxide.

Reference: R. H. Diebel and J. B. Evans, J. Bacteriol., *79*, 1960, 356.

Indole Production

The medium employed for this test must contain an adequate amount of tryptophane. Papain digest broth (p. 241) is excellent but may not be suitable for some organisms. The addition of 1.0 per cent casein digest to a suitable growth medium usually suffices.

Incubate the cultures for a minimum of 1 to 3 days, and test at 24-hour intervals on a sample of the culture.

Procedure: Layer 1 to 2 ml. of the Ehrlich-Böhme Solution No. 1 on the surface of the liquid culture. A red color develops at the junction if indole is present. The

author finds that no advantage is gained by the addition of Solution No. 2, as recommended in many texts.

PREPARATION OF SOLUTIONS

Solution 1

Para-dimethylaminobenzaldehyde...	4 gm.
96% ethanol...................	380 gm.
Concentrated HCl..............	80 gm.

Solution 2

Saturated aqueous solution of potassium persulfate

Goré's Modification: Remove the plug (which must be of white absorbent cotton wool) from the tube, and moisten with 0.5 ml. of Solution No. 2 and then with 0.5 ml. of Solution No. 1. Replace the plug and push it down to within 1 inch of the medium. Place the tube in a boiling water bath for 15 minutes; avoid any direct contact between the plug and the medium.

A red color on the plug indicates indole. The method differentiates between indole and methyl-indole, inasmuch as the latter is nonvolatile.

Reproduced by permission from S. N. Goré, Indian J. Med. Res., *8*, 1921, 505.

The Cholera-Red Test

The test has been used to help to identify the cholera vibrio, *V. comma*. It depends on the simultaneous production of nitrite and indole. The addition of sulfuric acid to the culture results in the production of nitroso-indole, which yields a pink to violet color.

The test is negative when the concentrations of nitrite and indole become disproportionate. When positive, the color depends on the ratio of the two, changing from orange-red to violet as the ratio of indole to nitrite changed from less than 1 to greater than 2, in the presence of 0.004 per cent indole.

When indole and nitrite are both present, a positive indole test by the Kovacs method is obtained only if the molar concentration of nitrite exceeds that of the indole. The Gnezda method, which depends on the volatility of indole but not of nitrite, is not affected.

The optimal concentration of the strongest cholera-red reactions is obtained with a molar ratio of indole to nitrite of approximately 2:1.

This can be achieved in practice by using the following medium:

Difco-peptone................ 10 gm.
Sodium chloride.............. 5 gm.
Sodium nitrate .... 0.01 gm.
Distilled water.............. 1000 ml.

Dissolve the ingredients. Adjust the pH to 7.2, and distribute in 5-ml. amounts in 150- by 13-mm. tubes. Sterilize at 120° C. for 15 minutes.

Inoculate and incubate for 22 hours at 37° C.

To 1 ml. of the culture, add 2 to 3 drops of concentrated sulfuric acid. The development of a pink to violet color is a positive test.

Reference: W. E. Beam, J. Bacteriol., 77, 1959, 328.

Growth in Moeller's KCN Broth

The original medium contains the following:

Peptone Orthana special*........ 10 gm.
NaCl......................... 5 gm.
KH_2PO_4.................... 0.225 gm.
$Na_2HPO_4·2H_2O$ .... 5.64 gm.
Distilled water.............. 1000 ml.

Adjust the pH to 7.6. Sterilize by autoclaving.

To the cold medium add 15 ml. of 0.5 per cent KCN. Dispense in 1-ml. amounts in sterile 6- by ½-inch tubes and stopper quickly with corks sterilized by heating in paraffin. The medium may be stored for 2 weeks at 4° C.

Inoculate with 1 loopful of a 24-hour broth culture grown at 37° C. Incubate at 37° C. and read daily for 2 days. Positive results are indicated by development of

* Three grams of Difco-proteose peptone No. 3 may be substituted for the Orthana peptone.

turbidity. *Citrobacter, Providence, Proteus, Klebsiella,* and *Enterobacter* species will grow in this medium. *Shigella, Salmonella, Arizona,* and *Escherichia coli* are inhibited.

Reference: W. H. Ewing, Enterobacteriaceae, Biochemical Methods for Group Differentiation. U. S. Department of Health, Education and Welfare, Public Health Service Publication No. 734, 1962.

Test for Deamination of Phenylalanine to Phenylpyruvic Acid

Yeast extract..................... 3 gm.
DL-Phenylalanine................. 2 gm.
(Or L-phenylalanine)............ 1 gm.
Disodium phosphate.............. 1 gm.
Sodium chloride................. 5 gm.
Agar........................... 12 gm.
Distilled water................ 1000 ml.

Tube and sterilize at 121° C. for 10 minutes and allow to solidify in a slanted position (long slant).

Test Reagent: Ten per cent (w/v) solution of ferric chloride.

Inoculation: Inoculate the slant of the PA agar with a fairly heavy inoculum from an agar slant culture.

Incubation: Four hours or, if desired, 18 to 24 hours at 37° C. After incubation, 4 or 5 drops of ferric chloride reagent are allowed to run down over the growth on the slant. If phenylpyruvic acid has been formed, a green color develops in the syneresis fluid and in the slant.

Reference: W. H. Ewing, Enterobacteriaceae, Biochemical Methods for Group Differentiation, U. S. Department of Health, Education and Welfare, Public Health Service Publication No. 734, 1962.

Tests for Decarboxylase Activity against Arginine, Ornithine, and Lysine

MOELLER METHOD (1955)

Basal Medium

Peptone (Orthana special)†........ 5 gm.
Beef extract..................... 5 gm.

† Peptone special Orthana Meat USP XV from A/S Orthana Kemish Fabrik, Copenhagen, Denmark.

Bromocresol purple (1.6%).... 0.625 ml.
Cresol red (0.2%).............. 2.5 ml.
Glucose...................... 0.5 gm.
Pyridoxal..................... 5 mg.
Distilled water............... 1000 ml.

Adjust pH to 6.0. Divide the basal medium into four equal portions, one of which is tubed without the addition of any amino acid. These tubes of basal medium are used for control purposes. To one of the remaining portions of basal medium add 1 per cent of L-lysine dihydrochloride; to the second, add 1 per cent of L-arginine monohydrochloride; and to the third, add 1 per cent of L-ornithine dihydrochloride. If DL-amino acids are used, incorporate them into the media in 2 per cent concentration, inasmuch as the microorganisms apparently are active only against the L-forms. Tube the amino acid media in 3- or 4-ml. amounts in small (13 by 100 mm.), screw-capped tubes and sterilize at 121° C. for 10 minutes. A small amount of floccular precipitate may be seen in the ornithine medium. This does not interfere with its use.

Inoculation: Inoculate lightly from a young agar slant culture. After inoculation, add a layer (about 4 or 5 mm. in thickness) of sterile mineral (paraffin) oil to each tube, including the control. A control tube should be inoculated with each culture under investigation.

Incubation: Incubate at 37° C. Examine daily for 4 days. Positive reactions are indicated by alkalinization of the media and a consequent change in the color of the indicator system from yellow to violet or reddish-violet. The majority of positive reactions with *Enterobacteriaceae* occur within the first day or two of incubation, but sufficient delayed reactions occur to warrant a 3- or 4-day incubation and observation period.

FALKOW METHOD (1958)

Comparative studies by Ewing (unpublished) have shown that the Falkow modification can be used successfully in most areas of the family *Enterobacteriaceae*. Results obtained with cultures that belong to

the *Klebsiella* and *Aerobacter* groups may be equivocal. The method cannot be recommended for use with members of these groups.

Basal Medium

Bacto-peptone................... 5 gm.
Yeast extract.................... 3 gm.
Glucose......................... 1 gm.
Bromocresol purple (1.6% solution). 1 ml.
Distilled water................. 1000 ml.

Adjust the pH to 6.7 to 6.8, if necessary. Divide the basal medium into four parts and treat in the same manner as that given above for the Moeller medium, except that only 0.5 per cent of L-amino acid is added. After the addition of the amino acids to three of the four portions of basal medium, tube the media in small (13 by 100 mm.), screw-capped tubes and sterilize at 121° C. for 10 minutes. The remaining portion of basal medium, without amino acid, serves as a control.

Inoculation: Inoculate lightly from a young agar slant culture. Oil seals are not used with this method. Inoculate a control tube with each culture under investigation.

Incubation: Incubate at 37° C. Examine daily for 4 days. These media first become yellow because of acid production from glucose; later, if decarboxylation occurs, the medium becomes alkaline (purple). The control tubes should remain acid (yellow).

Lysine-Iron Agar

Peptone.................... 5 gm.
Yeast extract................ 3 gm.
Glucose..................... 1 gm.
L-lysine.................... 10 gm.
Ferric ammonium citrate...... 0.5 gm.
Sodium thiosulfate........... 0.04 gm.
Bromcresol purple........... 0.02 gm.
Agar....................... 15 gm.
Distilled water............. 1000 ml.
Adjust to pH 6.7

Dispense in 4-ml. amounts in 13 x 100 mm. tubes and sterilize at 121° C. for 12 minutes. Slant tubes so as to obtain a deep butt and a short slant.

Inoculation: Inoculate with a straight

wire by stabbing to the base of the butt and by streaking the slant.

Incubation: 37° C. 18 to 24 hours.

This medium was designed primarily for the examination of blackened colonies on bismuth sulfite agar plates.

Reference: P. H. Edwards and M. A. Fife, Appl. Microbiol., *9*, 1961, 478.

Reference: W. H. Ewing, Enterobacteriaceae, Biochemical Methods for Group Differentiation. U. S. Department of Health, Education and Welfare, Public Health Service Publication No. 734, 1962.

Ammonia from Arginine for *Streptococcus*

Prepare a medium with the following composition:

Yeast extract	5 gm.
Tryptone	5 gm.
K_2HPO_4	2 gm.
Glucose	0.5 gm.
D-Arginine-HCl	3 gm.
Water	1000 ml.

Dissolve the ingredients; adjust the pH to 7; distribute in 5-ml. quantities in 120-by 13-mm. tubes; and sterilize at 100° C. for 30 minutes.

Also prepare a control medium without arginine; incubate for 2 days at 37° C. and test for ammonia with Nessler's reagent.

NESSLER'S SOLUTION

Dissolve (a) 3.5 gm. of KI in 15 ml. of water; (b) 1.7 gm. of mercuric chloride in 30 ml. of water; and (c) 12 gm. of sodium hydroxide in 30 ml. of water; add solution (b) to (a) gradually, while shaking, until a slight red precipitate remains permanent. Then add (c) and dilute the mixture to 100 ml. Finally add a little more of (b) until a faint permanent turbidity again forms. Set the mixture aside until it clears and then decant into a bottle fitted with a rubber stopper.

References: C. F. Niven, K. L. Smiley, and J. M. Sherman, J. Bacteriol., *43*, 1942, 651; and C. A. Cumming and S. A. Kay, Quantitative Chemical Analysis, Gurney and Jackson, 1934.

Methylene Blue Reduction Tests

Although these tests have been used as general tests with many microorganisms, their specific application has been mainly with the genus *Streptococcus* and the genus *Bacillus*.

For Streptococcus:

Methylene blue (medicinal)	0.5 gm.
Distilled water	1000 ml.

Sterilize at 121° C. for 15 minutes. Sterilize unskimmed milk in 10-ml. amounts in 150- by 13-mm. tubes. After sterilization, add 1 ml. of the dye to each tube. Mix well.

Inoculate the tubes with 24-hour-old culture and incubate at 37° C. Note (a) the ability of the organisms to reduce the dye, (b) the time taken for the dye to be reduced, and (c) whether reduction occurs before or after curdling of the milk.

The test should be read for 6 days. The advantage of unskimmed milk lies in the formation of a fat layer over the surface, which aids in the exclusion of air.

Reference: J. M. Sherman, and W. R. Albus, J. Bacteriol., *3*, 1918, 153.

NOTE: Despite the recommendation of the original authors, most workers prefer the use of fat-free milk.

For Bacillus:

Prepare the following medium:

Tryptose	20 gm.
NaCl	5 gm.
Agar	8 gm.
Water	1000 ml.

Dissolve the ingredients and sterilize at 121° C. for 15 minutes. After autoclaving, cool the medium to 55° C. and add sufficient sterile aqueous 1 per cent methylene blue solution to give a distinct pale-blue color. Adjust the pH to 7.2 to 7.4 and distribute aseptically into 150- by 13-mm. tubes in 10-ml. amounts.

Inoculate by a single stab with a straight needle. Check the cultures for growth and loss of color, in comparison with incubated, but uninoculated, controls after incubation for 24 to 48 hours.

Reference: K. L. Burdon, J. Bacteriol., *71*, 1956, 25.

Methylene Blue Tolerance

This test is used mainly in the genus *Streptococcus*. Medicinal methylene blue (0.1 per cent) is employed in a medium prepared as specified for the methylene blue reduction test, with the use of skim milk.

Growth of the organisms in the medium constitutes a positive test.

Reference: J. M. Sherman, P. Clark, and J. C. Mauer, J. Bacteriol., *33*, 1937, 483.

Slide Culture Technique for the Examination of Microcolonies

For this technique, specially cleaned slides and clarified agar are used.

Clean and bake new slides in a 400° C. oven for 15 minutes to remove grease (it is quite safe to place cold slides directly in the oven). They are then ready for use.

Clarified Agar: Removal of dead bacterial cells from commercial agar is essential. A 2 per cent agar solution containing the required nutrients is used. Cut a piece of closely woven cloth the size of the base of a Buchner funnel and place it in the funnel. Put about 20 gm. of Super-Cel in a liter of hot water, stir, and then pour into the funnel while suction is applied. Empty and rinse the flask. Melt the agar solution; cool to between 50° and 60° C., and add horse serum (3 ml. per L.). Heat again, with continuous stirring until the serum coagulates, and then add 20 gm. of Super-Cel to the agar solution and pour through the pad. Repeat if microscopic examination shows that bacterial cells are still present.

Dispense in 20-ml. amounts at 121° C. and autoclave for 15 minutes.

To prepare slides, melt and pour a clarified agar deep into a Petri dish placed on a hot plate (60° C.). Submerge sterile slides into the agar, drain slightly, and allow to set in a sterile, moist chamber.

To prepare a suitable chamber, place a circular filter paper in the base of a Petri dish and insert two glass rods to support the slides. Moisten the paper and autoclave. Add sterile water to the paper as required to keep it moist during incubation.

Preparation of Inoculum: Suspend the cells to a barely perceptible density in any suitable suspending fluid in a 13-mm. diameter tube. Place 1 drop on a test agar slide and carefully spread over the surface with a small, sterile spreader made of thin polythene film fixed to the end of a glass rod. To prepare a spreader, cut out a piece of thin polythene film, as illustrated in Figure 8.

Heat a piece of 3-mm, glass rod in a flame until it is hot enough to adhere to the polythene film on contact. Roll it on the narrow end of the film as indicated.

Sterilize the spreaders by immersion in sterile 70 per cent alcohol for 10 to 15 minutes before use.

It is most important to obtain a uniform spread and not to injure the agar surface. Dry the slide immediately in an oven at 105° C. Stain with filtered dilute carbolfuchsin and cover with a coverglass while still wet. Examine under oil immersion and count the average number of cells per field. Dilute the suspension so that the count will be reduced to not more than 1 cell per field, and use for the preparation of slide cultures by the same general technique.

Incubate in the humid chambers and remove slides at predetermined time intervals, depending on the rate of growth. Remove the agar from the under side of the slide, and then dry at 105° C., stain, and examine. If desired, a coverslip may be applied directly to the moist agar culture without addition of mounting fluid and the culture examined with a phase contrast microscope.

Reference: Author's recommendation.

Measurement of Organisms

Optical Instruments for Measurement of Organisms: For this purpose, an "ocular scale" is usually employed. It consists of a circular glass disc that is placed on the platform inside the ocular of the microscope. Etched on the surface is a scale of 50

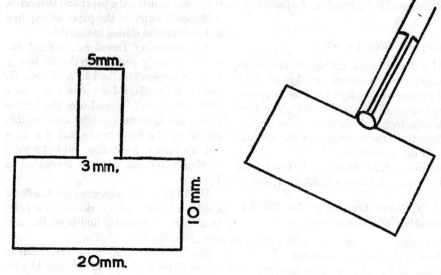

F‍IG. 8

uniform divisions. The linear value for each division depends on the ocular magnification, draw tube length, and objective magnification, and hence the scale is left unnumbered. For use in measurement, the scale must be calibrated for each combination of ocular, objective, and draw tube length.

Calibration is done with the aid of a "stage micrometer"—a glass slide, in the center of which is usually an accurately calibrated scale 1 mm. long and divided into 0.1 and 0.01 mm. The stage micrometer is placed on the stage of the microscope and the ocular scale into the ocular. The objective lens in use is then focused carefully on the slide scale, and the number of stage micrometer divisions (0.01 mm.) corresponding to the 50 divisions of the ocular scale is determined. Thus, if 50 ocular divisions = 10 scale divisions, 1 ocular division = $10/50 \times 0.01$ mm., which = 0.002 mm. or 2 μ.

It is important that the combination of ocular magnification, objective, and draw tube length be recorded for each calibration.

Once the calibration has been done, the stage micrometer is replaced with the preparation and the size of the organisms is estimated.

Measurement with Polystyrene Particles: Polystyrene particles prepared by the Dow Chemical Company have proved most useful for measurement of cells. Prepare a dilute suspension of the particles in water and use in place of water in the preparation of smears. Allow the smears to air-dry, and then cover with filtered dilute aqueous safranin (see Gram stain) and mount wet under a coverslip. The particles do not stain and can be used to measure the size of the stained cells.

The 0.8-μ particles are the most useful size for general purposes.

Reference: Author's recommendation.

Preparation of "Hanging Drops" for Motility Tests

Match Stick Technique: Carefully clean a slide and put it in a clean place on the bench.

Remove the head from a safety match and cut the match stick in two.

Adhere the two sticks to the slide with a small daub of grease; place them sufficiently close together to support a No. 1 square coverglass by its outer edges.

Remove any adhering dirt from a coverglass with a clean cloth and place it on the bench.

Use the 4-mm. loop to transfer a loopful of the broth culture aseptically to the center of the coverglass, and then sterilize the loop.

Place a small daub of grease on the top of each match stick, and then invert the slide over the coverglass and press down gently until the coverglass adheres to the sticks.

Revert the slide quickly but carefully. The drop should remain suspended from the coverglass.

Examination of Hanging Drop Preparation for Motility: Place the preparation on the stage with the drop over the center of the condenser.

Close the iris diaphragm completely; then open it slightly. With low power, focus with the coarse adjustment until the drop comes into focus (See Note 2 below). It may be necessary to open the iris diaphragm slightly.

Move the edge of the drop to the center of the field; focus with the fine adjustment and then swing in high power. (See Note 1 below).

Adjust the light and focus with the fine adjustment until the drop is again in focus. Organisms should be seen either swimming or motionless near the edge of the drop.

For an organism to be considered motile, at least *one* organism should be seen to alter its position in relation to at least two other organisms. It is *not* necessary for all organisms in a drop prepared from a *pure culture* to be in motion. Nonmotile organisms either all remain stationary or exhibit Brownian movement.

NOTE: 1. Not all microscopes are so constructed as to allow the high power objective to be swung in after the low power without touching the coverglass. When they do not allow this, the barrel of the microscope must be raised before the high power is swung in. The high power should then be carefully lowered until it barely touches the coverglass, and the drop is brought into focus by adjusting upwards.

2. If difficulty is experienced in focusing on the drop under low power, focus first on the edge of the coverglass. Then move the slide across and look for the drop.

3. An orange light is more suitable for observing hanging drops than white light or daylight.

4. Excessively long exposure to oxygen or an excessively rapid drop in temperature can result in an apparent nonmotility. Motility tests should be performed as quickly as possible after preparation of the drop to avoid undue temperature changes. In the case of organisms sensitive to oxygen, the hanging drop test is not recommended. Instead, a small drop should be placed on a slide, immediately covered with a clean coverslip, sealed on the margins with nail lacquer, and examined under oil immersion.

Reference: Author's recommendation.

Leifson's Flagella Stain

Young liquid cultures are preferred for this procedure.

Transfer the broth cultures to 15-ml. centrifuge tubes, and centrifuge at 3000 r.p.m. for 5 minutes.

Pour off the supernatant and gently resuspend the cells in about 7 ml. of distilled water. Centrifuge. Pour off the supernatant and gently resuspend the cells in distilled water to give a just visible turbidity. Incubate at 37° C. for 10 minutes and check for motility.

Select a perfectly clean slide. Do not use a cloth or wash in soap or detergent.

Flame the slide for a few seconds, and before it has cooled, use a grease pencil to mark a heavily defined band around an area of about 1.5 square inches at one end of the flamed side of the slide. This acts as a retarding margin around the stained area.

When cool, incline the slide, and place loopfuls of the washed suspension at two points at one end of the enclosed area and allow them to run to the end. If this does not occur readily, the slide has not been correctly cleaned. Allow the slide to dry in air and then place on a staining rack.

Shake the bottle of Leifson's stain thoroughly. Using a pipette, slowly run 1.0 ml. of stain into the marked area with care that the stain does not flow over the grease pencil marks.

Staining Time: Leifson states as follows: "The proper staining time is best determined by the formation of a fine precipitate in the stain on the slide. As soon as the precipitate is formed the flagella are stained. The formation of the precipitate is best observed by placing the slide on a black background and illuminating the stain with a beam of light. The precipitate has the appearance of rust coloured cloud which generally starts forming along one edge of the slide and then quickly spreads throughout the stain. As soon as the precipitate is formed throughout the stain, the time is up and the slide should be washed. This technique eliminates all guess work as to the proper time to wash the slides."

Flood the stain off the slide with a gentle stream of water. Counterstain for 1 minute with 1 per cent methylene blue.

(NOTE: It has been found in this laboratory that some flagella stain more readily after fixation in formalin.)

Preparation of the Stain: Three solutions are prepared: (a) 1.5 per cent sodium chloride in distilled water, (b) 3.0 per cent tannic acid in distilled water, and (c) 1.2 per cent basic fuchsin (special, for flagella stain) in ethyl alcohol. To effect complete solution, it is necessary to shake frequently for several hours.

Mix the three solutions in exactly equal proportions and store either at $-10°$ to $-20°$ C. (stable indefinitely) or at $0°$ C. (stable for a few weeks) for 1 day or more to clear before use.

Reproduced by permission from E. Leifson, J. Bacteriol., *62*, 1951, 377; and Stain Technol., *33*, 1958, 249; and from E. Leif-

son and L. Hugh, J. Bacteriol., *65*, 1953, 263.

Modified Fontana Method for Flagella Stains

Use two reagents.

1. FERRIC TANNATE MORDANT

Add 5 ml. of saturated aqueous potash alum to 10 ml. of 10 per cent (w/v) tannic acid, and follow by 1 ml. of saturated solution of aniline in water. Redissolve the curd that forms by shaking. Add 1 ml. of 5 per cent (w/v) ferric chloride. This gives a black solution. Allow to stand for 10 minutes before use.

2. AMMONIACAL SILVER NITRATE SOLUTION

Set aside *c.* 10 ml. from 100 ml. of 5 per cent (w/v) aqueous solution of silver nitrate. Add concentrated ammonia solution (sp. gr. 0.88) slowly to the 90-ml. portion until the brown precipitate just redissolves. Then add drops of the 10-ml. sample of silver nitrate solution until the solution remains faintly cloudy, even after shaking. Stored in the dark, this solution remains stable for several weeks.

Method of Making a Preparation and Staining to Show Flagella: Grow the organisms on yeast extract agar slopes in 6- by ⅝-inch tubes, to each of which are added 1 to 2 ml. of sterile distilled water, because motile organisms are most readily obtained from the liquid at the base of such slopes. Routine staining of these cultures is made after 18 to 24 hours of incubation, or after 48 hours in the case of the few cultures that grow slowly, *e.g., Pseudomonas lachrymans.* After incubation, inoculate two 4-mm. loopfuls of the liquid at the base of a slope into 5 ml. of sterile distilled water and incubate for 1 hour at $25°$ C. to remove debris and excess mucilage from the organisms. Transfer a drop of this suspension to a slide previously cleaned in chromic + sulfuric acid mixture. After allowing the drop to air-dry, cover the film with the iron tannate mordant reagent (No.

1) for 3 to 5 minutes. After very thoroughly washing the film with distilled water, apply the silver reagent (No. 2), heated nearly to boiling, and leave in contact with the film for 3 to 5 minutes. Again wash the film with distilled water, blot it, and either examine it directly or make it permanent under a coverslip by sealing with neutral Canada balsam.

Exposure to air causes disintegration of these silver-plated preparations after about 1 week. Use a light microscope with a $\frac{1}{12}$-inch oil immersion objective and × 10 ocular to examine the preparations. The silver-plated flagella are found to be easily visible provided that the substage condenser has been carefully centered and focused.

Reference: Muriel E. Rhodes, J. Gen. Microbiol., *18*, 1958, 639.

Gliding Motility

The *Myxobacterales* and the *Beggiatoales* glide over the surface of solid media or along solid surfaces. The larger forms are very easily observed, but others, because of their smallness and often very slow movement are observed with difficulty. To observe this movement, remove the cultures from the incubator, and taking care to exclude air bubbles, cover a portion of the growth with a clean coverglass. Press it down gently to insure close contact, and examine with an oil immersion lens. Concentrate on small groups of cells at the margin of the colony and note their relative positions from time to time.

Preliminary observation of groups of cells separated at the margin of the main growth is usually indicative of gliding organisms. Their slime trails may be visible in the uncovered growth on the agar under the high dry power.

Gram Stain

Prepare a smear and fix by heat. Cover the smear with crystal violet and leave for 1 minute. Wash in a beaker for 3 or 4 seconds with tap water, which should be running at a rate of about 30 ml. per second into a 250-ml. beaker. Rinse with Burke's iodine and leave the iodine on for 1 minute. Wash with water for a few seconds.

Hold the slide in a position where the smear is clearly visible against a white filter paper laid on the edge of the sink. Then apply 95 per cent alcohol, drop by drop, on the top edge of the smear until no more color runs out of the lower edge of it. The decolorization time is usually about 10 to 20 seconds. Wash; counterstain with 0.25 per cent safranin for 60 seconds. Wash, blot, dry, and examine.

Result: A blue color indicates Gram positive; red, Gram negative.

NOTE: The presence of a number of red cells among a mass of blue usually indicates the presence of dead, unstainable cells.

Mature spores are not stained by Gram and will appear as clear areas in the blue or red rod.

REAGENTS FOR THE GRAM STAIN

Hucker's Crystal Violet—Stock Solution

Crystal violet*.................. 2 gm.
Ethanol, 95%.................. 20 ml.

For use, mix 20 ml. of the stock solution with 80 ml. of 1 per cent aqueous ammonium oxalate. This should stand for 48 hours before use. The solution is stable and can be stored for months.

Safranin†—Stock Solution

Safranin..................... 0.25 gm.
Ethanol, 95%................. 100 ml.

For use, dilute 10 ml. of stock solution with 90 ml. of distilled water. The solution is stable and can be stored for months.

Iodine—Burke's

Place 2 gm. of KI in a mortar. Add 1 gm. of iodine and grind with a pestle for 5 to 10

* Cert. No. NC-35; 96% dye content specified. Pharmaceutical Laboratories, National Aniline Division, 40 Rector Street, New York.
† Cert. No. NS-19; 86% dye content specified. Pharmaceutical Laboratories, National Aniline Division, 40 Rector Street, New York.

seconds. Add 1 ml. of water and grind, and then add a further 5 ml. of water and grind again. This should effect solution of the iodine. Add 10 ml. of water and mix. Pour the reagent into a bottle, and rinse the mortar and pestle with successive rinses to bring the final volume to 100 ml. The solution is stable and can be stored for months.

Iodine—Gram's

Dilute Burke's iodine 1:2 with distilled water.

Alternative Procedure for Gram Stain

Prepare very thin smears (c. 100 cells per field = 50 × 10⁶/ml.) and fix by gentle heating.

Use the reagents specified in the previous method.

1. Flood the slide for 1 minute with Hucker's crystal violet.

2. Wash for 5 seconds by dipping the slide into tap water in a 250-ml. beaker. The tap water in this beaker should be constantly replaced by running water into the beaker at a rate of about 30 ml. per second.

3. Rinse off the excess water with Burke's iodine; then flood the slide with iodine solution for 1 minute.

4. Wash for 5 seconds in water, as above.

5. Decolorize the *wet* slide by immersing it for 1 minute in each of three coplin jars containing *n*-propanol, agitating the slide while it is in the decolorizer. Replace the propanol in the first jar after every 10 slides and place it last in the series to prevent excessive dilution of the decolorizer.

NOTE: the allowable time range in *n*-propanol (undiluted) is 30 seconds to 30 minutes. For 95 per cent propanol it is 15 seconds to 6 minutes. An equal time should be allowed in each jar.

6. Wash for 5 seconds in water, as above.

7. Rinse off the excess water with the 0.25 per cent safranin; then flood the slide with safranin, and stain for 1 minute.

8. Wash for 5 seconds, as above. Blot, air dry, and examine.

Reference: J. W. Bartholomew, Stain Technol., *37*, 1962, 139.

Cell Wall Stain

Procedure: Make smears of cultures on coverglasses, rather thickly to allow for loss of a portion of the material by washing.

Immerse the wet, unfixed smears in 1 per cent phosphomolybdic acid at room temperature (20° C., approximately) for 3 to 5 minutes. Stain with 1 per cent methyl green for 3 to 5 minutes. Wash well with water. Dry and examine under oil immersion. The cell walls stain dark green, and the cytoplasm is unstained.

Reproduced by permission from K. A. Bisset and C. M. F. Hale, Exptl. Cell Research, *5*, 1953, 449, Academic Press, Inc.

Detection of Iron Deposited on Bacterial Cells or Their Capsules or Sheaths

Prepare a dense smear of the cells on a clean slide, and cover the smear with a drop of a 0.1 per cent aqueous solution of potassium ferrocyanide. Place a coverglass over the preparation and observe under the low or high dry power of a microscope.

Place a drop of 3 N sulfuric acid on one edge of the coverslip, and draw it under with a piece of filter paper placed on the opposite side. When the acid reaches the cells, the ferric iron dissolves and reacts with the potassium ferrocyanide to form Prussian blue.

Care must be taken to see that the cells are first carefully washed to remove soluble ferric iron, which may still adhere from the medium.

Reference: Author's recommendation, based on material from an unknown source.

Neisser's Stain for Volutin or Metachromatic Granules

METHOD

1. Cover the fixed preparation with Neisser's blue for 2 minutes.

2. Wash the Neisser blue off the prepa-

ration with chrysoidin, and allow the chrysoidin to remain on the preparation for 3 to 5 minutes.

3. Wash lightly with running water.

4. Dry and examine.

Result: The metachromatic granules (volutin) stain bluish black, whereas the rest of the cell stains a light brown.

NOTE: If difficulty is experienced in detecting the cells, repeat the stain but omit the final washing with water. Remove the excess chrysoidin with a filter paper and dry.

SOLUTION A

Methylene blue	1 gm.
Alcohol, 95%	50 ml.
Glacial acetic acid	50 ml.
Distilled water	1000 ml.

SOLUTION B

Crystal violet	1 gm.
Alcohol, 95%	10 ml.
Distilled water	300 ml.

Before use, mix together 2 parts of Solution A and 1 part of Solution B. This mixture is Neisser's blue.

CHRYSOIDIN

| Chrysoidin | 1 gm. |
| Distilled water | 300 ml. |

Dissolve by gentle heat and filter.

Reference: M. Neisser, Hyg. Rundschau, *13*, 1903, 705. Reproduced by permission from Lange and Springer, Berlin.

Detection of Calcium Carbonate in Cells

1. Evolution of Carbon Dioxide: Mount a dense suspension of the cells on a slide under a coverslip. Examine under the low or high power of the microscope. Draw 4 N HCl under the coverslip by means of a piece of filter paper applied to the opposite side. Note any evolution of gas from the cells.

2. Staining for Calcium: Fix the cells in 10 per cent formalin. Centrifuge and suspend the packed cells in a small quantity of 0.1 per cent alizarin red S for 1 hour.

Wash and counterstain in 0.1 per cent aqueous toluidine blue, thionin, or methylene blue.

Calcium deposits appear red.

Reproduced with modification by permission from Medical Public Health Laboratory Methods, p. 1081, Lea and Febiger, Philadelphia, 1955.

Macchiavello's Stain for Rickettsiae

Stain a fixed smear with fuchsin solution (by filtering it over the preparation through a coarse filter paper in a funnel) for 4 minutes. Drain and wash rapidly with 0.5 per cent citric acid solution.

Wash immediately with tap water. Stain with a 1 per cent aqueous solution of methylene blue for 20 seconds.

The rickettsiae, intracellular and extracellular, are stained red; the cellular elements, blue. This method is effective for culture smears but not for tissue sections of typhus-infected animals.

Fuchsin Solution: 0.25 per cent solution of basic fuchsin in a M/30 phosphate solution buffered to pH 7.4.

Reproduced by permission from D. T. Smith and N. F. Conant, Zinsser's Textbook of Bacteriology, 11th ed., Appleton-Century-Crofts, New York, 1957.

Giemsa Stain for Chromatinic Structures in Bacterial Cells

Inoculate the surface of a nutrient agar plate by dropping a dilute suspension (c. 1000 organisms per ml.) on the surface and spreading the drop with a sterile bent glass rod. Incubate until microcolonies are visible under the low power ($\times$ 10) objective of your microscope.

To make an impression smear, cut a square centimeter of the agar from the plate and lift it carefully with a narrow-bladed scalpel slipped under the center so that the agar droops slightly on either side. While holding a clean slide horizontally over a disinfectant tray, raise the agar block to the underside until it touches. It will be drawn up to the slide, excluding air as it goes. Leave it in contact with the slide for 30 seconds and then carefully prize the agar away into the disinfectant tray with the tip of the scalpel without dislodging it laterally across the glass.

Expose the slide to the vapor of a freshly prepared 2 per cent osmic acid solution for 2 to 3 minutes.

Place the slide in N HCl at 60° C. for 10 minutes to hydrolyze the cytoplasmic proteins and render them less stainable. Wash thoroughly with distilled water.

Stain with Giemsa for 30 to 60 minutes. Wash thoroughly and mount in water.

The chromatinic structures stain a darker color than the rest of the cells.

Reproduced by permission from C. F. Robinow, in Addendum to R. J. Dubos, The Bacterial Cell, Harvard University Press, Cambridge, 1949.

A Method for Staining the Nuclei of Blue-Green *Algae*

Place filaments of the alga on a clean slide.

Flood with Bouin's fluid for 4 to 6 hours.

Carefully wash off the Bouin's fluid with tap water until none of it remains.

Flood with 1:20 dilution of Giemsa for about 40 hours.

Wash with tap water.

Allow to dry thoroughly before mounting in Depex mounting medium.

The nuclei stain a dark blue against a paler background.

Reference: Author's recommendation.

Toluidine Blue Stain for Nuclear Structures in Yeast Cells

Make a smear of yeast cells from a 6- to 8-hour culture, and allow it to dry in air. Flood the slide with 40 per cent ethanol for 2 minutes. Wash with tap water.

Flood with 0.1 M KOH for 1 hour at 28° C. Wash well with tap water.

Stain with 0.1 per cent toluidine blue in 10 per cent ethanol for 2 minutes. Wash with 10 per cent ethanol. Blot the slide and dry before mounting.

The nuclei stain a dense blue against a pale-pink background.

Reproduced by permission from G. F. Townsend, Stain Technol., *32*, 1957, 302.

A Method of Staining the Nuclei of *Fungi*

Place sterile slides in a humid chamber and onto each drop 1 drop of a liquid Czapek-Dox or other suitable medium. Inoculate the drop with fungal spores and then incubate at 28° C. for 18 hours.

Carefully flood the slide with Bouin's fluid for 4 to 6 hours in the moist slide chamber. Remove the slides and wash carefully with tap water until all the Bouin's fluid is removed.

Stain with 1:20 dilution of Giemsa for 24 to 48 hours.

Wash with water and allow to dry before mounting in Depex mounting medium.

The nuclei stain a dark blue against a paler background.

Reference: Author's recommendation.

Iron Hematoxylin Method

Fix the preparation in alcohol or by exposure to the vapor of 2 per cent osmic acid for 1 minute.

Mordant with 5 per cent iron alum for 10 to 20 minutes.

Rinse rapidly in distilled water. Stain with Heidenhain's iron hematoxylin solution for 10 to 20 minutes.

Differentiate in 0.5 per cent acid alcohol; control the degree by observation under the microscope. Rinse in tap water to arrest differentiation. Rinse finally in distilled water and blue with Scott's solution. Wash in running water for 5 to 10 minutes. Counterstain as desired. Dry and examine.

SOLUTIONS

1. 5 Per Cent Iron Alum in Distilled Water

Use the violet crystals of iron alum.

2. Hematoxylin Solution

Hematoxylin.................... 5 gm.
Absolute alcohol.............. 100 ml.
For use, dilute 1:5 with distilled water.

3. Scott's Bluing Solution

NaHCO$_3$..................... 3.5 gm.
MgSO$_4$·7 H$_2$O............... 20.0 gm.
Distilled water............... 1000 ml.
Dissolve the salts separately, mix, and add a crystal of thymol to preserve.

Bouin's Fluid (Fixative)

Picric acid, saturated aqueous
solution..................... 75 ml.
Formalin..................... 25 ml.
Glacial acetic acid............... 5 ml.

Giemsa Stain

Azur II-eosin................... 3 gm.
Azur II...................... 0.8 gm.
Glycerol (pure)............... 250 gm.
Methanol (acetone-free)........ 250 gm.

Giemsa Stain (Alternative)

With a pestle and mortar grind 0.5 gm. of Giemsa powder with 33 ml. of glycerol at 55° to 60° C. for 1.5 to 2 hours. Add 33 ml. of methanol and allow to stand for 24 hours.

The Ziehl-Neelsen Stain for Acid-fast Bacilli

1. Place the fixed preparation on the hot plate.
2. Flood the slide with concentrated carbolfuchsin. Continue to heat the slide for a period of 10 minutes, and add fresh stain to it if there is any tendency for the original stain to dry off.
3. Wash the slide thoroughly with tap water, and then, with a filter paper moistened with alcohol, carefully clean all the stain deposits from the back of the slide and also from the surface of the slide away from the smear itself. Wash again with water.
4. Immerse the slide in 25 per cent sulfuric acid for 5 minutes. The red stain immediately turns brown and begins to decolorize. Remove the slide and rinse under running water. As the acid is washed out, any remaining stain deposit will again take on its original pink color. Continue the sulfuric acid treatment until the smear,

upon washing with water, is colorless or only a very faint pink. Finally, wash well with water. Never prolong treatment beyond 20 minutes.

5. Counterstain with Loeffler's methylene blue or 0.1 per cent malachite green for 2 minutes.
6. Wash lightly with running water, dry, and examine. Acid-fast organisms usually appear as isolated bundles of 3 to 6 organisms in tuberculous sputa and stain red in a blue or green background.

NOTE: The prolonged treatment in step 4 above is necessary only for the removal of stain from extraneous material. Nonacid-fast organisms decolorize in a few seconds.

LOEFFLER'S METHYLENE BLUE

Methylene blue, saturated solution in alcohol............... 30 ml.
Potassium hydroxide, 0.0001%
aqueous.................... 100 ml.

CONCENTRATED CARBOLFUCHSIN

Basic fuchsin.................. 1.0 gm.
Absolute alcohol............... 10 ml.
Phenol, 5% aqueous........... 100 ml.
Dissolve the dye in the alcohol and add the phenol solution.

Slide Agglutination Test

This test is usually employed as a qualitative test for the detection of antibodies to a particulate antigen. It should be apparent, however, that, with the exercise of a little care, the technique could be used for quantitative purposes.

Prepare two wax cells on a slide, as illustrated below, by dipping the end of a hot slide in wax and pressing it down on the surface of a second slide.

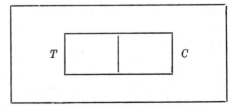

Place a drop of 0.85 per cent NaCl in

compartment C, and with the same pipette place a drop of antiserum (1:20 for "O" or 1:100 for "H") in compartment T.

With another pipette, transfer one drop of antigen (approximately 3×10^9 cells per ml.) to both T and C.

With a wire loop, mix the contents of C and then of T. Sterilize the loop, and then rock the slide with a fairly rapid rolling motion, holding it in such a position over a lamp so that the cells can be clearly observed. Clumping of the cells in T without similar clumping in C is a positive agglutination test. Clumping in C indicates an unstable autoagglutinable suspension which is unsuitable for serological work.

Reference: Author's recommendation.

A Technique for Dispensing Oxygen-Free Media and for Subculturing of Strictly Anaerobic Organisms

An important and often overlooked factor in the successful culture of anaerobes is the virtual total exclusion of oxygen during the collection and subsequent handling of the samples. The most explicit description of a technique that has proved successful in the hands of several investigators is that of Hungate, given below. Such precautions are not necessary with all anaerobes but should be adopted if less exacting methods fail.

Method

Prepare oxygen-free CO_2, H_2, or N_2 by bubbling the cylinder gases with low O_2 content through a chromous acid solution prepared as follows:

To 75 gm. of twenty-mesh metallic zinc, add 50 ml. of 3 N HCl and stir vigorously for 30 seconds. Then dilute 2.5 ml. of a saturated aqueous solution of mercuric chloride to 50 ml.; add this and stir the mixture for 3 minutes after the evolution of gas ceases.

Wash the zinc by decantation, and place it in the gas-washing bottle. Then dissolve 50 gm. of chromium potassium sulfate, $Cr \cdot K \cdot (SO_4)_2 \cdot 12 H_2O$, in a minimal amount of distilled water, and place the solution in the washing bottle; also add 10 ml. of 5 N H_2SO_4.

Pass the cylinder gas through the bottle to displace all air and allow to stand for 24 hours. The slow evolution of H_2 from the Zn reduces the chromium, and the solution turns a brilliant, clear blue. The reduction of the chromium can be speeded up by forcing the solution back and forth through the zinc several times.

This preparation effectively absorbs oxygen for weeks, even months, if the gas contains only small quantities. Tank nitrogen contains more oxygen than the other gases, and the absorbent is soon exhausted. In such a case, use hot reduced copper instead of, or preceding, the chromous solution. Alkaline pyrogallol removes not only oxygen but also carbon dioxide, which may be required for the growth of some organisms and which stimulates many others. Bicarbonate-CO_2 buffers cannot be employed when pyrogallol is the absorbent. It is therefore not recommended.

TECHNIQUE FOR DISPENSING AN ANAEROBIC CULTURE MEDIUM WITH MINIMAL ACCESS OF AIR

1. For Media That Cannot Be Heat-Sterilized: In applying this technique, it is presumed that the medium to be transferred has been prepared and sterilized under conditions in which oxygen has been rigidly excluded. The technique as described is intended for the preparation of roll tubes. Modification for other purposes should be obvious.

Sterilize empty culture tubes (16- by 150-mm. Pyrex tubes without lips) without cotton wool plugs, and upon removal from the autoclave close with sterile rubber stoppers.

Transfer the medium as follows: Connect two bent Pasteur pipettes with the gas source via a Y-tube and insert one in the culture tube and one in the flask of medium; flush out all the air.

Insert a sterile cotton-plugged 10-ml.

pipette provided with a mouth suction tube into the gas above the culture medium in the flask and suck gently so that air in the pipette is replaced with CO_2. The taste indicates when this has been accomplished.

Then draw in the medium and transfer 10 ml. quickly to the culture tube. Expel the last drop, but do not blow through the pipette. Stopper the tube and keep at 45° C. until it has been inoculated. To stopper the tube, hold it between the palm and the last two fingers of one hand, and hold the stopper between the index finger and thumb of the same hand. Insert the stopper as the capillary is withdrawn. Then, using both hands and a rotary motion, seat the stopper. The stopper can be seated more tightly by tipping so that the medium wets the lower surface of the stopper; the film of agar that occupies the space between the stopper and the glass then effectively prevents the entrance of air.

Culture tubes closed in this way have been found to remain anaerobic almost indefinitely. The *absolute* exclusion of oxygen by means of a rubber stopper is not claimed or implied, but any oxygen that is present is not sufficient to change the color of the oxidation-reduction indicator.

2. For Media That Can Be Sterilized by Heat: Dispense the medium in 4- to 5-ml. quantities in 150- by 16-mm. tubes. Flush with a mixture of 80 per cent hydrogen and 20 per cent carbon dioxide and seal with rubber stoppers. Secure the stoppered tubes in a rack so designed that the stoppers cannot be blown out of the tubes during sterilization; then sterilize at 120° C. for 20 minutes.

ANAEROBIC PROCEDURE FOR INOCULATION AND DILUTION

1. When Tubes Must Be Opened during Transfer: To inoculate, extend the open end of a bent sterile capillary pipette 5 or 6 cm. into the gas space above the medium in the first dilution tube. Stand the stopper upside down on a clean surface and leave until it is to be reinserted. Insert a second

bent sterile pipette into the tube from which a colony is to be picked. Pass sterile gas through both tubes during the entire time the stoppers are removed.

Flame a Pasteur pipette; cool in the medium to be inoculated and use this to pick up the colony that is to be transferred to the first dilution tube. Stopper the first dilution tube with minimal access of air and mix thoroughly. Then open and gas again with the same capillary.

Fill a sterile 1-ml. pipette with a large bore with the oxygen-free gas in the tube and transfer 0.1 or 0.2 ml. of this dilution to tube 2. Close tube 1 aseptically with the exclusion of air. Flame the capillary and use for tube 3 and so on. While doing this, have the tubes immersed to half their depth in a water bath at 45° C.

Cool the inoculated tubes under running water, rolling them in the horizontal position to keep the medium flowing over the inner surface of the tube until just before the agar is ready to set.

Then invert the tubes momentarily for the last time, thus forming a seal of medium around the stopper and leaving on the upper portion of the tube a thin film of agar, which will solidify almost immediately.

Hold the tubes stationary in a vertical position under the tap until the rest of the agar has set.

2. When the Tubes Are Not Opened during Transfer (as in Preparations of Liquid Dilutions): Make transfers with a sterile hypodermic syringe and a 1¾-inch, 19-gauge needle. Flush the syringe several times with the sterile gas mixture, and then insert through the sterilized rubber stopper; transfer the required sample to the next tube, mix, and repeat the process until dilutions are complete.

NOTE: Total exclusion of oxygen may prove impossible or, as Hungate suggests, even in its total absence, the E_h of the medium may be too high for some anaerobes. To control the entry of minor amounts of oxygen and to establish a low

E_h, Hungate has employed the following method:

To the medium during preparation, add 0.003 per cent sodium dithionite and 0.1 per cent sodium pyruvate. Dispense and sterilize. Inoculate with 2 per cent inoculum of a broth culture of *Escherichia coli* and incubate for 12 hours at 39° C. Then heat the cultures to 75° for 45 minutes to kill *E. coli;* cool and inoculate.

For many organisms 0.1 per cent cysteine may be employed in place of the dithionite, should the latter be too toxic. Cysteine will not, however, develop the low potential obtainable with dithionite or by the *E. coli* oxidation of pyruvate.

Solid media may be prepared by the addition of agar to the liquid media. The techniques are the same.

Reproduced by permission from R. E. Hungate, Bacteriol. Revs., *14*, 1950, 1; and from P. H. Smith and R. E. Hungate, J. Bacteriol., *75*, 1958, 713.

Transfer in an Oxygen-free Atmosphere

Consideration may now be given to the use of collapsible plastic bags for anaerobic transfers. One of the major difficulties in the use of anaerobic chambers has been that of removing the air, which necessitates evacuation and repeated flushing with an oxygen-free gas. The construction of a transfer chamber offers some advantages over the method of Hungate. This consists of a large polythene bag fixed to a ring on a flat metal plate containing two 15-cm. armholes. These are sealed with arm-length surgical gloves, an entry port, and a gas inlet tube.

The bag may be inflated with any inert oxygen-free gas; the cultures, culture media, and sterile transfer instruments are inserted through the port in an outflow of the gas, and the bag is reinflated once or several times before transfer is effected.

Reference: Author's recommendation.

Pyrogallic Acid-Sodium Carbonate Plates for the Culture of Anaerobes

Two grams of pyrogallic acid mixed with an excess of sodium hydroxide will absorb at least 200 ml. of oxygen. When sodium carbonate is used, carbon dioxide is liberated in the formation of the sodium pyrogallate. This materially aids the growth of most anaerobes.

To prepare single anaerobic plates, inoculate the medium and then invert the base over a piece of sheet glass or the unused lid of a 2-lb. can (obtainable from most can manufacturers). Fold a filter paper double, and place in the center of the fold approximately 1 gm. of pyrogallic acid and 1 gm. of washing soda. Slip the fold between the edge of the Petri dish and the glass plate and pull firmly outwards to compress the sealed reagents against the side of the dish. Take care that it does not touch the agar. If so, reduce the quantity of reagents. Tear off the protruding paper and seal with a mixture of 50 per cent petrolatum and 50 per cent paraffin wax. The wax should be heated until white vapors rise from it before being used, and it should be possible to ring the dish with wax from a pipette before solidification takes place. Wax that is too cool will crack and later admit air.

Reference: Author's recommendation.

A GUIDE TO STUDY

The following is a suggested grouping of bacterial genera for purposes of study. Some important common characters and suggestions about the type of differentiating characters that should be sought, tabulated, and memorized are given.

Except where specifically stated otherwise, the organisms should be regarded as unicellular, rigid, and straight.

Only the genera that appear in the *Manual* and those published in more recent papers are listed. The relationship between these and the nomenclature of Prévot and Krassilnikov will be found in the Key.

1. Red and Purple Photosynthetic Sulfur Bacteria

All contain bacteriochlorophyll and carotenoid pigments, with the latter predominating to give a reddish-purple color.

All deposit sulfur internally when exposed to H_2S.

All are anaerobic so far as is known.

Differentiation is based on the shape and arrangement of cells.

Thiosarcina, Thiopedia, Thiocapsa, Thiodictyon, Thiothece, Thiocystis, Lamprocystis, Amoebobacter, Thiopolycoccus, Thiospirillum, Rhabdomonas, Rhodothece, Chromatium.

2. Red and Purple Photosynthetic Nonsulfur Bacteria

All grow anaerobically with exposure to light and obtain energy both from oxidation of carbon compounds and from radiation. Some species of *Rhodopseudomonas* and possibly *Vannielia* will grow aerobically in the dark. Differentiation is based on morphology.

Rhodopseudomonas, Rhodospirillum, Rhodomicrobium, * *Vannielia.*

3. Green Photosynthetic Sulfur Bacteria

All contain chlorobium chlorophyll so far as is known.

All are anaerobes.

All deposit sulfur externally in the presence of H_2S so far as is known.

Differentiation is based on morphology and association with symbionts.

Chlorobium, Pelodictyon, Clathrochloris, Chlorobacterium, Chlorochromatium, Cylindrogloea, Chloropseudomonas.

4. Nonphotosynthetic, Strictly Autotrophic, Straight, Gram Negative Rods with Polar Flagella if Motile

All fail to grow on organic media.

Differentiation is based mainly on morphology and on nutritional differences.

Nitrosomonas, Nitrosocystis, Nitrosogloea, Nitrobacter, Nitrocystis, Thiobacillus†, Ferrobacillus.

Note: Other autotrophs *not* included above are *Nitrosococcus* and *Nitrosospira,* neither of which are straight *rods.*

5. Nonphotosynthetic, Facultatively Autotrophic, Straight, Gram Negative Rods with Polar Flagella

These organisms are heterotrophic and grow well on organic media but may need

* Also included in another group.
† Also has some facultatively heterotrophic species.

287

a special gas phase. They can also be grown autotrophically with energy obtained from the oxidation of simple inorganic substances.

Differentiation is based on the energy substrate.

Thiobacillus,* Methanomonas, Hydrogenomonas, Carboxydomonas.

6. Miscellaneous Colorless, Nonphotosynthetic Organisms Depositing Sulfur Internally

Differentiation is based principally on morphology.

Thiovulum, Macromonas, Thiospira, Thiobacterium, Achromatium, Thiodendron.

7. Nonphotosynthetic, Heterotrophic, Gram Negative Rods with Polar Flagella

Differentiation is based on morphology, pigmentation, luminescence, nitrogen fixation, salt tolerance, and biochemical reactions, particularly in regard to the type of compounds oxidized and the byproducts produced.

Pseudomonas, Comamonas, Fergusonia, Xanthomonas, Acetomonas, (Acetobacter),† Aeromonas, Photobacterium, Azotomonas, Zymomonas, Protaminobacter, Alginomonas, Mycoplana, Zoogloea, Halobacterium.

8. Colorless, Nonphotosynthetic Organisms Normally Fixed to a Substratum by Means of a Stalk

They do *not* form sheaths.

Differentiation is based on morphology, the nature of the stalk, deposition of iron, and mode of division.

Caulobacter, Asticcacaulis, Gallionella, Siderophacus, Nevskia, Pasteuria, Blastocaulis.

9. Colorless Nonphotosynthetic Organisms Noted for Deposition of Iron in Capsules or on Cells

Do *not* form sheaths or stalks.

Differentiation is based on cell morphol-

* Some species only.
† Peritrichous flagella.

ogy, presence or absence of capsules, and mode of iron deposition.

Siderocapsa, Siderosphaera, Sideronema, Ferribacterium, Sideromonas, Naumanniella, Ochrobium, Siderococcus, Siderobacter, Ferrobacillus,‡ Thiobacillus,‡ Metallogenium, Lieskeella.

10. Colorless, Nonphotosynthetic Organisms with Distinctly Curved Axis; No Stalk Formation; Motile with Polar or Lateral Flagella

Differentiation is based on morphology, location of flagella, mode of reproduction, specific metabolic characters, and oxygen tolerance.

Vibrio, Desulfovibrio, Methanobacterium, Cellvibrio, Cellfalcicula, Microcyclus, Mycoplana,§ Selenomonas, Photobacterium,§ Thiospira,§ Campylobacter, Bdellovibrio, Butyrivibrio, Succinovibrio, Lachnospira.

11. Organisms with Helical (Spiral) Axis; Motile with Polar Flagella or Nonmotile

Differentiation is based on photosynthetic pigments, and on morphological and nutritional characters.

Rhodospirillum,§ Spirillum, Paraspirillum, Myconostoc, Nitrosospira, Sporospirillum.

12. Organisms Occurring in Sheaths

Differentiation is based on unicellular or multicellular forms, morphology, intracellular deposition of sulfur, deposition of iron, type of motility (if any), presence of aerosomes, and type of sheath.

Sphaerotilus, Leptothrix, Toxothrix, Peloploca,§ Pelonema,§ Crenothrix, Phragmidiothrix, Clonothrix, Thioploca,§ Thiothrix,§ Coleomitus (?).

13. Organisms Reproducing by Extruding a Tube from the End of the Cell

Differentiation is based on pigmentation, oxygen sensitivity, and metal oxidation.

‡ Also in Group 4.
§ Also included in another group.

Rhodomicrobium,* *Hyphomicrobium, Pedomicrobium.*

14. Colorless Organisms Capable of Fixing Atmospheric Nitrogen Nonsymbiotically

Differentiation is based on morphology and type of flagellation.

Azotobacter, Azotomonas,† *Azotococcus, Beijerinckia, Aerobacter.**

15. Gram Negative Rods with Peritrichous Flagella That Produce Water-insoluble Pigments

Differentiation is based principally on the nature of pigment and also on biochemical reactions.

Chromobacterium, Flavobacterium, Serratia, Escherichia.‡

16. Colorless, Gram Negative Rods Producing Nodules and Malformations on Roots of Plants

Differentiation is based on the nature of the nodule or malformation and the fixation of nitrogen.

Rhizobium, Agrobacterium.

17. Colorless, Gram Negative Rods, with Peritrichous Flagella or Non-motile, Growing Well on Meat Infusion Agar Aerobically

Differentiation is based on hydrolysis of agar, alginates, chitin, pectins, and gelatin; presence or absence of flagella; production of acid or acid and gas in glucose; fermentation of lactose (positive or negative and rapid or delayed) and other carbohydrates; production of indole and urease; methyl red and Voges-Proskauer reactions; growth on various carbon substrates: growth in the presence of KCN; deamination of amino acids; pathogenicity; and temperature of growth.

Alcaligenes, Achromobacter, Agarbacterium, Beneckea, Escherichia, Shigella, Salmonella,

Arizona, Citrobacter, Klebsiella, Enterobacter, (Aerobacter), Hafnia, Serratia,* Proteus, Morganella, Rettgerella, Providencia, (Paracolobactrum), Alginobacter, Erwinia, Herellea, Colloides.

18. Small, Colorless, Unicellular Rods of Nonenteric Origin Requiring Amino Nitrogen and Frequently Growth Factors

Aerobic, Gram negative.

Differentiation is based on nutritional requirements, liquefaction of inspissated serum, motility, and pathogenicity.

Pasteurella, Bordetella, Brucella, Haemophilus, Actinobacillus, Calymmatobacterium, (Moraxella), Noguchia, Streptobacillus, Cardiobacterium, Yersinia.

19. Anaerobic, Gram Negative Rods

Differentiation is based on morphology (size, shape, and pleomorphism), motility, and nutritional characters and reaction in peptone water.

Bacteroides, Fusobacterium, Dialister, Sphaerophorus.

20. Gram Positive Cocci

Differentiation is based on morphology, arrangement of cells, sensitivity to oxygen, production of gas from peptone, production of methane, bile solubility, catalase, production and rotation of lactic acid, and utilization of ammoniacal nitrogen.

Micrococcus, Staphylococcus, Aerococcus, Gaffkya, Sarcina, Peptococcus, Diplococcus, Streptococcus, Pediococcus, Leuconostoc, Peptostreptococcus, Nitrosococcus, Mycococcus.

21. Gram Negative Cocci

Differentiation is based on morphology and arrangement and on sensitivity to oxygen.

Mima, Herellea, Colloides, Lampropedia, Neisseria, Veillonella, Methylococcus.

* Also included in another group.
† Also included in group 7.
‡ Some strains only.

22. Aerobic, Gram Positive, Nonsporing, Nonacid-fast, Unbranched Rods*

Differentiation is based on morphology and arrangement of cells, motility, production of acid or acid and gas from glucose, production of acid from lactose, fermentation of lactate, acidification and clotting of milk, tolerance of high temperatures, tolerance of low pH, hydrolysis of cellulose, cyclic development as cocci and rods, and pathogenicity.

Lactobacillus, Propionibacterium, Corynebacterium, Listeria, Erysipelothrix, Microbacterium, Cellulomonas, Kurthia, Brevibacterium, Arthrobacter, Leptotrichia.

23. Anaerobic, Gram Positive, Nonsporing, Nonacid-fast, Unbranched Rods

Differentiation is based on morphology and arrangement of cells, motility, production of butyric and propionic acids from lactate, production of gas from peptone, and production of large amounts of alcohol from glucose.

Butyribacterium, Propionibacterium,† Catenabacterium, Ramibacterium, Eubacterium, Cillobacterium, Leptotrichia, Bifidobacterium.‡

24. Rod-shaped, Unicellular Organisms Producing Endospores

Differentiation is based on sensitivity to oxygen and production of methane.

Bacillus, Clostridium, Methanobacterium, Fusosporus, Desulfotomaculum, Metabacterium.

25. Gram Positive, Acid-fast Nonmotile Multicellular Rods

The only genus represented is *Mycobacterium.*

* Odd bifurcations are not considered here to be branches.
† Included also under aerobic rods.
‡ These genera have been included in other groups. They do not branch in the accepted sense but may, under some conditions of growth, produce bifurcated cells or angulated cells.

26. Branching Gram Positive Rods

Differentiation is based on formation of a true branching mycelium in the early stages of growth, persistence of the branching character, multicellularity, production and arrangement of conidia, production and the nature of sporangia, motility of conidia, sensitivity to oxygen, and optimal temperature of growth.

Arthrobacter,‡ Mycobacterium,‡ Propionibacterium,‡ Bacterionema, Nocardia, Pseudonocardia, Promicromonospora, (Jensenia), Actinomyces, Micromonospora, Actinobifida, Thermomonospora, Thermoactinomyces, Microbispora (Waksmania), Micropolyspora, Thermopolyspora, Streptomyces, Chainia, Dermatophilus, Actinopycnidium, Microellobosporia, Actinoplanes, Streptosporangium, Ampullariella, Spirillospora, Amorphosporangium.

27. Organisms Clearly Multicellular without Application of Special Cell Wall Stains

Rigid or flexible; some cells greatly exceed 2 μ in diameter.

Differentiation is based on morphology, presence or absence of a sheath, motility, endospores, flagella, intracellular deposition of sulfur, flexibility of cells, and sensitivity to oxygen.

Caryophanon, Oscillospira, Arthromitus, Coleomitus, Beggiatoa, Thiospirillopsis, Saprospira, Thioploca, Thiothrix, Leucothrix, Vitreoscilla, Simonsiella, Alysiella.

28. Aerobic, Gram Negative Rods Forming Long, Motile, Articulated Chains

Differentiation is based on the presence or absence of flagella.

Lineola, Bactoscilla, Flexibacter.

29. Flexible, Rod-shaped Organisms, Motile with Gliding Action on Solid Surfaces or along Adjacent Cells in Liquids

No flagella; unicellular; Gram negative.
Differentiation is based on the size of the

cells, presence or absence of microcysts, and the development and nature of fruiting bodies.

Microscilla, Flexibacter, Cytophaga, Sporocytophaga, Archangium, Stelangium, Sorangium, Polyangium, Synangium, Podangium, Chondromyces, Myxococcus, Chondrococcus, Angiococcus, Moraxella.

30. Colorless, Flexible, Spiral-shaped Organisms without Flagella, Actively Motile in Solutions

Differentiation is based on the size of the cells, presence of an axial filament or a crista, which is visible with a standard microscope, sensitivity to oxygen, hooking of cell ends, and general morphology.

Spirochaeta, Cristispira, Borrelia, Treponema, Leptospira.

31. Pleuropneumonia and Pleuropneumonia-like organisms

Mycoplasma.

32. Intracellular Parasites of Man and Animals, Arthropods and Trematodes

Differentiation is based on the type of tissue or blood cells invaded, nature of growth in or on the cells, growth in chicken embryos, morphology, nature of the disease produced, symptoms of the disease, transmission by arthropods or trematodes, and mode of transmission by arthropods. *Rickettsia, Coxiella, Ehrlichia, Cowdria, Neorickettsia, Wolbachia, Symbiotes, Rickettsiella, Chlamydia, Colesiota, Ricolesia, Colettsia, Miyagawanella, Bartonella, Grahamella, Haemobartonella, Eperythrozoon, Anaplasma.*

INDEX

In the following Index the names of genera recognised in the seventh edition of Bergey's Manual and new generic names which have appeared in the literature since the publication of the Manual are printed in boldface. Alternate generic names employed by Prévot and Krassilnikov appear in italics. Page references in boldface refer to descriptions in the Digest of Genera.

---

* The specific epithet *rhusiopathiae* was recently conserved against the epithet *insidiosa* for the type species of Erysipelothrix.